PRINCIPLES OF ASTRONOMY

STANLEY P. WYATT

Professor of Astronomy
University of Illinois

ALLYN AND BACON, INC.
BOSTON

PRINCIPLES OF

ASTRONOMY

First printing: May 1964
Second printing: November 1964

Title page: The Whirlpool Galaxy, near the end of the Big Dipper. Photographed with the 200-inch telescope. (*Mount Wilson and Palomar Observatories photograph*)

Library of Congress Catalog Card Number: 64–14267.

Printed in the United States of America.

PREFACE

TIME WAS, centuries and even decades ago, when most people thought of the astronomer as a gentle and unexcitable soul who spent his nights peering patiently through his telescope, checking up on the moon and stars to see that they were indeed where they ought to be. His daylight hours were supposedly dedicated to teaching every comer the names and colors of the stars and the shapes of the constellations. But these popular ideas were way wide of the mark then, and they are even more of a myth now. Today's astronomer is both physicist and mathematician; he may be a theorist and go to work in the daytime, or he may be primarily an observer and do his job at night, or he may be both. But whatever he does, he loves the stars. And at his best he has two strong drives: one is to make his own contributions to astronomical knowledge; the other is to maintain a general mastery of his subject as it grows.

In the pages that follow I have tried to set down that subject, the story of the physical universe as we understand it today. Here is the background against which astronomers do their work; here is the physical setting in which men and women live. The subject of astronomy is certainly far more than a collection of isolated facts. It deals with the structure and motions and evolution of the bodies in the physical universe and of the universe itself. What binds the subject together and makes it coherent are some of the great principles of physics, such as the law of gravitation and the law of conservation of energy. I have attempted to emphasize principle rather than lonesome fact, to discuss physical ideas where appropriate, and to show *how* as well as *what* the astronomer knows. I have pondered here and there about some of the things we may someday understand but do not right now. Recently radio and radar astronomy have come of age, and many experiments in space are beginning to reveal new knowledge. These bold new phases of the subject are treated here, but not so much for their own sakes as for their growing impact on our total learning about the universe.

My aim has been to present a unified account of contemporary astronomy, beginning here at home with our earth and moving outward toward infinity—through our solar system, beyond to the stars of our home galaxy, and out into the physical universe. Our voyage ends at the present frontier of research: the most remote known galaxies, stellar systems whose light and radio waves have spent billions of years traveling to the earth. I have assumed that the reader is acquainted with algebra and geometry; to do less would be to violate the essentially quantitative spirit of astronomy. Various physical laws are formulated algebraically here and there, and many of the diagrams demand a measure of geometrical intuition. Integral logarithms are introduced and explained in Chapter 13, and physical principles are introduced and described where needed. I hope the story provides a balanced view of astronomy, although it is of course inevitable that no two practitioners will ever agree precisely on the relative emphasis that the various topics should be accorded.

I am indebted to a number of astronomers who have reviewed various parts of the manuscript and made valuable suggestions and criticisms. I am especially grateful to several of my associates at the University of Illinois. Dr. G. C. McVittie, Dr. Ivan King, and Dr. J. Myron Atkin have not only read and commented on various chapters, but on-the-spot discussions with them have been happily provocative. What errors may remain are of course my responsibility alone, and I shall be glad to know of them. I also wish to record my personal thanks to some thirty astronomical colleagues around the world for their great help in supplying me with the photographs that are reproduced here. Mr. Raymond E. White has given me extensive assistance with the construction of the star maps, and his fine efforts are much appreciated. I am also grateful to Mrs. Nancy Stone and Mrs. Lillian Taylor for their excellent work and great care in transcribing my handwriting onto typewriter paper. And above all I thank my wife, Catherine B. Wyatt, not only for a large amount of editorial assistance, but for constant encouragement and for putting up with my periodic hiding during the years this book was taking shape.

STANLEY P. WYATT

Urbana, Illinois

CONTENTS

ix

PRINCIPLES OF ASTRONOMY

1

PROSPECT

THE province of astronomy stretches from here, the surface of our home planet, outward to the most remote celestial objects that can be detected by present-day optical and radio telescopes. Light waves and radio waves, which bring us nearly all of our astronomical knowledge, travel through the void of space at a speed of 186,000 miles per second. Those waves reaching us from our nearest natural neighbor, the moon, take only a little over one second to get here. Sunshine journeys for 8 minutes to reach the earth. Light from the nearer stars spends years moving through space before it arrives at our eyes. And the radiation reaching us today from the farthest outposts of the observable universe was emitted long ago from ultradistant galaxies; these waves have crossed the depths of the universe for several billion years before they finally enter our telescopes. Astronomers are therefore able to survey an enormous volume of space. They also deal with tremendous spans of time because they witness astronomical objects as they were at some past moment. The moon is seen as it was about a second ago, the sun as it was 8 minutes ago, and a very distant galaxy as it was several billion years ago. The farther we look outward into the physical universe the deeper we penetrate backward into history.

The business of the astronomer, like that of any scientist, is both observational and interpretive. He has eyes, and he has instruments that extend his sight in many ways and provide him with enormously more information than can be learned by eyesight alone. But an astronomer is not a mere collector of information. Like other men he is endowed with curiosity: he yearns to put order and harmony into the complex universe of experience; he seeks to explain what he sees. His explanation may start as an intuitive but educated hunch. But unless he is a fool he does not announce his hunch to the world and go on to something else. Instead he asks himself whether the consequences of his proposed idea fit the known facts of observation. He also tries to learn whether his theory can be used to predict this or that phenomenon in the observable universe. If so, he will probably investigate to see if his prediction is borne out. At every step of the way he must either reshape his hypothesis or invent a new one so that no violence is done to the data of observation. Not only must the astronomer respect the unassailable facts he gathers, but his ideas must be consistent with known physical laws as well.

The universe explored by astronomy is of course immense in scope. At the same time astronomy as an intellectual discipline interacts strongly with many other disciplines. Its language is often mathematics, and the principles that govern the workings of the universe belong to physics. A voyager to the moon ought to be a chemist and a geologist, and a man going to Mars ought also to be a knowledgeable biologist because we suspect some kinds of vegetation there. But the interplay of astronomy with other fields is not restricted to the sciences; it spreads out to history, philosophy, and literature. Various systems of astronomical thought have shaped the activities and ideas of men over the centuries; they have put their imprint on the work of Homer, on the Bible, and on the writings of Dante, Shakespeare, and Milton, to name but a few. The subject of astronomy cuts across traditional boundaries more than most.

The strongest alliance of astronomy is with physics, the science of matter, energy, and motion. Several major physical concepts and principles weave through and through the astronomical story. From beginning to end astronomy uses the universal law of gravitational attraction to account for the motions of celestial bodies. Now and again it needs to bolster its arguments by appealing to the celebrated conservation principles: the conservation of energy and of angular momentum. Because the vast majority of matter in the universe is in the gaseous state, our interpretations must be rooted in a familiarity with the behavior of gases. And because our knowledge of the stars is carried to us by the light they emit, it is also essential that we know something of the physical laws of radiation and of how radiation is produced and destroyed by atoms. Where occasion demands we shall pause to introduce various physical concepts and principles, but our story remains that of astronomy.

The hierarchy of objects in the astronomical universe has at its top the largest isolated units we know, the *galaxies*. Each galaxy is an enormous collection of stars and of microscopic matter between the stars; collectively galaxies are found here and there throughout the entire universe which we can observe today. The second fundamental units are the *stars*. Each star is a hot gaseous sphere, radiating energy from its surface into space; collectively stars are found here and there throughout each galaxy. For want of a better name, we may designate the third and last units in the astronomical hierarchy as *planets*. Each planet is small compared to a star and the majority of its matter is solid; collectively planets are members of a planetary system.

The great galaxies are not distributed uniformly throughout the universe; here is a single isolated galaxy and there a pair. One also finds trios, quartets, larger groups, and even great clusters of a thousand or more galaxies. The vast gulfs between galaxies are not totally devoid of matter; there is recent evidence that some parts of intergalactic space are occupied by an ultrararefied medium of atoms. The individual stars within galaxies are not distributed uniformly either. Some stars are single and some are members of a star pair or trio. Other stars belong to clusters whose total membership may be 100 or even 100,000. In addition, ultrasmall matter—atoms, molecules, and dust particles—lies in the spaces between the stars. It is more difficult to generalize about the smallest units in the hierarchy, the planets, because our own solar system is the only system of planets we know much about. And it is probably the only one we *can* know much about with present-day telescopes based at the earth's surface. With only one or two examples at hand it is impossible to guess how planetary systems are similar to or different from one another, even though it appears likely that they may be abundant elsewhere in our own and in other galaxies. Our solar system is dominated by its central star, the sun, but it also contains nine relatively large and nearly spherical planets, a number of satellites, as well as asteroids and comets. All of these bodies ply through a tenuous collection of atoms and small particles, the interplanetary medium.

In developing the story of astronomy, we shall not start at the top of the hierarchy. Rather we shall first examine our own neighborhood, then move farther abroad, ending with the largest voyage of all. Because this ordering parallels the historical evolution of the subject, we shall in a general way be treating the best-known and longest-known aspects of astronomy first. Our knowledge of the outer objects depends strongly on what we have already learned from the inner ones, and we thus leave the outermost galaxies until last.

Planet *earth* is the one we know best. It is one of the nine principal planets that wheel in orbits around the sun. The tracks of the planets are strongly confined to a single plane, and so the space through which these bodies move is shaped like a very thin coin. Around most of the planets circle subplanets or *satellites*. Of the 31 known satellites in the solar system, our *moon* is the one we know best. The earth is the only planet with a single natural moon; the other planets have none or two or several.

In addition to the nine principal planets there are thousands, and maybe billions, of little planets in the system. These are the *asteroids*, each one of which sweeps around the sun in its own orbit. The *comets*, occasionally spectacular sights in the sky, also move around the sun but along much longer paths than ours.

A good part of our knowledge of the small bits of matter that roam the solar system comes from studying *meteors*, the bright but evanescent "shooting stars." These are the small grains in space that happen to collide with our earth's atmosphere. Bodies larger than a basketball occasionally ram the atmosphere and are able to get all the way to the ground without being consumed by the upper air. These objects are called *meteorites*. Also between the planets moves the rarefied *interplanetary gas*, which is best studied through experiments on spacecraft that orbit around the sun.

The *sun* itself dominates the solar system. Because it contains more than 99 percent of the entire mass of our planetary system, its gravitational effects are enormous. But for its ruling presence all of the planets, asteroids, and comets would fly away from each other indefinitely. The sun is also the single self-luminous body in our neighborhood. It is the abundant donor of virtually all of our light and heat here on earth. Even so, our planet receives only half of one-billionth of the entire radiant energy emitted by the sun.

The star we know best is the sun. But we can see thousands of others on a clear night, and several billions more are observable with today's telescopes. The nearest is nearly 300,000 times as far away as the sun; its light takes four years to travel to the earth. Although all of the stars are intensely hot and radiant spheres of gas, they differ importantly one from another in mass, size, luminosity, chemical composition, age, and life expectancy.

Probably more than half of the stars are members of multiple systems. These constitute the *binary stars* or *multiple stars*. In any given pair of stars each member moves restlessly in an orbit in response to the gravitational pull of its partner. We can think of our own solar system as an extreme type of multiple star, with a single bona fide star attended by a group of much smaller bodies—bodies too small ever to have become gaseous and self-luminous stars.

It is fortunate for us that the sun is a fairly constant star; we do not alternately roast and freeze because of intrinsic changes in the sun. But not all stars are so built. The *variable stars* rhythmically swell and contract, and major changes in output of light accompany these pulsations. Most unusual of the variables are the *novae*, which suddenly explode and expel great quantities of their surface gases into space at speeds of 1000 miles per second or faster. The light of a nova increases a hundred-thousand-fold in a day or two and then declines more slowly.

Larger groups of stars are congregated in *clusters* and *associations*. Some have a membership of only one or two dozen. The census of others may run to a million. The stars in clusters are far more neighborly than the run of typical stars but are far less neighborly than the components of multiple stars.

Although we count stars by the billions, they occupy but a tiny fraction of the room available. Big as they are as individuals, there is much space between them. The stars we see at night are spread more thinly than a collection of golf balls spaced 100 miles apart. But the vast and solitary reaches between the stars are not entirely vacant. They are permeated by the *interstellar matter* in the form of individual atoms, molecules, and "dust particles." The denser clouds of atoms and dust are the *nebulae*, some of which we can see without telescopic aid. The general interstellar medium, detectable only with sensitive instruments, is extremely tenuous, as though the air in an average-sized office building were spread out uniformly in all directions to the distance of the moon, a quarter of a million miles.

Stars, star clusters, and interstellar matter together form an isolated larger unit in space, our *galaxy*. Our great stellar system spins, every one of its members moving at high speed in a path around a central core of stars. A consequence of this spin is flatness, the system being shaped something like a coin. What we see of it from here—halfway from center to edge—is a circle of dim light, the *Milky Way*.

Far beyond the outer bounds of our home galaxy are the other galaxies. These are systems comparable to our own, each one being inhabited by billions of stars. Most of them also contain appreciable amounts of interstellar matter, and most of them wheel and flatten like our galaxy. A light ray emitted from a star in one galaxy does not reach a neighboring galaxy for some million years. The galaxies are clustered here and there, and once in a while two of them pass through each other in a grandiose collision that lasts for millions of years.

With today's telescopes it is possible to record perhaps as many as a billion galaxies, stretching into the greatest depth of space yet known. And these stellar systems are not motionless; they all appear to rush away from us and from one another, like dots on a balloon that is being inflated. The farthest galaxies are moving away fastest, and speeds of nearly 100,000 miles per second have been recorded for the most distant ones. The universe of galaxies is expanding.

2

THE EARTH:
STRUCTURE

OUR earth is but one of the nine principal planets that wheel about the sun. It ranks third in distance from the sun, second or third in brilliance as seen from the sun, and fifth in size. Its physical statistics are scarcely impressive. But because its surface is the habitat where we live, dream, and think, the earth is the astronomical body we know most about. Our study starts, then, here at home. First for consideration are the fundamental physical characteristics of our planet: what they are and how we know them. Then follows an inquiry into the structure of the earth's interior and of its atmosphere. The next chapter is devoted to the motions of our earth in space and time: its daily spin, its annual journey around the sun, and its slow gyration. Because our measures of astronomical direction, distance, and time are inevitably geared to the physical characteristics of the planet we live on and observe from, the subject of coordinates and time falls naturally within the scope of our look at the earth. The fourth chapter therefore deals with astronomical measures of place and time.

1. The Earth from Afar

SEEN FROM ITS surface, the earth fills almost exactly one-half of the sky. This division into an upper hemisphere of visible sky and a lower hemisphere of earth is best appreciated from a ship at sea or from a treeless plain. Seen from a point some billions of miles off in space, the earth would fill just about none of the sky. Viewed from any

7

8

THE EARTH: STRUCTURE

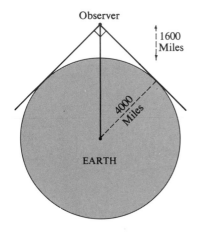

Observer

1600
Miles

4000
Miles

EARTH

Fig. 2.1:1. The angular diameter of the earth as seen from 1600 miles above its surface is 90°.

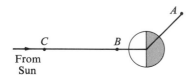

A

C   B

From
Sun

Fig. 2.1:2. Observer *A* sees the earth as a bright crescent, but for observers *B* or *C* it is a luminous circle.

Fig. 2.1:3. Photograph taken from a Viking Rocket 155 miles above ground, looking southeast. The Gulf of Mexico, 650 miles away, is overlain by clouds. (*National Aeronautics and Space Administration*)

intermediate point in space, the nearly spherical earth would block off a circle filling somewhere between none and one-half of the sky, the fraction depending only on the distance of the place of observation from the earth. For example, if our planet is to be comfortably included in a single look without turning the head, its angular diameter should be less than about 90°, which would require a height of observation greater than 1600 miles above its surface (see Fig. 2.1:1).

If our planet were self-luminous like the sun, it would be a bright circular disk when seen from a distance. But because it is an intrinsically dark body shining by means of reflected sunlight, the shape of the luminous part of its disk depends on where the observer is located in space. The various possible shapes are the same as the sequence of shapes the moon shows to us during its monthly cycle. Observer *A* in Fig. 2.1:2 sees the earth as a crescent. The earth is "full," or a bright disk, only for observers like *B* or *C*, who are at some point on a line joining sun and earth. These witnesses are looking at the daytime hemisphere of our planet.

From an airplane 3 or 4 miles up the ground usually looks hazy and pallid. When viewed from farther afield, the earth likewise lacks the crispness of outline and vivid coloration of a map. Perhaps the most striking feature is the intense whiteness of most of the globe. Not only are the polar and part of the temperate regions covered with snow, but at any given moment a good fraction of the earth's area is overlain by clouds. Although to us on the surface cloudiness means grayness and gloom, the observer from afar looks down on an earth that on the average is about 50 percent covered by brilliant white cloud tops. Note the clouds in Fig. 2.1:3.

As seen from the moon at the time of "full earth" each month, our planet has an angular area about 13 times that of the full moon we see from here. The earth's brightness as seen from the moon, however, is about 70 times that of the full moon seen from here because our clouds reflect light much more efficiently than does the moon's dark surface. Under very special conditions, when a part of one of our oceans or a large lake is very calm, it will act as part of a great spherical mirror, and the observer on the moon will then see an intense dot of reflected sunlight. Ordinarily, however, this solar light will be smeared out into a yellow patch by the rippling wave patterns on the water's surface, much like the sunbeams or moonbeams seen from an ocean beach.

When viewed from the sun, which is some 400 times farther away than the moon, planet earth would always be "full." In a telescope its shape would be a bright circle, but it could not be resolved as a disk with the unaided eye any more than we from here can see the neighboring planets as disks without a telescope. Its brilliance would be comparable to that of Venus, the brightest planet in our sky.

From Pluto, the most distant planet from the sun, the earth could not been seen with the unaided eye for two reasons: (1) it would be too faint for human vision; (2) since Pluto averages 40 times the earth's distance from the sun, the angle between earth and sun as seen from there would at most be $1\frac{1}{2}°$, the approximate width of a finger held at arm's length. The earth would be lost in the overwhelming brilliance of the sun.

From the nearest star beyond the sun, Alpha Centauri, which is 270,000 times as far as our sun, not even a 200-inch telescope could detect the earth or any other of the planets of our solar system. They are simply too small and too faint and lost in the glare of their parent star. It is little wonder, when we turn the tables, that our own telescopes here on earth have never yet directly revealed other systems of planets surrounding their parent stars.

BASIC PHYSICAL CHARACTERISTICS

2. Shape

ALTHOUGH IT IS perhaps natural to think of the earth's surface as being essentially flat, abundant evidence shows it to be approximately spherical. It is wrinkled, of course, for mountains rise as much as $5\frac{1}{2}$ miles above the surface of the sea and the greatest known ocean deeps extend about $6\frac{1}{2}$ miles beneath sea level. The daily rotation of the earth also keeps the shape from being a perfect sphere, as we shall see later. Altogether, however, these deviations are small when we think of the planet as a whole. The earth is a truer sphere than a ball one yard in diameter with fluctuations in diameter ranging up to $\frac{1}{8}$ inch.

That the earth is globular rather than flat was recognized 2500 years ago by the Greeks. They noted that whenever the moon enters the earth's shadow and an eclipse of the moon occurs, the shadow on the moon's disk is always the arc of a circle. The only body that at all orientations can cast a conical shadow with circular cross section is a

THE EARTH: STRUCTURE

sphere. More familiar testimony that the ocean surface curves is provided by a ship sailing out to sea (see Fig. 2.2:1). Watched from shore, her hull first sinks below the horizon, and later her stacks, her masts, and ultimately even her smoke. The achievement in 1522 of

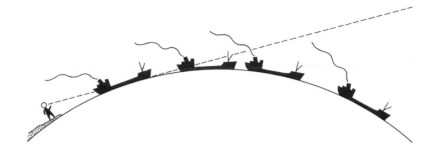

Fig. 2.2:1. Evidence of the earth's curvature.

Magellan's crew in sailing around the world revealed that there were no sharp "edges." The uniform curvature of the horizon is nicely demonstrated in the present era by photographs made from high-altitude rockets and orbiting satellites (see Fig. 2.2:2).

3. Size

THE MEAN OR AVERAGE diameter of the earth is, in round numbers, 8000 miles; more precisely, it is 7917.79 miles. The average difference among five investigations over the past century is only about ± 0.07

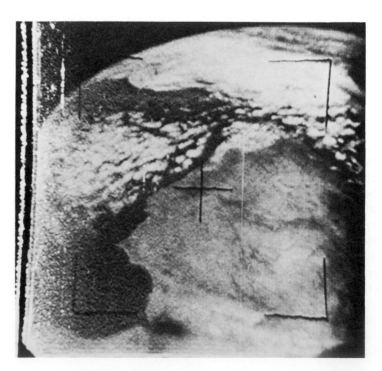

Fig. 2.2:2. The curvature of the distant horizon is striking in this photograph taken from the Tiros III satellite. The Straits of Gibraltar and the Spanish and Portuguese coasts are well defined. Clouds lie over England near the top of the picture. (*National Aeronautics and Space Administration*)

mile from the latter value. Of the many ways of obtaining the earth's size, the simplest in principle is to stretch a tape measure around the equator and thus find its circumference. More practically, the round-the-world flight time of an aircraft divided by its average speed over the surface yields the circumference. But navigational errors and the effect of head winds and tail winds conspire to make this method imprecise. A better way, if we can correct for the effect of refraction (Section 14), is to measure the distance at which a lighthouse or coastal mountain of known height disappears below the sea horizon. Figure 2.3:1, which is exaggerated for clarity, shows the earth as a sphere of radius R and capped by a mountain of height H above sea level. The distance D is the greatest distance from which the peak can be seen from sea level. The angle at the observer is 90° if the earth is a sphere, and thus we can utilize the theorem of Pythagoras, which tells us that

$$R^2 + D^2 = (R + H)^2 = R^2 + 2RH + H^2.$$

The square of the earth's radius cancels and therefore

$$D^2 = 2RH + H^2.$$

When each term is divided by $2H$, the radius turns out to be

$$R = \frac{D^2 - H^2}{2H}.$$

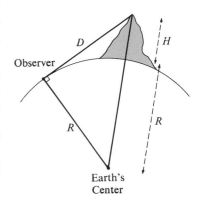

Fig. 2.3:1. Measuring the radius of the earth.

In applying this formula, it is necessary always to use the same units for all measured quantities; when D and H are both expressed in miles, R will come out in miles. If a mountain one mile high can be detected by a ship's radar at a distance no greater than 90 miles, the deduced radius of the earth is about 4050 miles, a value that is not far in error.

As long ago as 250 B.C. the Greek scientist Eratosthenes knew that the noontime sun on the first day of summer cast no shadows at Syene on the upper Nile in Egypt. At Alexandria, some 500 miles north of Syene on the Mediterranean coast, Eratosthenes found that the noontime sun on this same date was not directly overhead. Measurements of the height of a vertical stick and its shadow length revealed that the sun was some $7\frac{1}{2}°$ south of the zenith at this time. Assuming the earth to be spherical in shape and the sun to be so very far away that its incoming rays are all parallel to one another, we may repeat Eratosthenes' reasoning (see Fig. 2.3:2). The zenith direction at any point lies opposite to the direction of the earth's center and at right angles to the tangent plane or plane of the horizon at that place. The angle of $7\frac{1}{2}°$ at A is reproduced at C if the sun's rays are indeed parallel. To find the circumference of the earth, we need only recognize the simple proportion that the distance AS is to $7\frac{1}{2}°$ as the total distance around the circle is to the total number of degrees in a circle:

$$\frac{AS}{7\frac{1}{2}°} = \frac{\text{Circumference}}{360°}.$$

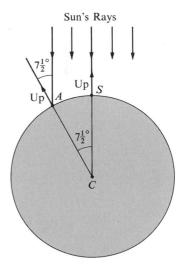

Fig. 2.3:2. Eratosthenes' method of establishing the size of the earth.

THE EARTH: STRUCTURE

Solving, and recalling that AS is 500 miles, we find that

$$\text{Circumference} = \frac{360}{7\frac{1}{2}} \times 500 \text{ miles}$$
$$= 24{,}000 \text{ miles.}$$

Division by $\pi = 3.14$ shows the diameter to be some 7600 miles.

Notice two instructive features of this calculation. (1) The result is only approximate because we never can get out of a computation more accuracy than is put into it. To find the earth's diameter with a precision to one more meaningful figure, we would have to measure the distance from Syene to Alexandria to the nearest mile and measure the angular distance of the sun from the zenith to the nearest hundredth of a degree. Modern methods of finding the earth's size resemble the ancient one; the greater precision today is rooted in the development of surveying and astronomical instruments for highly accurate measurement of distances on the earth's surface and of angles among the stars. (2) There is an alternative interpretation of Eratosthenes' results: he would have seen the same effect if the earth were flat and the sun not very far away. Sketching the figure to scale on graph paper or solving by trigonometry would put the sun at a distance of only 3800 miles (see Fig. 2.3:3). The dilemma can be resolved by making observations from one or more additional points along the north–south arc or meridian that passes through the two cities.

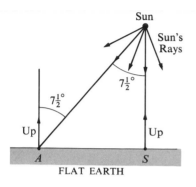

Fig. 2.3:3. An incorrect interpretation of Eratosthenes' results.

4. Mass

THE IDEA OF MASS is of fundamental importance. Intuitively, one is usually tempted to think of the mass of a body as its weight. Weight, however, is always a force. One's weight on the moon is very much less than it is here on the earth, and one's weight in a spaceship may be just about zero. But the mass of an object is precisely the same under all circumstances. Mass is a measure of the inertia of a body, its resistance to change of motion. Numerically, the mass of any object is the ratio of some amount of force exerted on it to the amount the object is accelerated in response to the action of that force. Push a large rowboat and a small toy boat with the same force. The latter is accelerated more; its mass is correspondingly less.

The fundamental unit of mass used in scientific work is the *gram*, intended to be the mass of one cubic centimeter of water at a temperature of 4°C, although in practice it is one-thousandth of the standard kilogram mass, which is housed in the International Bureau of Weights and Measures at Sèvres, outside Paris. In turn, the *centimeter* is the basic unit of length used by most scientists. One inch equals 2.54 centimeters. The centimeter was intended to be one-billionth of the distance from either pole of the earth, north or south, to any point on the equator, although in practice it is one-hundredth of the standard meter, the distance between two marks on a bar made of platinum and iridium when the bar is at 0°C. Like the standard kilogram of mass, the standard meter bar is kept at the Bureau in Sèvres. A thimble has a volume of about 3 cubic centimeters; a $\frac{1}{4}$-teaspoon measuring spoon about one cubic centimeter. The gram, representing the mass of one cubic centimeter of water, is therefore a small quantity; there are 454 of them in a one-pound mass. It will sometimes be useful to employ the metric ton (or, briefly, ton), which is one million grams.

The mass of the earth is 6×10^{27} grams (more precisely, 5.974×10^{27} grams). These figures are written in exponential form, a most economical way of writing very large and very small numbers, and one that we shall use freely. The number 10^{27} is simply a 1 followed by 27 zeros; 10^3 is a 1 followed by 3 zeros, or 1000; 10^0 is a 1 followed by no zeros, or unity. The notation continues for small numbers. The number 10^{-1} is the reciprocal of 10^1, or $\frac{1}{10} = 0.1$; 10^{-3} is the reciprocal of 10^3, or $\frac{1}{1000} = 0.001$. Written in decimal form, the number 1 occurs at the first place to the right of the decimal point for 10^{-1}, in the third place for 10^{-3}, and so on. Table 2.4:1 reveals the simplicity and economy of

TABLE 2.4:1.   Writing Numbers in Exponential Form

Short Form	Long Form	Customary Form
⋮	⋮	⋮
10^3	1000.0000	1000
10^2	0100.0000	100
10^1	0010.0000	10
10^0	0001.0000	1
10^{-1}	0000.1000	0.1
10^{-2}	0000.0100	0.01
10^{-3}	0000.0010	0.001
⋮	⋮	⋮

the exponential notation. In spite of this way of expressing the earth's mass, 6×10^{27} grams represents a lot of material. Imagine 5 million trucks, each of 5-ton capacity, and each depositing a full load of material at a central collecting point every 10 minutes. The pile will not accumulate to equal the earth's mass for 5 billion years, the approximate age of the earth and solar system.

5. Introducing the Law of Gravitation

MEASUREMENT OF THE earth's mass can scarcely be achieved by an Atlas; we must instead introduce some physical law that involves the mass of a body. Let us examine the basically important law of gravitation discovered by Isaac Newton in the seventeenth century. Thinking of a falling apple and the moon's motion about the earth as but two specific manifestations of some general law of nature, Newton concluded that there exists a force of attraction between every pair of things in the universe. Imagine any two isolated particles in space as in Fig. 2.5:1, one endowed with mass M_1, the other with mass M_2. By a particle we mean an idealized "point" which has a definite mass but occupies

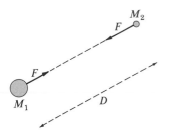

Fig. 2.5:1. Illustration of the universal law of gravitation.

only an infinitesimal volume of space. These particles are at a certain instant separated by a distance D. Then the law of gravitation says that each of these particles exerts a pull or force, F, on the other one, of amount

$$F = \frac{GM_1M_2}{D^2}.$$

The symbol G stands for the universal constant of gravitation and is always the same for any application of the law. It is one of the few fundamental constants of nature, another of which is the velocity of light. The *numerical* values of such constants of nature depend on the units in which they are expressed, but as physical quantities they do not vary from place to place or from moment to moment. The numerical value of G need not concern us in what follows, although if needed it may be found in Chapter 7, Section 7. Examining the gravitation formula further, we notice that for bodies of a given separation, the force is greater the larger the masses. Two planets a billion miles apart attract each other with a much greater force than a planet and a marble separated by the same distance, and the force between two marbles a billion miles from one another is less than either. For given masses, on the other hand, the force of attraction is less the greater the separation. If we should double the distance between earth and sun, the mutual force of attraction would be only one-fourth as much.

In addition to discovering this law for particles, Newton was able to show that it is also applicable in a simple way to certain bodies of finite size. In particular, a symmetric sphere attracts another body as though its entire mass were concentrated at its center; it may be replaced, in other words, by a particle of the same mass located at its center without in any way affecting the validity of the law. Since many celestial bodies are very nearly spherical, the law of gravitation can be successfully extended to them. For example, the weight of an object at the earth's surface is the force of attraction exerted on it by the mass of the earth. If the mass of the earth is M_1 and the mass of the object is M_2, then the weight of the object is

$$W = \frac{GM_1M_2}{R^2}.$$

The symbol R is the radius of the earth, since this is just the distance of the object from the center of attraction. The earth exerts gravitational attraction, therefore, as though its entire mass, M_1, were at its center.

An early approximate estimate of the earth's mass was made two centuries ago by N. Maskelyne, a British astronomer. On a level plain a pendulum at rest will respond to the earth's gravitation alone and define precisely the direction of the vertical. But near a massive isolated mountain, the pendulum will deviate by a small angle toward the mountain, its rest position governed by the combined effect of the earth's downward pull and the mountain's more or less horizontal pull. Detection and measurement of this effect permits a crude determination of the earth's mass.

A simpler method requires clocking the time of fall of an object dropped from a tower of known height. When let go, the object responds to the pull of the earth's gravitation and is accelerated downward toward the center of the earth. As one knows from ordinary experience, the time of fall depends on the height of the tower. In addition, the time taken depends on how rapidly the object is accelerated by the earth's pull, and this in turn depends on the earth's radius and its mass. Granted that we know beforehand the measured time and height, the radius of the earth, and the value of G, the mass of the earth can then be computed. The experiment ought to be conducted in a vacuum or with a fairly massive object; otherwise molecules of air will slow the time of fall, as with a feather floating to earth. Without such precaution, the measured time of fall will come out too large and the deduced mass of the earth will be erroneously low. Similar careful experiments at the surface of any other spherical celestial body will allow a determination of its mass. But there are other less direct but time-tested techniques for finding the mass of objects beyond the earth, and we shall describe them later. It is well to remember, however, that these indirect methods, like the more direct ones just discussed, all depend on the law of gravitation.

6. Density

A FAMILIAR OLD riddle asks which weighs more, a pound of feathers or a pound of lead. But the physical quantity that differs drastically for these items is not weight, but density. The average density of any object is defined as the ratio of the mass of the object to the volume of space it occupies. We can extend this definition to any point of a body, for example the center of the earth, the density "at a point" being the ratio of the mass of a very small sample surrounding the point to the volume the sample occupies. The unit of density we shall employ is grams per cubic centimeter. Since we earlier defined the gram as the mass of 1 cm³ of water, the density of water is 1 gm/cm³; the density of cork is only about 0.15 gm/cm³ and that of lead is some 11 gm/cm³. We can now compute the average density of the whole earth since we know its mass, M, and its radius, R. The volume of space occupied by any sphere is

$$V = \frac{4\pi R^3}{3},$$

and for the earth in particular this amounts to 1.08×10^{27} cm³ (or 2.60×10^{11} cubic miles). Division of M by V shows that the earth's average density is 5.52 gm/cm³, somewhat less than that of iron. Since the outer rocky layers of the earth are known to average only half of this value, it is clear that the central regions of our planet must be considerably denser than the average for the whole planet. With the possible exception of remote Pluto, whose mass we do not know, the earth leads the parade of the principal planets in having the highest average density.

INTERIOR OF THE EARTH

7. Earthquake Waves

OUR DIRECT EXPERIENCE of conditions beneath the earth's surface is limited to depths of only a few miles. To explore the vast majority of the earth's bulk, geologists must resort to indirect techniques, the most useful one of which utilizes the energetic natural phenomenon of earthquakes. All is not placid beneath the surface, and an earthquake is the product of a sudden adjustment to the long build-up of stresses to an intolerable point. At the focal point of an earthquake, which may lie very near the surface or as deep as 400 miles, the sudden motion of matter produces waves which travel out in all directions from the seat of the disturbance. Two chief types of waves are emitted. The primary or longitudinal waves are transmitted by back-and-forth motions of the matter; vibrations of the material through which these waves are traveling are along the direction of travel of the waves. Such, for example, are sound waves traveling in air. A person hears a distant gunshot because at a point on the line joining him and the gun the molecules of air are set into a back-and-forth motion. These knock the next batch of molecules into motion, and the disturbance moves toward the person at the "speed of sound," about $\frac{1}{5}$ mile per second. The secondary or transverse earthquake waves are transmitted by sidewise motions of the matter through which they are traveling; vibrations of the matter are at right angles to the direction of motion of the wave. Ocean swells exemplify transverse waves. A floating chip bobs up and down only; it does not move forward with the wave. It is important to remember that in both types of waves it is not matter, or mass, that is moving from one place to a distant point. The quantity being transported is energy.

Both primary and secondary waves travel through solid material, but only primary waves are transmitted through liquids. Although the path of a wave through any medium of changing physical characteristics is complicated by the effects of refraction, it is known that primary waves travel considerably faster than secondary waves, the speed at any point depending on the density, compressibility, and rigidity of the matter there. Detection of the arrival times of the two kinds of waves at a point on the earth is achieved by the *seismograph*. The difference in time between the arrival of the primary and the secondary waves from an earthquake depends in a complex way on the distance to the focal point of the quake and the interior conditions along the path of the waves. However, if the same disturbance can be detected at many seismograph stations over the earth, it is possible both to locate the focal point of the quake and to infer certain properties of the earth's interior. An important result of such studies is that at points in a zone of the earth opposite to the focal point the secondary waves fail to arrive, although the primary waves are readily recorded. The inference is that a part of the earth's interior is fluid.

THE MODEL OF PLANET earth that has emerged from seismological studies is still tentative, although likely correct in its main features. The nucleus of the earth, called the *inner core*, is probably solid and may be imagined as an extremely dense sphere with a radius of about 800 miles. The density of the matter at the center itself must necessarily be greater than the average for the whole earth, and most estimates lie between 12 and 18 times that of water. Intrinsically dense materials like iron and nickel may dominate there; another possibility is that the central regions are composed chiefly of rocky surface-like materials that are compressed by the enormous weight of overlying layers into very dense and unfamiliar forms. Evidence from the meteorites, although not conclusive, supports the hypothesis that iron or an iron-nickel alloy is the dominant component near the earth's center. The temperature there is not known, but it is likely that it must be measured in thousands of degrees. The *outer core* is a spherical shell with an inner radius of 800 miles and an outer radius of 2200 miles. Seismological studies indicate fairly conclusively that the materials of the outer core, although very dense and probably of about the same chemical composition as the inner core, are in the liquid state (see Fig. 2.8:1).

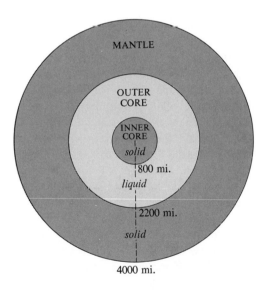

Fig. **2.8:1.** The three major parts of the earth's interior.

At a distance of 2200 miles from the earth's center, or 55 percent of the earth's radius, the nature of the materials changes abruptly. The great spherical envelope stretching from this level virtually to the surface is called the *mantle*. It is solid throughout, fairly homogeneous in composition, and its chief component is silicon dioxide, the chief building block of rocks. Seismological data show another abrupt change in physical characteristics near the surface, and this change divides the mantle from the outer veneer of the earth. This outer *crust* averages 20 miles in depth beneath the continents and only about 3 miles beneath the muds of the ocean floors. Most of the crust is composed of igneous rocks—materials that have solidified from a previous hot and molten state. The igneous rocks under the seas and in the lower half of the subcontinental crust are basaltic, composed chiefly of oxygen, silicon, and magnesium. The continents themselves are granitic, with oxygen, silicon, and aluminum as their dominant components. Being structures of lower density, they float atop the denser basalt (see Fig. 2.8:2). Above the igneous strata in many places lie

Fig. 2.8:2. The surface layers of the earth.

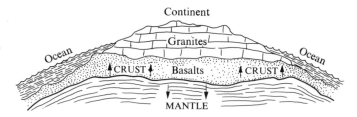

sedimentary rocks, formed from the matter carried by rivers and deposited in the oceans. Altogether, the sedimentary rocks comprise only a very small fraction of the total mass of the crust. The average of thousands of typical samples of material reveals that the crust as a whole is made up of 47 percent oxygen and 28 percent silicon. Aluminum forms 8 percent of the mass, iron 5 percent, calcium 4 percent, sodium and potassium 3 percent each, and magnesium 2 percent. Other elements are present only in smaller amounts. We shall see later that spectrographic study of the gaseous sun and stars enables us to estimate the relative abundances of the chemical elements at their surfaces. The stars are rather similar to one another in chemical composition, and the results accord roughly with those for our igneous rocks, with the fundamental differerence, however, that the stars also contain vast quantities of the two lightest and simplest atoms— hydrogen and helium.

Only 29 percent of the globe is land; the oceans flood the rest. Mount Everest juts 5.5 miles above sea level; the greatest known ocean deep, off the Mariana Islands in the western Pacific, extends 6.7 miles below sea level. It is fortunate for us that the surface is as wrinkled as it is, for if mountains and valleys were completely smoothed out the ocean would be 1.7 miles deep everywhere. Vast as the seas may seem, however, their total mass amounts to only $\frac{1}{4000}$ that of our whole planet.

9. The Earth's Magnetism

NAVIGATORS HAVE USED the magnetic compass for many centuries to aid them in maintaining course at sea, because a magnetized needle, if free to turn only in the horizontal plane, stays pointed toward magnetic north. If such a needle is suspended perfectly freely at a given point on the earth's surface, it indicates the direction of the earth's magnetic field at that place. Those points on the earth where the needle hangs vertical are the north and south magnetic poles, located in Hudson's Bay in far northern Canada and in Victoria Land in Antarctica, their positions varying somewhat with the years. The line around the earth where such a needle points horizontally is the magnetic equator; although not identical with the geographic equator, this line lies entirely within the tropics. The magnetic field of the earth, inferred from the angle of dip of the needle at points all over the earth, is shown in Fig. 2.9:1.

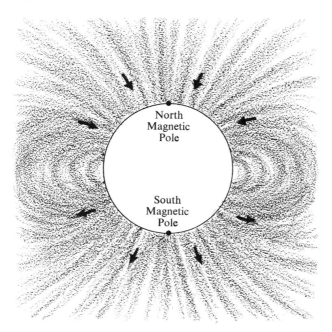

Fig. 2.9:1. The earth's magnetic field; arrows indicate the direction of the field at several points.

A magnetic field is always produced when an electric current flows. It seems certain that the seat of the magnetic forces we can measure at the surface lies deep within the earth and that the field accompanies a circulatory flow of electrically charged particles. The slow variability of the field offers evidence that at least part of the interior is in motion and thus molten. Whatever the precise explanation of the earth's magnetic field may be, we know at least that the earth is not unique. Jupiter is also known to possess a magnetic field; strong magnetic fields occur with spots on the sun; certain types of stars behave like magnetized spheres; and a weak but vast magnetic field pervades the nearly empty interstellar spaces of our Milky Way galaxy.

THE EARTH'S ATMOSPHERE

10. How High the Sky?

THE HEIGHT OF THE SKY depends on a definition of sky. If we mean the distance our greatest telescopes can probe into space, then the answer is a few billion light-years. But if we mean the height of our atmospheric ocean of air or of the blue daytime sky, the result is counted only in miles. Because the air density tapers off gradually with height, the determination of the height of the atmosphere depends strikingly on the method used.

One useful method requires the triangulation of phenomena high in the atmosphere (see Fig. 2.10:1). Assume that two observers are

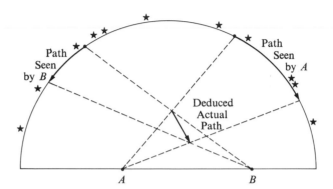

Fig. 2.10:1. Triangulating a meteor from two places to estimate the height of the atmosphere.

located many miles apart, with their watches synchronized. Each one sees a bright meteor flame across the sky at the same instant and plots its path through the stars on a star chart. They can then deduce the height of the meteor when it began to shine. Before seen, a typical meteor is a tiny grain of interplanetary matter orbiting around the sun. Suddenly meteor and earth arrive at the same place in space, and the first thing the meteor encounters as it approaches us with a relative speed of perhaps 20 miles per second is the host of gas atoms in the upper reaches of our atmosphere. Collisions ensue, and the particle is battered, broken, and usually consumed in about one second. Much energy is released and communicated to neighboring atmospheric atoms, and some of it is emitted as light. What one sees as a fast-moving "star" is actually a small traveling sphere of radiating atoms. The height at which a typical meteor runs into dense enough strata to luminesce is found by triangulation to be approximately 70 miles.

Photography of the *aurora borealis*, or northern lights, from two stations has revealed that these radiations originate in atoms in the outermost part of the atmosphere. Auroras are produced when occasional clouds of charged particles, ejected from the sun at speeds of some 1000 miles per second, ram the upper strata of air. Following the earth's magnetic field, most of the incoming particles arrive at high latitudes. The radiations emitted as a consequence of these violent collisions constitute the beautiful and ephemeral auroras, which occur also as the *aurora australis* in the southern hemisphere. The average height of these emanations is about 100 miles, with an extreme as high as 600 miles.

Strictly, there is no end to the atmosphere; it merges gradually with the extremely tenuous gas of atoms that pervades interplanetary space and which may be thought of as the outermost atmosphere of the sun. It is convenient, however, to remember that one-half of the total mass of the earth's atmosphere lies below some $3\frac{1}{2}$ miles above sea level and that all but one-millionth lies below about 70 miles.

11. Chemistry and Physics

SINCE THE BLANKET of air surrounding our planet is a gas, a small cube of it can be pictured microscopically as a host of atoms and molecules flying about at high speed and colliding with one another very frequently. Near the earth's surface, when the temperature is 32°F, each nitrogen molecule must endure about 5 billion collisions per second and has an average speed between collisions of 1000 miles per hour. If the individual particles had no energy of motion or, to say the same thing, if the temperature of the atmosphere were absolute zero (-460°F), the molecules would all fall like rocks to the surface in response to the gravitational pull of the earth. Conversely, if our atmosphere were suddenly to become many times as hot as it is now, the gas particles would be moving so fast that they would all soon escape from the hold of the earth's gravitation and move out into interplanetary space. Happily, the earth's situation is intermediate; the steady supply of radiant energy from the sun keeps the air aloft and yet the planet is massive enough to keep our ocean of air from seeping off into space.

In the lower atmosphere most of the particles are nitrogen molecules, accounting for 78 percent of the total. Oxygen molecules, requisite for the breathing of men and animals, constitute 21 percent. Most of the rest, about 1 percent, is the inert gas argon. There are small traces of carbon dioxide, added to by the decay of organic matter but tapped again by plants for food-building. Water vapor occurs in small and varying quantities, lost to the atmosphere as rain and snow while cycling back aloft by evaporation from the oceans. Dust and smoke particles also become part of the atmosphere, erupting from volcanoes and factory chimneys.

The density of air decreases with altitude. At sea level it is 0.0013 times as dense as water. Although impalpable when indoors, air has appreciable mass, the air molecules in a room of average size amounting to about the same mass of 10 gallons of water. The tininess of each individual particle may be appreciated from the fact that one cubic inch of air contains 4×10^{20} molecules and yet all together they occupy less than one-thousandth of the space in the cube. The number 4×10^{20} by itself conveys little impression of magnitude, but in terms of a classroom of 100 students counting at the rate of one number per second, it may. If they all count for a 40-hour week for 30 years (2 weeks of vacation per year) and then pool their individual results, their combined total will be 2×10^{10}. Squaring the result gives the number of molecules of air per cubic inch near the surface of the earth. Moving aloft, the density halves itself about every $3\frac{1}{2}$ miles. The inner layer of the atmosphere, within which virtually all clouds occur, is called the *troposphere* and extends to 7 miles, where the density is only $\frac{1}{4}$ the surface value. At 70 miles, where meteors incandesce, the air is a million times as tenuous as at the surface, although a cubic inch still contains about 4×10^{14} particles. The total mass of the atmosphere is about one-millionth the mass of the earth.

The atmospheric pressure, as measured by a barometer, varies with the weather at any point on or near the surface. But the average atmospheric pressure is a stable quantity at any level. Like the density of air, the pressure goes down as one moves up. Bubbling of the ears when mountain-climbing or flying is a familiar example. A measure of the force exerted by the bombarding molecules on a real or imaginary surface at any point, pressure depends (1) on the number of molecules per unit volume and (2) on the average energy of motion of each one. It is thus proportional to density and temperature. In our atmosphere the density decreases so sharply with height that its effect completely dominates any variations of temperature; thus the pressure also decreases steadily with height.

The highest mountains are always snow-swept and one can ski for most months of the year at many high-altitude resorts—an indication that average temperature decreases with height too. But unlike density and pressure, the temperature does not continue to plummet as one ascends. At the top of the troposphere it has cooled to about $-70°$F. Above 7 miles lies the *stratosphere*, and the temperature remains approximately constant at $-70°$F in the lower stratosphere, up to some 20 miles. The air then gets warmer, reaching $+200°$F in a stratum at 35 miles. Then follows a decrease to $-30°$F at 50 miles, the top of the stratosphere. Above 50 miles lies the *ionosphere*, so-called because many of the particles there are kept broken up into electrified subparticles or ions by the intense ultraviolet sunlight. From 50 miles on up the temperature goes higher and higher; at 75 miles it is 200°F and is still on the rise. At several hundred miles it is measured in thousands of degrees. It is not surprising that the temperature variation with height, as documented by meteor, balloon, rocket, and satellite research, is an odd and intricate one, for many factors are involved. The temperature at a given level, for example, depends on how much of the sun's radiation is able to penetrate to that level, and this in turn is governed by the numbers and kinds of atoms at all higher levels and the manner in which each kind of atom absorbs and emits radiation. The problem is clearly a complicated one, and much remains to be learned.

When contemplating regions very far from the earth, it is perhaps tempting to think of interplanetary space as being utterly cold. Actually, in a complete vacuum, temperature as defined by the speeds and collisions of atoms has no meaning, for in a vacuum there are, as a matter of definition, no atoms. However, if a small, perfectly absorbing sphere is placed in a vacuum at any point in space, it will soon reach a definite equilibrium temperature. At the earth's distance from the sun this is $+40°$F, far from "utterly cold."

12. The Atmosphere as a Filter

IF THE NIGHT SKY is cloudy, no starlight penetrates to the ground because the clouds, although scarcely very massive, scatter the light of Betelgeuse or Arcturus that otherwise would get through. Their water droplets filter out the incoming light so efficiently that not even a large telescope can detect a star behind a moderately thick cloud. If the evening weather is clear, however, the light of the stars reaches the ground because a cloudless atmosphere is fairly transparent to those wavelengths of light—from violet through the colors of the rainbow to red—to which the eye is sensitive.

The visual part of the spectrum spans only one octave of the entire keyboard of electromagnetic radiation. Short-waveward of violet light is the ultraviolet part of the spectrum, and beyond that is the region of X-rays, followed by the highly energetic gamma rays at the extreme short-wave end of the spectrum. Practically all of the radiations by celestial bodies at these short wavelengths are absorbed by the molecules of the atmosphere and never reach the ground. The electromagnetic spectrum is shown in Fig. 2.12:1, in which the depth of shading indicates

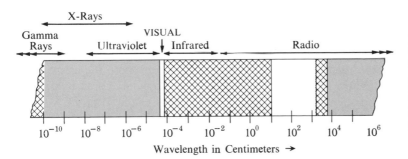

Fig. 2.12:1. The transparency of the atmosphere in different parts of the electromagnetic spectrum. At visual and some radio wavelengths radiation can penetrate the atmosphere. At other wavelengths the ocean of air is partially or completely opaque.

the atmospheric opacity at the various wavelengths. At longer waves than red is the infrared part of the spectrum, and beyond that is the extremely long-wave radio portion of the spectrum. Some of the infrared radiation of the stars penetrates the atmosphere, although much of it is stopped by water molecules in the air. The atmosphere is completely opaque in most of the radio spectrum, but in that part of it extending from wavelengths 10 thousand to a million times that of light there is a transparent window. Here is the realm of operation of television, FM radio, and radar, and it is this second window that has made possible the dramatic findings of the new radio astronomy. Long-waveward of this window, in the realm of the standard broadcast band of AM radio, the ground is again cut off from stellar radio radiations by our atmosphere. But absorption by molecules is not responsible for the atmospheric opacity at these longest wavelengths. Instead, the process is one of refraction; incoming waves are turned back into space by the electrified medium of the ionosphere (see Fig. 2.12:2). Similarly, waves transmitted from the ground are turned back down again by the ionosphere. It is this latter process that makes long-range radio communication possible; and the different state of electrification in hot daylight and cooler nighttime is responsible for the different reception characteristics of an AM radio at different times of day.

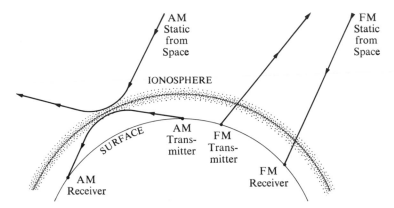

Fig. 2.12:2. At radio frequencies short-wave radiation travels in straight lines and can pass through the entire atmosphere. Long-wave radiation, however, is turned back.

Astronomical research is thus restricted to two wavelength bands as long as observations are made from the surface. But exciting developments have begun with photographs taken from rockets and satellites in the outer reaches of the atmosphere. Potentially richer than the harvest of knowledge from actual visits to the moon and planets is the enormous wealth of information that is accruing from research just a few hundred miles above the earth. From there the entire range of radiations is available and therefore remote and unreachable celestial bodies can be examined at all wavelengths of the spectrum.

13. Brightness and Color of the Sky

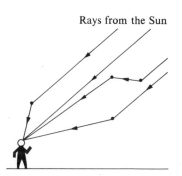

Fig. 2.13:1. Because some sunlight is scattered by the atoms and molecules of air, light reaches the eye from all parts of the daytime sky.

WHY IS THE DAYTIME sky bright instead of black as at night? Clearly, the ultimate source of the brightness must be the sun, which as a matter of definition is above the horizon by day and below by night. The sky owes its brightness to the fact that atoms and molecules scatter light. The blue light reaching us from any particular patch of the sky has traveled a devious path from the sun (see Fig. 2.13:1). A familiar example of scattering is a late-afternoon sunbeam coming through a west window; another is a searchlight beam stretching upward into the night sky. Here, as with skylight, we are not seeing light running along to some other target, for we can respond only to rays that actually enter our eye. The searchlight beam we see is only that tiny portion of light scattered by atmospheric particles in the primary beam and sent straight to our eye and focused on the retina. We may ask how these rays are clever enough to pick out our small eye a mile or two away, no matter how capriciously we might move around. The answer of course is that the process is a statistical one and light is scattered in all directions. It is conceivable that in looking at the daylight sky one might chance to see a black hole in the sky for a few seconds. It is also conceivable that one might take a one-mile walk in a smart rain shower and never get wet. But neither of these events has ever happened. When night comes the scattering atoms and molecules are still in the atmosphere and the same process goes on, but the stars are such faint primary sources that scattered starlight is not detectable to the eye. Intermediate between the bright sunlit sky and the black starlit sky is the easily noticeable moonlit sky. When the moon is nearly full, the background sky is milky in appearance and the faintest stars visible on a moonless night are no longer seen. Atmospheric scattering is similarly responsible for this faint luminescence. Other indirect effects are the nighttime loom of light above a distant city and the slow dimming of twilight after sunset; these occur because the upper air is illuminated and scatters light to us, although the primary source is below our horizon. From the observed fact that the last vestige of fading twilight in the west occurs when the sun is 18° below the horizon, we can estimate by yet another method the height of the atmosphere; the answer this time is 50 miles.

The sun's radiation, being a mixture of all colors in various relative amounts, appears yellow. It would thus seem reasonable that the daylight sky should be yellow in color rather than blue, much as the stage reflection of a yellow spotlight is itself yellow. The explanation is that atoms and molecules scatter the violet and blue waves of sunshine with much greater efficiency than the yellow and red waves. An imperfect but suggestive analogy is a sieve which lets through all small objects, some middle-sized objects, but no big ones. In the atmosphere nearly all of the red rays get through, but many of the violet rays are scattered. Therefore the sun we see has had some of the violet radiation removed and is somewhat redder than it would be if we did not have an atmosphere. The color of the scattered radiation from the sky is blue. When the sun or moon or a star is rising or setting, it is excessively red because the rays must pass tangentially through an extremely long path of atmosphere. Depletion of violet from the beam is therefore exaggerated, and this is augmented by the low-lying atmospheric dust particles which also scatter violet light more than red.

14. Refraction and Twinkling

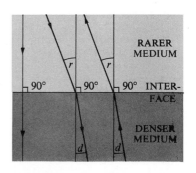

Fig. 2.14:1. The refraction of a light ray when moving from one medium into another.

LIGHT MOVES IN straight lines when it is traversing a uniform medium, but at an interface between two media the course of a ray changes—the ray is refracted. Imagine a perpendicular to the interface surface. The law of refraction states that the angle d between this perpendicular and the ray in the denser medium is less than the angle r between the perpendicular and the ray in the more rarefied medium (see Fig. 2.14:1). The only exception is a ray perpendicular to the interface, in which case both angles r and d are zero and the ray goes through without changing course. If a pencil is held vertically in a partly filled glass of water and viewed from the side, the immersed part appears considerably thickened because of refraction; the ray paths sketched in Fig. 2.14:2 indicate that the angular diameter of the pencil when viewed through water is greater than when it is viewed through air. Unlike the abrupt density change between air and a

THE EARTH: STRUCTURE

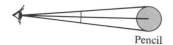

Pencil

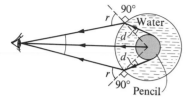

Fig. 2.14:2. Because of refraction the angular diameter of a pencil when seen in water is greater than when it is seen in air.

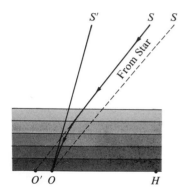

Fig. 2.14:3. Refraction by the atmosphere causes the observed altitude of a star to be greater than its true altitude.

water surface, the earth's atmosphere is a medium of continuously changing density. A light ray from a star has moved for some years on a straight course through the nearly perfect vacuum of interstellar space. But as it moves down into the atmosphere it is refracted, curving continually toward the vertical. Now the direction in which a person sees the star is the direction along which the ray is finally traveling when it meets him. Therefore, as shown in Fig. 2.14:3, the observed angular altitude of the star above the horizon is $\angle S'OH$. If the earth had no atmosphere, the ray would arrive at O'; the star's true altitude is therefore $\angle SO'H$. If we disregard the slight curvature of the earth's surface and recall that light rays from a distant star are parallel to a precision far greater than we can measure, it follows that $\angle SOH = \angle SO'H$. Thus the observed angular altitude of a celestial object above the horizon is always greater than its true altitude, except that if the body is directly overhead both are the same and are equal to 90°. The effect is small, about 3 percent of the angular diameter of the sun for an object 45° above the horizon. The maximum effect is for objects at the horizon, which are lofted by refraction by an amount slightly greater than the angular diameter of the sun or moon. The sun therefore rises earlier and sets later than it would if the earth had no atmosphere. In temperate regions of the earth the difference is 3 to $3\frac{1}{2}$ minutes depending on the time of year, so that the duration of daylight each day is extended 6 or 7 minutes at the expense of the duration of darkness.

A star twinkles, scintillating "like a diamond in the sky." But this effect is not an intrinsic property of the star itself; rather it arises from the imperfections of our atmosphere as a refracting medium. The ever-changing motions of smoke from a chimney or of the rustling leaves of a tree signify that the atmospheric air is continually in turbulent motion. In any isolated small volume of air occur random changes of motion and density. The detailed path of one light ray is not quite the same as that of the next one, as with two rising smoke

Fig. 2.14:4. Some effects of atmospheric refraction on the apparent shape of the setting sun. (*Lick Observatory photographs*)

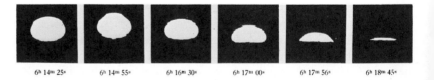

6ʰ 14ᵐ 25ˢ   6ʰ 14ᵐ 55ˢ   6ʰ 16ᵐ 30ˢ   6ʰ 17ᵐ 00ˢ   6ʰ 17ᵐ 56ˢ   6ʰ 18ᵐ 45ˢ

particles. The light reaching us from a star now reaches us from one direction, now from another; what we see therefore is a random dance around an average position. On some nights, for example in northern middle latitudes after a winter cold front passes and the wind veers to the northwest, the atmospheric turbulence is greater than usual, and thus stellar twinkling is enhanced. Striking as these scintillations may be, they are not at all pretty to the astronomer at his telescope. Magnification amplifies the turbulent dancing of the image, and when the astronomer wishes to take a photograph, he is faced with the task of taking a time exposure of a wildly wriggling subject. If the "seeing" is poor enough, the finished picture will be too blurry to be useful. Photography from satellites above the earth's atmosphere therefore has decided advantages over photography from the bottom of our gusty ocean of air.

THE EARTH'S ATMOSPHERE

15. The Highest Atmosphere

WE SHALL SEE in Chapter 7 that detailed observations of the motions of earth satellites can reveal a wealth of information on the properties of the atmosphere at very great heights. The first few years of the space age have revolutionized our ideas about conditions far aloft. The density of air decreases much less rapidly there than near the surface; instead of halving itself every 3.5 miles, it halves itself perhaps every 50 miles at a height of 1000 miles. The temperature there is about 2000°F, varying by several hundred degrees between day and night. The input of solar ultraviolet radiation by day heats and expands and raises the highest strata, which then collapse at night. During the maximum of the sunspot cycle, described in Chapter 12, the solar ultraviolet radiation is excessive and the daily rise and fall are exceptionally vigorous. At 600 miles the air density is 10 times as great shortly after noon as it is during the night when the atmosphere has settled again. At the level of the Echo I balloon, some 1000 miles, the material of the atmosphere can scarcely be called air any longer, for the heavier

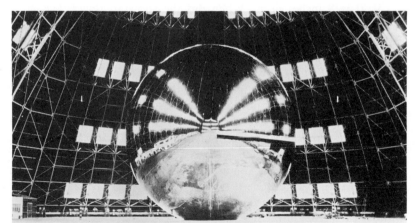

Fig. 2.15:1. The Echo I balloon undergoing a prelaunch inflation test. With its low mass and a diameter of 100 feet, this satellite has revealed much about the nature of the atmosphere at great heights. (*National Aeronautics and Space Administration*)

nitrogen and oxygen cannot ordinarily rise to such heights. The major element at 1000 miles is helium; at even greater distances above the surface the lightest atom, hydrogen, is probably in the ascendancy.

At still greater distances are the Van Allen radiation belts. These belts are approximately doughnut-shaped regions in the extended plane of the earth's magnetic equator, with the inner one about 1.5

earth-radii from the center of the earth, or some 2,000 miles from the surface, and the outer one about 4 earth-radii from the center, or some 12,000 miles above the surface. The main components of these regions are broken-up hydrogen atoms—positively charged protons and negatively charged electrons. These tiny but energetic particles are trapped in the outer magnetic field of the earth, bouncing northward and southward from one magnetic hemisphere to the other, and spiralling very rapidly as they go. A particle may spend days or weeks in these concentrated regions. Beyond the Van Allen belts the earth's magnetic field seems to exert control over the motions of charged particles out to about 10 earth-radii, or some 40,000 miles. Farther out the environment is that of interplanetary space.

AGE OF THE EARTH

16. Salinity of the Seas

DOZENS OF WAYS of guessing the age of the earth, the sun, and our galaxy have been suggested, and answers have ranged from a few thousand years all the way to eternity. Those estimates that are valid within the framework of known physical laws range from some 10 million years to perhaps 10 trillion years. Evidently, if such diverse answers have been found, the problem is not an easy one, but because of its importance we shall revert to the theme of age-finding many times. For now, let us consider the age of the earth only. The general approach to age determination may be illustrated as follows. Suppose one awakens at 7 A.M. to find 6 inches of snow on the ground, and at 9 A.M. it is 8 inches deep. When did the snowfall start? The most reasonable guess is probably 1 A.M., since at the morning rate of one inch per hour the snow must have fallen for 6 hours to accumulate to 6 inches by 7 A.M. and for 8 hours to accumulate to 8 inches by 9 A.M. But this estimate may of course be very wrong. For example, one may have failed to notice the night before that the ground was already covered by 5 inches of snow from a previous storm. On the other hand, the ground may have been warm at the start of the storm and much of the early snow may have melted as it fell. Moreover, the rate of fall may not have been constant with time, the fall possibly being light at first and not becoming a blizzard until dawn. This illustration shows (1) that to determine a time or age we must divide an amount by a rate, and (2) that the deduced age may be very far from correct without adequate knowledge of other factors.

The age of the oceans can similarly be estimated by measuring the present saltiness of the sea and the rate at which it is increasing. In the sea the total mass of sodium (one component of sodium chloride, common salt) is about 1 percent of the mass of all the oceans, or 1.3×10^{22} grams. The rate at which sodium is at present being carried down all of the rivers to the sea is 1.6×10^{14} grams per year. Division indicates that the oceans were formed some 80 million years ago. But is this estimate valid? For one thing, the rate of deposit may have varied in the past. For another, we are implicitly assuming that the primeval oceans were fresh, containing no sodium. If they were salty, our age estimate is too great. Conversely, if we have neglected the fact that much of the ocean salt may have formed salt deposits, our estimate of the total deposition of salt in the oceans and hence our age estimate would be too low. Most important of all considerations is that much of the sodium now flowing to the sea has been eroded from sedimentary rocks, and these sedimentary rocks (as opposed to igneous rocks) were formed from ancient deposits of sediment in the oceans. This sodium therefore has been at sea before and should not be counted; the rate of addition of new sodium is much less than 1.6×10^{14} grams per year. Thus the estimate of 80 million years is likely to be very much too low.

17. Rocks and Radioactivity

A MAJOR ADVANCE in dating began with the discovery of radioactivity by Becquerel and of the chemical elements radium and polonium by the Curies at the turn of the twentieth century. Although we shall not consider the details of atomic structure until later, it is possible to understand the principle of radioactive dating without that knowledge. Radioactive atoms, such as those of radium and uranium, have the remarkable property that their nuclei are unstable and spontaneously break up into other kinds of less massive nuclei. Given one such atom, nobody can say when it will break apart, any more than one can predict which kernel of corn will be the next to pop. But from a large collection of atoms, which is what the experimenter must always work with, it is found that a group of radioactive atoms of a given type disintegrates at a perfectly definite rate. For example, an assemblage of ordinary uranium atoms, with 238 particles in the nucleus of each (U^{238}), will be half gone in 4.5 billion years; the remaining half will be half gone in another 4.5 billion years; and so on. This figure is the so-called "half-life" of U^{238}, and the half-life of any type of radioactive atom can be deduced after measuring experimentally the amount present at two separate times. As far as is known, the rate of disintegration is completely independent of surrounding physical conditions such as pressure and temperature; a group of any number of U^{238} atoms will always halve itself in 4.5×10^9 years. This law of decrease is similar to that of the density of the earth's atmosphere, which, as we have seen, halves itself with every increase in height of $3\frac{1}{2}$ miles.

The transuranic elements, heavier than uranium, are not found naturally in rocks or air or ocean, but a few such substances can be made artificially by accelerators in the physics laboratory. They are all radioactive, and their inherent instability is so great that their measured half-lives are relatively short. Thus, if such transuranic elements as neptunium and plutonium were present in rocks when first formed, they would be virtually all gone now, having turned into other more stable atoms such as helium and lead. Since the longest half-lives among the transuranic elements are only a few million years, the rocks and the earth must be much older than this—an estimate agreeing with that determined from the saltiness of the ocean.

But is it possible to discover how old? There are three kinds of radioactive atoms that decay at quite leisurely rates. As we have seen, the most abundant kind of uranium, U^{238}, has a half-life of 4.5×10^9 years. Each atom undergoes 14 rapid-fire transmutations, ending up as one atom of lead (Pb^{206}) and 8 helium atoms (He^4). Since the time taken for an average atom to fall down the ladder is less than 1/10,000 the time it stays on the roof, we shall not dwell on the details of the fall, although they are well known. The lighter kind or isotope of uranium, U^{235}, has a half-life of only 7.1×10^8 years, decaying also to lead, but this time to Pb^{207}. Thorium (Th^{232}) has a half-life of 1.4×10^{10} years and decays to Pb^{208}. Helium atoms are created in these latter processes also. In principle, by measuring the present relative amounts of any one of these three radioactive atoms to its final decay product, we can find the age of the parent rock. For example, if one analyzes an ancient igneous rock and finds that U^{238} and Pb^{206} are equally abundant, then half of the original U^{238} has decayed, and the age of the rock is 4.5×10^9 years. But there are difficulties, since there may *originally* have been some Pb^{206} present. If so, the time taken for the establishment of the 50–50 ratio is less than 4.5×10^9 years. This uncertainty can be reduced by studying the relative abundance of the several isotopes of lead in rocks that contain no uranium. Assuming this to be the *original* lead abundance in the earth, we may subtract these amounts from the measurements of a uranium-bearing rock. What remains is the desired ratio of U^{238} to Pb^{206} that once was U^{238}. In spite of the minute quantities measured, the radioactivity method of dating is a superior one. From many rock samples and from measures of the relative amounts of various kinds of suitable radioactive atoms and their decay products, the oldest rocks are estimated with some confidence to be 3 or 4 billion years old. The age of the earth itself is presumably somewhat greater, perhaps 5 billion years; it is reassuring that age estimates of the sun and of meteorites are about the same. It appears then that our solar system formed a few billion years ago.

PROBLEMS

1. Supposing that the earth were shaped like an extremely elongated egg, what kinds of evidence might reveal this shape?
2. An observer on a spherical planet finds that a mountain 2.0 miles high can be seen from the ocean surface at a distance of no greater than 71 miles. (a) What is the radius of the planet? (b) What is its circumference?
3. Write the following quantities in exponential form: (a) 5 billion years, (b) 0.00042 ton, (c) three-millionths.
4. Write the following quantities in customary form: (a) 3.7×10^6 grams, (b) 7.413×10^2 cm, (c) 3.14×10^0.

5. Two one-gram masses are situated a distance D apart. **(a)** If they are replaced by two 100-gram masses, how many times as strong is the gravitational force? **(b)** If they are replaced by a 2-gram mass at one point and a 20-gram mass at the other, how many times as strong is the gravitational force?

6. Two objects are at first separated by 10 miles. **(a)** When they are later separated by 30 miles, by what factor is the gravitational force reduced? **(b)** When they are then separated by only $\frac{1}{2}$ mile, by what factor is the gravitational force increased?

7. **(a)** What would be your weight if you were at the surface of a sphere only 1 percent as massive as the earth but with the same radius as the earth? **(b)** What would be your weight if you were on the moon, whose mass is roughly 1 percent that of the earth and whose radius is about $\frac{1}{4}$ that of the earth?

8. The planet Saturn is about 100 times as massive as the earth, and its radius is about 10 times that of the earth. Estimate its average density in grams per cubic centimeter.

9. Suppose you take an imaginary trip from the center of the earth outward in a straight line into space. List the different layers through which you would pass, the distance traveled in each, the state of matter (solid, liquid, or gaseous) in each, and the known or probable most abundant types of atoms in each.

10. Given that the density of air is halved with every 3.5 mile increase in height above sea level, **(a)** how many molecules are there in one cubic inch of air 7 miles above sea level? **(b)** 28 miles above sea level?

11. List the various broad subdivisions of the electromagnetic spectrum in order of increasing wavelength and tell in which of these subdivisions the earth's atmosphere is transparent.

12. Explain why the daytime sky is very dark as seen from a space capsule 100 miles above the earth's surface.

13. Explain why fewer stars are visible on a night when the moon is full than on a night when the moon is below the horizon.

14. A sample of U^{238} originally contains 1.0×10^{20} atoms. Into what kinds of atoms will this sample turn, and how many of each kind will there be after 9.0 billion years?

3

THE EARTH:

MOTIONS

Our planet participates in a variety of motions. Fundamental among them are the daily *rotation* of the earth and its yearly *revolution*. We shall examine each of these motions in turn: the important characteristics of each, the consequences of each for our view of the world from here, and some proofs that the earth is indeed rotating and revolving. Of considerable interest over long stretches of time is the slow *precession* of the earth, the properties and causes of which are considered at the end of the chapter. Other motions of our planet need not concern us yet.

Because all things in the universe move and because much of this motion is recurrent or repetitive, it is important at the beginning to clarify the rather strict distinction the astronomer makes between rotation and revolution. A body *rotates* if it spins around an axis. Electrons and atomic nuclei spin; so do drills, figure skaters, planets, stars, and galaxies. Indeed, nobody has yet found a celestial body that is definitely without rotation. By contrast, a body *revolves* if it moves periodically in a path through space. A normal atom comprises a relatively massive nucleus around which electrons revolve; a miler circling a track is in revolution. Planets revolve in orbits around the sun, and double stars revolve around each other. Each star visible at night is, over the course of hundreds of millions of years, revolving in an enormous path around the nuclear region of our galaxy.

DAILY ROTATION OF THE EARTH

1. Period, Direction, and Speed

THE EARTH ROTATES *once a day from west to east around a straight axis that extends from the north pole through the center of the earth to the south pole.* All of the facts relevant to rotation appear in this one sentence; let us examine it closely.

The day, as a unit of time, is defined by the earth's rotation. The ordinary day of our experience is called the *mean solar day*, or *civil day*, and it is defined as the average time for the earth to turn once relative to the sun. To find the duration of the mean solar day, imagine inverting a giant egg-timer or sand clock at the instant the sun reaches its highest altitude of the day. At the moment of the same event the next day, stop the sand clock and count the number of grains that have passed through the aperture. Repeat this operation every day of the year and you will find that the results vary a bit from day to day. Compute the average number of grains, and let this number fall through the clock. The time taken is the mean solar day, which we subdivide into 24 hours, into 60 minutes per hour, and into 60 seconds per minute. A perfectly regulated watch runs at precisely this rate.

Astronomers often use another kind of day, the star day or *sidereal day*, which is in essence the time taken by the earth to turn once relative to the remote "fixed" stars. The sidereal day is subdivided into sidereal hours, sidereal minutes, and sidereal seconds, just as is the mean solar day, but each of these sidereal time units is shorter in duration than its solar counterpart by one part in 366. The sidereal day is thus shorter than the mean solar day by about 4 minutes. The difference between the two kinds of day is rooted in the earth's annual revolution about the sun. Because we round the sun once a year, the sun appears to move through the stars around us once a year. The two kinds of time, one geared to the sun and the other to the stars, are therefore different; we shall defer looking critically at this matter until later.

The sense or direction of the earth's daily rotation is from west to east. Imagine looking down on a globe of the earth from above the north pole. The direction east then corresponds to *counterclockwise* spin, as California moves toward New York, New York toward England, England toward Siberia, Siberia toward Japan, and Japan toward California (see Fig. 3.1 : 1). Next look at the spinning globe from above the south pole and notice that easterly rotation is then in the clockwise sense. To avoid confusion, let us adopt the convention that we always look down on the earth and solar system from a point in space far to the north. Easterly motion is then counterclockwise and westerly motion clockwise.

Because an object at the earth's surface participates in the daily spin, it moves in general at high speed relative to the earth's axis or center. Now speed is distance traveled divided by time taken, and in one day a surface object travels in a complete circle, with radius equal to its distance from the axis. A body at the north or south pole is located on the axis itself, and thus its speed is zero. At the equator the distance from the axis equals the radius of the earth. Thus, if we call the rotation period of the earth P, the velocity of a surface particle is

$$v = \frac{2\pi R}{P} = \frac{2 \times 3.14 \times 3960 \text{ mi}}{24 \text{ hr}}$$
$$= 1040 \text{ mi/hr.}$$

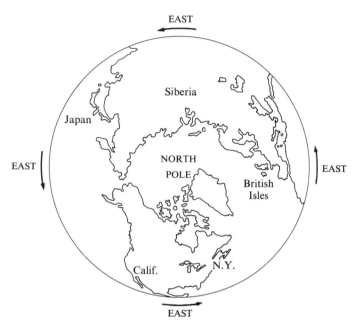

Fig. 3.1:1. The earth rotates eastward, or counterclockwise as viewed from above the north pole.

In other latitudes the speed is less, amounting for example to 800 mi/hr at latitude 40°. At this moment, then, one is moving relatively to the earth's axis at high speed toward the east point of his horizon.

2. Oblateness of the Earth

WE LEARNED IN Chapter 2 that the earth is very nearly spherical in shape. More precisely its oceans are the surface of an *oblate spheroid*, the three-dimensional volume swept out when an *ellipse* is spun round its shortest axis. In Fig. 3.2:1, which is exaggerated for clarity, the equatorial radius of the earth is a and the polar radius is b. The measure of polar flattening is the *ellipticity*, $(a - b)/a$, and for the earth is $1/298$. Since $a = 3960$ miles, the quantity $a - b$ (the difference between the equatorial radius and the polar radius) is only 13.3 miles. The flattening can be established by refining Eratosthenes' work. The *astronomical latitude* of a place is the angle between the vertical there and the plane of the equator and can be found with high precision from astronomical observation of stars or of the noon sun. If the astronomical latitudes of many places on a north–south line are known, and if the distances between them are established by surveying, it is found that the distance per degree of latitude increases slightly in going toward the pole, from 68.7 miles at the equator to 69.4 miles at either pole. The ellipticity of the earth can then be calculated from these observations.

The polar flattening is a consequence of the earth's rotation. Every particle in the solid earth moves in a circular path once a day about the axis of rotation, and for this motion to be maintained a constant *centripetal force* must be exerted on each particle. This type of center-directed force is exemplified by the inward pull on a ball at the end of a whirling string. When the string is let go, the centripetal force ceases and ball and string fly away. The centripetal force on a particle is

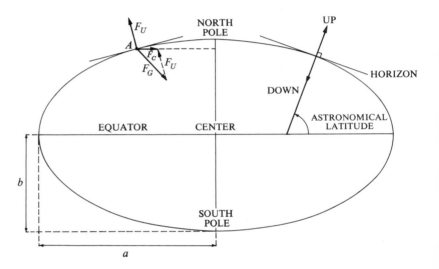

Fig. 3.2:1. The flattened earth, much exaggerated.

proportional to its distance from the axis of rotation and to the square of the angular rate of rotation. When dealing with the entire earth, we must examine the interplay of *two* forces, centripetal and gravitational. Imagine a ball at the surface of the spinning earth, as at A in Fig. 3.2:1. If the ball is to *remain* in circular motion, the *net* force on it must be the centripetal force, F_C. Now the gravitational force, F_G, exerted on the ball is directed nearly toward the center of the earth. To the gravitational force we must add a partially compensating force which will result in precisely the centripetal force, F_C; otherwise the ball will not stay in circular motion but will begin to wander. This force is found by constructing a *vector*, the dotted arrow labeled F_U, and the forces F_G and F_U add to give the net force F_C. The upward force F_U represents the upward push of the ground on the ball and defines the vertical; the tangent plane at A is the horizon there. It is clear from Fig. 3.2:1 that the vertical intersects the center of the earth only at the equator and at the poles. At latitude 45° a hole dug "straight down" would cut the plane of the equator 9 miles from the center. The maintenance of solid rotation, in which each particle moves in a circle, demands that the earth be flattened at the poles and distended at the equator. A large nonrotating mass is spherical, for there are no centripetal forces acting on any particle. A rotating body, on the other hand, adjusts its shape in response to these forces so that it is approximately an oblate spheroid.

Because rotation, as we have seen, is a universal phenomenon, so also therefore is flattening. The larger planets spin rapidly and are conspicuously oblate, and spiral galaxies are enormously flattened, being shaped something like coins.

3. Daily Spin of the Celestial Sphere

PROBABLY THE FACT of astronomy most obvious to the casual observer is the alternation of day and night. The sun, rising in the morning to the east, slants up the forenoon sky, reaches its peak altitude above the horizon at about noon, swings down the western sky, and finally sinks beneath the western horizon, only to rise once

Fig. 3.3:1. Stars setting in the west. The three stars of Orion's Belt are at the upper left when the time exposure starts and move downward and to the right as time passes. (*Lick Observatory photograph*)

again in the east the following morning. The moon, although it may rise at any hour of the day, follows the same pattern; once it rises the moon also wheels across the sky from east to west. So too do the stars and constellations. Although the stars do not change their positions relative to each other at all rapidly and the Big Dipper of tonight will still be dipper-shaped thousands of years from now, close inspection reveals that every star in the sky circuits around the earth every 24 sidereal hours, or every 23 hours and 56 minutes of ordinary time. This daily motion of celestial objects is best pictured by imagining that the stars are fixed to the inner surface of a black sphere of extremely and arbitrarily large radius, and that this *celestial sphere* spins at a

Fig. 3.3:2. An 8-hour exposure of the region surrounding the north celestial pole. Each star during this time moves counterclockwise one-third of a circuit because of the earth's rotation. The trail of Polaris is the bright arc close to the center. (*Lick Observatory photograph*)

perfectly uniform rate once every sidereal day from east to west around two points in the sky, the *north celestial pole* (*NCP*) near the star Polaris and the *south celestial pole* (*SCP*) in the opposite direction. The convenience of adopting an enormous radius for the figmentary celestial sphere is simply that the earth by comparison is only a point. Therefore, whether the stars and constellations are observed from the United States or Africa or Australia, the map of the sky and the shapes of the constellations are the same.

The daily spin of the celestial sphere from east to west is a consequence of the earth's daily rotation from west to east. Although the earth in fact spins, we are not aware of it because of the preponderant force of gravitation which defines "down" for us at all times; wherever we may be on the earth, we always feel "on top of the world." Since we personally feel stationary, the stars must yield. A detached observer in space would say that the earth spins from west to east daily; an earth-bound observer says that the celestial sphere spins from east to west daily. They are equally valid descriptions, but we shall soon see that the former is the simpler way of looking at the matter.

4. The Sky from Middle Northern Latitudes

IMAGINE AN OBSERVER at latitude 40° north, located on "top" of the small globe of the earth, at point X of Fig. 3.4:1. Next sketch in the extremely large celestial sphere centered at the center of the earth, noting that any such diagram drawn on a single sheet of paper must be greatly out of scale. With the earth scaled down to the size shown in Fig. 3.4:1, the celestial sphere ought to be drawn with a diameter of at least 100 miles. The vertical at point X is defined by a hanging plumb line; if this direction is extended down through the earth and out the other side it pierces the celestial sphere at the *nadir*; the opposite point, straight up, is the *zenith*. The great circle everywhere 90° from each of these two points is the *celestial horizon*, more or less equivalent to the visible horizon or dividing line between earth and sky. Let us adopt the convention that N, the north point of the horizon, is to the left, so that one is looking at the celestial sphere from a point far outside it to the west. The great circle passing through the north point, the zenith, the south point, and the nadir is the *celestial meridian*. Since the observer's latitude is 40° north, the angle between his vertical and the equator plane must also be 40°; this allows us to draw in the earth's equator and also its rotation axis, as shown in Fig. 3.4:1. Now if the earth's axis is extended until it cuts the celestial sphere, the points so defined are the *celestial poles*, NCP and SCP. The great circle everywhere 90° from each celestial pole is the *celestial equator*, the intersection of the earth's extended equator plane with the celestial sphere. The celestial equator passes precisely through the east and west points of the observer's horizon.

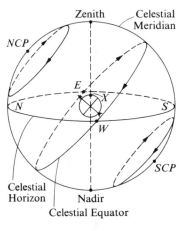

Fig. 3.4:1. The celestial sphere seen from a middle northern latitude.

Recalling that the earth spins from west to east daily but that any observer always feels stationary "on top of the world," let us keep the earth fixed and spin the celestial sphere in the opposite sense, from east to west. Then stars like those of Orion's Belt, which rise almost exactly at the east point, cross the meridian high in the south about 6 hours after rising, set in the west some 12 hours after rising, cross the meridian again to the north well below the horizon some 18 hours after rising, and finally rise again in the east after one full day. Stars like those of the Big Dipper, whose angular distances from the north celestial pole are less than the observer's latitude, continually wheel about this pole, never setting; these are the *north circumpolar stars*. Stars whose angular distances from the south celestial pole are less than the observer's latitude never rise; these are the *south circumpolar stars*. The observer who has never traveled away from 40° north latitude has never made acquaintance with the Southern Cross.

Stars located in a belt of the sky flanking the celestial equator alternately rise and set. In our example the angular half-width of this belt is 50°. Apart from the small effect of refraction, a star on the equator rises due east, sets due west, and is up half the time and down half the time. A star like Vega rises in the northeast, sets off to the northwest, and is above the horizon more than half the time; one like Antares rises in the southeast, sets in the southwest, and is above the horizon less than half the time. Polaris, the moderately bright North Star, happens in our century to lie only about one degree from the north celestial pole. Moving in its tiny daily circuit about the pole, it is a useful compass, lying always very close to the direction true north. Moreover, since the angular altitude of the celestial pole above the horizon equals the observer's latitude, observations of Polaris provide a convenient way of finding that latitude.

5. The Sky from the North Pole

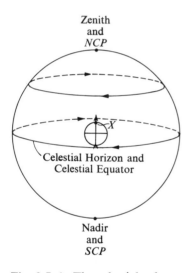

Zenith
and
NCP

Celestial Horizon and
Celestial Equator

Nadir
and
SCP

Fig. 3.5:1. The celestial sphere seen from the north pole.

THE OBSERVER at the north pole, at point X in Fig. 3.5:1, also feels "on top of the world." "Down" defines his nadir, "up" his zenith, and the infinitely extended tangent plane at his location defines the celestial horizon, as in our previous diagram. But the observer here is astride the earth's axis, and extension of this axis outward to the celestial sphere shows now that the north celestial pole is the zenith, the south celestial pole coincides with the nadir, and the celestial equator and celestial horizon are the same great circle. We cannot label compass directions here because at the north pole there is no direction except south. With the celestial sphere set into its daily east-to-west spin, every star sweeps out a circle of constant altitude once each day. The belt stars of Orion, when watched through the hours, skim around the horizon from left to right, and Polaris circles very nearly overhead. When observed from the pole, no star can rise or set; all stars in the north celestial hemisphere are circumpolar, remaining above the horizon, while those south of the equator are never visible. At the south pole the situation is reversed: Polaris, the Big Dipper, and Vega are never seen, whereas Antares, Canopus, and the Southern Cross are always up, each sweeping out a circle of constant altitude, this time from right to left.

6. The Sky from the Equator

FROM A POINT on the earth's equator, in Ecuador, in Borneo, or in the mid-Pacific, an observer also feels on top of things, and accordingly Fig. 3.6:1 is also oriented with the zenith at the top of the diagram. Let us again put the north point of the horizon to the left. Here, because the observer is 90° from each pole, the extended axis of rotation pierces the north and south points of his horizon. The celestial equator passes through the east point, the zenith, the west point, and the nadir. Orion rises in the east, swings up the eastern sky, passes overhead, and sinks down the western sky, while Polaris circles due north on the horizon, counterclockwise, and the Southern Cross wheels clockwise, to the south. At the equator no stars are circumpolar: every star's daily circle is bisected by the celestial horizon, and therefore all stars and constellations alternately rise and set. Apart from refraction and obstructions on the horizon, every star is up for 12 sidereal hours and then down for 12 sidereal hours.

In summary, the passing view of the sky depends only on the latitude of the observer. We have seen that (1) at the poles half of the stars are up all of the time; (2) at the equator all of the stars are up half of the time; and (3) at any intermediate latitude some of the stars are up all of the time, some of the stars are down all of the time, and the rest are up some of the time and down some of the time. Although this statement summarizes the situation concisely, it is worth remembering that during the daylight hours we cannot see stars even though, according to the rules in the preceding sentence, they may be above the horizon.

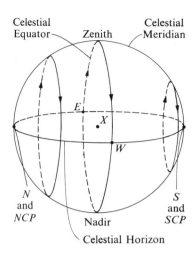

Fig. 3.6:1. The celestial sphere seen from a place on the equator.

7. Proofs That the Earth Rotates

GALILEO IN 1609 WAS the first man to scan the heavens with a telescope. From that day to this, evidence has accumulated that other celestial bodies spin: the parade of sunspots across the solar disk, the surface features on the face of Mars, the flattening of Saturn and of remote galaxies. By analogy one can argue that the earth, being one of the celestial bodies, ought to spin too. But argument by analogy, although often suggestive, scarcely constitutes proof.

About a century ago Foucault performed his celebrated pendulum experiment in Paris; let us repeat it, but at the north pole and more elaborately. A large cylindrical glass building is erected and a massive ball suspended from a frictionless bearing on the ceiling. Attached to the bottom of the ball is a small pin. Around the inside of the building is a balcony, with its inner edge covered with a ridge of sand. To start the experiment, the ball is first pulled to one side so that the pin makes a mark in the sand. When let go, it swings back and forth like a pendulum, making a mark in the sand at each crossing (see Fig. 3.7:1). But the pin does not strike the same point each time; the plane of swing slowly but steadily moves clockwise as seen from above the building. The cycle is completed in exactly 24 sidereal hours; the plane of swing has moved steadily around a vertical axis through 360°. Let us repeat the experiment during the long Arctic night, letting the ball go at the instant when the plane of swing is lined up with a bright star like Vega, seen through the glass wall. As the hours go by, the plane of swing *remains* lined up with Vega, for, as we have already seen, a star watched from the north pole moves steadily around the sky once each sidereal day. The plane of swing thus remains *fixed* relative to a frame of reference defined by the stars. There is no centripetal force here on the earth's axis; there are no frictional forces in our idealized experiment. Only gravitation is acting, straight down. There is no force

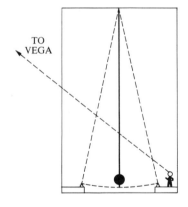

Fig. 3.7:1. The Foucault pendulum experiment conducted at the north pole.

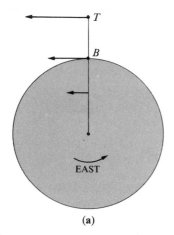

(a)

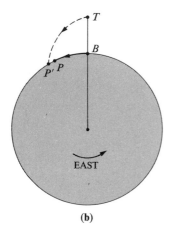

(b)

Fig. 3.7:2. Because of the earth's rotation, an object dropped from a tower hits ground slightly east of the base.

tending to make the plane of swing turn; therefore it does not. Rather, the building (and the earth on which it is built) turns once a day in the opposite sense. Looking down on earth from a point in space far out toward Polaris, the plane of swing of the pendulum is fixed, while the earth and dome turn easterly or counterclockwise. Thus it is the earth that rotates, not the celestial sphere. When the experiment is done elsewhere on earth, the interpretation is more difficult because the direction of the observer's vertical, or zenith, changes during the day as the earth rotates. The rate at which the plane of a Foucault pendulum swings turns out to be less than 360° per day at places other than the poles, and it is zero at the equator.

An object dropped from a high tower falls exactly vertically only at the north or south pole; elsewhere it lands slightly to the east of the vertical, providing another demonstration of the earth's rotation. Imagine, for simplicity, a ball dropped from a tall building located on the equator. When released it has, relative to the earth's axis, an easterly velocity a bit greater than that of the ground below because it is farther from the earth's axis. In Fig. 3.7:2(a), where we look down on the earth from above the north pole, are shown the easterly speeds of points at different distances from the axis. Because of the greater velocity at the top, *T*, the path followed by the dropped ball *as seen from space* will arc out and the ball will hit ground at *P'*. The bottom of the building, *B*, in this *same* time interval will move only to *P*. The ball thus hits east of the building, as is seen in Fig. 3.7:2(b). For a one-mile drop the deflection is about 6 feet. Similarly, if an object should fall down a vertical mine shaft at the equator, it would soon carom off the east wall of the shaft.

Drift is a consequence of the earth's rotation that must be allowed for in long-range gunnery. In the northern hemisphere a shell fired due north will travel over regions spinning less fast than the eastern velocity at the gun. The shell gets ahead of or east of the north–south meridian through the gun's position; a plot of its path on a map shows a drift to the right. If a projectile is shot due south, it moves over regions where the rotational speed is faster and thus it lags behind; plotted on a map, the drift is again to the right. The situation is reversed in the southern hemisphere, where a shell drifts to the left. The spiraling winds of typhoons and hurricanes, opposite in the two hemispheres, exemplify the influence of the earth's rotation on the ways of the weather; so too do the easterly trade winds of the near-tropical regions and the prevailing westerlies of the middle latitudes. By utilizing the Doppler principle (Chapter 11, Section 7), astronomers can measure the velocity of approach or recession of celestial objects. It turns out that the moon is approaching us at several hundred miles per hour at the time of moonrise in the east. This result is at first sight distressing, since it implies the moon will be perilously close in a few weeks, but reassurance comes when it is found that the moon is receding at several hundred miles per hour at the time of moonset in the west. The reason for these motions is, once again, our own rotational motion toward the eastern horizon.

8. Irregularities in the Earth's Rotation

THE PRIMARY requirement of a good time-keeper is a uniform rate. The human heart, for example, does not provide a very suitable basis for measuring time because it pulses at a changing rate depending on whether its owner has been napping or running a race and because one person's average pulse is faster or slower than another's. On the other hand, a good watch ticks at the same rate whether it is Monday or Thursday, winter or summer, morning or evening. Since the earth's daily rotation is used for time-keeping, we wish to find out how good a clock it is.

It is clear of course that our rotation rate cannot be very far from uniform, for otherwise the celestial sphere would appear to turn by fits and starts. Additional evidence that we should not expect much nonuniformity in the length of the day is afforded by the celebrated physical principle known as the *conservation of angular momentum*, which we shall now examine. The ordinary momentum of a body, such as an automobile, is the product of its mass and its velocity. The *angular momentum* (or rotational momentum) of a particle moving in a circle about an axis is the product of its mass, its distance from the axis, and its speed. In Fig. 3.8:1 the particle of mass M lies a distance D from the rotation axis and is moving at velocity v; its angular momentum is $L = MDv$. The total angular momentum of a body of finite size is the sum of the angular momentums of all particles in it; for example, a solid sphere of the same density throughout has $L = \frac{2}{5}MRv$, where M is its total mass, R its radius, and v the equatorial speed of a surface point about the axis. The idea of conservation is akin to that in forestry. For every tree cut down and carted to the lumber mill, ideally a new seedling is planted, the total number of trees at any time thus remaining constant. The principle of conservation of angular momentum states that the total amount of this quantity in the universe stays the same; it can neither be created nor destroyed. The angular momentum of any totally isolated system also remains constant. In view of this principle and because the earth is a fairly isolated system, we anticipate that its angular momentum is virtually constant and therefore that the product of its mass, its radius, and its equatorial velocity must remain constant. Thus the length of the day, the time for the earth to turn once, can change only if the earth's mass changes or if our globe swells or shrinks in size. We have no evidence for such variations in mass or size apart from the altogether negligible rate of infall of meteors from space and of projection of man-made objects into space.

Precise modern observations have nevertheless shown that the earth is not quite a perfect clock. For one thing, the length of the day has been increasing slowly, and is now about two-hundredths of a second longer than it was two thousand years ago. This effect is largely due to the ocean tides raised by the moon, the decrease in the angular momentum of the earth being compensated by an increase in that of the

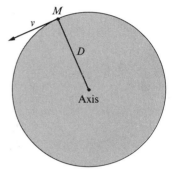

Fig. 3.8:1. The angular momentum of the circling particle is $L = MDv$.

moon. We shall consider these tidal effects later. In addition, small seasonal effects have been found, with extreme changes in the length of the day of about ± 0.002 second, the earth running a bit faster in the fall and slower in the spring. Such variations perhaps can be explained by seasonal melting of ice and snow at high latitude and consequent slight raising of the sea level everywhere; or seasonal changes in location and movement of air masses may be responsible. Whatever the reasons, seasonal changes in the angular momentum of all water and ice at the surface and of the whole atmosphere must be compensated by a change in that of the earth. To the long-term and seasonal effects we must add random fluctuations. From one decade to the next the average length of the day varies from its average over a century by about ± 0.002 second, but what causes these random changes we do not know. It should be added that observations have also proved that the precise location of the north and south pole changes by a few feet from decade to decade. Conservation of angular momentum requires that both this motion and the random time fluctuations be compensated elsewhere; a likely source of such compensation is irregular flow of the fluid matter in the earth's core.

The three known types of irregularity in our rotation conspire to make our planet a slightly capricious time-keeper. In 1955 a new kind of more uniform time was introduced; it is called *ephemeris time* and is based on the earth's orbital period rather than on its rotation. We shall read more about it in the next chapter.

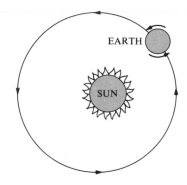

Fig. 3.9:1. The rotation and revolution of the earth are both described in the counterclockwise sense as seen from north of the solar system.

ANNUAL REVOLUTION OF THE EARTH

9. Period and Direction

THE EARTH REVOLVES *around the sun once a year from west to east in an orbit that is not far from circular.*

The year, as a unit of time, is defined by the earth's revolution. Although several kinds of year may be defined, the *tropical year* or *year of the seasons* is the ordinary year we are concerned with in everyday life. It is the time elapsed from the beginning of spring one year to the beginning of spring the next year; its length is 365.2422 mean solar days. The easterly direction of the earth's orbital motion has the same significance as with the earth's rotation: the motion is counterclockwise as watched from far to the north of our solar system (see Fig. 3.9:1).

10. Size of the Orbit

THE MEAN DISTANCE of the earth from the sun defines a new unit of length which we shall often need, the *astronomical unit*. Its measured value is about 93,000,000 miles. Although known to a precision of about one part in one million, the adopted value of the astronomical unit in miles changes a bit every time scientists make an improvement in determining its length. It should be stressed that 1 a.u. is a perfectly definite length; the fluctuations are only in our measurements of it. The precise meaning we attach to the term *mean distance* is given in the next section. For now, let us assume the earth's orbit is a perfect circle and examine the principles involved in finding the distance from sun to earth by triangulation. For the observer at point A on the earth (see Fig. 3.10:1), the sun at a given moment lies at a definite point among the stars on the celestial sphere. At this instant of time the sun is projected, as B sees it, onto a slightly different part of the celestial sphere. Comparison shows that the angular shift is 17.6″, or about 1 percent of the angular diameter of the sun itself. The procedure would of course be invalid if the stars were as close as shown in Fig. 3.10:1 because they too would be in different directions as seen by A and B In truth, the stars are so enormously distant it makes no practical difference whether one observes them from A or from B. The half-angle, 8.8″, is called the *geocentric parallax* of the sun. It is the angle at the sun subtended by the radius of the earth, AC in the diagram. Solving the right triangle, with the parallax and the earth's radius known, yields the distance of 93,000,000 miles.

It is a difficult matter, instrumentally, to see the stars in the daytime, which is the only time solar observations can be made. Moreover, A is observing the sun at sunset and B at sunrise. Because of such practical objections it is preferable to find the distance to the sun in other ways. We shall study them later.

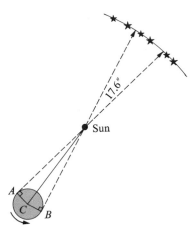

Fig. 3.10:1. The sun appears in slightly different directions when viewed from opposite points on earth, thus allowing deduction of its distance from us.

11. Shape of the Orbit: Kepler's First Law

JOHANNES KEPLER announced in 1609 the first two of his celebrated three laws of planetary motion. The first law deals with the shape of planetary paths and states that *the orbit of a planet is an ellipse with the sun at one focus.* An observational check on the shape of the earth's orbit can be made by plotting the annual path of the sun around *us.* Think of a boy and girl on opposite sides of a rotating merry-go-round; it is simply a question of whim whether one chooses to describe the relative path of the boy around the girl or the girl around the boy; the results are the same. Now the data we need are (1) the location of the sun among the constellations every day of the year, and (2) the relative distance to the sun. The latter can be found by measuring the angular diameter of the sun precisely, at the telescope, every clear noon. The bigger the angular diameter the closer the sun; the reciprocal of the measured angular diameter is proportional to the distance. The results of such a survey are shown in Fig. 3.11:1, where a smooth curve is passed through the daily measured values. Then, when the direction and relative distance of the sun are plotted, the resulting curve turns out to be an ellipse. Figure 3.11:1 shows that the extreme range of variation in angular diameter is only about one part in 32. Therefore our distance from the sun changes only by about 3 percent, the elliptical orbit being nearly circular. The illustration also reveals that we are closest to the sun early in winter (about January 2) and farthest in summer (about July 4). At first sight these dates may be puzzling because it is obvious that one is hotter when near the fire and colder when far from it. Actually, the dominant causes of the seasonal variations in temperature must be sought elsewhere, as we shall see in Section 17.

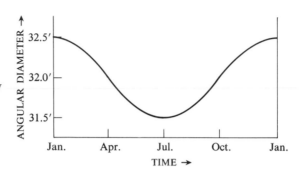

Fig. 3.11:1. The changing distance of the sun is revealed by the annual variation in its angular diameter.

12. Geometry of the Ellipse

TAKE A PHONOGRAPH record or a circular piece of cardboard and hold it in front of a large piece of cardboard which is kept perpendicular to the sun. When the circle is face-on to the sun, its shadow is a circle; when edge-on to the sun, it is a straight line. The sequence of shapes as the disk is rotated from face-on to edge-on is the whole family of elliptical figures. In Fig. 3.12:1 we look directly down on the earth's

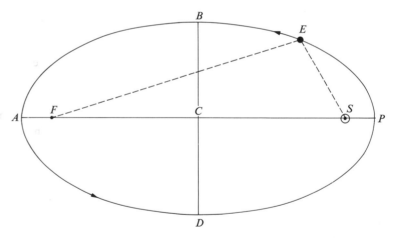

Fig. 3.12:1. The orbit of a planet is an ellipse, and the sun occupies one focus of the ellipse.

elliptical orbit (the flattening is exaggerated for clearness). The line *AP* is the *major axis* and the line *BD* is the *minor axis*, and the two axes bisect each other at right angles at *C*, the *center* of the ellipse. The *semimajor axis* is called *a*, and $a = AC = CP$; the *semiminor axis* is *b*, and $b = BC = CD$. The two *foci* of the ellipse are located equidistant from *C* on the major axis. One is marked by *S*, the sun, in accord with Kepler's first law; the other focus, *F*, is simply a point in space, occupied by nothing. In any ellipse the sum of the distances from any point on the curve to both foci remains constant; the earth (E) therefore moves always so that $SE + EF$ stays the same. This sum is exactly equal to AP, the major axis, as can be seen by putting the earth at the special point P.

The astronomer's definition of the mean distance of a planet from the sun, although to some extent arbitrary, is a very convenient one. It is simply a, the semimajor axis of the planet's orbit. In Fig. 3.12:1, then, $a = AC = CP = 1$ a.u. When the earth is at P, it comes as close to the sun as possible. This is the *perihelion* of our orbit (from the Greek "near sun"), the earth passing this point every year about January 2. The most distant point is at A, the *aphelion* of the orbit (from the Greek "away from sun"), aphelion passage occurring yearly about July 4. An alternative definition of mean distance is the average of perihelion distance and aphelion distance, because this average is $\frac{1}{2}(SP + AS) = \frac{1}{2}AP = AC = CP = a$, in agreement with the definition above.

Although a measures the size of the ellipse, we need a quantity to measure the flattening. The axis ratio, b/a, is one such quantity; the ellipticity, $1 - b/a$, which we used for the earth's polar flattening, is another. The one commonly used to describe the shape of an orbit is the *eccentricity*, e, its formula being $e^2 = 1 - b^2/a^2$. The concept of eccentricity may be pictured from Fig. 3.12:1; it is the distance from center to focus divided by the semimajor axis. Thus $e = CS/CP$. In the illustration the sun is shown some 80 percent of the way from C to P, and thus $e = 0.80$. The actual orbit of the earth has $e = 0.017$, and thus the sun is located fairly close to the center of the orbit; from above, $CS = e \times CP = 0.017 \times 93,000,000$ miles $= 1.6$ million miles. An orbit with eccentricity exactly zero implies $CS = 0$ and $CF = 0$. Here both foci coincide and the orbit is a circle. An elliptical orbit with eccentricity nearly 1 is a highly flattened curve; one with e exactly 1 is a straight line. Although according to Kepler's first law it is perfectly legitimate for an actual body to move in such a path, the motion would not last long, for soon the body would meet calamity, being engulfed by the sun. The eccentricity of any ellipse lies in the range from 0 to 1. Eccentricities greater than 1 and in some instances exactly 1 describe the shapes of curves that are not closed. We shall study them in Chapter 7.

13. Speed in the Orbit

SINCE THE EARTH'S path is nearly circular, we can, without appreciable error, say that the earth each year sweeps out the circumference of a circle whose radius is a. Thus our average orbital speed is

$$v = \frac{2\pi a}{P} = \frac{2 \times 3.14 \times 9.30 \times 10^7 \text{ mi}}{1 \text{ yr}} \times \frac{1 \text{ yr}}{3.16 \times 10^7 \text{ sec}} = 18.5 \text{ mi/sec.}$$

The actual speed in an elliptical orbit is variable, however. Kepler's second law of planetary motion, known as the *law of areas*, states that *the line joining a planet to the sun sweeps out equal areas in equal times.*

Think of the area swept out for an eight-week interval lasting from four weeks before perihelion (December 5) until four weeks after perihelion (January 30), as shown in Fig. 3.13:1. Kepler's second law tells us that in any other eight-week interval the area of the wedge swept out must be exactly the same. Specifically, think of the time from four weeks before aphelion (June 6) to four weeks after aphelion (August 1). To match the area of the short and fat wedge flanking perihelion, we must here construct a long and narrow wedge. Accordingly, the distance traveled by the earth in eight weeks along the periphery of the wedge is less near aphelion than near perihelion. In general, the farther the earth is from the sun the slower it moves; it moves fastest at the time of perihelion passage in January and slowest at aphelion passage in July. The variation is not great, from 18.8 mi/sec to 18.2 mi/sec, because our orbit is nearly circular. In a *precisely* circular

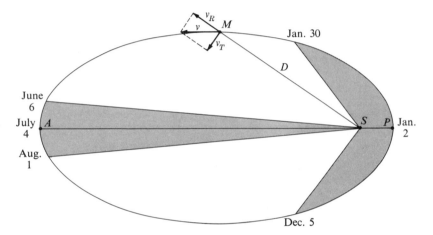

Fig. 3.13:1. A planet moves so that the line joining it and the sun sweeps out equal areas in equal intervals of time.

orbit the law of areas predicts constant speed, whereas in a highly elongated orbit, like that of a typical comet, the speed changes through a very large range: akin to that of a tortoise at its remote aphelion and to that of a hare when swinging round perihelion close to the sun.

Kepler's law of areas is an alternative and historically earlier statement of the law of conservation of angular momentum, which was described in Section 8. Stated more generally than our definition there, the orbital angular momentum of a body moving around the sun is the product of its mass, its distance from the sun, and its *transverse velocity*, v_T. In Fig. 3.13:1 the total velocity of body M is symbolized by v and its direction at any point is tangent to the orbital path. The velocity vector is composed of two parts: the *radial velocity*, v_R, is the rate of change of distance from the sun; the transverse velocity is at right angles to the radial velocity. The total velocity is the diagonal of the rectangle formed by the radial velocity and the transverse velocity. The constancy of angular momentum, L, requires

$$MDv_T = \text{constant.}$$

A body moving directly toward or away from the sun has no transverse velocity and thus its angular momentum is zero. Another body in a circular orbit has no radial velocity and thus its transverse and total velocities are identical; from the formula the speed in circular motion must be constant because D is fixed. In general, a body must move so that MDv_T is an unchanging quantity. The equivalence of this law and Kepler's law of areas may be seen as follows: in a very short time interval the line joining M and S sweeps out a long but extremely thin triangle. In one second, for example, the sides of this triangle are of length D and $v_T \times 1$ sec and therefore its area is $\frac{1}{2}Dv_T \times 1$ sec. Kepler's law of areas states that this quantity, which is about 0.86 billion square miles for the earth's orbit, is a constant. The formula for angular momentum says the same thing, providing the mass of the body is constant.

14. Sun and Ecliptic

A CONSEQUENCE of the fact that we orbit about the sun easterly once each year is that the sun appears to move easterly around *us* once each year. If we plot the position of the sun among the background stars and constellations each day, we find it is moving slowly but steadily through them. As a practical matter it is hard to locate the sun among the stars, because when the sun is visible the stars are not, but one way around this difficulty is to notice each evening what star group is rising exactly opposite the sunset point. The antisun point will be found to move steadily eastward through the stars at about 1° per day, and hence the sun itself moves in this same way. The annual path of the sun is the *ecliptic*; it is a great circle in the sky, splitting the celestial sphere exactly in half. Although the sun always lies on the ecliptic, as a matter of definition, almost all of the other bodies in our solar system—moon, planets, and most asteroids—move fairly close to the ecliptic. The *zodiac* is a belt around the sky of angular width 18° and centered on the ecliptic. Within its confines at any time lie most of the celestial bodies of our solar system.

The sun, as it moves easterly 360° per year, or some 30° per month, passes through the 12 constellations of the zodiac at the rate of one per month. Figure 3.14:1 shows that at the beginning of April the sun lies in the constellation of Pisces the Fishes. The opposite zodiacal constellation, rising in the east at sunset on this date, is Virgo the Virgin. A month later, at the beginning of May, the sun has moved easterly into Aries the Ram; the antipoint off to the east at sundown is now in Libra the Scales. Virgo, lying next west to Libra, has at sunset in early May already climbed well up the eastern sky as it participates in the westward spin of the celestial sphere. By the first of June the sun has moved farther east into Taurus the Bull; the antipoint is then located in Scorpio the Scorpion. At sunset in June Libra is well up, and Virgo even higher in the sky. Viewed from the earth, both the sun and the point opposite the sun move easterly one constellation per month. For any particular month the zodiacal constellations on or above the horizon at sunset are those reckoned from the sun's direction counterclockwise (east) to the constellation opposite the sun. For example, on the first of October the sun is in Virgo. At sunset, therefore,

Virgo is setting in the west, Libra and Scorpio are in the western celestial hemisphere, Sagittarius is on the meridian, Capricornus and Aquarius are in the eastern hemisphere, and Pisces is just rising. As the evening hours pass, sun and stars all wheel west, as we have already seen.

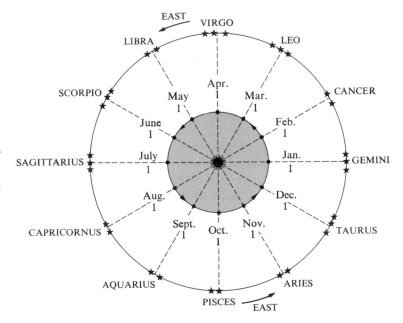

Fig. 3.14:1. Because of the earth's orbital motion, the sun as seen from the earth moves easterly through the stars, completing a circuit in one year.

You are probably aware that if your birthday is early in April, or indeed anywhere in the interval between March 21 and April 20, you are said by the astrologer to have been born under the "sign" of Aries the Ram, in spite of the fact that in our time the sun in early April is located one constellation to the west, in Pisces the Fishes. The confusion arises because the location of the sun among the stars on any given date of the year is slowly changing. When the original system of astrological "signs" was established a few thousand years ago, it was correct, but the *precession of the equinoxes*, to which we shall turn our attention presently, has changed things considerably since those days.

15. Annual March of the Constellations

BECAUSE WE CIRCUIT easterly once a year around the sun without being aware of it, the sun seems to circle us annually, moving easterly along the ecliptic through the background stars. Alternatively, it is equally valid to say that the whole celestial sphere shifts slowly *westward* relative to the sun. Thinking now of both the daily westward spin of the celestial sphere *and* the slight westward gain of the celestial sphere on the sun each day, notice that the sphere gains exactly one lap on the sun each year. This gain of 360° in 365 days amounts very closely to 1° per day. The stars and constellations thus cross the meridian a bit earlier each day, when we reckon time by the sun. Star time and star positions gain 24 hours or 360° per year on the sun, amounting to 2 hours per month or 4 minutes per day. If we are keeping ordinary civil time, every star rises 4 minutes earlier and sets 4 minutes earlier each day; every star crosses the meridian due north or due south of a specific point 4 minutes earlier each day.

In addition to their daily circuits, therefore, the constellations march progressively west with the seasons. Pegasus is a harbinger of autumn, rising in the east at sunset in August; by November it is rising 6 hours earlier and thus in early evening is high on the meridian; in February at sunset it is deep in the west; during late spring and early summer it is below the horizon at sunset and therefore not visible at all. The following August, a full year later, Pegasus is back in the east at sunset once again. One who knows the sky and watches it at all seasons cannot fail to relate its aspect to the time of year: the first early evening appearance of Pegasus in the east foretells the fall; Orion announces winter; Leo foreruns the spring; and Arcturus in Bootes tells of summertime. Indeed, thousands of years ago the annual march of the constellations was utilized as a practical calendar to regulate the planting and harvesting of crops.

16. Equator and Ecliptic

THE CELESTIAL equator in the sky is the circle where the earth's equator plane, projected out into space, intersects the celestial sphere. The ecliptic, on the other hand, is the circle in the sky where the earth's orbit plane, projected, intersects the sphere of stars. Are these two circles the same? Phrased otherwise, is the rotation axis of the earth exactly at right angles to the plane of our orbit around the sun? If the answers were yes, life would be considerably simpler for those learning astronomy, although considerably duller for all citizens of the world. For, if the ecliptic were the same as the celestial equator, the sun would always be somewhere on the equator; it would therefore always rise exactly in the east and set exactly in the west, and the day would always be 12 hours long, followed inevitably by a night of 12 hours. The amount of solar heat received in any town would under these conditions be very nearly the same every month of the year. There would thus be no seasons at any point on the earth, although it would still be hotter at the equator than at the poles.

The two circles, however, are *not* the same; the angle between them, called the obliquity of the ecliptic, is 23.5° (see Fig. 3.16:1). The ecliptic poles, where the perpendicular to our orbit pierces the celestial sphere, lie 23.5° from their celestial counterparts, the north ecliptic pole lying in the northern constellation of Draco the Dragon, the south ecliptic pole far to the south in Dorado the Swordfish. The sun, as it moves easterly around the ecliptic once a year, must cross the celestial equator twice a year. These intersection points are the *vernal equinox*, where the sun crosses into the northern celestial hemisphere, and the *autumnal equinox*, where the sun crosses into the southern celestial hemisphere. Spring begins the moment the sun reaches the vernal equinox, about March 21; autumn starts when it passes the autumnal equinox, about

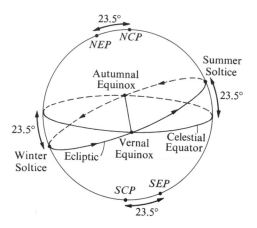

Fig. 3.16:1. The sun's annual motion against the stellar background defines the ecliptic. Spring and autumn begin when the sun passes the equinoxes; summer and winter begin when it passes the solstices.

September 23. When the sun reaches its greatest angular distance north of the celestial equator, on about June 21, it is at the *summer solstice*, and summer begins. Similarly, around December 22 the sun reaches its greatest angular distance south of the equator; it is then at the *winter solstice*, and winter begins at this instant.

17. The Seasons

THE FUNDAMENTAL reason why we have seasons is the obliquity of the ecliptic. To see why this is so, first imagine expanding the diagram in Fig. 3.16:1 so that it also shows the earth's orbital plane and spin axis. Figure 3.17:1 has been rotated through 23.5° so that the ecliptic

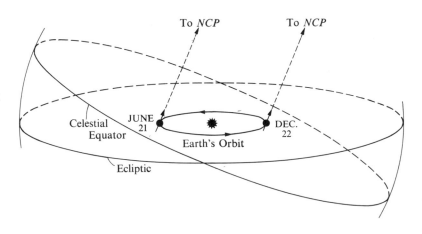

Fig. 3.17:1. The earth's rotation axis points in a fixed direction while the earth revolves in its orbit around the sun.

and therefore the the earth's orbital plane, which defines the ecliptic, are horizontal. The sun appears at the center of the diagram and the earth is shown at two sample points of its orbit. We are looking at the diagram from an extremely remote point in space off in the direction of Pisces the Fishes. Notice that the rotation axis of the earth is inclined

23.5° at all times, because it must be perpendicular to the equator of the earth and hence to the celestial equator. The spin axis remains pointed toward Polaris while the earth is traveling independently in its orbit around the sun. Of course if the celestial sphere were restricted in size, as we have had incorrectly to depict it in Fig. 3.17:1, the NCP would sweep out an annual loop among the stars. But because we imagine the sphere of stars as being indefinitely large, the earth's axis points toward a fixed point on it all year long.

The interrelation of the earth's two fundamental motions is not easy to conceive at first. Perhaps you may wish to think of an analogous situation. Picture a plane floor tilted 23.5° from the horizontal, as in the fun house at an amusement park (see Fig. 3.17:2). You walk around the room, hoping that gravity will keep you vertical and spinning 365 times for each orbit round the floor. Here, the floor is your orbital plane, which maintains a fixed orientation in space. Your spin axis also maintains a fixed direction in space, defined in this example by the direction of gravity.

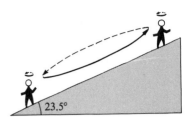

Fig. 3.17:2. Illustration of the relationship between the earth's axis of rotation and its orbital plane.

Now, to see in detail the factors that are relevant in causing seasons, let us further expand Fig. 3.17:1 so that we are looking at the earth itself on June 21 and on December 22. Figure 3.17:3(a) shows the earth on June 21. The sun's rays are coming in from right to left, and thus the right-hand hemisphere is in daylight while the left-hand hemisphere is in darkness. Remembering that the globe is spinning once each day, suppose first that a person is located at point A on the equator. It is noontime there, but as the earth turns he is carried around the hindside of the planet and 6 hours later enters the nighttime hemisphere; the sun sets. At midnight he is at point B, and six hours after that he is carried into daylight. Finally at noon he arrives at point A once again. Notice that his daily path is exactly bisected by the sunset–sunrise line and therefore that the duration of daylight is 12 hours and of nighttime 12 hours.

Next think of a person at the north pole. He simply turns around once a day; the sun is up all day, wheeling around the sky once a day at an altitude of 23.5° above the horizon. But at the south pole on June 21 the sun never rises; it circles 23.5° below the horizon.

At point D, for example on the north coast of Iceland, the daily track of an observer is from D around the near side to C at noon, then around the far side to D again. Notice that he remains in the daylit hemisphere all of the time and that at midnight the sun is on his horizon. This circle on the earth is located at north latitude $90° - 23.5° = 66.5°$, and is called the *Arctic Circle*. All points on or north of the Arctic Circle experience the midnight sun at least once a year. Let us next imagine being at point E, say on the Palmer Peninsula of Antarctica, on June 21. Here at noon the sun is on the horizon; as we swing round to F and back to E again the sun never rises during the day, if we disregard the lofting effect of refraction. Here is the *Antarctic Circle*, at south latitude 66.5°. All points south of it are in darkness at noon and indeed all day long on June 21.

Starting from point G, in a middle north latitude, notice that on

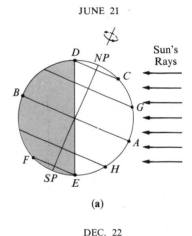

(a)

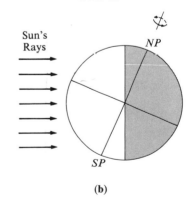

(b)

Fig. 3.17:3. On June 21 days are longest and nights are shortest at any place in the northern hemisphere, while the opposite holds in the southern hemisphere. The situation is reversed on December 22.

June 21 the daily track lies largely in sunshine; daylight lasts a long time and the night is short; at noon the sun rides very high in the southern sky. But if we go to a middle south latitude, starting our daily trek at point *H*, the night is long on June 21 and the sun is up for less than 12 hours; even at noontime the sun is low in the sky.

Two other circles deserve mention. On June 21 the noontime sun is directly overhead in north latitude 23.5° and directly in the nadir at midnight in south latitude 23.5°. These circles are called the *Tropic of Cancer* and *Tropic of Capricorn* respectively. The Tropic of Cancer passes very near Havana, through southern Egypt, central India, and Formosa. The Tropic of Capricorn runs near Rio de Janeiro, through the far southerly part of the African continent, and across central Australia. People who live in the tropics, the belt bounded by these two circles, may experience the sun passing through the zenith at some time during the year; in other regions of the earth the sun is never seen directly overhead.

On December 22 the situation is precisely reversed. Figure 3.17:3(b) shows the solar radiation arriving from left to right, with the left-hand hemisphere this time in daylight. At the equator the day and night are each 12 hours long, as always throughout the year. But now, on December 22, midnight sun is the rule in Antarctica and darkness at noon prevails in the high northern latitudes, while the noon sun is overhead at the Tropic of Capricorn. Places in the middle northern latitudes have short days and long nights, while the inhabitants of the middle southern latitudes enjoy long days and short nights.

Figure 3.17:3 shows only the extreme situations. At the equinoxes, on March 21 and September 23, the polar axis is tilted neither toward nor away from the sun but at right angles to the direction of the sun. On these dates every point on earth has days and nights of 12-hour length, if again the small effect of refraction is ignored. At the north pole the sun rises on March 21, circles daily in a slowly ascending spiral until on June 21 it is 23.5° above the horizon; it then slowly descends until it crosses the equator on September 23 and therefore sets once again. Because refraction raises the sun by 35′ and because the angular radius of the sun is 16′, the top rim of the sun actually swings into view at the north pole two days before the vernal equinox and finally disappears two days after the autumnal equinox. In the middle latitudes it is a good idea to turn on the car headlights about half an hour after sunset, but at the poles one can wait until about two weeks after sunset. At the south pole the sun is also up for some six months and then down for half a year, but the dates are reversed. As is clear from Fig. 3.17:3, the seasons in the two hemispheres are opposite. When it is winter in the United States, it is summer in Australia; when it is autumn in Europe, it is spring in Argentina; when the sun is shining at the north pole, it is dark at the south pole.

The alternation of the seasons at any one point on earth, for example at latitude 40° north, is attended by an alternation of the average temperature during the year. The yearly temperature pattern at any place is largely governed by the changing amount of solar radiation received by a horizontal square foot of ground there. Two specific effects conspire so that our heat receipt is a maximum at the summer solstice and a minimum at the winter solstice. (1) The duration of daylight is greatest on the first day of summer. At latitude 40° north the sun is above the horizon for some 15 hours on June 21 and below the horizon for only about 9 hours; it rises well before 6 A.M. and sets well after 6 P.M. On December 22 the sun rises late, is up only about 9 hours, and sets during the late afternoon. (2) The sun's altitude above the horizon averages greater on June 21 than on December 22. Think of a square-foot beam of radiation arriving from the sun. If the sun is overhead, and hence has altitude 90°, the energy arriving in one minute will strike a square one foot on a side. But if the sun is at a low altitude, this same amount of energy will be spread into a rectangle one foot wide but greater than one foot long. The amount of energy per square foot reaching the ground is thus smaller the lower the sun in the sky. As an extreme, imagine the sun right on the horizon; there its energy is infinitely diluted. The consequence of these two effects is that at latitude 40° north the energy received per square foot of horizontal surface during June 21 is 1.5 times that on March 21 and September 23; that on the latter dates is in turn 2.2 times that on December 22. Multiplying these two numbers, we find the heat receipt on the longest day of the year is 3.3 times that on the shortest day of the year at latitude 40° north. The same figures apply to latitude 40° south, except that the dates are reversed.

We can now understand the puzzle of Section 11, where we found the earth to be closest to the sun in early January and farthest away in July. At perihelion the amount of solar energy reaching the entire earth is naturally greatest; at aphelion it is least. But because of the small eccentricity of the orbit our distance from the sun does not vary much. The total daily amount of incident sunlight only changes by ± 3.3 percent from the yearly average; the maximum on January 2 is only 1.07 times that on July 4. At most points on the earth this effect is very small as contrasted with the changing duration of daylight and the average altitude of the sun. What little effect there is, however, ought to moderate the seasons in the northern hemisphere and intensify them in the southern. In the southern hemisphere summer begins on December 22 and perihelion happens to occur only about two weeks later; everything conspires to make it hot. On June 21 the day is short, the sun is low, and the earth has nearly reached aphelion; thus each effect reduces the incident solar energy. Actual weather records do not reveal any increased severity there, however, because of the moderating influence of the great southern oceans. The planet Mars happens to have the same characteristics: the southern hemisphere winter there begins at approximately the same time that Mars reaches aphelion; southern summer nearly coincides with perihelion passage. In contrast with the earth's nearly circular orbit, however, the Martian path is appreciably eccentric, and, as we shall see, the extremities of the southern Martian seasons are marked enough to be observable from here on earth.

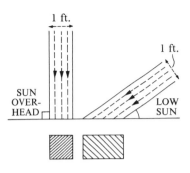

Fig. 3.17:4. When the sun is overhead, the solar energy reaching a given area in one minute is a maximum. When it is low in the sky, this same amount of energy is spread out over a larger area.

18. Why the Seasons Lag

ALTHOUGH THE MAXIMUM sunshine at any point in the temperate or polar latitudes is received on the date of the summer solstice, it is common knowledge that the hottest days of summer come along about a month and a half later. Similarly, the coldest spells of winter occur on the average about six weeks after the winter solstice. Likewise, on any given date the incident solar energy is a maximum when the sun is on the meridian at about noon, but the maximum temperature usually does not occur until midafternoon. Hottest temperature coincides with maximum heat or energy *content* of the air at a specific place, whereas up to this time we have been considering the arrival *rate* of energy. At the summer solstice, although the arrival rate of solar radiation is a maximum, the reradiation of energy by the earth into space is not; the fund is still increasing. Gain and loss do not balance until several weeks later. This lag is analogous to the changing population of a large city during the day. The arrival rate is a maximum in the morning as commuters and shoppers pour into the city. Although a few night workers and city-dwellers with suburban jobs are outbound, the inflow is much greater and thus the population is increasing. Late in the afternoon a mass outflow to the suburbs begins and the total number of people in the city declines. The maximum population occurs during the middle of the day when the numbers of inbound and outbound passengers are equal, and there is thus a considerable lag from the time of the crowded morning influx to the moment of peak population.

19. The Kinds of Year

THE MOST FUNDAMENTAL kind of year is the *sidereal year*. It is the interval of time that would be recorded by a detached observer in space watching the earth orbit around the sun exactly once relative to a frame of reference defined by the stars. Otherwise stated, it is the time taken by the sun to move exactly once around the ecliptic from a certain star back to that star again. Its duration is 365.25636... mean solar days. The kind of year we use in everyday life is called the *tropical year*, the *year of the seasons*, or the *ordinary year*. It is the time the sun takes to move from the vernal equinox around the ecliptic back to the vernal equinox. Its duration is 365.24220... mean solar days. The ordinary year is thus 0.01416... mean solar days or some 20.4 minutes shorter than the sidereal year.

The discrepancy arises from the slow precession of the vernal equinox westward through the background stars. We shall examine this effect shortly, but for now let us recall that spring begins when the sun annually reaches the vernal equinox and that maximum energy is received at the summer solstice. The heat budget at any point on earth is accordingly linked to the sun's progress relative to the equinoxes and solstices rather than to the background stars. Our calendar must therefore accord with the year of the seasons rather than the sidereal year.

THE NATURAL UNITS of time are the day, governed by the coming and going of the sun, the year, governed by the coming and going of the seasons, and to a lesser extent the month, governed by the coming and going of the moon. We have already seen that the particular kind of day most suitable for society is the mean solar day and that the appropriate kind of year is the tropical year, which is 365.24220... mean solar days in length. The most natural kind of month to employ is the time from one full moon to the next full moon; its duration averages 29.53059... mean solar days. The number of full moons per year thus averages 12.36.... Notice that none of these larger time units is an integral multiple of any smaller one; indeed there is no physical reason why such round numbers should be expected. Calendar problems turn largely on efforts to reconcile these various time intervals with one another.

Many of the early calendars either were based on the moon or attempted to harmonize both sun and moon. Today's Islamic calendar is reckoned from the moon, and its year of 12 ordinary months is some 11 days shorter than the ordinary year. The date of Easter Sunday in the Christian calendar changes from year to year in what perhaps seems a random manner. Actually, Easter is based on the moon: it is celebrated on the first Sunday after the full moon that occurs on or after March 21. Between the years A.D. 1800 and 2000, for example, the date of Easter varies from March 22 to April 25.

In 45 B.C. the *Julian calendar* was born. The Roman calendar had been in a snarl, and Julius Caesar reformed it after counsel with the astronomer Sosigenes. The Julian calendar is strictly solar; the moon is disregarded. Each year has 365 days, except that there is an extra day every fourth year; accordingly, the average length of the Julian year is 365.25 days, not far from the actual value of 365.24220... days. Without a leap year every four years, the moment of the vernal equinox would come 0.24220... days later each year, its occurrence being delayed by one day each $1/0.24220... = 4.13...$ years. Without leap years, after 750 years January would presage hot weather and July cold. The Julian calendar got around this difficulty very nicely and was used extensively until the sixteenth century.

But the average length of the Julian year is a bit too long, by $11\frac{1}{4}$ minutes. Thus the sun's equinoctial crossing gradually shifted to earlier and earlier dates of the Julian calendar, at the rate of about eight days every thousand years. In 1582 Pope Gregory XIII, advised by the astronomer Clavius, decreed that the date of the vernal equinox, which had crept forward to March 11, should revert to March 21, its date at the time of the Council of Nicaea in A.D. 325. The only way to effect such a change was to skip ten days; and thus in Catholic countries the day after October 4, 1582, was October 15, 1582. Most non-Catholic nations, however, did not go along with this jump, and England and the British colonies held out until in 1752 September 2 was followed by September 14. Many citizens thought they were being cheated out of 11 days of life and the resultant riots killed a number of people. Russia adopted the Gregorian calendar after the Revolution, in 1918.

In addition to bringing the vernal equinox to March 21, it was desirable, in order to prevent future date-jumping, to bring the calendar year into better alignment with the tropical year by shortening the average length of the calendar year. To this end Pope Gregory ruled therefore that only those century-end years divisible by 400 should be leap years. The *Gregorian calendar*, which we use today, resembles the Julian calendar closely, the only difference being that years divisible by 100 are not leap years unless also divisible by 400. The years 1800, 1900, and 2100 thus have no February 29, but 2000 and 2400 do have the extra day. In one complete cycle of 400 years there are thus 97 leap years; the average length of the Gregorian year is therefore $365\frac{97}{400} = 365.2425$ days, remarkably close to the duration of the ordinary year. The difference is only 0.00030 day, or 26 seconds, and the Gregorian calendar will get out of step with the year of the seasons only one day every 3000 years. One can always develop a scheme that will keep the calendar year and the tropical year in as close step as desired, but the scheming rapidly gets elaborate and complicated. Here is one occasion where it is perhaps wisest to retain the Gregorian calendar and adopt the motto, "Let George do it—in A.D. 5000."

21. Proofs That the Earth Revolves

UNTIL THE SIXTEENTH century most men believed that the sun moved around the earth each year. Today evidence abounds that the sun is essentially fixed at the center of the solar system and that the earth is doing the moving.

Try moving your head in a circle while looking out the window. You will notice that any near object, for example a speck on the glass, moves in a small path relative to a more distant tree or house. Analogously, if the earth is indeed moving around the sun, you would expect all relatively near stars to loop in little ellipses against the very much more distant galaxies. Imagine a relatively near star located on the ecliptic in Pisces the Fishes, as in Fig. 3.21:1. On April 1 it cannot be seen because the sun too is in Pisces. But on July 1 the star is some 90° west of the sun and rising in the east about midnight; a photograph

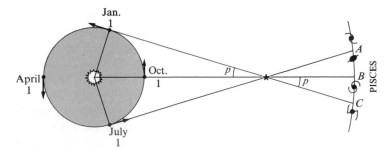

Fig. 3.21:1. As measured from the earth, each of the nearer stars moves in a small ellipse once a year, proving that the earth revolves around the sun.

shows it to lie at point *A* on the celestial sphere. On October 1 it is at point *B* and on January 1 at point *C*; during the next half-year it moves back to *A* again, completing its round trip in just one year. Being on the ecliptic, the star moves in a little arc on the sky. For a star not in the ecliptic the annual path is a small ellipse. If the earth is not moving around the sun, on the other hand, such motions are not to be expected.

These loops were not observed at the telescope until 1838, when Bessel detected the motion of the faint star 61 Cygni. Today these reflex motions are known for more than 6000 stars, each star completing its small circuit exactly once a year, each star offering proof that the earth indeed moves around the sun. It is fair to ask why more than two centuries elapsed from the invention of the telescope to Bessel's discovery; the point is that the stars are extremely far away and thus their reflex motions are very small. The angular semimajor axis of the star's ellipse is called the *annual parallax* of the star and is shown in Fig. 3.21:1 as the angle *p*. The largest known parallax, that of α Centauri, is only 0.78″, smaller than the angular diameter of a nickel three miles away. It is little wonder that the parallactic motions of the stars were not discovered until the development of large and precise instruments.

Today we accept the fact that the earth moves around the sun and utilize the measured parallax of a star in combination with the 93,000,000-mile separation of earth and sun to solve for the star's distance. Essentially, the earth's annual motion provides a base line for triangulation, and solution of the right triangle in Fig. 3.21:1 tells us how far away the star is.

Not only do the stars execute parallactic ellipses as a consequence of our earth's motion, but also their velocities of approach or recession vary throughout the year. Imagine that the star in Fig. 3.21:1 is at rest relative to the sun. On April 1 the earth is neither approaching nor receding from the star, on July 1 it is moving toward the star at some 18.5 mi/sec, on October 1 its approach speed is zero, and on January 1 it is receding from the star at 18.5 mi/sec. Because of the Doppler principle, this annual cyclic change in *radial velocity* should be detectable in the spectrum of the star's light. Such yearly changes have been observed for thousands of stars, excepting those at or near the ecliptic poles where the annual change is too small to measure. Each of these thousands bears witness to the earth's motion around the sun; if the earth were stationary no such changes would occur.

Several other proofs are known for the earth's revolution around the sun, but we shall pause for only one more: the *aberration* of light. "Aberration" stems from the Latin word for "wander," and its effect on the wandering of stars was discovered by Bradley in 1727, more than a century before annual parallaxes or the Doppler effect were known. Like the parallactic motion discovered by Bessel, the aberrational motion of a star is an annual ellipse on the celestial sphere. But the angular size of the ellipse is here much bigger, and unlike the parallax effect the size of the ellipse here is not dependent on the star's

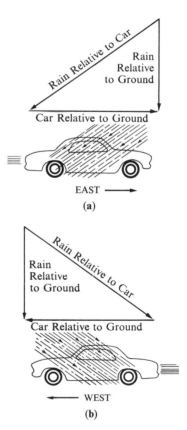

Fig. 3.21:2. When rain is falling vertically on a windless day, its motion relative to any moving object is downward and rearward.

distance. To understand aberration, let us look at an example closer to common experience. Imagine it is raining and because there is no wind the drops are falling vertically. Your car is parked and you look out the side window; the drops indeed are falling vertically. Now drive east along the road as in Fig. 3.21:2(a); looking out the side window you see the drops moving down and to the rear or west. Make a U-turn and head west, as in Fig. 3.21:2(b); now the drops are moving down and to the east, but still to the rear. Drive around a traffic circle and all the way around the drops move down and to the rear; stop, and they fall vertically again. Here we are dealing with a problem in relative motion: the speed and direction of the rain relative to you is a combination of its motion relative to the ground and your motion relative to the ground. The solution is found by sketching the vector triangles shown in Fig. 3.21:2.

Now let us compare the direction of arrival of the rays from a star as seen from the sun and as seen from the circling earth. Figure 3.21:3 shows that the direction of the star as we see it makes a smaller angle with the direction of our motion than does the true direction. Because the velocity of light is 186,000 mi/sec, or about a thousand times the earth's orbital speed, the difference in angle is fairly small, never exceeding 20.5″. The angular displacement is a maximum for all stars at right angles to the direction of our motion; it is zero for stars ahead and behind. Returning to the star in Pisces, Fig. 3.21:1, the aberration effect is zero on July 1, when we head toward the star. On October 1 the star and all the galaxies in Pisces are displaced by the maximum amount of 20.5″, on January 1 there is again no effect, and on April 1 the shift is a maximum but in the opposite direction. Stars on the ecliptic oscillate along an arc once a year, whereas those not on the ecliptic move in small ellipses. But wherever the star may be on the celestial sphere, the angular semimajor axis of its annual path is always 20.5″, the angle subtended at the tee by a nickel held on the green of a par-three golf hole of 230 yards. It is far greater than the largest known stellar parallax, and accordingly it is not surprising that the discovery of aberration occurred a century before that of the parallactic motions of the stars.

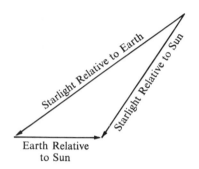

Fig. 3.21:3. Because of the aberration of light, the direction of a distant star if observed from the earth is not quite the same as its direction if observed from the sun.

PRECESSIONAL MOTION OF THE EARTH

22. Period and Direction

WE HAVE SEEN that the year of the seasons is a bit shorter than the true sidereal year, for as the sun moves easterly around the ecliptic, the vernal equinox moves west a bit through the stars to meet the sun. Hipparchus discovered this motion in the second century before Christ, and at that time the vernal equinox was located in the constellation Aries; in the intervening two thousand years it has, as we have seen, moved westward into Pisces. The annual westward rate is 50.2″ per year, and therefore one full cycle of 360° takes 25,800 years. Thus 258 centuries from now our successors will again find the vernal equinox located in the constellation Pisces. In the interim the intersection of the ecliptic and the celestial equator will be sliding slowly but steadily westward along the ecliptic through the constellations of the zodiac.

THE IMPLICATION of the backsliding of the equinoxes is that the celestial equator is not a fixed great circle among the stars and that the locations of the north and south celestial poles among the stars change with time. Because the celestial poles are *defined* by the earth's rotation axis, Hipparchus' discovery shows that the earth's spin axis gyrates once every 25,800 years. The root of this complication is the spheroidal shape of the earth. As Newton found, a perfectly spherical earth would be attracted gravitationally by the sun like a point-mass, but the actual oblate earth behaves more like a sphere with a massive equatorial doughnut wrapped around it. Point P in Fig. 3.23:1 represents the sun, lying far from the earth. Its gravitational pull on A is greater than on C (at the earth's center); its pull on B is less than on C. The difference between attractions on the parts of the doughnut at A and B tends to turn the earth until its extended equatorial plane contains the point P. Imagine for a moment that the line BCA is an ocean liner and that three tugs are hauling on it with lines attached at A, B, and C, in the directions indicated by the arrows. The engines of tug A are at full speed ahead, those of C at half speed, and those of B at slow speed. In addition to a motion of the whole ship through the water, which does not concern us here, the ship rotates in response to the tugs, its compass heading in this example changing in a counterclockwise direction.

Why, then, has the earth's equatorial plane not moved into coincidence with its orbital plane in response to this force? Unlike the ship, our earth is spinning rapidly. The response of the rotating earth to this turning force is at first sight surprising: the direction of the earth's spin axis does not creep toward the north ecliptic pole, as one might expect, but instead always moves at right angles to the direction of the north ecliptic pole. Figure 3.23:2 shows the similarity between the behavior of a spinning top and that of the spinning earth. If set on its pivot without spin a top falls over in response to gravity, but if set to spinning rapidly with its rotation axis vertical it does not fall over. If it spins rapidly with its axis inclined by 23.5°, then the combination of the rapid rotation and the downward force of gravity yields a slow precession of the axis, the upper point of the axis describing a horizontal circle while the angle from the vertical remains at 23.5°. The behavior of the earth is analogous, although complicated by the fact that both the sun and moon exert separate turning forces on the earth; the precession of the equinoxes arises from their combined action.

A CONSEQUENCE of the earth's precession is that the north celestial pole slowly sweeps out a small circle around the north ecliptic pole of

23. Physical Cause

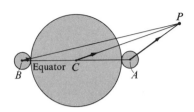

Fig. 3.23:1. The sun's gravitational attraction on the spheroidal earth tends to bring the equatorial plane into coincidence with the plane of the earth's orbit.

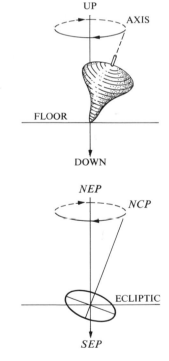

Fig. 3.23:2. The precession of the earth's axis resembles that of a fast-spinning top.

24. Motion of the Poles and the Equinoxes

angular radius 23.5°, the motion being counterclockwise through the stars. Now only about 1° from Polaris, the pole will move to within $\frac{1}{2}°$ of Polaris during the next half-century and then on past it; it will enter the constellation of Cepheus early in the twenty-first century, moving slowly through Cepheus and entering Cygnus about the year 10,000. Some 12,000 years from now the bright star Vega will serve as the north star, as it did 14,000 years ago. We found earlier that those stars lying close to the celestial pole are circumpolar, but, since the pole moves, a quite different group of stars will be circumpolar for the observer several thousand years from now. A star that now rises due east will in general rise to the north of east or to the south of east in the distant future. The Southern Cross, now in the invisible south polar cap for most northern observers, will be visible from the entire United States and southern Europe in the year 15,000. Other constellations that are today in the invisible polar cap will be familiar to observers many millennia from now, as they were long long ago.

PROBLEMS

1. **(a)** What is the speed of a particle around the earth's rotation axis if it lies in the plane of the equator and halfway between the surface and center of the earth? **(b)** Of an ice crystal that lies one mile from the south pole of the earth?

2. Assume the length of the day is suddenly increased from 24 hours to 48 hours. **(a)** What would the equatorial velocity of rotation then be? **(b)** Would the earth's oblateness be different? **(c)** By what factor would the rotational angular momentum of the earth change?

3. The bright star Capella lies 44° from the north celestial pole. **(a)** Is Capella circumpolar in Houston (latitude 30° north)? **(b)** In Minneapolis (latitude 45° north)?

4. The stars of the Southern Cross all lie at least 27° from the south celestial pole. What is the northernmost latitude at which the Cross in its entirety can be seen above the horizon? Consult a map of the world to find several cities that lie near this latitude.

5. A star is located on the celestial equator. Describe its daily path as seen from **(a)** a place on the equator, **(b)** from the south pole, and **(c)** from a place at latitude 30° north.

6. Describe the results you would expect if a Foucault pendulum experiment were conducted at the south pole.

7. Sketch an ellipse and its major and minor axes and two foci. Place a planet at one end of the minor axis and use the theorem of Pythagoras to demonstrate that $e^2 = 1 - (b^2/a^2)$.

8. The orbit of Mars has a semimajor axis of 142,000,000 miles and an eccentricity of 0.093. **(a)** What is the distance from the center of the sun to the empty focus of the Martian orbit? **(b)** What are the perihelion and aphelion distances of Mars from the sun?

9. In early January what zodiacal constellations are above the horizon at sunset? At midnight? At sunrise? At noon?

10. A star rises in the east at 8:30 P.M. standard time on May 1. What time does it rise on May 2? On May 15? On June 1? On September 1? On February 1? On April 15?

11. Describe the apparent path of the sun throughout the year as observed from the south pole.

12. What effects are chiefly responsible for the seasonal variation of temperature at a place in a temperate latitude?

13. When during the year does a town on the equator receive the greatest daily amount of solar energy? The least daily amount?

14. Discuss one proof that the earth revolves around the sun.

15. (a) What is the maximum possible angle between Polaris and the north celestial pole as the earth's axis precesses? (b) In what century will Polaris next lie at this maximum angle? (c) And in what latitudes of the earth will Polaris then be a circumpolar star?

4

MEASURES OF PLACE AND TIME

A N important part of daily living is the business of getting to certain places at certain times, and all members of a community must agree on where a place is and what the time is if they hope to live together with a minimum of confusion. Astronomers too have found it essential to settle on certain conventional and precisely defined ways of specifying where and when—where to find Arcturus now, when the sun will set tonight. Although a rather abstract subject, astronomical measurement of place and time must be understood if one is to grasp clearly the spatial arrangement of the bodies comprising the physical universe and the changes of this arrangement with time.

1. Dimensions and Coordinates

AN UNAMBIGUOUS definition of a location or event requires listing one or more quantities or *coordinates*; the number of coordinates listed is the *dimensionality* of the system. The mileposts on the Pennsylvania Turnpike exemplify a one-dimensional coordinate system, indicating distance along the highway from the Ohio border. A city map is two-dimensional because two coordinates are required to specify a point; the New York Public Library, for example, is located at Fifth Avenue and Forty-second Street. A relief map is three-dimensional, because to construct it one must know the height of the surface above sea level at each point on the two-dimensional plane. The path of an airplane in flight requires four coordinates in order to keep track of its changing location. At 8:12 P.M. the craft is 22,000 feet above O'Hare Airport in Chicago and at 8:39 P.M. it is 16,000 feet above downtown Milwaukee; its path between the two cities is a succession of events, each one of which is specified by three space coordinates and one time coordinate.

Every coordinate system, whatever its dimensionality, must have an *origin* from which measures are made, an orientation in space, and one or more units, such as miles or degrees, in which the coordinates are expressed. A convenient choice for charting the path from Chicago to Milwaukee is to adopt O'Hare Airport as the origin. At a time t minutes later, the airplane is x miles east of a north–south line through O'Hare ($-x$ miles if west of this line), y miles north of an east–west line through O'Hare, and at altitude z feet above that of O'Hare. It should be stressed that there is nothing absolute about the number of dimensions, the location of the origin, or the orientation of coordinate systems; all are chosen for convenience and simplicity in dealing with the problem at hand. The astronomer at one time will use a three-dimensional coordinate system whose origin is the nucleus of the Milky Way galaxy; at another time he will need a two-dimensional system on the celestial sphere with origin at the center of the earth.

MEASURES OF PLACE

2. Angular Measure

OUR SPECIAL CONCERN now is in designating the direction of a celestial body rather than its distance from us; we therefore deal with angles. The most familiar angular unit is the *degree*, of which there are 360 in a full circle and 90 in a right angle; the degree is subdivided into 60 *minutes of arc*, and the minute of arc is further subdivided into 60 *seconds of arc*. Thus $1' = 60''$, and $1° = 60' = 3600''$. The average angular diameter of the sun is $32'$; the angular diameter of Mars ranges from less than $4''$ up to $25''$, depending on its distance from the earth.

Instead of degrees, minutes of arc, and seconds of arc, the astronomer often finds it convenient to use time units to measure angles. Although at first sight it may appear unjustifiable to express angles in terms of time intervals, remember that the 24-hour circling of the celestial sphere provides us with a natural time unit, and one circuit is of course 360° of angular travel. From the equivalences listed below, it can be seen that a star located on the celestial equator moves 15° in an hour, 1° in 4 minutes of time, and 15″ in one second of time.

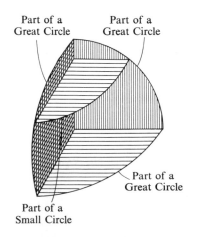

Part of a Great Circle   Part of a Great Circle

Part of a Great Circle

Part of a Small Circle

Fig. 4.3:1. Any great circle divides a sphere into two equal parts; a small circle does not.

$$24^h = 360°$$
$$60^m = 1^h = 15°$$
$$4^m = 1° = 60'$$

$$60^s = 1^m = 15'$$
$$4^s = 1' = 60''$$
$$1^s = 15''$$

3. Coordinates on a Sphere

LOCATING A STAR or the moon or a man-made satellite on the celestial sphere at a given instant requires only two numbers. For example, if Jupiter at a certain time is south of you and halfway from horizon to zenith, its location on the sky is accurately specified. Astronomers find it necessary to use a variety of such two-dimensional coordinate systems. But before studying them individually, we will find it useful to discover that these several systems have much in common with one another.

(1) Each of the astronomer's spherical coordinate systems has a definite *physical basis*, such as the direction of gravity or the rotation axis of the earth. (2) Whatever this physical basis may be, it defines a *fundamental great circle* on the sky, such as the celestial equator. By a great circle we mean the circle of intersection of a sphere and a plane passed through the center of that sphere; any great circle divides a sphere into two exactly equal parts. A small circle, on the other hand, is the circle of intersection of a sphere and any plane that does not pass through the sphere's center. The distinction between the two types of circle is shown in Fig. 4.3:1. (3) Given the fundamental great circle, the location of its two *poles*, lying 90° from all points of the great circle, follows automatically. (4) There is the family of all *secondary great circles*, each of which passes from one pole to the other and cuts the fundamental at right angles. (5) On the fundamental great circle there is always a *point of origin* from which angles are measured. The various features are shown in Fig. 4.3:2. The two coordinates of star *S* are the arc *AF*, which is defined to be the angle *AOF* at the center of the sphere between the lines *OA* and *OF*, and the arc *FS*, which is defined to be the angle *FOS*.

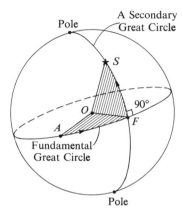

Fig. 4.3:2. Common features of any spherical coordinate system.

4. Azimuth and Altitude in the Sky

THE MOST STRAIGHTFORWARD set of coordinates to visualize is the *horizon system*, whose physical basis is the direction of gravity as defined by a plumb line at the point of observation. Its fundamental great circle is the *celestial horizon*, the circle of intersection of the observer's horizon plane with the celestial sphere. Because the celestial sphere is conceived to be indefinitely large, it is immaterial whether we imagine this plane passed through the observer at the surface or through the center of the earth. The poles of the celestial horizon are, as we saw in Fig. 3.4:1, the *zenith* and *nadir*. The secondary great circles are called *vertical circles*, the point of origin on the fundamental great circle is the *north point* of the horizon, and the special vertical circle passing through the origin is the *celestial meridian*. The two coordinates of a star in the horizon system are the *azimuth*, or compass direction, and the *altitude*, or angular elevation above the horizon. In Fig. 4.4:1 the azimuth of star *P* is the angle at observer *O* that is subtended by the points *N* and *F*, measured from the north point around through the east point to the foot of the star's vertical circle, or, what is the identical quantity, the *arc NESF*. The azimuth of an object in the sky may lie anywhere between 0° and 360°; for the star in Fig. 4.4:1, lying southwest of the observer, it is about 240°. The altitude of the star is the angle at *O* between the lines *OF* and *OP*, or, as we shall say subsequently, the arc *FP*. Altitude ranges from 90° for an object directly

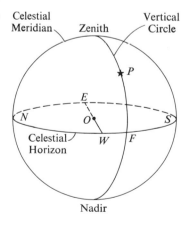

Fig. 4.4:1. The azimuth of star *P* is the arc *NESF* and the altitude is the arc *FP*.

overhead to 0° for an object on the horizon to −90° for an object directly beneath the observer. Of course no celestial body with a negative altitude can be seen because it is below the horizon. The altitude of the star in Fig. 4.4:1 is about 40°.

The azimuth and altitude of a celestial body change in a rather complex fashion as the celestial sphere turns through the day. Moreover, the azimuth and altitude of a given star at a given instant, say Betelgeuse at 10 P.M. tonight, depend on where the observer of Betelgeuse is located on the earth. Therefore these coordinates, useful though they may be in navigation and surveying, clearly need to be supplemented by coordinates of a more stable character.

5. Hour Angle, Declination, and Right Ascension

THE PHYSICAL BASIS of the *equatorial* system of coordinates is the axis of rotation of the earth. As we saw in Fig. 3.4:1, extension of this axis outward to the celestial sphere defines the *north celestial pole* and *south celestial pole*. The fundamental great circle here is the *celestial equator*, the secondaries are called *hour circles*, and the special hour circle passing through the observer's zenith is again the *celestial meridian*. The intersection of the celestial equator and the celestial meridian is called the *equator point*.

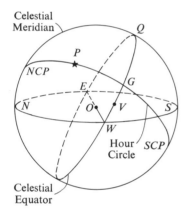

Let us distinguish two sets of equatorial coordinates, for reasons to be clarified soon. In the first set the coordinates are the *hour angle* and the *declination*. In Fig. 4.5:1, which is oriented in the same fashion as Fig. 4.4:1, the hour angle of star P is the arc QG and is measured westward from the equator point, Q, to the star's hour circle. Hour angle is reckoned either in degrees, from 0° to 360°, or in hours, from 0^h to 24^h. This coordinate is sometimes called the *local hour angle*, as a reminder that at any given moment the hour angle of a star is not the same for observers at different points on the earth. The hour angle of a star is simply the number of sidereal hours ago that the star, in its daily circuit of the sky, crossed the observer's meridian. The hour angle of star P in Fig. 4.5:1 is about 45° or 3^h. Declination is measured north or south from the celestial equator, ranging from +90° for a star at the north celestial pole to −90° for one at the south celestial pole. The declination of a star on the celestial equator is 0°; such a star rises due east of the observer and sets due west. In Fig. 4.5:1 the declination of star P is the arc GP and is about 40°.

Fig. 4.5:1. The declination of star P is the arc GP, the hour angle is QG, and the right ascension is VG. The arc QV is the observer's sidereal time.

The hour angle of a star, although a changing quantity, has a decided advantage over azimuth and altitude because it increases *uniformly* with time as the celestial sphere spins smoothly from east to west. Since a star does not move appreciably relative to its neighbors or relative to the celestial poles, the declination of a star remains virtually constant with time. If the astronomer wishes to catalogue the coordinates of stars on the celestial sphere, he requires that *both* coordinates remain fixed. For this purpose he uses the second set of equatorial coordinates, which again includes declination, but which replaces the uniformly varying hour angle by an east–west coordinate called the *right ascension*. The point of origin in this system is a fixed point among the stars and therefore, like the stars, moves around us once a day; it is the *vernal equinox*, V in Fig. 4.5:1. The right ascension of star P is the arc VG; it is counted east from the vernal equinox and may be expressed in either degrees or hours. Star P has a right ascension of about 30° or 2^h; the range of possible values is from 0° to 360° or 0^h to 24^h. The declination of star P is, as before, the arc GP.

6. Sidereal Time

WHAT IS THE relationship between the two sets of equatorial coordinates? Declination is of course common to both sets, but hour angle and right ascension differ from one another. Try adding these two coordinates together; from Fig. 4.5:1 and our definitions it follows that

$$\text{Hour angle plus right ascension} = QG + VG = QV.$$

Next imagine sketching in another star at some point P', its hour circle cutting the celestial equator at G'. Adding the two coordinates of this second star, we have $QG' + VG' = QV$, the same as before. Thus the sum of the hour angle and the right ascension of *any* star is the arc QV, a quantity independent of the particular star one is considering. This quantity is *time*; specifically it is the so-called *sidereal time*, or local sidereal time. Interpreted geometrically, the arc QV is the hour angle of the vernal equinox. Thus we have the important definition that *the sidereal time is the hour angle of the vernal equinox*. Alternatively, it is the right ascension of stars which at that instant are crossing the celestial meridian. Its value increases uniformly as the celestial sphere rotates from east to west, the sidereal day starting at 0^h when the vernal equinox crosses the celestial meridian and a new day starting 24 sidereal hours later when the vernal equinox again transits the meridian. We shall discuss astronomical time more fully later.

7. Other Celestial Systems of Measure

ALTHOUGH THE astronomer uses right ascension and declination more than any other set of coordinates, two other systems deserve brief consideration here because they are employed in a variety of problems.

The *ecliptic system of coordinates* has as its physical basis the orbital plane of the earth, and therefore its fundamental great circle is the *ecliptic*, the annual path of the earth as seen from the sun and the path of the sun as seen from the earth. The poles are the *north ecliptic pole* in the constellation of Draco and the *south ecliptic pole* in the constellation of Dorado, the great circles joining the poles are the *secondaries to the ecliptic*, and the point of origin is the *vernal equinox*. In Fig. 4.7:1, which is oriented with the north celestial pole at the top and which does not include horizon coordinates, the two ecliptic coordinates of star P are its *celestial longitude*, the arc VJ measured in degrees eastward from the vernal equinox, and its *celestial latitude*, the arc *JP* measured in degrees north or south from the ecliptic. Celestial longitude ranges from 0° to 360° and celestial latitude from +90° at the north ecliptic pole to −90° at the south ecliptic pole; the ecliptic coordinates of the star in Fig. 4.7:1 are about 35° and +45° respectively. Ecliptic coordinates are most useful in solar system studies. Since the sun is always on the ecliptic, its celestial latitude is zero; its celestial longitude always increases with time as the sun moves in the easterly direction indicated by the arrows in the illustration.

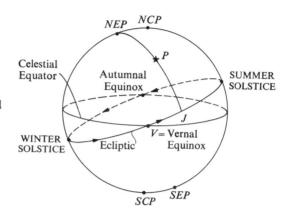

Fig. 4.7:1. The celestial longitude of star *P* is the arc *VJ* and the celestial latitude is *JP*.

The *galactic system of coordinates* has as its physical basis the plane of symmetry of our stellar system, the Milky Way. Its fundamental great circle is the *galactic equator*, the best great circle that can be plotted along the center line of the Milky Way. The poles are the *north galactic pole* in Coma Berenices and the *south galactic pole* in Sculptor; the family of great circles connecting the galactic poles are the *secondaries to the galactic equator*; and the point of origin is the direction to the center of our galaxy, which is located in Sagittarius. The plane of the galaxy makes an angle of 62.6° with the plane of the earth's equator, and thus the angle between the two poles in the sky is also 62.6°. The point of origin, *A* in Fig. 4.7:2, has right ascension 17^{h}42^m, declination −28.9°, while the north galactic pole has right ascension 12^{h}49^m, declination +27.4°. The two galactic coordinates of star *P* are its *galactic longitude*, the arc *AK* measured in degrees eastward from point *A*, and its *galactic latitude*, the arc *KP* measured in degrees north or south from the galactic equator. Galactic longitude ranges from 0° to 360° and galactic latitude from +90° at the north galactic pole to −90° at the south galactic pole. We shall find these coordinates useful in studies of the shape and motions of our galaxy.

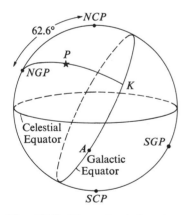

Fig. 4.7:2. The galactic longitude of star *P* is the arc *AK* and the galactic latitude is *KP*.

8. Longitude and Latitude on Earth

WE HAVE DEALT with various ways of specifying the location of an object on the celestial sphere; it is now necessary to consider the location of a point on the earth's surface. The physical basis of terrestrial coordinates is again the daily rotation of the earth; the fundamental great circle is the *equator*, and the points equidistant from all points on the equator being of course the *north pole* and the *south pole*. The secondaries are called *meridians*, and the point of origin is the intersection of the Greenwich meridian with the equator at a point in the Atlantic Ocean about 400 miles south of Ghana, labeled *E* in Fig. 4.8:1. The Greenwich meridian, in turn, is that particular meridian which passes through point *G*, the meridian telescope at the Royal Observatory in Greenwich, England. The *longitude* of a place *P* is the arc *EM* or angle *EOM* measured east or west to the intersection of the meridian of *P* with the equator; the longitude of *P* in the illustration is about 75°W. Longitudes range from 0° to 180° east or west.

One might suspect by analogy with the celestial coordinates we have studied that the *latitude* of *P* is the arc *MP* or angle *MOP*. This time, however, recall that we are not specifying position on the surface of a sphere but on a slightly flattened oblate spheroid. The angle *MOP* is the *geocentric latitude* of *P*. As shown in Fig. 4.8:2, this quantity in general differs from the *astronomical latitude*, which was defined in Chapter 3, Section 2 and is here shown as the angle *MXP*.

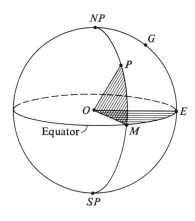

Fig. 4.8:1. The longitude of place *P* is the arc *EM* or angle *EOM*; the geocentric latitude of *P* is the angle *MOP*.

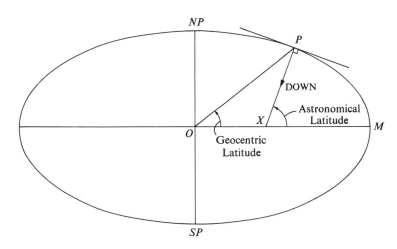

Fig. 4.8:2. Because of the earth's oblateness the astronomical latitude is greater than the geocentric latitude except at a pole or on the equator.

The two kinds of latitude are both 0° at all points of the equator and both 90°N or 90°S at the two poles; at all other points on earth the astronomical latitude is greater than the geocentric, amounting at most to about 12′ near latitude 45°.

To interrelate terrestrial and celestial coordinates, it is useful to recognize that, at any moment one cares to specify, any star one names is exactly in the zenith at some one point on the earth and at no other. The astronomical latitude of this *substellar point* is simply the declination of the star; the west longitude of this point is the Greenwich hour angle of the star. Alternatively, a star passing through your zenith has a declination equal to your astronomical latitude and its hour angle reckoned from the celestial meridian of Greenwich is equal to your west longitude.

MEASURES OF TIME

9. Astronomical Time

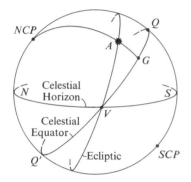

Fig. 4.10:1. A May afternoon in the northern hemisphere. The sidereal time, arc QV, is 6^h; the apparent solar time, arc $Q'QG$, is 14^h or 2 P.M.

INTUITIVELY, WE ALL sense the clear distinction between past, present, and future and that "now" flows steadily in the sense that there is more and more of the past and less and less of the future. This flow can be measured by counting any phenomenon that occurs over and over again, such as the beat of a heart or the rising of the moon. Any such recurrent event can thus serve as a *measure of time*, the interval between two successive such events being a *unit of time* and the device for counting them a *clock*.

The most natural unit of time is the rotation of the earth, because it is fairly regular and will not run down for a very long time and because it is relatively easy to determine the time by observing the daily meridian crossings of stars. As we saw in the last chapter, the earth's rotation is slightly irregular, and only recently have the demands for extremely precise time-keeping made it necessary to define a more uniform standard of time. But before considering ephemeris time, let us first understand the kinds of astronomical time that are based on the earth's rotation.

Because there are several kinds of time whose unit is the day, it will be useful to keep in mind a fundamental similarity among them: *any kind of astronomical time based on the earth's rotation is the hour angle of some celestial body (real or fictitious) plus a constant number.* The unit of time is therefore the interval required for the body in question to make exactly one circuit around the earth.

10. Time by the Stars

WE SAW IN SECTION 6 that *sidereal time* is the hour angle of the vernal equinox, and the sidereal day is the period of time from one meridian transit of the vernal equinox until the next one. Strictly, this interval is a bit shorter than the time for a star, such as Betelgeuse, to circle us once; because of the westward precession of the equinoxes the vernal equinox returns to the meridian about 0.01 second sooner than does a specific star. The sidereal time in Fig. 4.10:1 is the arc QV expressed in time units and is 6^h, since in this example the vernal equinox is setting in the west.

11. Apparent Solar Time

BECAUSE THE sidereal time of sunrise is 4^h at one time of year, 12^h at another, and 22^h at another, it is convenient for society at large to employ a kind of time based on the comings and goings of the sun rather than the stars. The most primitive kind of such time is *apparent solar time*, or time measured by the actual position of the sun in the sky. The adjective "apparent" here is synonymous with "actual" or "real." Apparent solar time is the hour angle of the real (apparent) sun plus or minus 12 hours. It ranges from 0^h to 24^h, and the constant

12^h is utilized to avoid changes of date at midday. When the sun is crossing the observer's meridian at local apparent noon, its hour angle is then zero; the local apparent time is therefore 12^h. In the morning when the sun is off to the east with hour angle 19^h, the local apparent time is $19^h - 12^h = 7^h$. The apparent afternoon sun is shown as A in Fig. 4.10:1; the time of year is late May since the sun has moved past the vernal equinox easterly along the ecliptic some $60°$. The hour angle of the sun is the arc QG, here 2^h; thus the apparent solar time is $2^h + 12^h = 14^h$. A device that records apparent solar time directly (if it is daytime and the sky is clear) is the *sundial*. A rod pointed at the north celestial pole casts a straight-line shadow on a horizontal plate; the azimuth toward which the shadow line points depends only on the hour angle of the sun, and thus the horizontal plate can be marked to indicate apparent solar time.

12. Mean Solar Time

WE SHALL SEE shortly that time by the actual sun does not proceed at a uniform rate; no clock can be built that mimics the now-slow and now-fast sun. To remedy this deficiency, it is essential to introduce a more suitable and regular kind of time known as *mean solar time* or *civil time*. Imagine a new kind of sun which moves at a uniform rate easterly along the celestial equator, taking precisely the same time needed for the actual sun to circle the ecliptic once each ordinary year. The mean solar time is the hour angle of the mean sun plus or minus 12 hours; it is defined in the same way as apparent solar time except that it employs the fictitious mean sun rather than the real sun as the reference body.

13. The Equation of Time

TWO EFFECTS conspire so that apparent solar time is ahead of mean solar time during some parts of the year and behind it at other times, the difference between the two being as much as 16 minutes in early November. The first source of difference is the eccentricity of the earth's orbit; the second is the obliquity of the ecliptic.

Let us consider these two effects separately by imagining yet another fictitious sun, which may be called the *intermediate sun*. Although it seems that we are indulging in a good deal of fiction, it is essential to an understanding of the difference between apparent solar time and mean solar time. The intermediate sun coincides with the real sun at the instant when the earth passes the perihelion of its orbit on about January 2 each year, the two being in the constellation of Sagittarius on that date. The intermediate sun moves easterly along the ecliptic at a uniform rate, completing its circuit in one ordinary year. The actual or apparent sun, however, moves at a variable angular rate along the ecliptic because the earth's orbit is eccentric and the earth obeys the law of areas. Since the earth is moving its fastest at perihelion, the real sun forges east of the intermediate sun and stays east of it until the latter catches up at aphelion on July 4. The real sun then moves west of the intermediate sun, since the earth is now moving slowest in its orbit, not overtaking the intermediate sun until perihelion the following January 2. Thus in the first part of the year the hour angle of the real sun is less than that of the intermediate sun; in the second part of the year the opposite is the case.

Although it moves uniformly, the intermediate sun is not suitable as a time-keeper because it moves along the ecliptic, whereas hour angle is measured along the celestial equator. The mean sun, which we have already met, is now defined more precisely than before as that fictitious body which coincides with the intermediate sun at the vernal equinox and moves uniformly along the celestial equator once each ordinary year. The hour angle of these two suns is identical at the two equinoxes and solstices. But the hour angle of the intermediate sun is the larger in spring and fall and that of the mean sun is the larger in summer and winter.

The combined effect of the orbital eccentricity and the tilt of the ecliptic is represented by the *equation of time*. The equation of time at any instant is the apparent solar time minus the mean solar time. Its value is thus positive when the hour angle of the real sun is greater than that of the mean sun, and negative when the real sun trails the mean sun. Figure 4.13:1 shows as thin curves the separate effects of

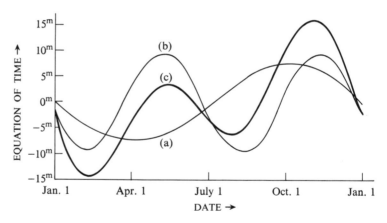

Fig. 4.13:1. The equation of time (c) is the apparent solar time minus the mean solar time. It is a joint effect of the earth's varying orbital speed (a) and the obliquity of the ecliptic (b).

(a) the eccentricity and (b) the obliquity at different times of year; the thick curve (c) gives the algebraic sum of these two, which is the equation of time.

14. Time and Longitude

THE SEVERAL KINDS of time studied thus far have been defined in terms of the observer's local meridian. If at a given instant the sidereal time at a specific place is 11^h, then it is 11^h at that same moment at all points on the meridian of longitude passing through that place. If at another instant it is local apparent noon at the Palomar Observatory in California, located at longitude 116°52′W or $7^h47^m28^sW$, then the sun is on the meridian at that same moment at all points on earth with the same longitude as Palomar but at no place else on earth. On the meridian of longitude 15° or one hour east of Palomar, the sun has already crossed the meridian and the apparent time at this same instant is 13^h. At the Greenwich meridian at this same time the Greenwich hour angle of the apparent sun is 7^{h}47^{m}28^s and thus the Greenwich apparent time is 19^{h}47^{m}28^s.

The general relationship between time and longitude is shown in Fig. 4.14:1. Suppose, hypothetically, that the star P is the reference body which serves as the origin from which we measure some given kind of time. Then its hour angle for the local observer with zenith Z is the arc QB. Point G represents the zenith at the Greenwich Observatory, and the arc from the north celestial pole through G to A passes through the stars which at that moment are on the celestial meridian there; the hour angle of P reckoned from Greenwich is the arc AB. The difference between the two hour angles and hence between the times at the two places is $AB - QB = AQ$, the west longitude of the place in question. *Time difference equals longitude difference.* More specifically,

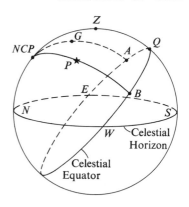

Fig. 4.14:1. West longitude, arc AQ, plus local time, arc QB, equals Greenwich time, arc AB.

> Greenwich Sidereal Time minus Local Sidereal Time equals West Longitude; Greenwich Apparent Time minus Local Apparent Time equals West Longitude; Greenwich Mean Solar Time minus Local Mean Solar Time equals West Longitude.

15. Standard Time

OF THE THREE KINDS of time so far examined, mean solar time is the best suited for daily living because it is geared to the sun rather than the stars and also because it runs at a uniform rate. However, since time difference equals longitude difference, the mean solar time on the east side of a room is about 0.01 second later than on the west side of the room. On a long westbound freight train the mean solar time in the caboose is 3 or 4 seconds later than in the locomotive, and, to add further complication, the watch of every person ought continually to be set back second by second as the train moves westward. With the advent of rapid transportation in the latter half of the nineteenth century and the desirability of avoiding excessive confusion in scheduling, timekeeping by zones was introduced. The *standard time* or *zone time* we keep today was adopted in the United States in 1882.

In principle, zone time works as follows. First, the fundamental time of the civilized world is agreed to be Greenwich mean solar time, usually abbreviated to Universal Time or U.T. People living in a 15° or one-hour zone of longitude centered on the Greenwich meridian keep this time. People in the next zone east, from longitude 7.5°E to 22.5°E, keep a time precisely one hour later than U.T.; people in the zone next west from Greenwich, from longitude 7.5°W to 22.5°W, keep a time precisely one hour earlier than U.T. In the continental United States, Eastern Standard Time is the local mean solar time at longitude 75°W, Central Standard Time at longitude 90°W, Mountain Standard Time at longitude 105°W, and Pacific Standard Time at longitude 120°W. Universal Time is accordingly exactly five hours later than Eastern Standard Time, six hours later than Central Standard Time, and so on. The zones run around the world until ultimately a ship in mid-Pacific at longitude 179°W is keeping zone time 12 hours *earlier* than U.T., and another nearby vessel at longitude 179°E is keeping time 12 hours *later* than U.T. The clocks of the two read the same *hour*, but the *date* at the ship in east longitude is one day later than at the other ship. It is necessary therefore to skip 24 hours when westbound into east longitude across the International Date Line at longitude 180° and conversely to repeat 24 hours when eastbound into the western hemisphere. The first merrymakers to greet the New Year are the Fiji Islanders, when it is only noon on December 31 in England. The moment comes successively later for the New Zealanders, Australians, and Japanese. A wave of noise moves westward around the world, reaching Europe, then the Americas, and finally ending in mid-Pacific when it is noon on January 1 in England.

In practice, the boundaries of the various time zones depend on local circumstances. The International Date Line, for example, is somewhat jagged to allow all parts of the Fiji Islands to have the same date and all of the Aleutian chain to have the same date as the rest of Alaska. The zone boundaries within the United States are highly irregular also, following state boundaries here and county boundaries there. For example, the state of Michigan, although almost entirely in the sixth time zone west from Greenwich, keeps Eastern Standard Time, and South Dakota keeps Central Time in its eastern portion and Mountain Time in its western counties.

When a state or community adopts Daylight Saving Time, usually from the last Sunday in April through the last Sunday in October, it simply shifts to the zone time of the next zone east. Thus a clock reading Central Daylight Saving Time agrees with one reading Eastern Standard Time; the two times are the same. Since the sun is perfectly indifferent to our advancing the clocks by an hour, the result of course is that on daylight time the sun rises and sets an hour later than if we had maintained standard time. Because, like the sun, animals and children are indifferent to clock-changing, vigorous controversy is engendered semiannually in those communities using Daylight Saving Time, particularly among farmers and young mothers. Daylight Saving Time does, however, have the advantage of saving lighting costs, since on this system most of us are up and about for one extra hour of daylight and abed for one extra hour of darkness.

16. Ephemeris Time

THE SEVERAL KINDS of time considered in the preceding sections are geared to the earth's rotation. As we saw in the last chapter, however, there are three recognizable kinds of minor fluctuation in the rate of our rotation, the most important in the long run being the lengthening of the day. In order to find a more uniform kind of time, we shall turn our attention away from the earth's rotation and focus it on the *orbits of the moon and planets.* We shall see in Chapter 7 that Sir Isaac Newton founded in the seventeenth century a most successful science of motion or mechanics. With its help and observations of the moon and planets it is possible to calculate with high precision the characteristics of the orbits of these bodies. It is then possible, using this information, to calculate an *ephemeris*, or list of predicted positions, for the moon and planets for many years in advance. Finally, a number of years later the astronomer compares the *predicted* positions with the positions as *observed* with the telescope. He finds that the moon and the planets are all *ahead* of the predicted locations by the same number of minutes. To obtain agreement of predicted and observed right ascensions and declinations, he introduces ephemeris time, and the loss of mean solar time relative to ephemeris time is simply the accumulating error in the earth's rotation. Ephemeris time, in other words, is that kind of time which is used in Newton's theory of planetary motions.

The basis of physical time in the past was the mean solar second, which equals 1/86,400 of the mean solar day and thus fluctuated a little with the earth's rotation. The second of ephemeris time, which is the new basis of physical time, is defined as 1/31,556,925.975 of the ordinary year at the beginning of the year 1900. A clock in the mid-twentieth century that keeps ephemeris time is about half a minute ahead of one keeping Universal Time.

MAPS OF THE SKY

17. Stars and Constellations

THE BRIGHTER STARS are arranged into a variety of different figures that make the groups readily recognizable after a bit of practice. One finds crosses and semicircles, pentagons and triangles, squares and dippers. The entire sky is divided into 88 areas, each one of which is a *constellation* and is assigned a Latin name. The brighter stars in any given constellation are designated by Greek lower-case letters, all of which are shown in Table 13.1:1 (p. 301), followed by the genitive form of the Latin constellation name. Usually the first letter of the Greek alphabet is assigned to the brightest star of a constellation, the second letter to the second brightest star, and so on. A few dozen prominent stars are also often referred to by their proper names. Thus the brightest star in the constellation of Leo the Lion is known as Regulus (little king) and also as Alpha Leonis; the second brightest star in Leo is Denebola (tail of the lion), also called Beta Leonis. Table 4.17:1 lists the 88 constellations by Latin name, genitive form, three-letter abbreviation, and English name.

18. Reading Star Maps

THE SIX STAR MAPS shown on pages 81–86 cover various zones in the sky and should assist in identifying the more prominent stars and

TABLE 4.17:1. The Constellations

Latin Name	Genitive	Abbreviation	English Name
Andromeda [a, c]	Andromedae	And	Andromeda
Antlia	Antliae	Ant	Air Pump
Apus	Apodis	Aps	Bird of Paradise
Aquarius [a]	Aquarii	Aqr	Water Carrier
Aquila [a]	Aquilae	Aql	Eagle
Ara [a]	Arae	Ara	Altar
Aries [a]	Arietis	Ari	Ram
Auriga [a]	Aurigae	Aur	Charioteer
Bootes [a]	Bootis	Boo	Herdsman
Caelum	Caeli	Cae	Graving Tool
Camelopardalis	Camelopardalis	Cam	Giraffe
Cancer [a]	Cancri	Cnc	Crab
Canes Venatici [a]	Canum Venaticorum	CVn	Hunting Dogs
Canis Major [a]	Canis Majoris	CMa	Larger Dog
Canis Minor [a]	Canis Minoris	CMi	Smaller Dog
Capricornus [a]	Capricorni	Cap	Goat
Carina [a, b]	Carinae	Car	Keel
Cassiopeia [a, c]	Cassiopeiae	Cas	Cassiopeia
Centaurus [a]	Centauri	Cen	Centaur
Cepheus [a, c]	Cephei	Cep	Cepheus
Cetus [a]	Ceti	Cet	Whale
Chamaeleon	Chamaeleontis	Cha	Chameleon
Circinus [a]	Circini	Cir	Compasses
Columba [a]	Columbae	Col	Dove
Coma Berenices	Comae Berenices	Com	Berenice's Hair
Corona Australis	Coronae Australis	CrA	Southern Crown
Corona Borealis [a]	Coronae Borealis	CrB	Northern Crown
Corvus [a]	Corvi	Crv	Crow
Crater	Crateris	Crt	Cup
Crux [a]	Crucis	Cru	Cross
Cygnus [a]	Cygni	Cyg	Swan
Delphinus [a]	Delphini	Del	Dolphin
Dorado [a]	Doradus	Dor	Swordfish
Draco [a]	Draconis	Dra	Dragon
Equuleus	Equulei	Equ	Little Horse
Eridanus [a]	Eridani	Eri	River
Fornax	Fornacis	For	Furnace
Gemini [a]	Geminorum	Gem	Twins
Grus [a]	Gruis	Gru	Crane
Hercules [a, c]	Herculis	Her	Hercules
Horologium	Horologii	Hor	Clock
Hydra [a]	Hydrae	Hya	Water Serpent
Hydrus [a]	Hydri	Hyi	Water Snake
Indus [a]	Indi	Ind	Indian
Lacerta	Lacertae	Lac	Lizard
Leo [a]	Leonis	Leo	Lion
Leo Minor [a]	Leonis Minoris	LMi	Smaller Lion
Lepus [a]	Leporis	Lep	Hare
Libra [a]	Librae	Lib	Scales

Latin Name	Genitive	Abbreviation	English Name
Lupus[a]	Lupi	Lup	Wolf
Lynx	Lyncis	Lyn	Lynx
Lyra[a]	Lyrae	Lyr	Lyre
Mensa	Mensae	Men	Table Mountain
Microscopium	Microscopii	Mic	Microscope
Monoceros	Monocerotis	Mon	Unicorn
Musca[a]	Muscae	Mus	Fly
Norma	Normae	Nor	Ruler
Octans	Octantis	Oct	Octant
Ophiuchus[a]	Ophiuchi	Oph	Serpent Carrier
Orion[a, c]	Orionis	Ori	Orion
Pavo[a]	Pavonis	Pav	Peacock
Pegasus[a, c]	Pegasi	Peg	Pegasus
Perseus[a, c]	Persei	Per	Perseus
Phoenix[a]	Phoenicis	Phe	Phoenix
Pictor[a]	Pictoris	Pic	Easel
Pisces[a]	Piscium	Psc	Fishes
Piscis Austrinus[a]	Piscis Austrini	PsA	Southern Fish
Puppis[a, b]	Puppis	Pup	Stern
Pyxis[b]	Pyxidis	Pyx	Mariner's Compass
Reticulum[a]	Reticuli	Ret	Net
Sagitta[a]	Sagittae	Sge	Arrow
Sagittarius[a]	Sagittarii	Sgr	Archer
Scorpio[a]	Scorpii	Sco	Scorpion
Sculptor	Sculptoris	Scl	Sculptor's Tools
Scutum	Scuti	Sct	Shield
Serpens[a]	Serpentis	Ser	Serpent
Sextans	Sextantis	Sex	Sextant
Taurus[a]	Tauri	Tau	Bull
Telescopium	Telescopii	Tel	Telescope
Triangulum[a]	Trianguli	Tri	Triangle
Triangulum Australe[a]	Trianguli Australis	TrA	Southern Triangle
Tucana[a]	Tucanae	Tuc	Toucan
Ursa Major[a]	Ursae Majoris	UMa	Larger Bear
Ursa Minor[a]	Ursae Minoris	UMi	Smaller Bear
Vela[a, b]	Velorum	Vel	Sails
Virgo[a]	Virginis	Vir	Virgin
Volans	Volantis	Vol	Flying Fish
Vulpecula	Vulpeculae	Vul	Fox

[a] May be found on one or more of the six star maps.

[b] Carina, Puppis, Pyxis, and Vela are modern subdivisions of the original very large constellation Argo Navis, the legendary ship Argo.

[c] In Greek mythology Andromeda was the daughter of Cepheus and Cassiopeia and wife of Perseus; Cassiopeia was the wife of Cepheus; Cepheus was a king of Ethiopia; Hercules was a son of Zeus and celebrated for his great strength; Orion was a hunter who chased the Pleiades and was slain by Diana; Pegasus was a winged horse; and Perseus was a son of Zeus and was the hero who rescued and married Andromeda.

constellations. Each polar map covers an entire polar cap within 40° of the celestial pole at its center. Each seasonal map covers a region 7 hours wide in right ascension and extending 60° in declination north and south of the celestial equator, overlapping its neighboring maps as well as the polar maps. The size of each star image is proportional to the brilliance of the star in question, and the magnitude of each star may be estimated from the scale at the bottom of Map 1. Magnitudes are the astronomer's measurements of the apparent brightness of stars and are explained in Chapter 13, Section 10. All stars in the sky brighter than magnitude 3.5 are included on the maps; a number of fainter stars are also shown where they are needed to assist in the identification of constellations. The alphabetical designations are listed for those stars that are assigned Greek letters, and the proper names of a few bright stars are also given. Dotted lines between stars suggest a characteristic shape to look for in finding a given constellation. Many of the constellations listed in Table 4.17:1 do not appear on the maps because their brightest stars are relatively faint. Included here and there as open circles are several star clusters and galaxies that are visible to the unaided eye; some are easily seen but others require a very keen eye.

An observer in the northern hemisphere should begin his studies with Map 1, which should be rotated until the proper date is at the top. The north polar constellations will then resemble the map at the hour of 8:30 P.M. standard time. For a time of observation later than 8:30 P.M. the map should be further rotated counterclockwise 15° (or one hour of right ascension) for each hour. Polaris, the Big Dipper, and Cassiopeia are prominent features of this part of the sky. An observer in the southern hemisphere should begin with Map 6, with the proper date at the top if it is 8:30 P.M. If it is later, the map should be rotated clockwise 15° for every hour. Among the major signposts of the south polar cap are Crux, known familiarly as the Southern Cross, the two Clouds of Magellan, and the very bright star Canopus.

To use the seasonal maps, select the one on which the proper date appears. Stars near the hour circle passing through the date of observation will be on or near the celestial meridian at 8:30 P.M. standard time. At a middle northern latitude an observer should face south. Stars near the bottom of the map will be near the southern horizon or perhaps below it; stars near the celestial equator will be moderately high in the south; and stars near the top of the map will not be very far from the zenith. An observer at a middle southern latitude should face north and use the seasonal maps held upside down. For hours later than 8:30 P.M., recall that stars of later and later right ascension come to the meridian as time goes by. Thus, although the central meridian of the autumnal map, at right ascension 22 hours, is suitable for use at 8:30 P.M. on October 15, a predawn observer at 2:30 A.M., 6 hours later, should use the winter map and the hour circle at 4 hours.

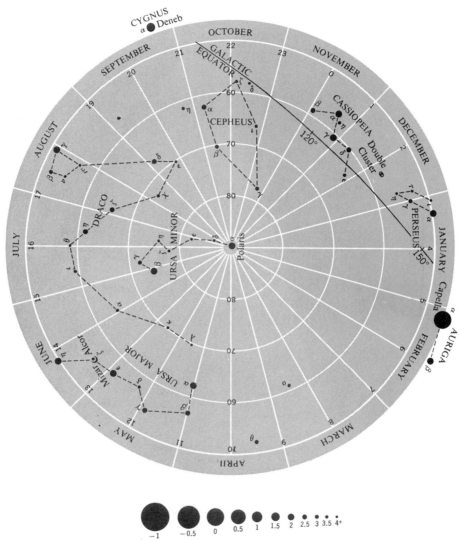

SCALE OF MAGNITUDES

Map 1. The North Polar Constellations.

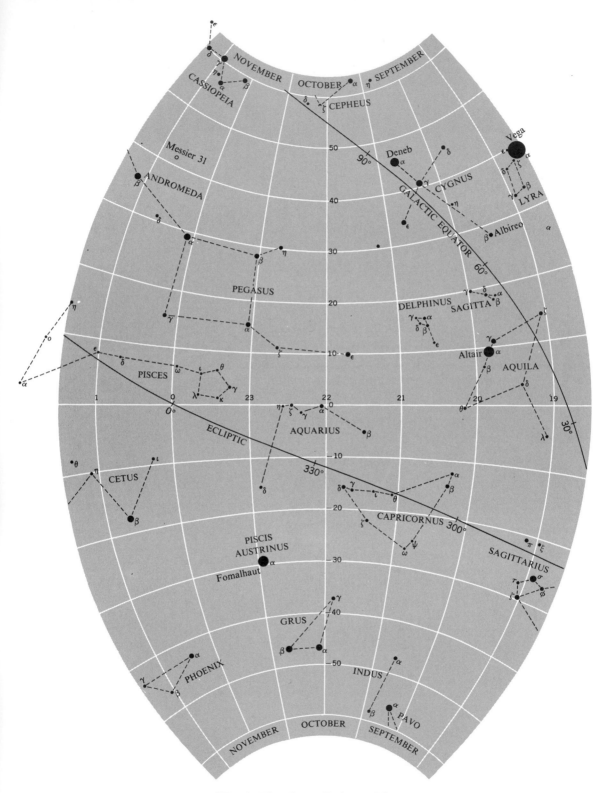

Map 2. The Constellations of Autumn.

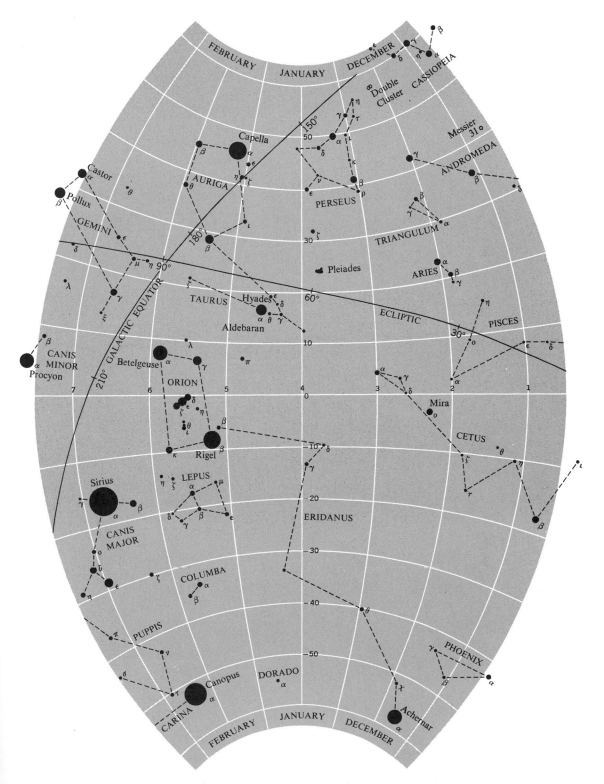

Map 3. The Constellations of Winter.

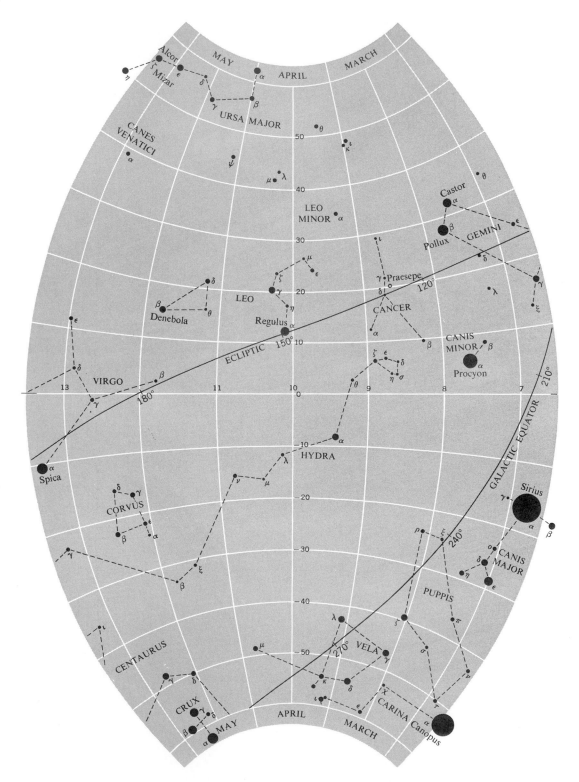

Map 4. The Constellations of Spring.

84

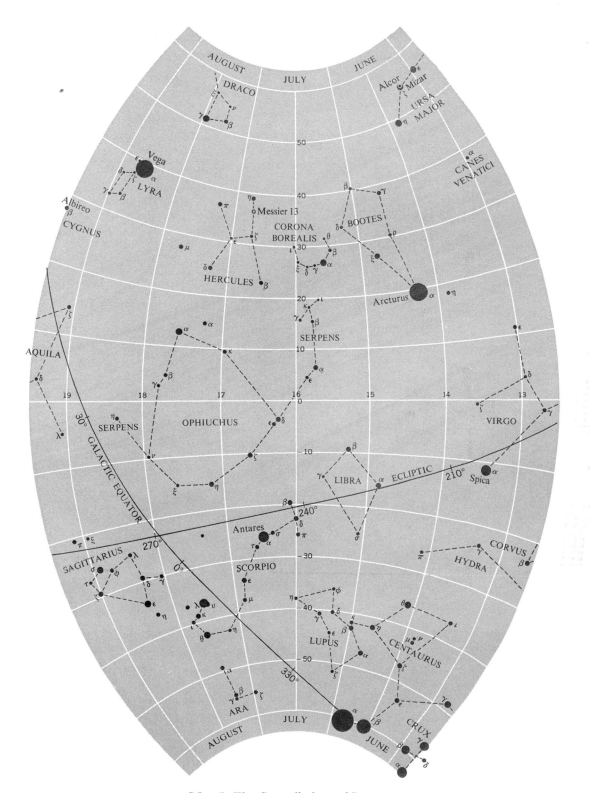

Map 5. The Constellations of Summer.

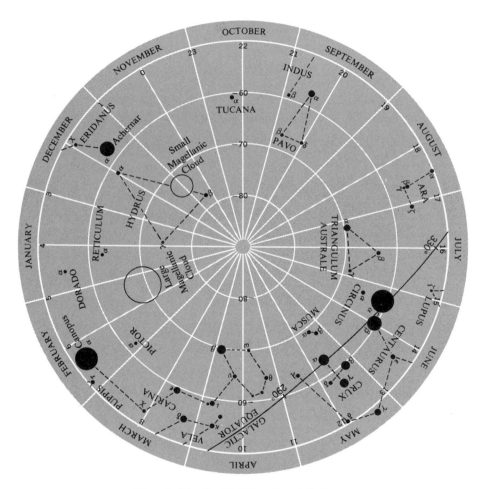

Map 6. The South Polar Constellations.

PROBLEMS

1. (a) Express the following hour angles in time measure: 180°, 10°, 30′, 2′, 1.5″. (b) Express the following right ascensions in degree measure: 20^h, 1^{h}16^m, 6^{h}43^{m}13^s.

2. Give the physical basis and the name of the fundamental great circle of each of the four commonly used celestial coordinate systems.

3. Give the azimuth and altitude of a star at each of the following points: (a) southwest and two-thirds of the way from horizon to zenith, (b) rising in the northeast, (c) in the nadir, (d) 20° above the north celestial pole as seen from latitude 35°N.

4. What is the declination of the southernmost stars you can see (a) if you live at latitude 40°N and (b) if you live at latitude 25°N?

5. (a) What is the hour angle of a star when it has its lowest altitude of the day? (b) What is its hour angle 12 hours of *mean solar time* later?

6. Give the right ascension and declination and the ecliptic coordinates of the sun when it is at the summer solstice.

7. What are the right ascension and declination of the two ecliptic poles? Use the star maps to find the nearest bright star to each of these points.

8. Vega has right ascension 18^{h}34^m and declination +38.4°. (a) At what latitude can Vega be seen in the zenith? (b) What is the sidereal time when Vega is passing through the zenith? (c) What is the sidereal time when Vega's hour angle is 20^{h}41^m?

9. Use the star maps to locate the two galactic poles. Identify the nearest bright star to each of these points.

10. On about what date is the local sidereal time at an observatory the same as the local mean time?

11. Estimate from the graph in Fig. 4.13:1 the equation of time on March 6. What is the local mean time on that date when the apparent sun is at its highest altitude of the day?

12. What is the Greenwich sidereal time when the vernal equinox is on the meridian at longitude 5^{h}52^{m}54^{s}W?

13. What are the Universal Time and the local mean time at longitude 8^{h}11^{m}27^{s}W if the Pacific Standard Time is 13^{h}42^{m}41^s?

14. On a trip from San Francisco to Tokyo the correct zone time and date as the International Date Line is approached is 14^{h}23^m, May 19. Five minutes later the Line has been crossed. What are the correct zone time and date at this later instant?

15. At what speed would a jet pilot have to fly westward at the equator so that his local mean time stood still?

5

LIGHT, RADIO, AND TELESCOPES

Almost all that we know of objects beyond the earth depends on analyses of the electromagnetic radiations received from them. What the ancients knew of the moon, planets, and stars depended solely on their unaided vision; what we know today depends on an extension of that vision through the development of instruments to supplement or supplant the eye in the detection and measurement of celestial bodies. The earliest step, more than three centuries ago, was Galileo's first use of the *telescope*, which revealed fainter objects than the eye alone could see and also magnified the angular sizes of objects. The nineteenth century saw the development of *spectroscopy*, wherein the light from a celestial source is broken into its component colors by a prism, and of *photography*, which not only permits the collection of light from the stars over a long period of time but also makes possible the accumulation of permanent albums of the sky. In the twentieth century a number of devices have been developed for amplifying and making more precise our knowledge of the radiation of celestial bodies in the visual and near-visual part of the electromagnetic spectrum. In addition, a fundamentally new branch of astronomy was born in 1932 when Karl Jansky first detected extraterrestrial radiation in the radio part of the spectrum at a wavelength 30 million times that of light. After the long span of visual astronomy, it is only in recent years that it has been possible to take advantage of the atmospheric window at the radio wavelengths shown in Fig. 2.12:1. Even more recently studies have begun at other wavelengths from rockets and satellites that have penetrated beyond the bulk of our atmosphere. Although by no means achieved, the aim of observational astronomy is to record precisely for every celestial body its position in space, its motions, and the intensity of the radiation from each of its parts at every wavelength of the electromagnetic spectrum; any changes of these quantities with time need also to be observed.

FUNDAMENTAL PRINCIPLES OF OPTICS

1. Waves and Rays

RADIATION FROM a source may be described as a series of spherical waves that move outward in all directions, much like the ripples that spread out when a stone is dropped into a quiet pond. In a vacuum light and radio waves travel at a fixed speed, 186,300 miles per second; the only difference between them is the wavelength, or distance from one wave crest to the following wave crest. For many purposes it is simpler to think of light as a series of rays, each of which is traveling in a direction at right angles to the wave crest, as shown in Fig. 5.1:1.

One of the fundamental principles of optics states that a light ray, and indeed radiation in any part of the spectrum, moves in a straight line when passing through a uniform or homogeneous medium. This principle is called the law of *rectilinear propagation*. Because the great gulfs of space between the stars are very nearly devoid of matter, they constitute a uniform medium that is almost perfectly vacuous, and thus any radiation crossing these spaces moves in a straight line at the "speed of light," 186,300 miles per second.

A second principle is the law of *reflection*. When a ray of light impinges on a surface, a part of it is reflected back into the medium from which it came. Figure 5.1:2 shows the surface of a plane mirror and the path followed by a ray arriving at the mirror. The angle

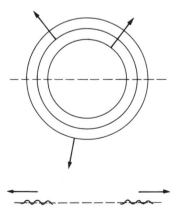

Fig. 5.1:1. Top view and side view of wave crests moving outward at constant velocity.

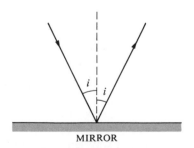

Fig. 5.1:2. The angle of reflection equals the angle of incidence, *i*.

between the arriving ray and a perpendicular erected at the point of impact is called the *angle of incidence*, and that between the departing ray and the perpendicular the *angle of reflection*. The law of reflection states that the angle of reflection equals the angle of incidence.

A third principle of optics is the law of *refraction*. When a ray of light strikes a surface, that part of it which is not reflected passes on through the surface and the direction of motion of the ray is changed. Our study of the earth's atmosphere necessitated a consideration of refraction in Chapter 2, but let us repeat here that a ray of light which crosses a surface from a rarer into a denser medium changes course *toward* the perpendicular to the surface and one which moves from a denser into a rarer medium changes course *away* from the perpendicular. In order to visualize more clearly what happens at an interface, it is useful to remember the rule that the *denser* the medium through which radiation is passing, the *slower* its speed. Figure 5.1:3 indicates successive positions of an advancing wave crest at equal intervals of time. Since the left part of the crest reaches the denser medium first, its speed is slowed down first; the entire crest thus changes its direction of motion toward the perpendicular.

A fourth principle of optics is that of *dispersion*: rays of different wavelength or color are refracted through differing angles. When a star's light, which is a mixture of all colors, strikes a refracting surface, the violet rays are slowed more than the red; therefore the course change of the violet light is greater than that of the red, the light being dispersed into the spectrum of all colors, as shown in Fig. 5.1:4. Dispersion creates difficulties in the construction of certain kinds of telescopes, as we shall see. Alternatively, the dispersion of starlight by a device such as a *prism* makes possible the important science of spectroscopy.

REFRACTING TELESCOPES

THE ESSENTIAL functions of any telescope are the *collection of radiation* at the receiving apparatus—whether it be the eye, a photographic film, or a radio antenna—and *resolution*, the capacity to distinguish between points that are close together in the sky. The earliest telescopes achieved these functions by utilizing *lenses* and the principle of refraction. Imagine first a hemisphere of glass and, as in Fig. 5.2:1, parallel rays from a star incident perpendicularly on the plane face of the glass. All rays strike the plane face at a 90° angle of incidence and thus are undeviated on entering the glass. But on emerging from the glass the only ray that strikes the second interface at 90° and stays on course is the central ray, labeled *b* in the illustration. Rays *a* and *c* change course away from the perpendicular on leaving the denser medium; they intersect each other and ray *b* at the *focus* of the lens. Here, then, is a suggestive method of collecting all of the light striking the glass at a single point, whereas without the lens only ray *b* would reach this point.

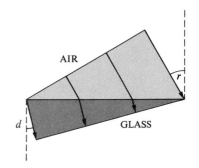

Fig. 5.1:3. Angle *d* in the denser medium is less than angle *r* in the more rarefied medium. Each ray is refracted at the interface and each completes the indicated path in the same interval of time.

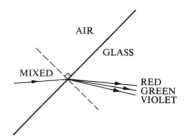

Fig. 5.1:4. Violet rays are refracted more than red, thereby accounting for the dispersion of light.

2. Lenses and Refraction

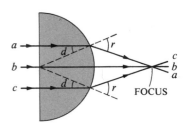

Fig. 5.2:1. A hemisphere of glass focuses rays *a*, *b*, and *c* at a point

Although the hemispherical glass reveals the principle of focusing light, in practice it is a rather useless lens because the location of the focal point differs for rays incident at different places on the plane face and also because of the dispersion of light. What is actually used is exemplified by the thin lens shown in Fig. 5.2:2, where the two faces are only very small parts of two large spheres. Here, because the arriving rays are deviated only slightly, the focal length of the lens, F, is quite long compared with its diameter, D. All rays incident on the

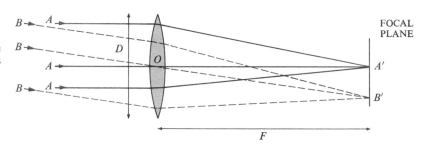

Fig. 5.2:2. The focal length of the lens is the distance F and the optical axis is the line OA'. Rays from stars A and B are focused at the points A' and B' respectively.

lens from a star, A, on the optical axis are refracted in such a way that they meet extremely close to a common point, A'. Furthermore, all parallel rays from another star, B, not on the optical axis, meet at B'. The plane through A' and B' perpendicular to the optical axis is the *focal plane*. A photographic film held at this point will map those stars in the sky in the near vicinity of star A.

3. Design of a Camera

THE ESSENTIAL parts of the simplest kind of photographic camera are a lens, a roll of photographic film, a light-tight box to keep out unwanted light and hold the film in the focal plane of the lens, and a shutter which covers the lens except when a picture is being taken. While the shutter is open, the subject is mapped onto the film, the effect at each point of the film varying as the intensity of light striking it. When the film is developed and fixed in chemical baths, washed and dried, there results a permanent record of the subject, whether it is a baby, an evergreen tree, or a field of stars.

4. A Refractor for Photography

A SUBSTANTIAL part of present-day observational research in astronomy is devoted to making celestial photographs, as with the instrument in Fig. 5.4:2. The essential difference between ordinary snapshot photography and astronomical photography is that most astronomical subjects are extremely faint. In order to collect enough light from the faint source to impress a latent image on the photographic emulsion, it is first necessary to have a large lens in order to accumulate the starlight incident on a good-sized area. Second, it is necessary to collect the light over a long period of time—in other words, to make a time exposure. What is needed, therefore, is a telescope of good size and a method of moving it at the same rate the stars move westerly across the sky so that it will remain pointed at the subject. We shall elaborate on the latter requirement later. In addition, because he may wish to make accurate measurements on his photographs, the astronomer usually uses a plate of glass rather than a pliant film for his work. Figure 5.4:1 shows a simple refractor; the side of the photo-

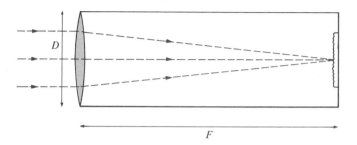

Fig. 5.4:1. For photography the photographic plate is positioned so that the emulsion lies in the focal plane of the lens.

graphic plate toward the lens is coated with emulsion and is focused so that it lies accurately in the focal plane of the lens.

Fig. 5.4:2. The 20-inch Carnegie Astrographic Telescope of the Lick Observatory, Mount Hamilton, Calif. (*Lick Observatory photograph*)

5. A Refractor for Visual Use

SUPPOSE ONE wishes to look at a region of the sky with the refractor pictured in Fig. 5.4:2. At first it may seem reasonable to remove the plate and put one's eye at the focus. Light from a star on the optical axis, however, would reach the eye from all points of the lens; the eye would thus see a bright lens instead of a star. For visual use, the converging light rays must be made parallel so that the retina of the eye will be able to focus them. This is achieved by using an *eyepiece*. In one simple kind of eyepiece, as in Fig. 5.5:1, the light passes beyond the focus, the beams diverging until they strike a small lens similar in shape to the telescope lens; the latter refracts the light back into a

Fig. 5.5:2. The 40-inch refractor of the Yerkes Observatory of the University of Chicago, at Williams Bay, Wis. (*Yerkes Observatory photograph*)

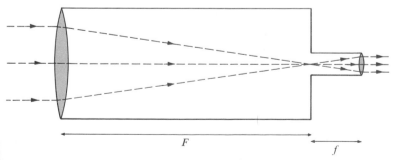

Fig. 5.5:1. For visual use, light is allowed to pass beyond the focal plane. It strikes the eyepiece lens, where it is refracted into a parallel beam that enters the eye.

6. Chromatic Aberration

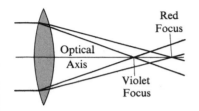

Fig. 5.6:1. The chromatic aberration of a single lens.

parallel beam of diameter less than the diameter of the pupil of the eye (about ¼ inch). The crystalline lens of the eye then intercepts the parallel beam and focuses it finally upon the retina.

NO OPTICAL SYSTEM is perfect, and the several kinds of deviations from perfection are known as aberrations. Our concern now is that particular aberration which arises in a lens owing to the dispersion of light of differing wavelengths. It is called *chromatic aberration* (from the Greek "chroma," meaning "color"). Because violet rays change course more than red rays on entering a lens like that shown in Fig. 5.6:1, the focal length of the lens is less for violet light than for red. A screen held perpendicular to the optical axis at the violet focus will reveal a star as a violet-blue point surrounded by a circular smear of reddish light; if the screen is moved away from the lens so that the red is in focus, the violet and blue are smeared out. Since a single lens brings light of only one color to a focus at a given point, chromatic aberration can be partially conquered only by using more than one lens, as was discovered in the middle of the eighteenth century. Two lenses of different refractive power and shape are placed close together; any two desired colors may thus be brought to a common focus, and the other colors focus very nearly at this point. Because the eye is most sensitive to the long-wave end of the spectrum, visual refractors are ordinarily designed to bring red and green light to a focus, and the orange and yellow rays reach almost precisely the same point. Blue and violet come to a focus sooner, and it is not uncommon to notice a violet-blue halo surrounding a star viewed through such an instrument. At first thought, it may seem that the best remedy for chromatic aberration would be to use a large number of lenses so that a large number of colors would come to a common focus. When one recalls, however, that part of the light incident on each air-glass interface is *reflected*, the ultimate absurdity turns out to be a telescope with an infinite number of lenses designed so that light of all colors is focused, but limited in utility by the unhappy fact that no light reaches the focal point.

REFLECTING TELESCOPES

7. Mirrors and Reflection

THE SECOND fundamental type of telescope uses a mirror and employs the principle of reflection of light; such an instrument is called a *reflector*. A telescopic mirror is made of glass and coated with a thin layer of highly reflecting material such as silver or, more usually, aluminum. What is the shape of the mirror surface needed for a reflecting telescope? The simplest shape, a plane reflecting surface like the usual household mirror, cannot function as a telescope because, as may be seen from Fig. 5.7:1, parallel rays from a star will all be reflected by the same amount and will return into space as a bundle of parallel rays. In particular, rays from a source that are incident perpendicularly on the plane mirror will be reflected straight back to the source. The next simplest surface is a portion of a sphere. Figure 5.7:2 shows several parallel rays incident on a hemispherical reflecting bowl, each reflected at equal angles. For rays incident near the optical

Fig. 5.7:1. A plane mirror returns starlight to space as parallel beams.

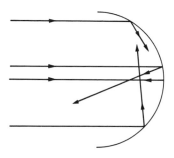

Fig. 5.7:2. A hemispherical mirror does not bring parallel light to a single focal point.

axis, the focal length, or distance from center of mirror to focus, is equal to one-half the radius of the sphere. But rays striking this mirror farther from the optical axis are reflected so that they cross the optical axis closer to the mirror. A ray incident at 60° will strike the optical axis at the mirror itself, whereas rays incident on the outermost parts of the hemisphere will be reflected more than once before crossing the optical axis. The imperfection of a spherical surface as a focusing device for parallel light is called *spherical aberration*. In order to use a sphere as a practical mirror it is necessary to use only a small fraction of its surface; the focal length must therefore be very long compared with the diameter of the mirror itself.

8. The Parabola

THERE IS ONE shape of surface which will reflect all parallel rays from a star to a common focus, providing that the star is in the direction of the optical axis of the surface. This is the *paraboloid*, the shape found when a *parabola* is spun around its axis. Figure 5.8:1 shows a parabola, with the paths of several incident rays meeting at the focus. Flashlights and searchlights utilize paraboloidal reflectors with the bulb located at the focus; rays diverging from the bulb are reflected into a parallel beam which will illuminate efficiently an object at some distance. The principle may be illustrated by reversing all the arrows in Fig. 5.8:1. The reflecting telescope is, in essence, a searchlight in reverse.

Although all rays from a star on the optical axis of a paraboloidal mirror are focused at a single point, it turns out that the parallel light from stars in other directions is not focused at a point. The images of stars on a photograph made with a reflector are crisp and circular for stars near the center of the picture but, because of the aberration of a paraboloid for off-axis stars, images are neither crisp nor circular at the edge of the picture.

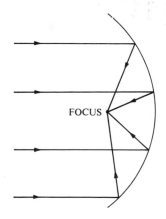

Fig. 5.8:1. A paraboloid focuses all incident light from a star on the optical axis at a single point.

The parabola is a curve of great interest to astronomers, and we shall encounter it again. Not only is the parabola employed in the optics of reflectors, but it is also a possible shape of orbits in space. We shall find in Chapter 7 that Kepler's law of ellipses, which we first met in Chapter 3 in connection with the earth's orbit, must be amended to include other types of curves, among them the parabola. A body

Fig. 5.8:2. The 74-inch reflector of the Mount Stromlo Observatory, Canberra, Australia. (*Mount Stromlo Observatory photograph*)

leaving the earth with parabolic velocity (often called escape velocity), about 7 miles per second, has just enough speed to move infinitely far from the earth in spite of the gravitational back-pull of the earth. Unlike a body in a closed elliptical orbit, it will never return to earth, for the parabola along which it moves is not a closed curve.

9. Where Is the Focus?

THE FOCAL PLANE of a reflector lies between the mirror and the stars at a point inside the telescope tube, and therefrom arises the problem of how to place a photographic plate in position in order to record in-focus starlight. The most straightforward solution is to place a plate-holder centrally in the tube, supported by thin metallic plates, or fins, attached to the tube; this location is called the *prime focus*. A person looking down the optical axis of a reflector sees an arrangement like that shown in Fig. 5.9:1(a); the cutaway view from the side is shown in Fig. 5.9:1(b). In very large instruments both the observer and the photographic plate he is exposing ride in a cage at the prime focus (Fig. 5.9:2). With such large instruments, only about 10 percent of the light arriving from a star is blocked by the cage. For smaller telescopes it is clearly impractical to put the astronomer inside the tube, since he would obstruct his own aims. Instead he has access to the plate-holder through an opening in the telescope tube.

A frequent alternative to the prime focus is the *Newtonian focus*, shown in Fig. 5.9:1(c). A small plane mirror is mounted at an angle of

45° to the optical axis and between the paraboloidal mirror and the prime focus. The converging beam from a star is thus reflected to the side of the tube, where the plate-holder is located. Another alternative is the *Cassegrainian focus*, shown in Fig. 5.9:1(d). The small secondary mirror interrupts the converging beam and reflects it back through a small hole in the main mirror to a focus just behind the mirror. If

(a)

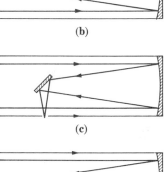

(b)

(c)

(d)

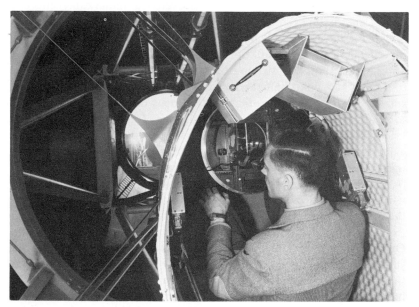

Fig. 5.9:2. The prime-focus cage of the 120-inch reflector on Mount Hamilton. (*Lick Observatory photograph*)

Fig. 5.9:1. (a) Looking down the optical axis of a reflector; (b) the prime focus of a reflector; (c) the Newtonian focus; (d) the Cassegrainian focus.

the secondary mirror in the Cassegrainian arrangement were plane, the focal plane would lie inside the tube. Instead it is convex so that the focus will be accessible; the effect of the curved secondary mirror is

Fig. 5.9:3. The 200-inch Hale telescope on Mount Palomar. The instrument is here aimed at the zenith. (*Mount Wilson and Palomar Observatories photograph*)

to increase the focal length of the telescope. The focal plane of the Cassegrainian reflector is located similarly to that of a refractor, and, unlike the Newtonian and prime focus arrangements, one looks at a star through the eyepiece in the same direction one looks at the star with the unaided eye.

10. The Schmidt Telescope

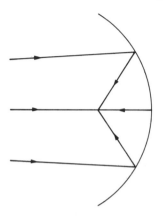

Fig. 5.10:1. Incoming rays are made slightly divergent in order to be sharply focused by the spherical mirror of a Schmidt telescope.

IN 1930 BERNHARD SCHMIDT discovered a remarkably effective way of eliminating the off-axis aberrations of the paraboloid and also of utilizing the more easily built spherical mirror. Recall from Section 7 that a spherical mirror will not focus parallel light from a star on the optical axis, that rays striking the mirror near the optical axis come to a focus at a point halfway between the mirror and the center of the sphere. In order to force other rays to focus here also, it is necessary to arrange that the incoming rays from a star follow slightly diverging tracks before striking the mirror, as shown in Fig. 5.10:1. This is achieved by placing a lens at the center of curvature of the spherical mirror, the lens being shaped in such a manner that rays incident from a star will be refracted outward by just the correct amount and will then be reflected by the mirror to a common focus. Because the amount of refraction is small, the lens does not differ very much from a plane slab of glass; it is therefore called a *correcting plate.* Off-axis stars do not come to focus on a plane surface but on a spherical surface concentric with the mirror. Because the focal surface is curved, the glass photographic plate must be bent slightly—occasionally a hazardous procedure. The optical arrangement of the several parts of a Schmidt telescope is illustrated in Fig. 5.10:2, the curvature of the correcting plate being highly exaggerated for clarity. A major advantage of the Schmidt telescope is that its aberrations are very small for stars lying some distance from the optical axis; it is therefore beautifully suited for making photographs which cover substantial areas of the celestial sphere.

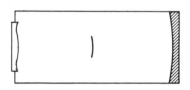

Fig. 5.10:2. Starlight is very slightly refracted by the Schmidt correcting plate, is reflected by the spherical mirror, and reaches a focus on the curved surface near the middle of the telescope tube.

Fig. 5.10:3. The 24–36-inch Curtis Schmidt telescope at the Portage Lake Observatory of the University of Michigan, photographed with a pinhole camera by Freeman D. Miller. (*Observatory of the University of Michigan photograph*)

PERFORMANCE RATINGS

11. Light-gathering Power

ONE MAY WONDER why there is such a wide variety of telescopes around the world. One reason of course is financial: a given amount of money will permit the purchase of this instrument but not that one. A more telling reason is that one astronomical problem is best solved by a telescope of a certain design, whereas another problem demands a different type of telescope. One astronomer may need a large-area photograph of bright gas clouds in the Milky Way; another may want to study the most distant faint galaxies; a third will wish to view the surface detail on Mars as critically as possible. Several criteria are used as indicators of the performance of a telescope for different requirements, and the first we shall consider is the *light-gathering power*.

When a star is observed with the unaided eye, the light focused on the retina enters the eye as a circular beam whose diameter equals the diameter of the pupil, about $\frac{1}{4}$ inch. When the same star is seen through a telescope, the pupil receives the light in a circular beam whose diameter, D, is the diameter of the lens or mirror. Since the amount of light reaching the pupil depends on the *area* of the aperture, it is proportional to the square of the diameter. The light-gathering power of a telescope, L, is defined as the ratio of light per unit time entering the eye at the telescope to that from the same source which enters the unaided eye per unit time,

$$L = \frac{D^2}{D_{\text{eye}}^2} = \frac{D^2}{(\frac{1}{4})^2} = 16D^2,$$

providing D is expressed in inches. Thus a 1-inch telescope collects 16 times as much light as the unaided eye and a 10-inch telescope 1600 times as much. It is clear, then, that the bigger the telescope objective (lens or mirror) the fainter will be the stars that can be seen or photographed.

12. Resolving Power

A SECOND criterion of the performance of a telescope is its ability to separate or resolve two stars which are so close together in the sky that the unaided eye sees them as a single point. Because light is a wave phenomenon, the waves from a star which strike a telescope objective and converge toward the focus interfere with one another. This effect is called *diffraction*. Even if an instrument is perfectly built, the image of a star at the focus is not a point but a small circular disc surrounded by faint rings. The angular separation of two stars just resolvable by a telescope of aperture D (in inches) may be calculated from diffraction theory; it is $5''/D$. Thus a 10-inch instrument can resolve an angle of $0.5''$ and a 50-inch an angle of $0.1''$. The 200-inch Hale telescope theoretically can resolve points only 150 feet apart on the moon, 240,000 miles away. In practice, full resolution is only rarely achieved with a large telescope because of the turbulence of the atmosphere and the resultant twinkling of the stars.

13. Scale and Magnification

WHEN A TELESCOPE is used for photography, the resulting picture has a definite *scale*, as does a map or a house plan. Instead of being expressed as $\frac{1}{8}$ inch per foot or 1 inch per 100 miles, however, the scale of a photograph is expressed as an angle in the sky per unit length on the photograph, such as 45″ per millimeter or 1° per inch. The light from two stars separated by an angle A in the sky is focused at two points separated by a distance x, and the relation between x and A depends only on the focal length of the telescope, as in Fig. 5.13:1.

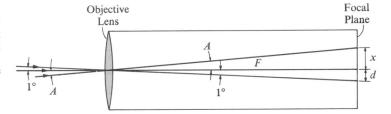

Fig. 5.13:1. All rays from a star on the optical axis are focused at one point on the focal plane; all rays from a star 1° away are focused at a second point on the focal plane d inches away.

Imagine a second telescope with a focal length twice as long as that in the figure, or $2F$. By similar triangles, the same two stars will be separated by a distance $2x$. If stars 1° apart in the sky are photographed with a telescope of focal length F, they will be separated on the plate by a distance

$$d = 0.017F.$$

If F is given in inches, d is also given in inches. For example, a telescope whose focal length is 100 inches will separate two objects a degree apart by 1.7 inches. Since the angular diameter of the moon is about $\frac{1}{2}°$, its linear diameter on a photograph taken with this instrument will be close to 0.9 inch.

When a telescope is used visually with a given eyepiece, everything viewed appears angularly larger. The moon, for example, may appear to have angular diameter 5° in a certain telescope as contrasted with 0.5° when viewed with the unaided eye, and the angular separation of two stars actually 2′ apart will appear to be 20′. The *angular magnification* of this particular telescope-eyepiece combination is thus 10. In Fig. 5.13:2(a) light from star 1 is brought to a focus in the focal plane at point 1 on the optical axis, while light from star 2 (separated from star 1 by angle A in the sky) focuses at point 2. For simplicity, only the rays passing through the center of the telescope lens are drawn in, although in actuality a whole cone of rays converges on point 1 from star 1 and another whole cone converges on point 2 from star 2. From each of these two families of converging cones, the illustration shows only those particular rays diverging from the focus which pass centrally through the eyepiece. All other beams from star 1 are refracted by the eyepiece so that they comprise a parallel beam on entering the eye. Similarly, all other beams from star 2 are refracted by the eyepiece into a parallel beam, this beam making an angle a with the optical axis. The eye thus sees the two stars separated by angle a, whereas their true separation in the sky is angle A. The angular magnification, M, is the ratio of these two angles, $M = a/A$. If the angles involved are not too

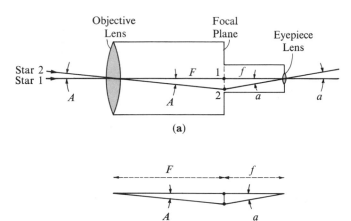

Fig. 5.13:2. The angular magnification of a telescope-eyepiece combination is $M = F/f$.

large, they are related, as one can see from Fig. 5.13:2(b), by $a/A = F/f$. Therefore the angular magnification of a given telescope-eyepiece combination is

$$M = F/f.$$

Here F is the focal length of the telescope and f is the focal length of the eyepiece.

Most visual telescopes are equipped with a variety of eyepieces of different focal length, which can be interchanged depending on the object under study and the quality of the seeing. The formula above implies that we can obtain as big a magnification as we wish by choosing an eyepiece with a small enough focal length. Actually the amount of magnification achievable with any telescope is limited by its resolving power. Remember that because of diffraction the image of a star in the focal plane is a disc. If too great a magnification is used, the star will appear as a smear rather than a point; the practical maximum magnification is about

$$M_{\text{max}} = 50D,$$

where D is, as before, the diameter of the objective in inches. Similarly, there is a minimum useful magnification. Reference to Fig. 5.5:1 will reveal that if an eyepiece of longer focal length is used, the parallel beam will have such a large area that only a part will enter the eye; the rest of the light will be wasted. The smallest useful magnification turns out to be about

$$M_{min} = 4D,$$

if D is again expressed in inches. Thus, for a 10-inch telescope,

$$M_{min} = 40 \text{ and } M_{max} = 500.$$

14. Refractor or Reflector?

A DISTINCT advantage of the reflecting telescope is its freedom from chromatic aberration. Even with two lenses, a refractor must be of fairly long focal length in order to avoid objectionable color aberration. The ratio of focal length to diameter of objective, F/D, is the *focal ratio* of a telescope; and in practice most refractors have focal ratios of about 15. Reflectors, on the other hand, usually have focal ratios of only about 5. Therefore for a given diameter of objective, D, the telescope tube can be much shorter in length for the reflector than for the refractor, with a consequent reduction in cost of mounting and housing. In addition, the lenses of a refractor must be of optically perfect glass, and four surfaces must be shaped with precision, whereas the glass forming the mirror of a reflector need not be perfect because it is coated with reflecting material, and only one surface has to be shaped with precision. The refractor has the advantage that there is no obstruction in the telescope tube, whereas in a reflector the secondary mirror blocks a small percentage of the incoming light. Furthermore, about 82 percent of incoming light passes through a system of two lenses whose surfaces are clean, whereas a reflector with two aluminized mirrors transmits somewhat less, about 75 percent.

Since mirrors can be supported from behind, because the required quality of their glass is not a severe restriction, and because the focal ratio of a reflector need not be large, it has been possible to build reflectors with apertures larger than those of refractors. The largest refractor in the world is the 40-inch instrument at the Yerkes Observatory in Williams Bay, Wisconsin, with a focal length of 760 inches and thus a focal ratio of 19. The second largest is the 36-inch refractor at the Lick Observatory, atop Mount Hamilton in California. The largest

Fig. 5.14:1. An aerial view of the Kitt Peak National Observatory in southern Arizona. This mountain-top site, 40 miles southwest of Tucson and 6800 feet above sea level, was chosen in 1958. (*Kitt Peak National Observatory photograph*)

reflector in the world is the 200-inch Hale telescope on Palomar Mountain in California; its focal length is 660 inches and therefore its focal ratio is 3.3. Second in size is the 120-inch reflector at the Lick Observatory, and third is the 102-inch instrument at the Crimean Astrophysical Observatory in Russia, and the fourth is the 100-inch on Mount Wilson in California. The largest Schmidt telescope in the world is located at the Karl Schwarzschild Observatory in East Germany. Next in size is the Schmidt telescope on Palomar Mountain, which has a correcting plate 48 inches in diameter and a spherical mirror 72 inches in diameter.

15. Mountings, Drives, and Domes

BINOCULARS AND spyglasses are lightweight portable instruments which can be easily aimed at the whim of the observer. Astronomical telescopes, on the other hand, must be mounted so that they can be pointed steadily at any object in the sky. A tripod is sufficient for a very small visual telescope, but the mounting requirements for a large telescope are far more strict. First, the astronomer must be able to find the object he wishes to study; second, the telescope must stay pointed at the object under study.

Nearly every telescope has an *equatorial mounting*: the direction in which such a telescope can be pointed is specified by the two equatorial coordinates, hour angle and declination. Figure 5.15:1 shows a typical equatorial mounting. On a fixed and massive pier extending into the ground is the *polar axis*, which can be rotated as desired. The polar axis points toward the celestial pole and is thus parallel to the axis of rotation of the earth. The angle between the polar axis and the horizontal floor is equal to the latitude of the observer. Attached to the upper end of the polar axis, at right angles, is the *declination axis*. Thus, when the polar axis is turned, the declination axis is directed toward various points on the celestial equator. Finally, the telescope tube itself is free to turn around the declination axis. In Fig. 5.15:1 the tube is pointed toward the celestial pole, but it may be turned to point toward any desired declination. The *hour circle* on the polar axis allows the astronomer to tell the hour angle at which the telescope is pointing; the *declination circle* attached to the declination axis tells him the declination toward which the instrument is aimed. The counterweight at one end of the declination axis balances the weight of the telescope at the other end so that the instrument is more easily maneuvered. The essential reason for employing the equatorial mounting is that once the telescope is pointed toward the Pleiades, for example, the declination does not need to be readjusted to follow them through the night, and the hour angle needs only to be increased proportionally to the time. If a telescope were mounted in azimuth and altitude, like large guns or the transit instruments of surveyors, following a celestial body during the night would be a complicated job.

To set out on a given star in the first place, the astronomer checks its right ascension and declination in a catalogue. He notes the sidereal time on the observatory's sidereal clock or on his sidereal watch (an ordinary watch rated to gain four minutes per day). Subtraction of the

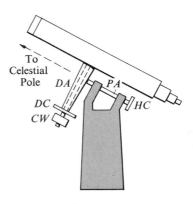

Fig. 5.15:1. A telescope mounting. The polar axis is *PA*; it carries the hour circle *HC* for setting the desired hour angle and it also carries the declination axis *DA*. The declination axis carries the telescope, a counterweight *CW*, and the declination circle *DC* for setting the desired declination.

right ascension from the sidereal time gives the hour angle of the star at that instant. The instrument is maneuvered to point at this hour angle and declination and, if no mistakes have been made, the object in question appears in the telescope. If the telescope is large and the magnification therefore high, the angular field of view will be very small and the chance of sighting the desired star on the first try is thus not much better than finding a hammer in a haystack during the first minute of search. To avoid fruitless hunting, a small telescope or *finder* is attached parallel to its parent. With its much larger field of view the star is easily found. The instrument is then maneuvered until the star is centered in the finder's field of view; it will then be seen in the big instrument.

Suppose our telescope is located at a middle northern latitude, the star in question is near the celestial equator, and we are observing it in the southern sky. We have centered the star in the field of view and are watching it. What does it do? Instead of staying in the center of the field, it marches steadily west across the field because of its daily motion around the sky. Its hour angle is increasing, but the hour angle toward which the telescope is pointing is fixed. If the angular field of view is 1° in diameter, for example, the star will move out of the field in only 2 minutes, since it moves 360° in 24 hours, 1° in 4 minutes, and thus $\frac{1}{2}$° in 2 minutes. In order to keep the star in view, the telescope must be moved at the same rate as the star. The mechanism by which this slow but steady motion of the telescope is achieved is the *drive* of the telescope. Like a clock, the drive of a telescope may be mechanical or electrical. Once it is set running, the telescope moves in hour angle at the rate of 360° per sidereal day, and therefore any field of stars toward which the telescope is pointed remains in view as the night hours pass. In other words, the drive of an equatorially mounted telescope exactly counteracts the earth's rotation.

Although a portable telescope can be taken indoors after use, a large telescope needs its own housing to protect it from bad weather. The housing must be designed so that the telescope can point at anything above the horizon. One structure that meets this need is a simple rectangular shed with a roof which can be rolled off when the telescope is in use. A disadvantage of such housing, however, is that when the telescope is pointed at high altitudes it is exposed to the wind and may vibrate, blurring the image of a star. Of greatest utility is the hemispherical *dome*. A vertical slice of the dome may be moved horizontally to reveal a slit of open sky from horizon to zenith. Furthermore, the entire dome can be rotated electrically so that the slit is in the desired compass direction. The telescope may therefore be pointed toward any azimuth and altitude desired.

The site chosen for an observatory depends on many factors. Of cardinal importance are good weather and good seeing. Weather records show that there is great variation from one region to another in the average number of clear days per year. The average degree of atmospheric turbulence and thus the quality of the seeing differ in various localities. Although accessibility is desirable, it is usually

Fig. 5.15:2. A moonlight view of the 200-inch Hale telescope dome with shutter open. (*Mount Wilson and Palomar Observatories photograph*)

overruled in choosing a site by the advantages of being at a high altitude above a good part of the atmospheric mass and also of being very far away from the loom of city lights and the drifting smog. The most favorable sites in the United States are in the southwest. The three largest reflectors in the United States are in California; the McDonald Observatory with its 82-inch reflector is in western Texas; and the National Observatory was established, after extensive testing of atmospheric conditions, on Kitt Peak in southern Arizona.

Fig. 5.15:3. An airplane view of the Mount Wilson Observatory, northeast of Los Angeles and 5900 feet above sea level. (*Mount Wilson and Palomar Observatories photograph*)

16. Spectrographs and Spectroscopes

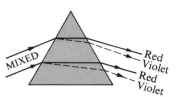

Fig. 5.16:1. Mixed light is dispersed by a prism into the colors of the rainbow.

AUXILIARY EQUIPMENT

THE LIGHT FROM a star is a mixture of all colors; if it can be unmixed, it reveals an enormous amount of information about the physical nature of the star. To break the mixed light into the several colors or wavelengths of the spectrum, we may use the principle of *dispersion*, which was discussed in Section 1. Earlier, in designing a refractor, we went to some lengths to overcome the effect of chromatic aberration. Now, however, we want to find an effective way of utilizing the principle of dispersion, and this involves the *prism*. If we allow the parallel mixed light from a star to strike one face of a triangular block of glass, as in Fig. 5.16:1, the red component of the light is refracted through a given angle on entering the glass and through another given angle on leaving the other face. On departing from the prism, it is a parallel beam of red light. The violet component is refracted more than the red, so that on leaving the prism it is a parallel beam moving in a different direction. Thus the prism breaks the parallel mixed light into a whole series of beams of different colors, each moving in a slightly different direction.

If the astronomer plans to utilize the telescope and a prism to examine the spectrum of an astronomical object, he has several options. Let us first describe the *slit spectrograph*, which is shown in Fig. 5.16:2.

Fig. 5.16:2. The optics of a slit spectrograph. Light from a star on the optical axis of the telescope converges at the focus, where the slit is located. The spectrograph is designed to focus light of each wavelength on the photographic plate. The spectrum of the star is a line or strip on the photograph, with red at one end and violet at the other.

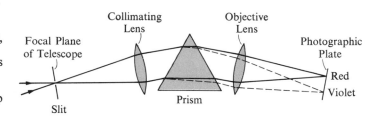

Remember that light from the stars reaches the focal plane of a telescope as a converging cone of rays. Precisely at the telescope focus is a very narrow *slit*, perpendicular to the plane of the figure. This opening prevents admission of light from other stars or from other parts of an extended surface such as the sun; otherwise the resulting spectrum would be a hopelessly tangled blend with the green light of one star superposed on the red of another. On passing the slit, the diverging cone of stellar rays must be made parallel before entering the prism, again to avoid unwanted blending. This function is the same as that of the eyepiece of a visual telescope; the *collimating lens* is placed at a distance from the slit equal to its own focal length and thus renders the beam parallel. The light then enters the *prism* and, as we have seen, is dispersed into all the colors of the rainbow. It is next necessary to bring all of the different-colored beams to a focus so that they may be photographed.

The problem here is similar to that encountered in an ordinary telescope, in which the various beams from different stars are focused on the focal plane. In the spectrograph, however, the different-colored beams from *one* star must be focused at the focal plane; this is achieved by the *objective lens*. A photographic plate placed in the focal plane of the objective lens will thus record a long thin strip of light from the star, indicating the relative amount of light emitted by the star at the various

Fig. 5.16:3. The 82-inch reflector of the McDonald Observatory in Texas, operated by the University of Chicago and the University of Texas, with spectrograph attached. (*Yerkes Observatory photograph*)

wavelengths of the spectrum. With their spectrographs astronomers use ordinary black-and-white photography rather than the more complex color photography. In spite of the fact that the resultant picture is not so pretty as one in color, a spectrogram of a star contains a great wealth of information, as we shall find in Chapter 11. As with a telescope, one can replace the photographic plate by an eyepiece and examine the spectra of stars visually; such an instrument is called a *spectroscope*.

An alternative way of combining a telescope and prism to record stellar spectra is the *objective prism*. Here, instead of obtaining a large, detailed, high-resolution spectrum of a single star, we are interested in getting small, low-resolution spectra of many stars on the same photograph. With the objective prism we dispense with the slit and the collimating lens, since light from the stars is already parallel on reaching the earth. Arriving light first strikes a narrow-angle prism at the upper end of the telescope, as shown in Fig. 5.16:4, is

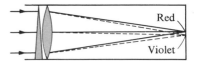

Fig. 5.16:4. An objective prism disperses the light of each star so that its image is a small streak on the photograph. Illustrated are rays arriving from a star on the optical axis.

dispersed by the prism, then enters the objective and is focused on the photographic plate. The resulting picture is similar to an ordinary photograph of a field of stars, except that the image of each star is spread out into a streak.

17. Photocells

A VERY IMPORTANT part of observational astronomy is the precise measurement of the *quantity* of light received from a star in different parts of the spectrum. Although this can be done with moderate accuracy by intercomparing the sizes of stellar images on a photograph, the intensity of light from a source is far more precisely measured by using the *photoelectric cell*. The principle of this device rests on the photoelectric effect. When light strikes the surface of certain metals such as potassium or cesium, negatively charged electrons are freed from their parent atoms. The number released is proportional to the intensity of the light source. Now, a flow of electrically charged particles is an electric current, and the strength of a current can be measured by a sensitive meter. Starlight is so feeble that several steps must be taken to produce a current large enough to be measured. (1) The photocell is placed at the focus of the telescope to take advantage of the light-gathering power of the instrument. (2) The weak current of ejected electrons is amplified. In the *photomultiplier tube*, the device most often used by astronomers, the electrons knocked off the photosensitive surface by the incident starlight are steered electrically to a second surface, knocking out other electrons. All of these are steered to a third surface, where more electrons join the current. By the time about ten stages have been completed, the current is enormously amplified and can be measured with precision.

18. Image Tubes

A DEVICE WITH a most promising future is the *image tube*. Its purpose is to increase the light-gathering power of a 20-inch telescope to that of a 100-inch or 200-inch instrument. The principle is akin to that of the photocell, except that the photocell records only one object at a time, whereas the image tube amplifies the light of all stars in the field. The stars deliver converging cones of light to the focal plane, where they impinge on a sensitive surface. At each point struck by light, electrons are knocked free in proportion to the intensity of the light. The electrons are accelerated and focused onto a fluorescent surface like a television screen, and this screen is then photographed. This technique is perhaps one hundred times as efficient as ordinary photography and thus, instead of collecting more light by using a larger mirror, each bit of light is made to produce a greater effect by utilizing the photoelectric process.

19. Telescopes in Reverse

ANOTHER PROMISING device is the *laser*, which is a short rod of synthetic ruby. When it is stimulated by flashes from a gas tube beside it, the ruby crystal emits an energetic pulse of red light into an extremely narrow cone. The laser may be attached to a telescope and aimed in any direction. In 1962 a laser was first used to spotlight the moon. Every minute a 1/2000-second pulse was emitted toward a dark point on the lunar surface. On the outbound trip each pulse occupied a region of space nearly 100 miles long, speading in width to about one mile on approaching the moon, the entire pencil receding from the earth at 186,300 mi/sec. At incidence on the rough lunar surface, much of the red light in each pulse was absorbed and the rest was scattered in all directions. Only about one part in 10^{19} of the radiant energy in each pulse rebounded along a track close enough to its outward path to reach the mirror of a companion receiving telescope. Here the feeble returning signals were detected by a photomultiplier tube, some 2.5 seconds after the emission of each pulse.

RADIO TELESCOPES

20. Comparison with Optical Telescopes

As WE HAVE already seen, radiant energy is emitted by the stars not only at wavelengths to which the eye responds, but in all parts of the electromagnetic spectrum. The earth's atmosphere, however, stops this energy at most wavelengths. There are only two windows through which we can look at the universe: the visual part of the spectrum and a portion of the radio part of the spectrum. The instruments we have considered thus far are designed for use at visual wavelengths; now we turn to *radio telescopes*, which are designed to provide us with information on the quantity of radio energy emitted by various celestial sources. Although the history of radio astronomy goes back only to 1932, the principles which guide the construction of a radio telescope are familiar. As with light waves, radio waves move in straight lines in a vacuum and are subject to refraction and reflection when moving through non-uniform regions. As with a conventional optical telescope, the two

Fig. 5.20:1. The twin 90-foot paraboloids at the Owens Valley site, about 200 miles north of Los Angeles. The distance between the pair can be varied to provide an interferometer of the desired base line. (*Owens Valley Radio Observatory, California Institute of Technology*)

LIGHT, RADIO, AND
TELESCOPES

essential functions of a radio telescope are (1) to collect radio energy and (2) to resolve sources that are angularly close together in the sky. The three basic parts of a radio telescope are the *antenna*, which receives the energy from a source in the sky, the radio *receiver*, which amplifies a trillion or so times the incredibly tiny signal intercepted by the antenna, and the *meter*, which records the information for the radio astronomer.

21. Antennas

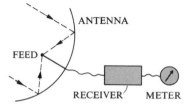

ONE POPULAR kind of antenna is paraboloidal in shape, like the mirror of a reflecting telescope. Figure 5.21:1 shows the radio waves from a celestial source on the axis of the dish being reflected to a common focus, where the *feed* is mounted. This small antenna collects the energy, which then is delivered to the receiver, amplified, and delivered to the meter.

In order to collect enough energy from the weak celestial sources, the paraboloid must be of substantial size. One of the largest dishes in operation is at the Jodrell Bank station of the University of Manchester, England, and its diameter is 250 feet. It is mounted so that it can be pointed at any part of the sky. The dish is surfaced with wire mesh rather than glass, and as an all-weather instrument it fortunately does not need to be housed in a dome.

Fig. 5.21:1. The essential parts of a radio telescope shown schematically.

The cost of mounting antennas much larger than that at Manchester becomes prohibitive. An alternative design is used at the University of Illinois, as shown in Fig. 5.21:2. The 400-foot by 600-foot antenna is trough-shaped rather than dish-shaped, and it is fixed in a north–

Fig. 5.21:2. Looking northeast on a partly cloudy evening at a portion of the six-acre radio telescope at the Vermilion River site. The collecting surface is a cylindrical paraboloid, here partially covered with snow. It focuses incoming cosmic radio radiation onto the north-south focal line, 155 feet high. During this 75-minute time exposure an airplane crossed the field of view, its lights leaving a straight trail against the sky. In the greater distance each star moved counter-clockwise through an 18° arc around the north celestial pole, off the picture above and left. Patchy clouds drifting across the sky caused the breaks in each star trail. (*Photographed by Arno Schriefer, Vermilion River Observatory, University of Illinois*)

south valley. An east–west slice through the surface is parabolic in shape, and energy from a source on the meridian is focused along a straight line. The daily rotation of the earth permits the instrument to examine all right ascensions. The declination to be examined on a given day is set electrically rather than by moving the instrument itself.

Many other varieties of single antenna structure are in use besides those using the focusing property of the parabola, but we shall not dwell on them at length. A major problem in any radio telescope is that its resolving power, or ability to see fine detail in the sky, is millions of times less than that of an optical telescope of the same size. To match the resolving power of a one-inch optical telescope, a radio telescope tens of miles in diameter would have to be built. Therefore a radio instrument must be big in order not only to collect adequate energy but also to provide angular resolution. By making use of the fact that radio waves interfere with one another like ocean waves in a confused sea, it has been possible to overcome in part the difficulty of low resolution by setting two or more simple antennas some miles apart and recording the joint signals from the individual antennas. These instruments are called *interferometers* and have permitted, among other things, precise determination of the position of radio sources on the celestial sphere and examination of the solar surface in some detail at radio wavelengths.

22. Performance Ratings

THE CRITERION that specifies the energy-gathering performance of a radio antenna is called its *effective area*. It is a measure similar to the light-gathering power of an optical telescope, but it is more complicated in concept because the effective area of an antenna is not necessarily equal to its actual area. To understand it, think of a large piece of cardboard with a one-foot-square hole in it and held so that its plane is at right angles to the sun. Then, at a given radio wavelength, a given amount of energy passes through the square aperture each second. Now, if the antenna of a radio telescope at the same place and time delivers, for example, 1200 times as much energy each second to the receiver, then its effective area is 1200 square feet. This quantity has to be defined for each direction, because clearly a parabolic dish is far more responsive to a source on its axis than, for example, to one $20°$ away.

In addition to specifying the sensitivity of a radio telescope in terms of effective area, we need a measure of its directional discrimination. Not only do we wish to detect the radiation from many celestial radio sources, but we also wish to resolve them one from the other. The resolving power of a radio telescope depends on the size of its antenna and the wavelength at which it operates. If the diameter (or, crudely, the square root of the effective area) is $100D$ feet, then the closest pair of sources that can be resolved is about $0.2°/D$ for an antenna operating at wavelength 10 centimeters, $2°/D$ at 1 meter, and $20°/D$ at 10 meters. Again, it is clear that radio telescopes must be big in order both to detect faint sources and to resolve them.

Although it is advantageous to have an optical observatory atop a mountain and thus above a good part of the atmosphere, a radio observatory requires a site that is as free as possible of interference from radio and television signals and the static from automobile and aircraft ignition systems. Thus many stations are located in sparsely populated regions where they are shielded by the terrain. The National

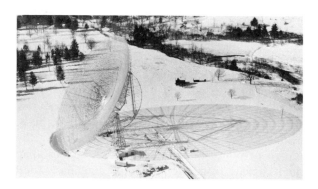

Fig. 5.22:1. The 300-foot steerable antenna at Green Bank, W. Va. (*National Radio Astronomy Observatory photograph*)

Radio Astronomy Observatory at Green Bank, West Virginia, for example, is located in a valley between ridges of mountains. Furthermore, because the antennas are large and exposed to the weather, it is important that they be located away from the ordinary paths of hurricanes and tornados, although cloudy and rainy weather do not hamper operations.

23. Radar Instruments

RADIO TELESCOPES and optical telescopes receive the radiation emitted by celestial objects. A radar set, on the other hand, transmits a burst of energy at radio wavelengths out from its antenna in a given direction. If there is a target in the beam, some of the outgoing energy will be reflected from it, and a minute fraction will come back and strike the antenna again, where it is fed to the receiver, amplified, and recorded. If a powerful radar is pointed at the moon, for example, the train of events resembles the operation of pointing a very powerful searchlight at the moon and snapping it on briefly every few seconds or of detecting the moon at visual wavelengths with a laser.

Radar detection of the moon was first achieved in 1946 with a U.S. Army radar set on the New Jersey coast. Electronically, it is possible to measure with high precision the time taken for a pulse of energy to make the round trip from earth to moon and back. Since it is known that the speed of radiation in a vacuum is 186,300 mi/sec, it becomes possible to measure the distance to the moon as well as to other objects, such as meteors, which are not prohibitively far away. Objects extremely far away return such a minute fraction of the signal to the antenna that they cannot be detected. Therefore astronomical radar observations are confined to the solar system. As of 1963 the sun and the inner planets had yielded to this technique.

Fig. 5.23:1. The 85-foot radar antenna at the Goldstone Station in California's Mojave desert, used for extensive observations of Venus in 1961 and 1962 and for detection of Mars in 1963. (*Courtesy National Aeronautics and Space Administration and Jet Propulsion Laboratory*)

PROBLEMS

1. On March 21 you are temporarily blinded by the image of the sun reflected into your eye by the windshield of a car approaching you on a level road from the north. Suppose the windshield is a plane piece of glass pitched at an angle of 30° from the vertical. (**a**) What time of day is it? (**b**) What is the altitude of the sun? (**c**) What is your approximate latitude?

2. The inner bright rainbow is caused by sunlight that follows a four-legged path. Each ray is incident on a spherical drop of water, is refracted there, and then is reflected internally at the far surface of the drop, passes back through the drop, and is finally refracted again on emerging from the drop. The ray then proceeds to your eye, having turned through a total angle of 138°. Sketch the path of such a ray.

3. What are the essential functions of an optical telescope? Of a radio telescope?

4. What is chromatic aberration, and how is its effect reduced in designing a refractor?

5. Dispersion operates in the atmosphere as well as in lenses and prisms. A bright star observed telescopically at a low altitude appears as a little vertical spectrum instead of as a point. Explain why the violet light from such a star is at a slightly higher altitude than the red light.

6. The radius of a hemispherical mirror is 14 feet. (**a**) What is its focal length for rays that are incident close to the center of the mirror and that arrive from a star lying on the extended optical axis of the

mirror? (b) What is its focal length for rays from this star that reach the mirror at an angle of incidence of 45°?

7. Distinguish between the prime focus, the Newtonian focus, and the Cassegrainian focus of a reflector.

8. A Schmidt telescope has features both of a reflector and of a refractor. Why?

9. Calculate the light-gathering power and resolving power of the 200-inch Hale telescope. What is the linear diameter of Venus on a photograph made at the prime focus of the 200-inch, given that the angular diameter of Venus at the time of exposure is 0.70′ and that the focal length of the mirror is 666 inches?

10. (a) What are the minimum and maximum useful magnifying powers of a 6-inch visual telescope with focal length 3 feet? (b) What should be the focal lengths of the eyepieces used with this instrument?

11. What are some of the reasons why a reflector performs better than a refractor of the same aperture? And a refractor better than a reflector?

12. (a) How should a telescope be set to find an object at right ascension 13^h52^m, declination $+3.7°$, if the sidereal time is 12^h19^m? (b) How should it be set to pick up the same object three sidereal hours later?

13. Name and state the function of each part of a slit spectrograph.

14. Calculate the resolving power of a radio telescope of diameter 200 feet and operating on a wavelength of 3 meters.

15. How far is Venus from the earth on an occasion when the round-trip time for a radar signal is 5.4 minutes?

6

OUR MOON

Accompanying the earth in its journey through space are a single large natural *satellite*, the *moon*, and, since the Russian launching of the first *sputnik* on October 4, 1957, a varying number of man-made objects such as balloons and copper needles. We shall consider the moon in this chapter, reserving discussion of man-made earth satellites until the theory of celestial orbits has been developed in the next chapter.

Although as viewed from beyond the solar system the moon is a relatively insignificant object, it ranks second to the sun in brilliance as seen from the earth. Its varying shapes and times of appearance gave impetus to astronomical studies thousands of years ago; in more recent times the neighborliness of the moon has made it possible to observe its motions and to map its surface features with great precision. By comparison, the satellites of other planets are so far away that we know little about them. In fact, since 3 of the 31 known satellites in the solar system have been discovered since 1940, it is likely that there remain a number yet to be found. The moon ranks fifth in size among the known satellites. Its most outstanding statistic is that it is more massive relative to its parent planet than any other satellite; the earth–moon system therefore is more like a double planet than any other of the 31 planet–satellite combinations.

THE LUNAR ORBIT

1. Distance to the Moon

JUST AS THE earth revolves around the sun, the moon orbits around the earth. If Kepler's first two laws of planetary motion, which we encountered in discussing the earth's orbit, are at all general, we are entitled to expect that the moon's orbit is elliptical in shape, with the center of the earth at one focus, and that the moon obeys the law of areas. This expectation is verified by observation.

The orbital period of the moon is established by plotting its easterly path through the background stars and finding the time taken to complete exactly one circuit. This period turns out to be 27.3 days and is of course the same interval of time an observer outside the solar system would clock as the moon wheeled 360° around the earth.

Of fundamental importance is a knowledge of the distance to the moon, and this can be established precisely by several different techniques. The first of these requires triangulation from two observatories far apart on the earth. Simultaneous photographs are made at the two points, and when they are compared the position of the center of the moon's disk among the stars is found to be different in the two pictures, as shown in Fig. 6.1:1. The angular separation of the two images is x. To simplify the geometry without sacrificing principle, observatories A and B in the illustration have the moon at the horizon so that triangles ACM and BCM are similar and are right triangles. In triangle ACM the angle AMC is $x/2$ and AC is the known radius of the earth. The distance from the center of the earth to the center of the moon, CM, can then be computed. In actuality observations at the horizon are scarcely practical. Instead, the two observatories are a few thousand miles apart and the base line between them can be computed from a knowledge of the latitude and longitude of each. In addition to taking the simultaneous photographs, the altitude of the moon above the horizon must be measured at both observatories. The mean distance of the moon from the earth, which is the semimajor axis of the lunar orbit, turns out to be 238,857 miles and is accurate to within about a mile. We shall often use the round figure of 240,000 miles for this distance.

A second technique for finding the distance to the moon involves the use of radar, the principles of which we considered in Chapter 5. The round-trip time for a signal to leave the antenna, strike the near face of the moon, and return to the antenna is measured electronically with high accuracy. Since the speed of electromagnetic radiation in a vacuum is also known with remarkable precision, the lunar distance is deducible to the nearest mile or so, in agreement with the computation by triangulation. One difficulty with the radar method is that the signal spends a small fraction of a second in the earth's atmosphere, where it is slightly refracted and travels a bit slower than when it is traversing a vacuum. A third technique, also considered in Chapter 5, is the use of a laser.

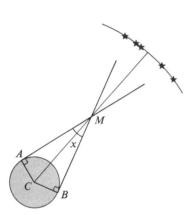

Fig. 6.1:1. The distance to the moon, CM, can be found by photographing it at the same time from points A and B on the earth.

2. Orbit Shape and Speed

THE ECCENTRICITY of the moon's orbit can be established by measuring the moon's changing angular diameter during the month. The average angular diameter of the moon is 31′, a shade smaller than the sun's. But it varies during the month, being a maximum when the moon is nearest the earth, at *perigee*, and a minimum about two weeks later when the moon is farthest from the earth, at *apogee*. The orbital eccentricity is 0.056, and thus the minimum distance of the moon is 5.6 percent less than the mean distance, or 225,000 miles, and the maximum is 5.6 percent more than the mean, or 253,000 miles.

Knowing the size, shape, and period of the lunar orbit, we can find the average speed of the moon; the velocity averages 2300 miles per hour. Because of the law of areas it varies up to 5.6 percent from the average, being a maximum at perigee and a minimum at apogee. The *angular* velocity of the moon through the stars can be found without any knowledge of its distance. Since it moves through the stars one circuit every 27.3 days, its average angular velocity must be 360°/27.3 days = 13.2°/day = 33′/hour. Thus on the average the moon moves its own diameter eastward through the stars in approximately one hour.

3. Inclination

THE MOON'S monthly path through the stars is nearly along the ecliptic, but not quite. At most it lies 5° north or south of the ecliptic. The two points at which the moon's path crosses the ecliptic are the *nodes*. When the moon crosses from south to north of the ecliptic it is at the *ascending node*; about two weeks later it passes the *descending node* (see Fig. 6.3:1). The moon's nodes are not fixed points among the stars but move west along the ecliptic, completing one circuit every 19 years. This *regression of the nodes* is reminiscent of the precessional motion of the earth, but it takes much less time than the 26,000-year cycle for the gyration of the earth's axis of rotation.

What these observations mean are (1) that the moon's orbit plane is inclined to the earth's orbit plane by 5° and (2) that this plane does not have a fixed orientation in space. Imagine placing a record on a record-player incorrectly so that it is tilted 5° from the horizontal, and then turning on the switch so that the turntable rotates not at 33 rpm but once every 19 years; this will give the picture of the behavior of the moon's orbital plane. The physical reason behind the regression of the nodes is the disturbing effect of the sun's gravitational pull on the moon.

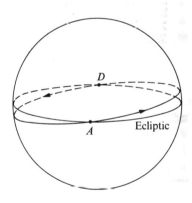

Fig. 6.3:1. The moon's orbit is inclined 5° to the plane of the earth's orbit. Point *A* is the ascending node of the moon's orbit and point *D* is the descending node.

4. The Moon's Path Relative to the Sun

WE HAVE LEARNED that the moon revolves around the earth once a month and the earth around the sun once a year. What sort of track does the moon make as it moves with the earth around the sun? Figure 6.4:1 shows five positions of the moon over the period of a month, during which the earth moves through an angle of about 30° around the sun. At *A* the moon is opposite the sun as viewed from the earth; at B, a week or so later, it has moved round a quarter of its orbit and is ahead of the earth; in another week it is at C, between the earth and the sun; at D it trails the earth; finally at E it is opposite the sun

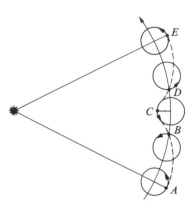

once again. From this illustration it is seen that the moon's motion is serpentine in character. The diagram has to be enormously exaggerated, however; actually the sun is about 400 times as far away as the moon, and a correctly scaled drawing would show that the monthly wiggle is small. In fact, if the tangent line to the moon's path is drawn at any point, the actual path always lies on the sunward side of its tangent line; that is, the path is everywhere concave to the sun.

Fig. 6.4:1. The moon moves on a serpentine path relative to the sun, as shown by the dashed-line track.

5. Center of Mass

OUR ILLUSTRATION in the previous section is a bit too simple. Actually, the point that moves around the sun once a year in an elliptical orbit is not the center of the earth, but the *center of mass* of the earth–moon system. The center of mass of two bodies joined by a massless straight rod is the pivot point, as shown in Fig. 6.5:1. It can be located by the formula

$$M_1 D_1 = M_2 D_2.$$

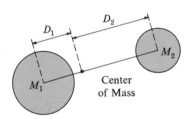

Fig. 6.5:1. The center of mass of two spheres lies on the line joining their centers and divides this line in the ratio of their masses.

Here M_1 is the mass of the first object and D_1 is its distance from the center of mass; similarly, M_2 is the mass of the second object and it lies at a distance D_2 from the center of mass. The total separation of the two objects is $D = D_1 + D_2$. A familiar application of this principle arises in seesawing when the participants are of distinctly unlike mass, such as a father and child. A successful seesaw requires that the father sit much closer to the pivot point than does his child.

The concept of center of mass carries over to objects not joined by rods. In particular, the center of mass of the earth–moon system lies fairly close to the earth's center because of the earth's far greater mass. Thus the earth's path around the sun is also serpentine, although the size of the earth's wiggles is much smaller than the moon's. The formula given above suggests that if the astronomer can measure these wiggles he can determine the mass of the moon. We shall see in a later section that this is how the moon's mass is deduced.

6. Two Kinds of Month

WE HAVE LEARNED that the orbital period of the moon is 27.3 days; this interval is called the *sidereal period* of revolution or *sidereal month* and is the time taken for the moon to make one circuit through the stars. Of importance too is the time taken for the moon to complete one circuit relative to the sun. As the moon moves easterly nearly along the ecliptic it overtakes the sun, and when it passes the sun it is said to be in *conjunction*. Continuing easterly, the moon moves through the stars at an average rate of 13.3° per day, while the sun moves 1.0° per day eastward as a consequence of the earth's orbital motion. Thus the moon gains only 12.3° per day on the sun. Consequently, the time required for the moon to gain one lap on the sun and come to conjunction again is somewhat longer than 27.3 days. It amounts to 29.5 days, and this is the *synodic period* of the moon, or the *synodic month* ("synod" signifying "meeting"). This interval is also called the *month of the phases*, because the sequence of phases or shapes of the moon depends on its place in the sky relative to the source that illuminates it, the sun. The time from full moon to full moon is therefore 29.5 days, whereas the true month has 27.3 days. Neither of these times corresponds to any calendar month, each of which has an integral number of days.

An alternative way of picturing the difference between the sidereal and synodic month is shown in Fig. 6.6:1. The instantaneous location of the moon's orbit is plotted at three different times. At *A* the moon is opposite the sun, as viewed from the earth. At *B*, 27.3 days later, the moon has completed one circuit and again is seen in the same direction among the stars as at *A*. But it takes 2.2 additional days to swing around the extra angle and be opposite the sun, at *C*.

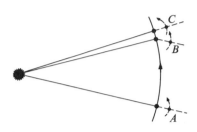

Fig. 6.6:1. At *A* and *B*, 27.3 days apart, we see the moon at the same point among the stars. At *A* and *C*, 29.5 days apart, we see the full moon at the antisun point.

7. Times of Moonrise and Moonset

WATCH THE crescent moon for a few consecutive evenings in the western sky a half-hour or so after sunset. Not only does it swing down the sky and set each evening, because of the earth's daily rotation, but there are progressive changes from night to night. Figure 6.7:1 shows the crescent moon on three successive nights at a given solar time, 30 minutes after sundown. The moon is seen to be higher in the western sky each evening; it therefore sets at a later time on successive nights. Just as the stars rise and set four minutes earlier each day because of the earth's orbital motion around the sun, so the times of moonrise and moonset are *retarded* each day because of the moon's easterly motion relative to our timekeeper, the sun. The amount of the delay can be determined from the knowledge that the moon loses exactly one lap on the sun in one synodic month. Therefore, although the average interval between meridian crossings of the sun is by definition 24 mean solar hours, the average interval between meridian crossings of the moon, since it makes one less diurnal circuit than the sun in 29.5 mean solar days, is

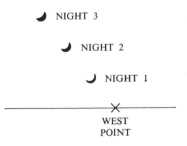

Fig. 6.7:1. The moon sets later from night to night.

$$24 \text{ hours} \times \frac{29.5 \text{ mean solar days}}{(29.5 - 1) \text{ mean solar days}} = 24 \text{ hours } 50 \text{ minutes.}$$

The *average* daily delay in moonrise and moonset is 50 minutes, although there are large variations in this figure for any given pair of successive days.

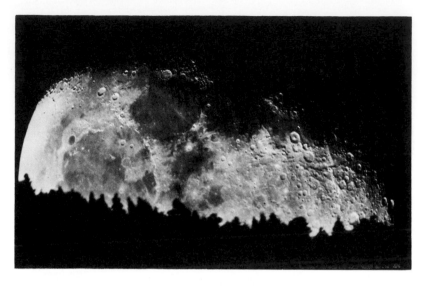

Fig. 6.7:2. The waning moon, rising over the horizon east of Flagstaff, Ariz., about 2½ hours after sunset. The trees are 9 miles away. Photographed by Arthur A. Hoag with the 40-inch reflector. (*Official U.S. Navy photograph*)

8. The Harvest Moon

EXAMPLES OF THE great variability in the delay of moonrise are the *harvest moon*, the full moon occurring nearest to the autumnal equinox, and the next-following full moon, the *hunter's moon*. The names arise from the fact that in the middle latitudes of the northern hemisphere the early-evening landscape is illuminated by bright moonlight for a large number of nights in autumn. The reason for this is that the daily delay in moonrise near the full of the moon is a minimum in early autumn, not much more than ten minutes. Half a year later, the Easter

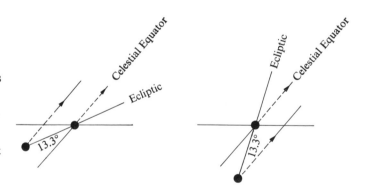

Fig. 6.8:1. At the left is the harvest moon effect. On one night the moon is at the vernal equinox and rising at the east point. On the next night it rises north of east a short time later. At the right is a springtime full moon. The first night it is at the autumnal equinox and rising at the east point. The following night it rises south of east about an hour and a half later.

full moon, the first following the vernal equinox, lags by nearly an hour and a half and is therefore in the sky for only a few nights. The explanation of these variations is given graphically in Fig. 6.8:1. Near the time of the autumnal equinox the full moon, being opposite the sun, is near the vernal equinox. The pitch of the ecliptic to the eastern horizon is therefore small and the delay in moonrise is a minimum. When the sun is near the vernal equinox in March or April, the full moon is near the autumnal equinox and the ecliptic is not far from vertical. The delay is then a maximum.

THE MOON IS a spherical solid body and is not self-luminous. It shines by reflected sunlight and, like the earth, has at any instant a daytime hemisphere and a nighttime hemisphere. The shape of the moon as seen from the earth depends on what part of the daylit hemisphere we see. Figure 6.9:1 shows the moon in various locations during the synodic month, as observed from far north of the solar

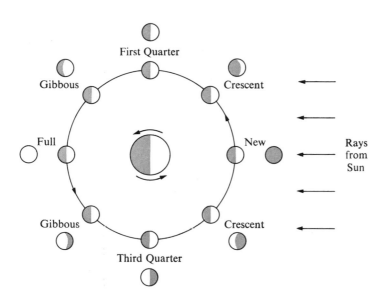

Fig. 6.9:1. The phases of the moon.

system. Also shown is the appearance of the moon to an observer on earth. *New moon* occurs when the moon is in conjunction with the sun. The sun shines on the hemisphere we cannot see; moreover, since the new moon is near the sun in the sky, it is up all day and down all night. The new moon is therefore not visible from the earth. About three days after new moon the moon has moved east of the sun and therefore rises and sets some three hours after the sun. By that time about one-fourth of the illuminated hemisphere has become visible from the earth; the moon is then in the *crescent* phase. As can be seen from Fig. 6.9:1, the sliver of visible moon is to the right, or west. The shape of the moon's geometrical edge, or *limb*, is a semicircle; the shape of the *terminator*, which is the dividing line between the day and night hemisphere of the moon, is a semicircle seen at an angle and therefore a semiellipse. This holds true not only when the moon is crescent, but at all phases. At the first and third quarters the terminator is a straight line—a special kind of semiellipse.

About a week after new moon the moon is 90° east of the sun; it therefore rises about noon, crosses the meridian at about sunset, and sets near midnight. Half of its daylight hemisphere is now visible and

OUR MOON

it looks like a coin sliced in half. The moon is then said to be at *first quarter* because one-fourth of a synodic month has elapsed since new moon. Ten or eleven days after new moon three-fourths of the daylight hemisphere can be seen from the earth. This is the *gibbous*

Fig. 6.9:2. The crescent moon, four days after new, photographed with the 36-inch refractor. South is at the top, to agree with the view of the moon as seen through a refracting telescope. (*Lick Observatory photograph*)

moon, a reverse crescent, rising in the east in midafternoon. Finally, about two weeks after new moon, the moon is *full*. Rays from the sun pass the earth and shine on the hemisphere that is exposed to the earth. As can be seen from Fig. 6.9:1, the full moon is above the horizon over the whole nighttime hemisphere of the earth. Being opposite the sun, the moon rises at sunset, is up all night, and sets at dawn. During the interval from new to full the fraction of the moon visible to us steadily increases; the moon is said then to be *waxing* (from the German "wachsen," meaning "to grow").

After full moon the phases are repeated in reverse order until the next new moon. The moon is now *waning*. The waning gibbous moon rises during the early evening hours and is often seen in the western sky before setting in the morning. The *third quarter* or *last quarter*

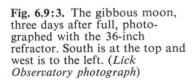

Fig. 6.9:3. The gibbous moon, three days after full, photographed with the 36-inch refractor. South is at the top and west is to the left. (*Lick Observatory photograph*)

moon rises about midnight and sets at noon. Its illuminated hemisphere is to the observer's left or east, opposite to the waxing moon. The waning crescent moon rises before dawn and can be seen in the eastern sky for a while before sunrise. Finally, after 29.5 days, the moon is new once again.

We can get good insight into the correlation between the moon's phases and the times of moonrise and moonset by referring to Fig. 6.9:1 and remembering that we are carried counterclockwise once a day, first into the night hemisphere of the earth, then back into daylight again. For example, three days after new moon, when we rotate into the night hemisphere and therefore the sun sets, the waxing crescent moon is still visible above our western horizon. It in turn disappears after the earth makes an extra eighth of a turn, which takes three hours. When we rotate into sunshine at dawn

Fig. 6.9:4. A composite photograph of the moon at last quarter, photographed with the 100-inch Hooker telescope. (*Mount Wilson and Palomar Observatories*)

the next morning, the waxing crescent moon is still below the horizon, not rising in the east until midmorning.

Also evident from Fig. 6.9:1 is the fact that the phases of the earth as viewed from the moon are just the opposite of the lunar phases we witness. At full moon the man in the moon sees new earth. While we see a waxing crescent moon, the observer on the moon sees a waning gibbous earth.

10. Earthlight

WHEN THE MOON is within a few days of new, we can see at night the entire circular disk: the bright crescent of reflected sunlight and the rest of the circle gleaming with a pale light. This effect is sometimes called "the old moon in the new moon's arms." The faint light is radiation that has made a three-legged trip, from sun to earth to moon to eye. Figure 6.10:1 shows the journey of one such ray. At first sight the path of this ray seems to violate the law of reflection, but it must be remembered that the earth and moon are rough surfaces and incident light is reflected out in all directions from any point. Because the earth is gibbous at this time, it reflects a large amount of sunlight onto the night hemisphere of the moon. In turn, the moon, although its *albedo*, or reflecting power, is only 7 percent, reflects enough of this radiation so that it is easily detectable by the eye. Measurement of the intensity of this *earthlight* allows computation of the average albedo of the earth and atmospheric clouds; it is 35 percent.

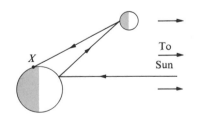

Fig. 6.10:1. The path of a sample of sunshine that contributes to earthlight as seen by the observer at *X*.

Fig. 6.10:2. Earthlight on the waxing crescent moon. (*Yerkes Observatory photograph*)

ROTATION OF THE MOON

11. Finding the Period of Rotation

LIKE THE EARTH, the moon not only revolves in an orbit but also spins on its axis. The time of rotation is readily found by watching the moon for a few months, particularly between first and last quarter when a majority of its face is visible, and noticing that we always see essentially the same face, or surface features. It is the "man in the moon" we see, never the back of his head. Therefore the moon's period of rotation must be exactly the same as its period of revolution, 27.3 days. Analogously, if one walks completely around a tree, keeping it always on his left hand, after one full circuit he has also rotated once, having faced all directions of the compass while circling the tree. The fact that the moon rotates and revolves with precisely the same period cannot be accidental; the explanation is rooted in *tidal forces*, which we shall consider presently.

12. Librations

Fig. 6.12:1. The moon's libration in latitude.

CAREFUL TELESCOPIC studies reveal that the moon does not present exactly the same face to us at all times. Although at any given moment of full moon we can see only 50 percent of the lunar surface, it has been possible to map 59 percent of the total area of the moon by observations from the earth. These slight alterations are called the *librations*, or balancing motions, of the moon, and they arise from three effects. (1) The moon's rotation axis is inclined to the perpendicular of its orbit plane by $6\frac{1}{2}°$. This results in the libration in latitude, or north–south libration, as shown in Fig. 6.12:1. At time *A* we can see beyond the north pole of the moon; two weeks later at *B* we can see beyond the south pole. (2) The moon rotates at a uniform angular rate, but its orbital speed is variable because of the law of areas, giving rise to the libration in longitude, or east–west libration. Figure 6.12:2, exaggerated for clarity, shows the moon at four points equally separated in time by 27.3/4 days = 6.83 days, *C* being the perigee and *E* the apogee. The location of the moon at *D* and *F* must be chosen so that the law of areas is satisfied and the shaded regions are all of the same area. Thus in moving from *C* to *D* the moon has revolved through more than 90° but has rotated exactly 90°, and therefore when the moon is at *D* we see more of its western hemisphere than usual. (3) The diurnal or daily libration arises from the fact that the earth is of finite size. In Fig. 6.12:3 the moon is setting at *G*, from which a slightly different hemisphere can be studied than from *H*, where the moon is just rising. Taken together, these three effects combine in such a way that 41 percent of the moon is always exposed to the earth, 41 percent never exposed, and 18 percent alternately visible and invisible.

ROTATION OF THE MOON

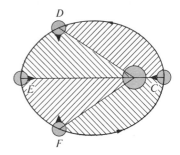

Fig. 6.12:2. The moon's libration in longitude.

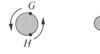

Fig. 6.12:3. The moon's diurnal libration.

Fig. 6.12:4. Two photographs showing libration. (*Lick Observatory photographs*)

13. Tides on Earth and Moon

THE MOON KEEPS the same face toward the earth because of the tidal forces exerted by the earth on the moon. By a tidal force we mean the *difference* in the gravitational force of attraction exerted by one body on two different parts of a second body. To understand better the tidal influence of the earth on the moon, let us first consider the more familiar tidal influence of the moon on the earth.

The moon, acting gravitationally as though all of its mass were at its center, exerts slightly different forces on different parts of the earth, as shown in Fig. 6.13:1. The force of attraction on unit mass at *C*, where the moon is overhead, is greater than on the center, *O*, because *C* is closer to the moon. Similarly, *O* is pulled harder than *A*, where the moon is at the nadir. At *B* and *D* the force vectors have about the same magnitude as at *O*, but they differ in direction. If we now regard the center of the earth as our reference point and subtract from each vector the force of pull at the center, we have left the differential tidal forces

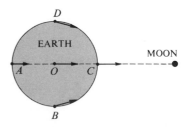

Fig. 6.13:1. The gravitational force exerted by the moon on unit mass at different points on the earth.

OUR MOON

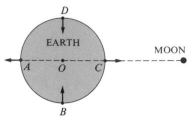

Fig. 6.13:2. The tidal force exerted by the moon on unit mass at different places on the earth. Because of the earth's rotation, the tide periodically rises and falls at any given location.

shown in Fig. 6.13:2. This amounts to a stretching force along the line AC and a squeezing force at B and D and at all other points where the moon is on the horizon. Therefore we may expect that since the earth is not perfectly rigid it will be deformed into an egg-shaped body whose long axis points toward the moon. In particular, if we imagine the earth covered by an idealized very deep ocean, there will be high tides at C and A and low tides at B and D.

The earth and moon are of course not stationary, and the average interval between successive transits of the moon at any one place on earth is 24 hours and 50 minutes. In Fig. 6.13:2 an observer on an island initially at C will experience a high tide there. After 6 hours and 13 minutes he will be at D and have a low tide. Then the water will start to rise, and 12 hours and 25 minutes after passing C the observer will experience a high tide again at A. Thus there will be two highs and two lows every 24 hours and 50 minutes.

Because of the peculiarities of topography on different coastlines, the moment of high tide at a given port does not coincide with the instant the moon is on the meridian. In a harbor that is joined to the ocean by a narrow channel, for example, the current will flow into the harbor for some time after high tide on the outside coast; later it will empty for some hours after low water outside. The lag in time of high and low water inside the harbor depends therefore on local geographical features, but the periodicity nevertheless follows the comings and goings of the moon. In addition to a definite lag in time at each place, the average *range* of the tides at each point can be measured. In the open ocean high water is only 2 or 3 feet above low water; on the coast, however, the range again depends on local topographical features. At ports in the Bay of Fundy between Nova Scotia and New Brunswick, the range attains an extreme of about 50 feet.

Although the sun is much farther away than the moon, its mass is about 27 million times that of the moon. The tidal force exerted by the sun on the earth is fully 45 percent of that exerted by the moon, and its

Fig. 6.13:3. The harbor at Cutler, Maine, one view at high tide and the other at low tide. (*Maine Department of Sea and Shore Fisheries*)

effects are also important. When the earth, moon, and sun are on line with each other, the stretching and squeezing forces are greater than average. Thus at new moon and full moon the high tides are higher than usual and the low tides are lower than usual; the tidal range is therefore a maximum. These are the so-called *spring tides*. At first and third quarter the moon and sun are 90° apart in the sky; the tidal effects of the two bodies counteract one another. At these times we experience *neap tides*; high water is not as high as usual, low water is not as low as usual, and the range is a minimum.

Oceans are not the only bodies of water affected by the tide-raising forces of the moon and sun; so too are inland lakes and ponds by small amounts. The gases of the atmosphere also undergo tides. The earth itself is not perfectly rigid and therefore it too responds to these forces; the solid tides at the earth's surface have been measured, and their range is nearly a foot.

If we next turn our attention to the much greater tidal forces exerted by the earth on the moon, we may understand why the moon keeps the same face toward the earth. Suppose that some billions of years ago the moon rotated faster than it revolved around the earth. In that remote time there thus were rising and falling solid tides at each point on the moon, just as we experience on earth today. These tides were accompanied by the continual expenditure of an enormous amount of energy in the form of heat generated by the frictional rubbing of adjacent matter. Because of the principle of conservation of energy, the rate at which energy appears as heat must be exactly balanced at all times by the rate of loss of energy of some other form. The rotational energy of the moon is the most obvious source; therefore to offset the energy going into heat the moon's rate of rotation must have continually decreased. Ultimately, when the period of rotation became as long as the period of revolution, the moon had a fixed and permanent tide in the form of bulges pointing toward and away from the earth, as demonstrated in Fig. 6.13:4. There were no further highs and lows at any point (except for the effects of the sun) and hence no further energy going from the rotation into friction. Therefore the moon now keeps its same face toward the earth; it is tidally coupled to the earth.

At first, it may seem that we have constructed too elaborate a theory to explain an isolated effect. Actually, however, every satellite in the solar system whose rotation period has been measured is found to be tidally coupled to its parent planet. Moreover, the sun's innermost planet, Mercury, keeps the same face always toward the sun.

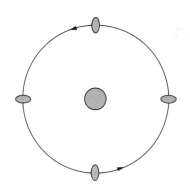

Fig. 6.13:4. The moon is tidally coupled to the earth and has permanent solid bulges, greatly exaggerated here.

14. Tidal Friction and the Future

WE SAW IN Chapter 3 that records of ancient eclipses provide evidence that the length of the day has increased on the average by about 0.0016 second per century over the last two thousand years. At this rate the decreasing rotational energy of the earth must be continually converted into heat energy at a rate of some two billion horsepower. This value is close to the rate calculated for the known ocean tides of the earth. The friction is especially large where there are strong currents and shallow waters, and about two-thirds of the heat energy is released in one body of water, the Bering Sea.

It thus is probable that the length of the day will continue to increase at a slow rate until some tens of billions of years from now the earth will always keep the same face toward the moon. The slow decrease in rotational energy also implies a slow decrease in the angular momentum of the rotating earth. Because of the conservation of angular momentum, however, this decrease must be compensated by an increase in the angular momentum of the moon in its orbit. The result is that the moon's orbital period and orbital size will very slowly increase. At the present time the semimajor axis of the moon's orbit is increasing by about a half inch per year. When tidal coupling is ultimately complete, the length of the day and of the month will both be about 50 of our present days.

STRUCTURE OF THE MOON

15. Size and Shape

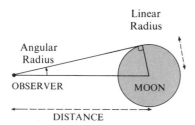

Fig. 6.15:1. To find the radius of a distant sphere, the astronomer must know both its angular radius and its distance.

IF THE ANGULAR diameter of the moon is measured precisely at the telescope and if the distance to the moon is known, it is possible to solve the triangle in Fig. 6.15:1 for the radius and thus the diameter of the moon. The diameter of the moon turns out to be 2160 miles, or 27 percent of the earth's diameter.

The shape of the moon is very nearly that of a sphere. There are deviations of a few miles owing to the ruggedness of the lunar terrain. Furthermore, the moon is somewhat flattened at the poles as a result of its monthly rotation. Compared with the earth, however, the moon's rotation is slow, and thus the moon's oblateness is very small. The solid tidal bulge of the moon is a third slight departure from sphericity, but measurement of its height is extremely difficult, as in trying to judge how much an egg held end-on deviates from the shape of a ball. The librations, however, make it possible to view the moon when it is not quite end-on, and it seems very likely that the end-on diameter does not differ by more than a mile from the equatorial diameter at right angles to it.

16. Mass and Density

IN SECTION 5 we saw that the earth and moon follow slightly serpentine paths around the sun as their center of mass follows an elliptical path around the sun. If in Fig. 6.5:1 we imagine the larger body to be the earth and the smaller one the moon, we can use the formula for the center of mass to find M_2, the mass of the moon, providing we know all other quantities. Since we already know the mass of the earth and the distance to the moon, all that remains is to measure D_1, the distance from the center of the earth to the center of mass. The latter can be established from precise measurements of the path of the sun along the ecliptic. When the moon is at first quarter, the earth in its orbital track is a bit ahead of the center of mass and thus the sun appears slightly too far east on the ecliptic. Later, at third quarter, the earth trails the center of mass and the sun's position is a few seconds of arc west. Measurement of these monthly reflex oscillations of the sun and of the nearer planets shows that the center of mass of the earth–moon system lies 2900 miles from the center of the earth when the moon is at its mean distance. The mass ratio of earth to moon is thus 81.3, or 80 in round figures.

Of some interest is the fact that the center of mass lies inside the earth itself. Because the radius of the earth is nearly 4000 miles, the center of mass is about 1000 miles beneath any observer who sees the moon in his zenith. It is of course a moving point, circuiting the interior of the earth on the average every 24 hours and 50 minutes.

The mean density of the moon can be computed from its mass and diameter; it is 3.3 grams per cubic centimeter, or 60 percent of the earth's average density.

17. Surface Gravity and Escape Speed

THE *surface gravity* of a large spherical celestial body is the rate at which a small object in free fall near the surface is accelerated by the gravitational force of the body. The surface gravity or acceleration of gravity of the earth is 32 feet per second per second; an object dropped from atop a tower has a speed of 32 ft/sec after one second of fall, 64 ft/sec after two seconds, and so on. Measurement of this quantity allowed us to determine the mass of the earth in Chapter 2. From the known mass and radius of the moon, its surface gravity is found to be only one-sixth that of the earth, or about 5 feet per second per second. A ball thrown upward at a given speed from the lunar surface will go six times as high and take six times as long to come down again as compared with the same ball thrown upward from the earth's surface. Because the weight of an object is the product of its unchanging mass and the surface gravity of the body on which it is located, one's weight on the moon would be only one-sixth his weight on the earth.

Every spherical celestial body has a definite escape speed, or *escape velocity*. The escape velocity of the earth, for example, is about 7 miles per second. Its significance is that any ball or rocket that leaves the earth's vicinity at 7 miles per second or any greater speed will permanently leave the earth, in spite of the backward pull of the earth's gravitational force. The formula for the escape velocity of any spherical celestial object is

$$v^2_{\text{escape}} = \frac{2GM}{R},$$

where G is the universal constant of gravitation, M the mass of the body in question, and R its radius. Because the moon has only some 1/81.3, or 1.23 percent, of the earth's mass and 27 percent of its radius, the moon's escape velocity is only $\sqrt{1.23/27} = 0.21$ of the earth's, or 1.5 miles per second.

18. The Interior

OUR KNOWLEDGE of the interior of the moon is highly limited; the chief clue we have is that the average density of the moon is substantially less than that of the earth. In fact, the value of 3.3 grams per cubic centimeter is but a little greater than the density of matter near the surface of the earth. If we assume, then, that the density of the surface rocks of the moon does not differ markedly from that of the earth's crust, it follows that the moon is of nearly the same density throughout its bulk, with only a slight increase toward the center.

19. Surface Features

CONTRASTED WITH the interior of the moon, about which our knowledge is indirect, the lunar surface features have been observed and mapped in great detail. Not only can we see the large-scale features of the moon's visible hemisphere with a good pair of binoculars or even with the unaided eye, but during excellent seeing conditions large telescopes are capable of revealing lunar details only one or two hundred yards in diameter. In 1959 a Russian satellite photographed most of the hindside of the moon for the first time. Since then astronomers have had a general idea of the nature of the far side to add to their detailed knowledge of the near side (see Fig. 6.19:1).

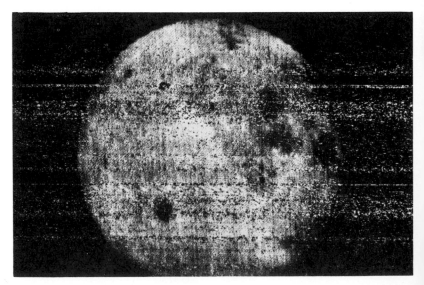

Fig. 6.19:1. A photograph of the moon's far side, taken from Lunik III on October 7, 1959, from about 40,000 miles, developed in the satellite and televised back to earth. South is at the top. On this date the moon was five days past the new phase as seen from the earth. Mare Crisium, which is very conspicuous from the earth when the moon is a waxing crescent, is here seen at the extreme right. The conspicuous dark feature in the lower left is the Sea of Moscow, and is about 150 miles in diameter. (*From N. P. Barabashov, A. A. Mikhailov, and Yu. N. Lipsky,* An Atlas of the Moon's Far Side, *translated by R. B. Rodman, Interscience Publishers, New York, N.Y., and Sky Publishing Corporation, Cambridge, Mass., 1961*)

To the unaided eye the most striking features of the moon are the dark-grayish regions that cover about half of the disk and vaguely resemble a face, "the man in the moon." They were named *maria*, Italian for "seas," by Galileo, who thought these dark smooth areas were oceans. The name is still retained, although we are now certain that there are no oceans on the moon. The maria range up to several hundred miles in diameter and are roughly circular in shape, although they appear elliptical if near the limb of the moon. Their shores tend to be rimmed by mountain ranges and their relatively level surfaces are dotted with many small features when viewed with high magnification:

Fig. 6.19:2. A part of Mare Imbrium, the Sea of Shadows, in the northern part of the lunar disk, photographed with the 120-inch telescope. The large craters are Archimedes, Aristillus, and Autolycus. (*Lick Observatory photograph*)

craters, hills, and solidified waves. The great dark maria are believed to be areas of lava which long ago were molten and able to flow but now are solid.

A small telescope reveals an enormous variety of *craters*, nearly circular structures ringed by mountains. They have been recorded by the tens of thousands and range in diameter from 150 miles for Clavius to less than a mile. Inside the elevated ring of a crater is a moderately level floor depressed below the outside ground level, and often near the center of the ring rises a mountain or a group of mountains. In general, the greater the diameter of a crater the deeper is its floor beneath the uplifted circular rampart. For craters of moderate size the depth runs about 5 percent of the diameter. Some craters sit in isolated splendor in the great maria; but most are located in the bright southern uplands of the moon, overlapping one another here, superposed on one another there.

Near the time of full moon one can see with the telescope the great *ray* system of the crater Tycho, radiating out in many directions from

Fig. 6.19:3. Crater Clavius and vicinity, photographed with the 200-inch telescope. This region may be identified on Fig. 6.9:4. (*Mount Wilson and Palomar Observatories*)

Fig. 6.19:4. Tycho and its surroundings, photographed with the 120-inch telescope. (*Lick Observatory photograph*)

the crater and resembling the meridian sections of a navel orange. The lunar rays are bright and extend out impartially over mountains, valleys, and maria. Several other craters, such as Copernicus, Kepler, and Aristarchus, have well-developed ray systems, with streaks extending some hundreds of miles from the parent crater. The rays from Tycho are the brightest and extend the farthest of any on the moon, thousands of miles. The overwhelming majority of craters, however, are without rays.

Mountains and mountain ranges are more peaked and rugged than on earth and their elevations above the surrounding plains run about as high as terrestrial mountains. The highest peak in the lunar Apennines range, along the southwest shore of Mare Imbrium, rises 18,000 feet above the surrounding plains. A few mountains near the south pole of the moon rival Mount Everest. Because there is no "sea level" on the moon, height measurements must be made relative to adjacent, more or less level regions. In mapping the three-dimensional topography of the moon, advantage is taken of the long shadows cast by mountain peaks when they are near the terminator. Figure 6.19:5 shows how it is possible to determine the height of a mountain by triangulation, after measuring the length of the shadow at a certain instant and computing the altitude of the sun above the lunar horizon. In a similar way it is possible to find the depths of craters, the heights of their central peaks, and a variety of additional information.

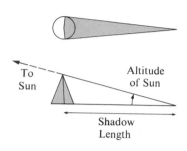

Fig. 6.19:5. Top view of the shadow cast by a conical mountain when the sun is low, and a side view showing how the height of a mountain can be computed indirectly from measurable data.

20. The Crater Controversy

How DID THE lunar craters originate? Many ideas have been announced in the past, some supported by reasonable evidence of one sort or another, others verging on the fantastic. Here, perhaps as notably as in any controversy in the field of astronomy, men have set forth theories with supreme disregard for the hypotheses and evidence presented by other men. At the present time the final answers continue to evade us, but most astronomers think that the maria and the vast majority of craters were formed by the impact of meteorites of various sizes in the early history of the moon. Although craters bear a superficial resemblance to terrestrial volcanoes, detailed examination shows that they are totally different structures, with their depressed floors and high ratio of diameter to depth. The cross section of a typical lunar crater closely resembles that of meteor craters and bomb craters on earth, although on a bigger scale. Such pits are nearly circular, even when the altitude of arrival of the missile is small. Further support of the impact hypothesis is that the measured volume of material in the elevated ring of a lunar crater equals the volume of the hole. The vast bulk of the uplifted material was lunar to begin with but displaced by the explosion accompanying the hit. The impinging meteorite, arriving at about 20 miles per second, is estimated to have been only 1 percent or so of the diameter of the resultant crater.

The distribution of craters on the moon ought to be random if the impact hypothesis is correct, since the moon exposes all faces to space, but a glance at the moon reveals immediately that the craters are not distributed randomly at all. This apparent difficulty is overcome when one reflects that these events did not all happen simultaneously. Imagine that a great mare is formed by the impact of a big meteorite and that part of the energy released goes into heating and melting the surface rock, with a subsequent outflow of molten lava. Such a great event will obliterate most traces of pre-existing craters, and only subsequently formed craters will stand out. Alternatively, old craters like Clavius have many small and thus more recent craters superposed on them. A second criticism that can be leveled at the meteorite hypothesis is that the earth, which travels the same part of space as the moon, has no known large craters. This can be answered when we realize that the moon is devoid of an atmosphere and thus has no appreciable erosion; things look much the same there as they did when the moon finished forming. On earth glaciation and volcanization build mountains and the erosion by wind and weather levels them again; today's surface bears no resemblance to its early self.

The lunar rays are probably dust particles and small pieces of debris that were ejected at greater than average speed from the scene of impact of a meteorite. Instead of landing on the rim, they orbited along an elliptical path and landed far from the scene. Older craters had their ray systems too, but these have been obliterated by the formation of more recent maria and craters. Only the late-formed craters parade their rays today, and it is very probable that Tycho is the most recent major modification in the moon's surface.

21. Brightness, Albedo, and Temperature

MEASUREMENTS OF the radiant energy received from the moon or from different parts of it at different phases allow an assessment of its brightness, reflectivity, and surface temperature. The brightness of the full moon is only about 1/500,000 of the sun's, although it delivers more light to us than all of the planets and stars combined. The average albedo of the moon is only 7 percent; the moon is therefore only 7 percent as bright as a perfectly reflecting body of the same size. The albedo of the dark maria is of course lower than the average value, whereas that of the bright uplands is higher.

Measurements of the center of the lunar disk at full moon show that the surface temperature is about 270°F at the point where the sun is in the zenith. The midnight temperature, on the other hand, is about −240°F. During an eclipse of the moon the surface temperature falls and rises with very little lag, showing that heat does not flow readily into and out of the moon. This is reminiscent of soil on the earth: although the surface follows the variations of air temperature, the temperature a few feet down is fairly stable, and underground water pipes do not freeze up in the winter. Soil is not, however, the surface material of the moon; the available evidence is consistent with a surface layer of pumice, a porous and dusty material that probably has accumulated from the continual impact of tiny meteors and also from the slow disintegration of rocks owing to their monthly expansion and contraction as day follows night.

22. The Atmosphere

SEVERAL CLUES indicate that the moon has no detectable atmosphere. No lunar clouds have ever blocked our view of the various parts of the surface. The spectrum of moonlight is a faithful copy of the solar spectrum; light reflected from the moon does not pass through any appreciable quantity of absorbing gases above the lunar surface. As the moon circles the earth, it crosses in front of or *occults* various stars. At any given occultation the star blacks out instantaneously as it moves behind the limb, rather than dimming gradually as do setting stars observed from the earth. Furthermore, if the moon had appreciable atmosphere, the ray path of a star about to be occulted would be refracted, delaying the expected time of beginning of the occultation. No such effect has been observed.

Indirect evidence of the absence of a lunar atmosphere is provided by the low escape velocity of the moon. We saw in Chapter 2 that a gas is composed of atoms and molecules speeding about and colliding frequently with one another. Now if the moon once had an atmosphere, each atom would after a time have had a series of collisions so that it would have moved upward at a speed sufficiently higher than usual to escape the moon and go into an orbit around the earth or sun. With an escape velocity of only 1.5 miles per second, a lunar atmosphere of atoms such as nitrogen and oxygen would have seeped into space in a matter of days or months. On the other hand, the earth, with an escape velocity of 7 miles per second, can retain such an atmosphere indefinitely, because a series of collisions that will speed an atom up to 7 miles per second almost never happens. The planet Mars is intermediate in size and therefore in escape velocity; observation confirms that Mars is able to retain some atmosphere, although a rarefied one.

23. Changes on the Moon

THE QUEST for natural changes in the lunar surface is beset with difficulty, because what the observer sees depends on the precise phase of the moon, the state of libration of the moon, the instrument used, the condition of the atmospheric seeing, and the nature of the observer himself. Comparison of the structure of a given crater today with a drawing made a century ago cannot prove that any change has occurred, because no artist can draw in all of the infinite detail of any natural structure. Although nearly all careful lunar observers believe that certain changes have occurred, the objective evidence of photography has shown no certain natural changes on the moon. Indirectly, however, we can infer that minor changes do occur. Solar tides stretch and squeeze the surface by a small amount twice every 29.5 days. Contraction and expansion of the surface rocks accompany the great difference of temperature between night and day, leading probably to a slow scaling and flaking. Although meteorites large enough to make a detectable crater on the moon are exceedingly rare events, the continual rain of small meteors onto the moon is comparable to that on the earth.

OUR MOON

Whereas nearly all such bits are consumed in the earth's atmosphere, the lunar surface is unprotected by any atmospheric blanket and is constantly bombarded by small grains at the rate of millions per day.

24. The Moon as a Place to Live

WITHOUT AIR, and without water except for what may be trapped in the rocks or frozen in polar craters where the sun never shines, the moon is inhospitable indeed, for it can support no vegetable or animal life. Sound cannot be transmitted through a vacuum, and therefore the lunar world is one of silence. Any small exposed area of the lunar surface is subjected to radiation of all wavelengths from sun and stars, to cosmic ray particles, and to occasional bombardment by a small but fast meteor. As an observatory, with eternal black sky and perfect seeing, the lunar surface offers fine possibilities; as a place to live comfortably it does not.

ECLIPSES OF MOON AND SUN

25. Shadows in the Sun

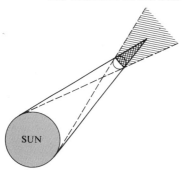

Fig. 6.25:1. The umbra is heavily shaded; the penumbra is lightly shaded.

EVERY SOLID body in the solar system carries a shadow with it wherever it moves in its orbit. In particular, any solid sphere smaller in size than the sun is attended by a conical shadow extending away from the sun. In Fig. 6.25:1 one pair of extended tangent lines bounds the cone-shaped volume in which the sun is completely blocked off; this is the region of total shadow called the *umbra*. The second pair of extended tangent lines, dashed in the figure, bounds that portion of space in which the solid sphere blocks off a part of the sun; it is the region of partial shadow, or *penumbra*, and anybody in it can see some but not all of the sun. In Fig. 6.25:2 the length of the umbra, L, can be found for any solid sphere of radius R, provided we also know R_s, the radius of the sun, and D, the distance of the sphere from the sun. These several quantities are related by two similar right triangles. From a comparison of the smaller triangle with the larger, it follows that

$$\frac{L}{R} = \frac{L + D}{R_s}.$$

This equation can then be solved for the length of the umbra to give

$$L = \frac{DR}{R_s - R}.$$

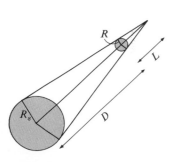

Fig. 6.25:2. Finding the length of the umbra.

The solar radius is known to be 432,000 miles, and the earth and moon in particular lie at an average distance of 93,000,000 miles from the sun. From the known radii of earth and moon, it follows that the earth's umbra is about 860,000 miles long and that the moon's umbra averages only about 233,000 miles in length, a figure not much different from the mean distance of the moon from the earth.

26. An Eclipse of the Moon

WHEN THE MOON is full, it usually rides above or below the earth's shadow as it moves eastward in its orbit. At the moon's average distance, the earth's umbra is a circular patch directly opposite the sun and 1.4° in diameter. Since the moon moves on a circle inclined 5° to the ecliptic, there is only a small chance that at any full moon it will lie close enough to the ecliptic to encroach on this patch. The conditions necessary for the occurrence of a lunar eclipse are therefore that the moon is full *and* that it lies on or very near the ecliptic. The average number of lunar eclipses per decade is about fifteen; the maximum number possible in any one year is three and the minimum number is zero. A *partial eclipse* of the moon occurs when only a part of the moon cuts the earth's umbra, a *total eclipse* when the entire moon is for a time immersed in the umbra, and a *central eclipse* when the moon is on the ecliptic and thus bisects the umbra as it moves eastward. Figure 6.26:1 shows the sequence of events at a central

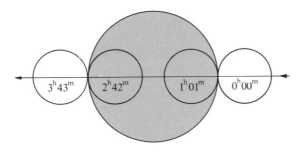

Fig. 6.26:1. A central lunar eclipse, with north up and east left. Times are reckoned from first contact and are for average conditions.

lunar eclipse. At first contact the moon begins entering the umbra and its eastern edge is darkened. From then until second contact about an hour later the moon moves farther and farther into the umbra, affording proof of the earth's spherical shape, as we saw in Chapter 2. From second to third contact, a period of nearly two hours for a central eclipse, the moon is totally immersed in the earth's shadow. It then emerges for about an hour and at fourth contact leaves the umbra. Before first contact and after fourth contact the moon of course spends some time in the earth's penumbra, but at these times its normal brilliance is not markedly diminished.

Barring local cloudiness, an eclipse of the moon is visible over the entire night hemisphere of the earth because the full moon is opposite the sun in the sky. During totality the moon does not black out completely, but remains readily visible as a dull-reddish or coppery circle. This weak light is not radiation from the lunar surface itself, nor is it the phenomenon of earthlight since the eclipsed moon is at this time exposed to the night hemisphere of the earth. Rather, this reddish light is sunlight that has passed through the lower strata of our atmosphere and been refracted into the geometrical umbra of the earth, as

Fig. 6.26:2. A time exposure of the moon during a total lunar eclipse, with star trails in the background. (*Yerkes Observatory photograph*)

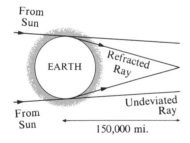

Fig. 6.26:3. The earth's atmosphere refracts sunlight so that the eclipsed moon lies beyond the region of complete blackout.

shown in Fig. 6.26:3. If the earth had no atmosphere, the moon would be blacked out, but because of refraction the effective umbra of the earth is only about 150,000 miles long. The ruddy hue of the eclipsed moon results from the scattering of the blue and violet components of sunlight by the molecules and dust motes in the earth's lower atmosphere, the same effects that redden the rising and setting sun. As seen from the moon at this same moment, the earth would be a black disk surrounded by a bright but thin ring of red light.

A lunar eclipse, besides being a pretty spectacle, offers some opportunities for research. We have already seen that it gives a proof of the globular shape of the earth. Measurement of the radiation received from the moon during a lunar eclipse also permits deduction of the nature of the surface materials of the moon.

27. Annular Eclipses of the Sun

WHEN THE MOON is new, it usually passes a few degrees north or south of the sun as it changes from a waning to a waxing moon. Occasionally, however, it is close enough to one of its nodes so that it partly or completely blocks off the sun; we then experience an eclipse of the sun. The conditions necessary for the occurrence of a solar eclipse are therefore that the moon is new *and* that it lies on or near the ecliptic. On the average there are about twenty-three solar eclipses per decade somewhere on the earth; the maximum number possible per year is five, the minimum number two. A *partial eclipse* of the sun occurs when some part of the earth is for a time immersed in the penumbra of the moon; an observer there sees the sun partly blocked off by the moon. A *central eclipse* occurs when the axis of the moon's umbra brushes the earth at some point. Because the moon's shadow length is comparable to the distance of the moon from the earth, some central eclipses occur when the moon's umbra fails to touch the earth; these are called *annular eclipses of the sun*. At other central eclipses the earth does cut the umbra; we then have a *total eclipse of the sun*. Figure 6.27:1 shows the three different kinds of eclipse. The average number of central solar eclipses per decade is fifteen, of which eight are annular and seven total.

An annular eclipse occurs when the angular diameter of the moon is less than that of the sun and therefore when the moon cannot fully cover up the sun. An observer on the axis of the moon's umbra beyond the vertex sees the new moon momentarily surrounded by a ring or annulus of brilliant sunlight. Because in its orbital motion the moon gains its own diameter on the sun in about one hour, the annular part of the eclipse will be preceded for about an hour and followed for about an hour by a partially blocked sun, as illustrated in Fig. 6.27:2. When the moon and sun are both at mean distance and a central eclipse of the sun occurs, the moon's umbra fails by at least 3000 miles to reach any part of the earth and the eclipse is annular. This accounts for the fact that annular eclipses are somewhat more frequent than total eclipses. The most extreme annular eclipse occurs when the moon is at apogee and the earth at perihelion in early January, because then the moon has its minimum angular diameter and the sun its maximum, and therefore the angular width of the annulus is as big as possible.

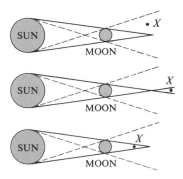

Fig. 6.27:1. Earthbound observer X is witnessing a partial eclipse in the top sketch, an annular eclipse in the middle sketch, and a total eclipse in the lower sketch.

BEFORE   DURING   AFTER

Fig. 6.27:2. Three views of an annular eclipse about 30 minutes apart. East is to the left in each view.

Fig. 6.27:3. Two annular eclipses of the sun. The left photograph was made in Senegal, West Africa, on July 31, 1962; duration of the annular phase was 3ᵐ25ˢ. On the right, with the same optical system, is a photograph made in South Africa 200 miles east of Cape Town on January 25, 1963; duration of the annular phase was 0ᵐ37ˢ. Both sun and moon are of greater angular diameter during the January eclipse. (*Lockheed-California Company and U.S. Air Force*)

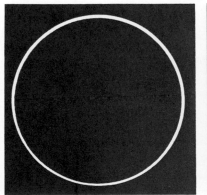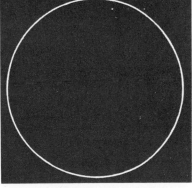

28. Total Eclipses of the Sun

ONE OF THE most beautiful and awesome sights of nature, a total eclipse of the sun occurs over a limited part of the earth a little less than once a year on the average. Not only must the moon be new and very close to the ecliptic, but its angular diameter must be greater than the sun's. For the very best of conditions the earth, moon, and sun must be directly in line with one another, the moon must be at

OUR MOON

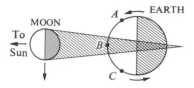

Fig. 6.28:1. A total eclipse of the sun. Arrows indicate the direction of rotation of the earth and of the orbital motion of the moon and its shadow.

perigee, and it must be early July so that the earth is at aphelion. Then, as shown in Fig. 6.28:1, the observer at *B* who has the moon at his zenith sees the biggest possible moon because he is 4000 miles closer to the moon than its perigee distance. At the same time the sun is its minimum size in the sky. Even so, the instantaneous circular black patch of totality on the earth's surface is only 170 miles in diameter, considerably smaller in area than the state of Maine.

As the moon moves easterly in its orbit around the earth, its shadow crosses the earth at about 2000 miles per hour in an easterly direction. The earth itself is rotating eastward at a speed of 1000 miles per hour at the equator and more slowly at higher latitudes. Therefore the net motion of the dark patch of totality is 1000 miles per hour or more in a generally eastward direction across the surface of the earth. It follows that at any one place totality cannot last long, with 7.5 minutes the maximum possible duration under the most favorable circumstances and 3 or 4 minutes the average duration. In Fig. 6.28:1, in which *B* is experiencing an eclipse at noon, we see that the eclipse began at *A* about two hours earlier when it was sunrise at *A*. Sweeping across the earth's diameter of 8000 miles at about 2000 miles per hour, the umbra lifts off the earth about four hours later at *C*, where by then it is sunset.

Fig. 6.28:2. The tracks of all solar eclipses for the years 1963 to 1984, computed by Oppolzer. Legend: ——— total; – – – – annular; —·—·— annular total; △ begins; ○ noon; ▲ ends. (*Yerkes Observatory*)

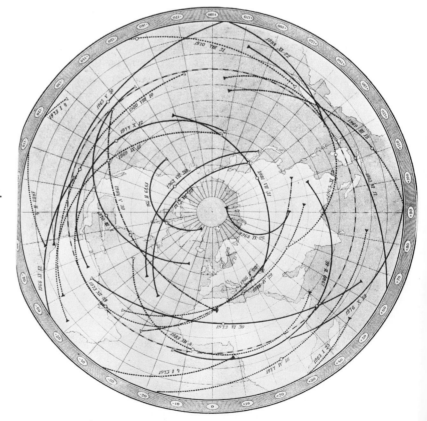

The path of totality is therefore a thin but very long strip across the earth. Any given total solar eclipse is seen as a partial eclipse by people thousands of miles on either side of the track of totality, but the area of the strip of totality itself averages only a fraction of 1 percent of the earth's surface area. Since the occurrence of such eclipses averages less than one a year, they happen at any given place on the average only once every four centuries. It is clear that the eclipse astronomer must make long voyages to out-of-the-way places, always running the risk that cloudy skies will prevent observation of the eclipse.

As with an annular eclipse, a total eclipse begins when the east limb of the moon makes first contact with the west limb of the sun. More and more of the sun is blacked out until after the better part of an hour it is a bright but thin crescent, and the earth and sky are dimmed and changed in coloration because the light from the limb of the sun is redder than that from the center. Just before totality, as the last hairline of sun is disappearing, it may be possible to see in the air the moon's dark umbra racing in from the west. For a fraction of a second before totality, the last bit of sun shines through valleys at the moon's east limb but is obstructed by mountains; the light is broken into bright beads. Then comes second contact, and the sun's disk is visible no more. The sudden darkness is like that of late twilight, and the pearly white

Fig. 6.28:3. The total solar eclipse of June 30, 1954, photographed from Minnesota. (*Photograph by D. C. Dornberg, St. Paul Dispatch and Pioneer Press*)

corona, the outer atmosphere of the sun, shines forth, sometimes accompanied by reddish-colored solar *prominences* extending out, tongue-like, from the red inner solar atmosphere, or *chromosphere*. The light from the sky is feeble enough so that the planets and brighter stars are easily visible. Too soon comes third contact, with instantaneous beads appearing once again and the moon's umbra hurrying off to the east. The sun is gradually uncovered again, with fourth contact coming about an hour after totality.

29. Eclipses and Research

THE FLEETING moments of totality during a solar eclipse give astronomers a rare chance to make daytime observations of crucial importance. Precise timing of the contacts tests whether predicted positions agree with observed positions. Photometric and spectrographic studies of chromosphere, prominences, and corona are possible with the millionfold brighter solar disk screened off. The sky near the sun can be photographed to see whether there are any planets inside the orbit of Mercury; but since no such objects have been found, it appears certain that no body as large as the nine principal planets can be moving in the innermost regions of the solar system. Also astronomers can attempt to verify the theoretical prediction of Einstein that a light ray grazing the limb of the sun will change course by 1.75″ as it moves through the solar gravitational field. Einstein's 1917 general theory of relativity is a theory of gravitation of greater generality than Newton's, proposed two and a half centuries earlier. One of the very few observational tests for the validity of this newer description of nature is the gravitational deflection of light, because Newton's theory predicts a course change only half as great as Einstein's. A photograph of the stars near the sun at total eclipse is compared with

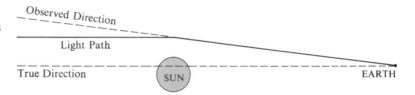

Fig. 6.29:1. Gravitational effect of the sun on a stellar light ray. The actual light path is shown as solid. The observed direction of the star coincides with the light path at the earth. The true direction of the star is the light path if the sun is removed.

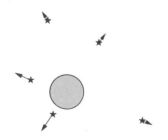

Fig. 6.29:2. Stars indicate the true directions of several stars, and the arrowheads show their locations resulting from gravitational deflection.

another photograph of the same star field when it is in the night sky. The stars on the eclipse plate are displaced radially outwards, their light being deflected as shown in Fig. 6.29:1. The angular deflection is inversely proportional to the distance of closest approach of the ray to the sun; it is thus a maximum for stars near the limb and extremely small for stars a few degrees away. The effect is akin to pushing a fist into a mass of dough: the dough close to the hand spreads out radially and the material farther out scarcely moves. An exaggerated picture of the effect is shown in Fig. 6.29:2. Although the observations are very difficult, many attempts at different eclipses show unquestionably that the deflection at the limb is close to the value of 1.75″, as predicted by relativity theory.

30. Other Kinds of Eclipse

IN ADDITION to eclipses of the moon and sun, the satellites of Jupiter can often be seen to black out as they enter the shadow of Jupiter. These phenomena are analogous to a lunar eclipse, because a body that is not self-luminous enters the shadow of another such body.

Of high importance in stellar astronomy is the study of eclipsing stars, pairs of stars which orbit around one another in a plane that is edge-on to the solar system. Twice each period one star gets in front of its partner and blocks off some or all of its light. Unlike the eclipses we have studied thus far, here is one self-luminous body eclipsing another

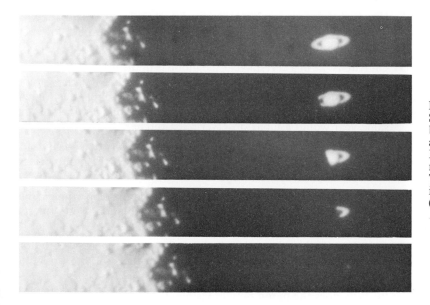

Fig. 6.30:1. Occultation of Saturn by the moon on September 11, 1962, photographed with a 9-inch refractor from Peoria, Illinois. The top photograph was made at $2^h19^m00^s$ Universal Time, and the others at 30-second intervals thereafter.
(*Photographs by Bernard and Donald Jackson*)

one. When the eclipsed body is angularly much larger than the foreground body, we have a *transit*, as when Mercury or Venus passes across the face of the sun. Alternatively, when the eclipsed body is much the smaller body, we have an *occultation*, as when the moon passes in front of Regulus or Spica.

PROBLEMS

1. Explain the principles involved in determining the distance of the moon by triangulation, by radar, and by laser.

2. If the moon is at apogee and in your zenith, in what direction and at what distance from you is the center of the moon's elliptical orbit?

3. Two spherical bodies are separated by 1,000,000 miles. Body A is four times as massive as body B. What is the distance of each from their center of mass?

4. Between new and full moon the moon moves east 180° relative to the sun. In this same interval (**a**) how far does the moon move relative to the stars? (**b**) The sun relative to the stars?

5. If there is a new moon on June 12, (a) what is the phase of the moon on June 17, and (b) about what hour does it set on that date?

6. (a) About what time of day does the last quarter moon rise? (b) At about what time does the full moon set?

7. For what reasons has it been possible to map more than half of the lunar surface without sending a spacecraft to the moon?

8. If a high tide occurs at a given point at 3:34 P.M. Thursday, at what hour and on what day of the week does the next low tide occur? The next high tide? The next following low tide?

9. On August 22 in a certain year the moon is in the first quarter phase. (a) On about what date will the ocean tides next have their maximum range? (b) About when would be the first suitable date after August 22 to look for earthlight? (c) On what date in October of the same year would a lunar observer see a full earth?

10. What is the ratio of each of the following physical constants of the moon to the same physical constant of the earth: radius, mass, mean density, escape velocity, surface gravity?

11. There is abundant evidence that the moon has no appreciable atmosphere. What evidence might a lunar inhabitant cite for the presence of an atmosphere surrounding the earth?

12. Calculate the length of the shadow of a solid sphere with radius one-tenth that of the sun at (a) 1 a.u. from the sun, and (b) 5 a.u. from the sun.

13. (a) Why does the moon remain visible during a total lunar eclipse? (b) Why is it then reddish in color?

14. Give all the conditions that must be fulfilled if a total solar eclipse is to last as long as possible. For simplicity, assume that the sun is in the zenith at the place of observation.

15. Describe an astronomical test of the general theory of relativity that can be carried out during a total eclipse of the sun.

7

PLANETARY

MOTIONS

THE solar system is dominated by our massive and self-luminous parent star, the sun. Not only do we depend crucially on the radiant energy it sends to us, but its great mass, which comprises 99.87 percent of the matter in the solar system, serves as the gravitational glue that holds our system together. If somehow the gravitational force of the sun could be turned off, each planet, asteroid, and comet would move away in an essentially straight-line path; the solar system would adjourn once and for all. Fortunately gravitation cannot be turned off; the planets and asteroids and most comets move permanently around the sun. The large planets, their satellite families, and the small asteroids wheel in nearly circular orbits, and the volume of space swept out by these objects is shaped like a thin coin, with the sun at its center. The sun's family of comets, on the other hand, is believed to occupy a spherical space extending out from the sun halfway to the nearest stars or beyond. Only those comets that come relatively close to the sun are detectable, even with large telescopes; the presence of the distant ones is inferred indirectly, as we shall see in Chapter 9. If we represent the space occupied by the planets as a silver dollar, the space occupied by the comets is a globe surrounding it and hundreds of feet in radius. This larger region encompasses roughly all those points in space where the gravitational attraction of the sun is stronger than that of any other star.

PLANETARY MOTIONS

1. The Nine Principal Planets

BEFORE DEALING with their motions, let us get acquainted very briefly with the planets themselves. Table 7.1:1 lists the nine principal planets, in order of increasing distance from the sun. Figure 7.1:1

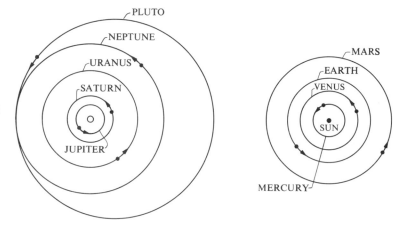

Fig. 7.1:1. At the right are the orbits of the inner terrestrial planets. At the left are the orbits of the Jovian planets and of Pluto. Mars moves on the small path inside Jupiter's orbit.

TABLE 7.1:1.   **The Principal Planets**

Planet	Mean Distance from Sun (a.u.)	Features
Mercury	0.39	Shortest orbital period
Venus	0.72	Brightest as seen from earth
Earth	1.0	Home base
Mars	1.5	Possibly supports vegetation
Jupiter	5.2	Largest
Saturn	9.5	Accompanied by a ring
Uranus	19	First to be discovered
Neptune	30	Discovered by prediction
Pluto	40	Longest orbital period

shows plan views of the inner and outer parts of the planetary system. Although the orbits of the planets are not precisely in the same plane, they are nearly so.

It is useful to classify the nine planets in two quite distinct ways. First, the two planets that move inside the earth's orbit, Mercury and Venus, are called the *inferior planets*; the six planets that move outside our orbit are called the *superior planets*. These terms are helpful in describing the motions of various planets as observed from our moving earth. A second and more fundamental classification is suggested by the physical nature of the planets. The four inner planets, Mercury, Venus, Earth, and Mars, have relatively small size, high average density, slow rotation, little or no atmosphere, and few or no satellites. They are called the *terrestrial planets* because they are generally similar to our earth. In the conspicuous gap between Mars and Jupiter move the asteroids or minor planets. The next four principal planets, Jupiter, Saturn, Uranus, and Neptune, are relatively large in size and of low average density. They rotate fast and have extensive atmospheres, and most are accompanied by large families of satellites. They are called the *Jovian planets* because they are similar to Jupiter. Pluto stands in a class by itself and may be called the *enigmatic planet*. Although its mass is unknown, Pluto is certainly very much smaller in size and slower in rotation than the Jovian planets; it probably was a satellite of Neptune long ago.

THE THEORY OF PLANETARY MOTIONS

2. Observed Characteristics

IN CONSIDERING the theory of planetary motions, we shall examine the historical development of the subject, because it is one of the finest examples in science of the long and tough fight to account for a series of complicated phenomena of observation. The battle has continued intermittently for more than two thousand years; it is now over in the sense that we do not know of any remaining adversaries, no remaining facts of observation that present theory fails to explain. There is no guarantee, however, that a few isolated rebels, new facts, will not come out of hiding to challenge today's theory of planetary motion. In earlier chapters we have generally first studied the fundamental results and then reasoned from them through the process of *deduction* to the particulars. Now we shall reverse our approach in order to see how the scientist more usually works, first noticing observational or experimental facts and then reasoning from them by the process of *induction* to find an explanation or an accounting of the facts.

One may ask at the outset why the subject of planetary motions has played such a prominent role in the history of science. The first reason is that the observed facts could be and were collected without any telescopic aid, by able and patient watchers of the skies. The second is that these observed facts were unusual enough to demand an explanation from those watchers who were endowed with curiosity. For one thing, the five planets known to antiquity are among the brightest objects in the sky. At their brightest Venus, Jupiter, and Mars send us more light than Sirius, the brightest star; Mercury and Saturn outshine all but a few of the stars. For another, the planets usually shine with a steady light rather than twinkling like the stars. But what sets the planets apart more than brilliance and steadiness of light is their unusual motion against the stellar background; indeed the word planet comes from the Greek word for "wandering."

What are the observed characteristics of planetary motions which any successful theory must explain? (1) The planets do not appear in all parts of the sky. Look at any planet at any time; you will find that it is close to the ecliptic, usually within the zodiac. (2) The motion of

PLANETARY MOTIONS

any planet follows a characteristic pattern within the zodiacal belt. It moves slowly easterly most of the time, on or near the ecliptic, but occasionally turns about and moves westerly relative to the stars. After a time the planet resumes its easterly motion once again. Unlike the sun and moon, which are always in easterly or *direct motion* through the stars, each planet spends a minority of its time in westerly or *retrograde motion* against the stellar background. Figure 7.2:1

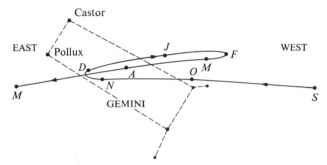

Fig. 7.2:1. The motion of Mars through Gemini during 1960 and 1961. The position of the planet on September 1, 1960, is labeled *S*. Positions are shown until May 1, 1961. Retrograde motion lasted from late November until early February.

shows the motion of Mars for a few months during the latter part of 1960 and the early part of 1961. (3) The motion of each planet along the zodiac takes a characteristic time called the *synodic period*. This is the interval from the date a planet is in the middle of its retrograde motion to the next date it is in the middle of its retrograde motion. Alternatively, when any planet is in direct motion, it will at some time be in line with the sun; it will then be invisible in the evening sky, just as the new moon is invisible. This moment is called *conjunction*, since the planet and sun are together in the sky. The interval between successive conjunctions of a planet is also equal to its synodic period. Mars has the longest synodic period among the bright planets, 780 days, followed by Venus with 584 days, Jupiter with 399 days, Saturn with 378 days, and Mercury with 116 days. The outer "discovered" planets have synodic periods only a few days in excess of a year.

Thus the three main features of planetary motion which call for explanation are (1) location near the ecliptic, (2) direct and retrograde motion, and (3) synodic periods. The first of these features has been accounted for from ancient times: whatever else they may do, the planets move in paths that are confined closely to a common plane. The fact that a distant landscape occupies a narrow circular belt around the observer's horizon implies that the trees, fields, and hills are more or less confined to a plane in three dimensions. Similarly, the fact that the planets are seen projected on a narrow belt around the ecliptic implies that they move in a flattened volume of space. Although there has been agreement since antiquity on the flatness of the planetary system, the other two essential observed characteristics have been interpreted in a variety of ways. We turn next to the story of these interpretations.

THE FIRST serious attempt at a theory of planetary motions was made by the mathematician Eudoxus, probably with the encouragement of Plato, in the first half of the fourth century B.C. Eudoxus accounted for the known motions of the celestial bodies by supposing the universe to be composed of 27 transparent spheres, each centered on the earth and turning at its own uniform rate around a given axis. One sphere carried all of the stars from east to west; various combinations of the other spheres represented the observed motions of the sun, moon, and the known planets. A given planet, for example Jupiter, was attached to the equator of a sphere which turns around its poles; the poles of this sphere in turn were attached to a second bigger sphere which turned at another rate around its two poles; and so on. A few decades later, and with the support of Aristotle, Callippus extended the system of Eudoxian spheres so that theory was in better accord with the facts. Aristotle himself elaborated the system by using 55 spheres. The several versions of the theory of concentric spheres were all *geocentric*, with the earth assumed to lie stationary at the center of the universe.

Heraclides, who probably studied with Plato, asserted that the earth rotates from west to east daily and also thought that Mercury and Venus move around the sun. Aristarchus, a great astronomer who worked in the first half of the third century B.C., foreshadowed Copernicus by nearly two thousand years; he framed a *heliocentric* theory, in which the sun is stationary at the center of the universe and the stars are stationary on the celestial sphere. The earth not only rotates daily but also orbits around the sun along with the planets. But the consensus of Greek scientific opinion was against a spinning and orbiting earth and, in spite of the daring ideas of Aristarchus, the geocentric framework continued to be sovereign.

As the years passed, the Eudoxian system of concentric spheres became inadequate in the face of increasing recognition that each planet goes through a cyclic change in brightness every synodic period. Because this change implies that the distance of a planet from the earth also varies with this same period, concentric spheres could no longer account for the observational facts. Although several clever geometrical schemes were proposed as improvements, we shall deal only with the one that came to rule astronomical thought for many centuries, the theory of *epicycles*.

The foundations of the theory of epicycles were laid by the mathematician Apollonius in the latter half of the third century B.C. Hipparchus, the greatest observational astronomer of ancient times and among the greatest of theorists, worked a century later. Although practically all of his writings are lost, the work of Hipparchus is known from Ptolemy's *Almagest*, which was written about A.D. 140 and served as the bible of astronomy for 14 centuries. Hipparchus contributed in two major ways to the development of the theory of planetary motions: (1) he used the theory of epicycles to account for the non-uniform motions of the sun and moon through the sky; (2) he left a legacy of observations of planetary motions. Then, after a gap of two and a half centuries in which very little of the science of astronomy was developed, Ptolemy inherited this legacy and utilized the theory of epicycles to originate a highly satisfactory geocentric theory of the motions of the bright planets. The resulting picture, called the Ptolemaic system, should be regarded as a joint product of Apollonius, Hipparchus, and Ptolemy.

The assumptions at the foundation of the Ptolemaic system are that (1) the earth is stationary, (2) the earth is at the center of the universe, and (3) celestial bodies move in perfect circles at constant speed. These assumptions are reconciled with the observed facts as shown in Fig. 7.3:1, which is deliberately simplified. The moon and sun revolve

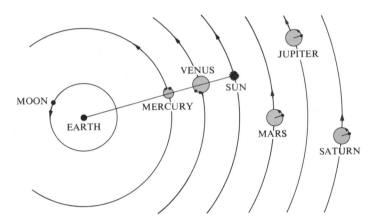

Fig. 7.3:1. The Ptolemaic system, not drawn to scale. Each planet moves around its small epicycle while the epicycle center moves around a larger deferent.

easterly around the earth, with periods of 27.3 days and one year respectively, just as we observe them to do. The planets, however, move quite differently. In the Ptolemaic system each planet moves at constant speed along a small circular epicycle whose center simultaneously moves at constant speed around a large circular *deferent*, the deferent being centered on the earth. An inferior planet, Venus for example, moves uniformly around its epicycle at such a rate that it comes as close as possible to the earth once each synodic period. At the same time the center of her epicycle stays always in line with the sun, thus moving around its deferent once each year. By these devices Venus is constrained always to appear as a morning or evening object and to execute its cyclic variations of brightness once each synodic period, in agreement with the observed facts. A consequence of combining these motions is that Venus moves 360° around her epicycle once every 225 days, which is the so-called sidereal period of the planet. A superior planet moves in a way quite different from an inferior planet. Jupiter, for example, moves around his epicycle once each year, with the line joining planet and epicycle center always parallel to the earth–sun line. Simultaneously, Jupiter's epicycle center moves round its deferent at a rate such that Jupiter will come closest to the earth once each synodic period. Combining these motions, Jupiter's epicycle must roll 360° around its deferent once every 11.9 years, which is Jupiter's sidereal period. These schemes, although placing the inferior and superior planets on different footings, ensure agreement with observation. First, it follows that each planet will appear in retrograde motion for a time every synodic period. Second, the sidereal period of a planet may be thought of as the long-run *average* time it takes for the planet to move once around the zodiac through the background stars, and here again the predictions of the Ptolemaic theory are in accord with the facts.

What has been said thus far refers to motions of the sun, moon, and planets relative to the background stars. But because one of the fundamental assumptions of the Ptolemaic theory is that the earth is at rest, it is finally necessary to have all of these motions going on inside a celestial star-studded sphere which itself is rotating from east to west every 23 hours and 56 minutes. That is, all of Fig. 7.3:1 except for the earth is to be imagined as rotating clockwise around the fixed central earth once a day.

Although in retrospect the Ptolemaic system may seem self-centered and artificial, it is nonetheless a skillful geometric construction which accounted for the behavior of the universe as it was then known, and as it was known for more than a thousand years. During these many ensuing centuries astronomy did not progress in Europe. It was kept alive, but not much advanced, by the Moslems, who translated many major Greek works into Arabic, built a number of observatories, and added to the fund of planetary observations. Although the Moslems made scattered efforts during the Middle Ages to improve on the Ptolemaic system, there were no important modifications. The essential contribution of the Islamic world was not in developing planetary theory but in preserving Greek astronomy. Not until the thirteenth century were more than a handful of Europeans acquainted with Ptolemy's work, which by then had been translated from Arabic into Latin. And not until the early sixteenth century were the fundamental assumptions of his cosmology challenged, by Copernicus.

4. The Copernican Revolution

THE CENTURIES of the Renaissance were transitional; they witnessed a revival of learning, an insistent effort to rediscover the writings of classical Greece, a swing toward learning by reason rather than by revelation, a turning of the mind outward from the self. In medieval times man was central in the universe, and therefore his earth was quite naturally central in the universe. There was no testimony to the contrary: his home was unique, big, and firm, whereas the things of the sky were little, far away, ethereal, and for man to enjoy looking at and to use in telling time and fortunes. But during the Renaissance horizons receded. Men began to travel and trade extensively, and at the market places they met diverse people, customs, and ideas; their thoughts turned outward. The great voyages of discovery around 1500 stretched thought further, and Magellan's cruise established dramatically that no longer was there any unique central geographical place on the surface of the globular earth. At the same time the Reformation meant that no longer was Rome the single center of Christian thought.

It was in this exciting time of transition, when men more and more were focusing their attention outward toward nature and when the doctrine of uniqueness was waning, that Copernicus took the ultimate revolutionary step and deposed the earth from its fixed place at the center of the universe. His contribution is a product both of the man himself and of the provocative and expansive world in which he lived. Born in 1473, Nicolaus Copernicus studied both in his native Poland and in Italy, receiving thorough training in mathematics, in astronomy, and in reading Greek. He returned home from Italy in about 1506 to become a canon at the Cathedral of Frauenburg; his duties were not heavy and from then until his death in 1543 he devoted much of his time to astronomy. Although Copernicus occasionally made observations, he worked chiefly at creating a new system of astronomy. His work, *De Revolutionibus Orbium Coelestium*, was published in the year of his death.

The assumptions at the foundation of the Copernican theory are that (1) the celestial sphere is stationary, (2) the sun is at the center of the universe, and (3) celestial bodies move in perfect circles at constant speed. As a consequence of the first two assumptions, the earth must rotate daily from west to east while revolving annually in an orbit around the sun. In the Copernican view the status of our own home is thoroughly different from its central and fixed status in the Ptolemaic system. From now on the retrograde motion and changing brightness of the planets are explained more simply, as we shall see when we consider Kepler's work. Now, the sidereal period of a planet is simply its orbital period around the sun. No longer must we fret over the puzzling relation of the five planets to the sun and the exalted status of the year in Ptolemy's theory of planetary motions. No more do all the stars have to circuit around the earth at incredibly high speeds; now they are stationary on a fixed sphere. Although the picture of the universe is greatly simplified in the Copernican theory, retention of the assumption of perfectly circular motion required that some epicycles be retained in order to explain the variable speeds of the planets. For not only can epicycles be made to account for the retrograde motions of the planets; they can also be made to represent noncircular motion at variable speed. Not until Kepler's time, some 60 years after *De Revolutionibus*, did all epicycles disappear from the theory of planetary motions.

What was the proof that the Copernican system was right and the Ptolemaic system wrong? The fact is that there was no observational proof whatever; both systems were adequate to account for the known facts. The appeal of the Copernican geometry therefore was rooted not in any proofs of its validity, but rather in its simplicity and harmony. Copernicus is not to be credited with making a discovery but with making a choice, the choice of simplicity. Needless to say, this revolution of thought was not completed in a day or a year or even a century.

Not only were there theological objections, both Catholic and Protestant, to dethroning man's home, but there were scientific objections as well. If the earth rotates, a falling body should strike ground to the west of its starting point; if the earth orbits around the sun, each star should appear to move around a little loop each year. These difficulties were not cleared up until later, and during the balance of the sixteenth century only the stoutest of mathematically trained people chose the Copernican theory over the Ptolemaic system.

5. Kepler's Laws of Planetary Motion

DURING THE last three decades of the sixteenth century there lived simultaneously three great astronomers, each of whom gave much to the establishment of the planetary laws we use today: Tycho Brahe, Galileo Galilei, and Johannes Kepler.

Tycho, born in 1546, was a Dane and a nobleman. Like Hipparchus 17 centuries before him, Tycho was a great observational astronomer, a devoted collector of information. In 1572 he observed the nova, or new star, in Cassiopeia, which for a few weeks rivaled Venus in brilliance; no longer could the celestial sphere be regarded as absolutely changeless. Tycho knew that what astronomy most needed was a long, continuing, and accurate series of observations of lunar and planetary positions, and to that end he established the first observatory in Renaissance Europe, on the Danish island of Hven, and equipped it with the most precise instruments until then devised. Although

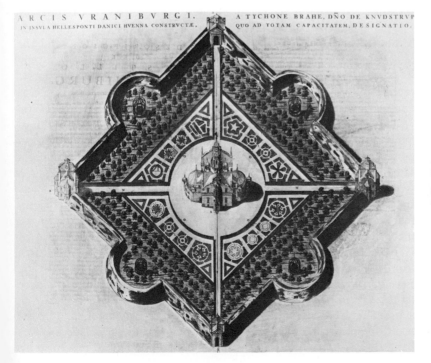

Fig. 7.5:1. Tycho's Observatory, Uraniburg, on the island of Hven, about 1584. (*Yerkes Observatory*)

Tycho's work was done before the invention of the telescope, he was able to achieve an accuracy of 1 or 2 minutes of arc in his angular measures. He observed completely and systematically for more than 20 years, not, like most of us, at only those odd moments when something spectacular like an eclipse or comet or nova is in the sky. Tycho was a good theorist too, although his conception of the universe was a hybrid, rather similar to that of Heraclides: the moon and sun move around the earth, while at the same time the five planets move around the sun. Although he revered the work of Copernicus, Tycho objected to a sun-centered universe for a variety of reasons, among them his failure to detect the annual parallax of stars. Neither he nor anybody else in his time could know that even the nearest stars have parallaxes less than 1 percent of what could have been discovered in pretelescopic times.

Tycho Brahe's essential contribution was not his system of the universe, but rather the bequest he left to Kepler. Tycho was tempestuous and quarrelsome and he finally had to leave Hven and Denmark. He settled in Prague, where Kepler joined and assisted him for a year and a half until Tycho's death in 1601. The bequest was twofold. First, Tycho's studies of the comet of 1577 showed that it was not an atmospheric phenomenon but moved far from the earth, probably along an oval-shaped path. Here was the first suggestion that celestial bodies might move in noncircular orbits. Second, and crucially important, Tycho accumulated a vast store of accurate observational data, better than anything the world had ever seen. Kepler was able to go to work immediately in trying his hand at a new theory of planetary motions which would fit Tycho's data.

Galileo Galilei was born in Italy in 1564 and lived until 1642; he was the first ever to turn a telescope to the sky, in the summer of 1609. In his earlier life Galileo had been a Copernican by choice, and the remarkable discoveries he made with his small refractors served only to confirm his choice. Among them was the discovery that large, round Jupiter was attended by four orbiting satellites. Further observations proved that the closer a satellite to Jupiter the greater its orbital velocity. Here was a miniature Copernican universe: small things moving around a big thing, the innermost moving fastest and the outermost slowest. Now too, the earth was no longer unique in having a satellite. More important, Galileo discovered that Venus during a synodic period shows all phases, like the moon. Given that planets shine by reflected sunlight, it follows from the Ptolemaic geometry that Venus must always be new or crescent, whereas the Copernican theory predicts all phases, as shown in Fig. 7.5:3 and as observed by Galileo. But the times were not auspicious for deposing the earth from its central position in the universe, and at Rome in 1616 *De Revolutionibus* of Copernicus was banned. Galileo wrote the *Dialogue on the Two Principal Systems of the World, Ptolemaic and Copernican*, a presumably disinterested comparison of the two theories. But the pro-Copernican arguments were too strong and the *Dialogue* too was banned; and Galileo, a sincere Catholic, had publicly to renounce his

Fig. 7.5:2. Two of Galileo's telescopes. (*Yerkes Observatory photograph*)

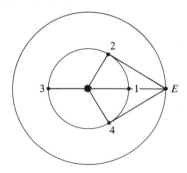

Fig. 7.5:3. In the Copernican scheme an observer on the earth, *E*, should see an inferior planet in all phases. At 1 it is new, at 3 full, and at both 2 and 4 a semicircle.

belief in a moving earth. During his final years he could do no astronomy, and he spent much of his time working on kinematics, the science of motion. Therefore he not only provided powerful observational verification of the Copernican view, but Galileo also, in his studies of the laws of falling bodies, laid the foundations for Newton's development of dynamics, the science of motion in response to forces. Galileo

Fig. 7.5:4. Venus at various distances from the earth. When closest, very little of the disk is visible; when farthest, Venus is nearly circular. (*Lowell Observatory photographs*)

is often called the founder of classical physics, for he was among the first to practice the peculiar blend of activities that science is: the exercise of logic and the accumulation of fact; reasoning and rereasoning in the light of the empirical data of experiment.

Johannes Kepler, born in Germany in 1571, became a staunch Copernican in his early years, and his overriding ambition was to discover the harmonious workings of the planetary system. Although he probably believed in astrology, and certainly cast horoscopes as had Tycho before him, Kepler was an able mathematician. He had both the drive and the patience to work out the consequences of his many fanciful hunches and to check them against Tycho's observational data on planetary positions. His wild ideas were products of his yearning to find the pattern of planetary motions, and his favorite discovery, made in his twenties, was that the planetary orbits were spaced so that one each of Euclid's five regular solids could be placed between each pair of planets: the cube between Saturn and Jupiter, the tetrahedron between Jupiter and Mars, and so on. Wild ideas or not, Kepler personifies the spirit of modern science: no discrepancy between theory and observation can be tolerated.

PLANETARY MOTIONS

Working persistently with Tycho's observations for many years, trying out idea after idea that failed, Kepler finally succeeded in finding his three laws of planetary motion. But as a prelude he needed to be able to map the orbits of the planets, in particular that of Mars. He achieved this by comparing the direction of Mars from the earth at two instants separated by 687 days, which is the Martian sidereal period. In this interval Mars has swept 360° around the sun and returned to its first position. Figure 7.5:5 shows the various angles that could be found from Tycho's data on Mars. It is then but a brief step to establish the distance SM in terms of $SE = SE' = 1$ a.u. Taking many such pairs at different times makes possible the mapping of the entire Martian orbit in terms of the astronomical unit.

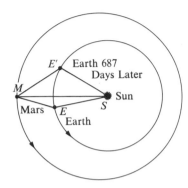

Fig. 7.5:5. In 687 days the earth moves 42° less than 2 complete revolutions; thus angle ESE' is 42°. The angle between sun and Mars at both times is found by observation. The distance of Mars in astronomical units may then be found.

Kepler's first two laws were a product of his work on Mars and appeared in 1609; the third law appeared in 1619. They are:

1. *The law of ellipses:* The orbit of a planet is an ellipse with the sun located at one focus.
2. *The law of areas:* The line joining a planet to the sun sweeps out equal areas in equal times.
3. *The harmonic law:* The square of the orbital period of a planet is proportional to the cube of its mean distance from the sun.

Although the Keplerian universe is essentially Copernican rather than Ptolemaic, the common axiom of both earlier systems was now abandoned. No longer must motion be circular at constant speed. The first law tells us that a planet moves in a plane, because an ellipse is a plane two dimensional figure. But no longer must it move in a circle; it may move in an ellipse of any eccentricity, with one focus at the sun and the other focus at some point in empty space. The second law is the earliest version of the law of conservation of angular momentum, discussed in Chapter 3; it implies, as we saw earlier, that a planet's speed is variable. We studied the first two laws in Chapter 3, in connection with the earth's orbit, and we now turn to consider the meaning of the harmonic law.

Let P be the orbital period of a planet, for example the time interval between any two successive perihelion passages; and let a be the mean distance of this planet from the sun, where this quantity is defined as the semimajor axis of the orbit. It then follows that the proportionality of Kepler's third law may be written as

$$P^2 \propto a^3.$$

The proportionality sign can be changed to an equality sign in any algebraic relation if we insert a constant of proportionality, let us say k. Thus an alternative statement of the third law is

$$P^2 = ka^3,$$

in which k is a constant quantity. This equation can now be applied to any planet. For example, the period and semimajor axis of Jupiter are related by

$$P_J^2 = ka_J^3,$$

and of the earth by

$$P_E^2 = ka_E^3.$$

Now the expression for k in terms of more fundamental physical quantities was not established until Newton's work later in the seventeenth century. However, it can be made to disappear by dividing the last two relations, and we find that

$$\frac{P_J^2}{P_E^2} = \frac{a_J^3}{a_E^3}.$$

Here the characteristics of Jupiter's orbit are expressed in terms of those of the earth as a standard. This relation can be simplified by the further device of forcing the denominators to have the value unity. To achieve this, we define P_E to be one year and a_E to be one astronomical unit. Thus if we express time in years and distance in astronomical units, the harmonic law becomes, for any planet,

$$P^2 = a^3.$$

For example, observations of Jupiter show that its sidereal period is approximately 12 years. What then is its mean distance from the sun? Substitution of the known quantity yields

$$a_J^3 = P_J^2 = (12)^2 = 144.$$

Now $(5)^3 = 125$ and $(6)^3 = 216$, so the mean distance of Jupiter from the sun falls between 5 a.u. and 6 a.u. To the nearest 0.1 a.u., $a_J = 5.2$ a.u. For another example, imagine an artificial planet moving around the sun with semimajor axis 0.25 a.u. What is its orbital period? Dispensing with subscripts, we find this time that

$$P^2 = a^3 = \left(\frac{1}{4}\right)^3 = \frac{1}{64}.$$

Therefore

$$P = \sqrt{\frac{1}{64}} \text{ yr} = \frac{1}{8} \text{ yr} = 46 \text{ days}.$$

For a third example, how long does it take a comet to complete one circuit around the sun if it comes very close to the sun at perihelion but is 20,000 a.u. away at aphelion? Its mean distance (average of perihelion and aphelion) is very close to 10,000 a.u.; hence

$$P^2 = a^3 = (10^4)^3 = 10^{12}.$$

Therefore

$$P = \sqrt{10^{12}} \text{ yr} = (10^{12})^{1/2} \text{ yr} = 10^6 \text{ yr} = 1,000,000 \text{ yr}.$$

Note that in all applications we have had to express periods in years and mean distances in astronomical units.

In order later to understand how the retrograde motions of the planets are explained by the Copernican–Keplerian system, let us use the harmonic law to discover how the orbital speeds of the planets differ from one another, and to determine whether Mercury moves faster or slower than Pluto. The speed of any one planet of course varies because of the law of areas, but since the planetary orbits are nearly circular we shall not go far astray if we simplify our analysis by deducing the constant speed of a planet in a precisely circular orbit. For such a path the mean distance from the sun is constant and equal to the radius of the circle, a. Since the speed or velocity, v, is distance traveled divided by time taken, we have

$$v = \frac{2\pi a}{P}.$$

Squaring both sides and inserting Kepler's third law, we have

$$v^2 = \frac{4\pi^2 a^2}{P^2} = \frac{4\pi^2 a^2}{ka^3} = \frac{4\pi^2}{ka}.$$

Thus we deduce that the square of the circular speed is proportional inversely to the distance from the sun, or $v^2 \propto 1/a$. Mercury, the innermost planet at about 0.4 a.u., accordingly moves faster than any other planet, averaging about 30 mi/sec. The earth's speed is $18\frac{1}{2}$ mi/sec. Pluto, at 40 a.u., is 100 times as far from the sun as Mercury; therefore its average speed is only $\sqrt{\frac{1}{100}}$ or $\frac{1}{10}$ that of Mercury, or 3 mi/sec. Unlike a spinning wheel, where a point on the rim moves fastest, a planet closer to the hub moves faster than one farther away.

6. How the Laws Explain the Observations

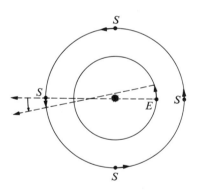

Fig. 7.6:1. Motion of a superior planet as observed from the moving earth. The dashed lines show that it is moving east when at conjunction.

In Section 2 we saw that there are three major observed characteristics of planetary motions that demand explanation in any successful theory. Let us see how the Copernican–Keplerian system accounts for them. First, that planetary motions are chiefly confined to the zodiac means that the planes of the planets' orbits are not very different from one another. This fact, also accounted for in the Ptolemaic system, is not a necessary consequence of Kepler's laws but rather a consequence of the processes by which the solar system originally formed. We shall deal with this problem in Chapter 10.

The observed retrograde motions of the planets, however, necessarily follow from Kepler's laws. Figure 7.6:1 shows the orbits of the earth and of a superior planet, S, as seen from a point far to the north of the solar system. The velocity of the superior planet is less than that of the earth, as we deduced in the last section. Imagine observing S from the moving earth, E, at various times. When S is at conjunction, in line with but beyond the sun, we see S moving east among the stars. First join the arrow ends and locate S among the stars. A week or so later each planet has moved to the arrow tip; join the tips of the arrows and locate S among the stars. The superior planet has moved counterclockwise or easterly through the background stars. The same easterly or direct motion holds for other locations of S except near the time of *opposition*, when S is closest to the earth and also brightest. The earth is moving faster than S and overtaking it. Joining arrow ends and the arrow tips, S is seen now to be moving clockwise, or westerly. Thus at and near the time of opposition a superior planet is in retrograde motion.

The apparent motion of an inferior planet, I, can be seen from Fig. 7.6:2. Notice first that an inferior planet can never be opposite the sun but instead must always lie less than 90° from the sun, as seen from the earth. Furthermore, an inferior planet is in conjunction with the sun both when it is closest to the earth and again when it is farthest from the earth. *Inferior conjunction* is the term for the former event and *superior conjunction* for the latter. When an inferior planet lies at its greatest angular distance from the sun, it is said to be at *maximum elongation*. This maximum angle is 28° for Mercury and 48° for Venus. Noticing that an inferior planet moves faster than the earth, and joining arrow ends and then arrow tips, we find that an inferior planet usually is in direct motion easterly among the stars. Only at and near inferior conjunction, when it is nearest the earth and in the new or crescent phase, is its motion retrograde. After inferior conjunction and until the next superior conjunction, an inferior planet lies west of the sun. In the diurnal motion it is then a *morning planet*, rising in the east before sunrise each morning. After superior conjunction and until the next inferior conjunction, it is east of the sun in the sky, thus setting in the west after sundown; during this interval it is an *evening planet*.

The characteristic synodic period of a planet is accounted for quite naturally in the heliocentric theory. For example, Mars is known to have a sidereal period of 687 days and a synodic period of 780 days. In Fig. 7.6:3 Mars is at opposition at time 1. At time 2, one year later, the earth has completed one circuit of the sun, but Mars, moving more slowly, has only described an angle of $(365^d/687^d) \times 360° = 191°$ and is located at position 2. At time 3, one more year later, the earth has completed another circuit, while Mars has moved through $191° \times 2 = 382°$, a bit more than a full circle, and is at position 3. A few weeks later, 780 days after opposition, the faster moving earth catches up with Mars, opposition again occurs at position 4, and one synodic period has elapsed.

Quite generally, the mutual synodic period of any two planets is simply the time it takes for the inner and faster body to gain one lap on the outer and slower body. Imagine watching two planets from the sun. To start with, they are in line with each other in the sky. Now the inner one, A, moves around the ecliptic once during its sidereal period, P_A. Its easterly angular rate of motion is thus $360°/P_A$, in degrees per year. The outer one, B, with Keplerian period P_B, is seen from the sun to be moving at the slower angular rate $360°/P_B$. The faster thus gains on the slower at a rate $360°/P_A - 360°/P_B$, getting steadily farther east of B. Ultimately, A will gain one full lap on B and the solar observer will see them together in the sky once more; A will again see B at opposition; B will again see A at inferior conjunction. The time to gain one lap is therefore the synodic period, P_{syn}, of the pair. It is simply the time taken for A to gain one lap of 360° on B. And since time taken is amount to be gained divided by rate of gain, it follows that

$$P_{syn} = \frac{360°}{360°/P_A - 360°/P_B} = \frac{1}{1/P_A - 1/P_B}.$$

THEORY OF PLANETARY MOTIONS

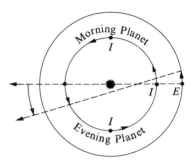

Fig. 7.6:2. Motion of an inferior planet as seen from the earth. The dashed lines show that it is moving east when at superior conjunction.

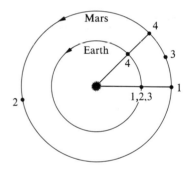

Fig. 7.6:3. The synodic period of Mars is 780 days, the interval required for both earth and Mars to move from position 1 to position 4.

If we take the reciprocal on both sides, we find

$$\frac{1}{P_{\text{syn}}} = \frac{1}{P_A} - \frac{1}{P_B}.$$

To find, for example, the synodic period of Mars as seen from the earth, the earth is the inner planet, A, with $P_A = 1.000$ year, and Mars is the outer planet, B, with $P_B = 687$ days $= 1.878$ years. Thus

$$\frac{1}{P_{\text{syn}}} = \frac{1}{1.000 \text{ yr}} - \frac{1}{1.878 \text{ yr}} = \frac{1.000 - 0.532}{\text{yr}} = \frac{0.468}{\text{yr}}.$$

Therefore, taking reciprocals,

$$P_{\text{syn}} = \frac{1 \text{ yr}}{0.468} = 2.137 \text{ yr} = 780 \text{ days}.$$

The same relation can be used to find the duration of the synodic month (Chapter 6). The moon in its easterly motion around the earth has an orbital period of 27.3 days, whereas the sun circuits the ecliptic only once every 365 days. Working out the formula, we find that the moon gains one lap on the sun every 29.5 days, and this of course is the time from new moon to new moon, the synodic month.

It is instructive to think of a few of the implications of the general formula for the synodic period of two planets. First, if planet B is extremely far from the sun and thus has a very long orbital period compared with that of the earth A, then the term $1/P_B$ is very small and therefore the synodic period of B is only slightly longer than one year. This prediction makes sense intuitively, for the remote planet moves scarcely at all against the stars during one year; it therefore reaches opposition (rising at sunset and setting at dawn) about once a year, its behavior reminiscent of the annual march of the stars. The synodic period of Pluto is only a day and a half longer than one year. Second, if planet A is much closer to the sun than is the earth, which we shall now identify as B since it is the more remote of the pair, then again the term $1/P_B$ is small compared with $1/P_A$, so the synodic period of B is only slightly longer than that of A. This result also makes sense, because this time the earth scarcely moves while the inner planet speeds around the sun. The innermost planet, Mercury, has an orbital period of 88 days and a synodic period of 116 days. Finally, imagine the earth and a man-made planet with orbital period one year. Here $1/P_A = 1/P_B$, and thus $1/P_{\text{syn}} = 0$, and $P_{\text{syn}} = \infty$. Thus the formula predicts an infinite synodic period in such a situation. Does this make sense? An object in the same plane as the earth and moving in the usual easterly sense will simply trail (or lead) the earth by the same constant amount. Such an object therefore can never come to opposition; its synodic period is infinite. The first spacecraft launched from the earth into orbits around the sun have extremely long synodic periods, whereas among the natural planets it is the earth's neighbors, Mars and Venus, that have the longest synodic periods.

Thus the Copernican sun-centered universe, amended by Kepler's three laws, accounts in a natural way for the observed characteristics of planetary motions. And yet, for all their simplicity, the laws are strictly empirical; they are terse statements about how the planets move. The fundamental principles underlying Kepler's laws, and from which they are deduced, were not understood until later in the seventeenth century, by Sir Isaac Newton.

NEWTON WAS born in England in 1642, the year of Galileo's death, and lived until 1727. Because of the enormous variety of his achievements and the unparalleled depth of his insight, he is usually regarded as the greatest physical scientist the earth has known. Most of his work was done in the earlier years of his manhood, and his monumental work, *Principia*, was published in 1687. Newton's essential contribution to planetary theory was to unite the celestial planets with the things of the earth in one all-embracing theory of motions; he discovered and he verified that the same laws of nature work throughout our solar system. The science of mechanics, partly foreseen by Galileo, was now established.

The founding axioms of mechanics are called *Newton's laws of motion*. They are:

1. Every particle moves in a straight line at constant speed unless compelled to change this motion by forces acting on it.
2. When a force acts on a particle, the motion of the particle is changed in the direction in which the force acts, and the acceleration of the particle is proportional to the force.
3. To every action there is always an equal and opposite reaction; or, the mutual forces of any two particles on each other are equal and are oppositely directed along the same straight line.

The first law implies that motion rather than rest is the natural state of affairs in the universe; rest amounts to the special case of a particle moving at zero speed. Uniform motion can never actually be realized in nature, because no object can ever lie completely away from pushes and pulls, from such forces as gravitation and radiation pressure. The first law is thus an idealization of experience. Perhaps the closest approach to fulfillment is the motion of an isolated star; it moves very nearly in a straight line at constant speed, since only ultraweak forces act on it. But the uniformity is not perfect, for the path of such a star in our part of the Milky Way system is curved by the weak gravitational pull of the central mass of stars in our galaxy; for every million miles of forward travel it is deviated sidewise about two-tenths of an inch.

Newton's second law is stated algebraically as

$$a = \frac{F}{M},$$

where F is for the magnitude and direction of the force exerted on a particle of mass M, and a is the magnitude and direction of the resulting *acceleration*, or the change of motion of the body. Both force and

PLANETARY MOTIONS

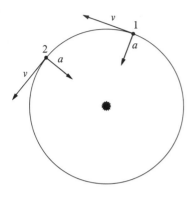

Fig. 7.7:1. A planet at two points in a circular orbit. The velocity vector is constant in amount but steadily changes direction because of the acceleration toward the center.

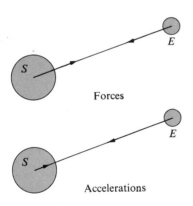

Forces

Accelerations

Fig. 7.7:2. Earth and sun exert equal and opposite forces on each other, but the acceleration of the earth is by far the greater.

acceleration are vector quantities, having both amount and direction. By acceleration is meant change of velocity, and velocity too is a vector quantity. A bullet fired from a gun is accelerated rapidly from zero speed to a rapid exit speed at the muzzle; the forces producing the acceleration are the expanding gases of the exploded charge. A planet moving around the sun in a circular orbit at constant *speed* is nevertheless in accelerated motion, because the *direction* of its *velocity* continually changes, as shown in Fig. 7.7:1; the force here responsible for the acceleration is the gravitational attractive force exerted by the sun on the planet. The second law implies further that, for a given fixed force exerted in turn on a variety of objects of different mass, the lightest mass will be accelerated by the greatest amount; the heaviest, the least. The mass of a body is thus a measure of its inertia, or resistance to acceleration. Next, if we imagine a given fixed mass and exert different forces on it in turn, its acceleration each time will be proportional to the force impressed.

The third law states that forces come in pairs: the book pushes *down* on the desk with the same force that the desk pushes *up* on the book; the gravitational downward force on a falling raindrop is paired with an equal upward pull on the earth by the raindrop. There are two difficulties in appreciating the law of action and reaction. (1) One may ask how anything can ever move if forces come in equal and opposite pairs. The answer is that the raindrop accelerates according to the net of all forces exerted *on* it, such as the gravitational downward force of gravity and the upward resisting force of air molecules in its way; the raindrop is quite oblivious to the forces *it* exerts on *other* objects. (2) If the earth and raindrop exert forces of equal strength on one another, as Newton's third law asserts, one may ask why the earth does not move halfway up to meet the drop. To understand the reason, refer back to the second law; the acceleration of the raindrop, which is the vector governing how the drop moves, is very large because the mass of the drop is very small; the acceleration of the earth owing to the pull of the raindrop is negligibly small because of the overwhelmingly greater mass, or inertia, of the earth. The force vectors and acceleration vectors resulting from the mutual gravitational attractions of sun and earth are shown in Fig. 7.7:2.

Although Newton's laws of motion serve as the foundations of mechanics and are applicable to forces of all types, something more was needed to account for the specific way that planets move. If these laws are valid, then how do they relate to the empirical findings of Kepler? Legend has it that Newton was in his garden one day and saw an apple fall from a tree; he began to wonder if the fall of the apple and the monthly "falling" of the moon around the earth were two disparate manifestations of some general force between bodies. He knew that the downward acceleration of a body at the earth's surface is 32 ft/sec² = 32 × 3600 ft/min², and he computed that the earthward acceleration of the moon in its orbit was about 32 ft/min², or only 1/3600 of the surface acceleration. Now, the moon's distance from the earth's center averages about 240,000 miles, whereas the earth's surface is only some

4000 miles from its center. Thus the ratio of distances is 60 and the ratio of accelerations is $1/3600 = 1/(60)^2$. The acceleration of an object therefore appears to be proportional to the inverse square of its distance from the center of the attracting body. These considerations led Newton to the formulation of his universal law of gravitation, which we have already considered in Chapter 2. To reiterate, the force of attraction, F, between two bodies of masses M_1 and M_2 that are separated by a distance D is

$$F = \frac{GM_1M_2}{D^2},$$

where G is the universal constant of gravitation, whose value is fixed by laboratory measurements. It turns out that

$$G = 6.67 \times 10^{-8} \frac{cm^3}{gm\ sec^2}$$

and that the force between two one-gram masses a centimeter apart is

$$F = 6.67 \times 10^{-8} \frac{cm^3}{gm\ sec^2} \times \frac{1\ gm \times 1\ gm}{1\ cm^2} = 6.67 \times 10^{-8} \frac{gm\ cm}{sec^2}$$

$$= 6.67 \times 10^{-8}\ dyne.$$

For convenience the unit of force in the cgs system is called the dyne, and its definition is

$$1\ dyne = 1 \frac{gm\ cm}{sec^2}.$$

To clear up two points, let us substitute Newton's second law of motion into his law of gravitation. First, Galileo found experimentally that balls of different mass fall at the same rate (apart from air resistance). If ball A has mass M_A, and B has a greater mass M_B, and the earth has mass M_E and radius R_E, then the forces in question are different; they are respectively

$$\frac{GM_EM_A}{R_E^2} \quad \text{and} \quad \frac{GM_EM_B}{R_E^2}.$$

But the acceleration of ball A, which is the quantity that counts in determining how it moves, is

$$\frac{GM_E}{R_E^2},$$

and this is precisely the same for ball B. This quantity is therefore independent of the mass of the body being dropped, be it a marble or a truck. It is called the surface gravity of the earth and is symbolized by g, or, better, by g_E. Its value is

$$g_E = \frac{GM_E}{R_E^2} = 6.67 \times 10^{-8} \frac{cm^3}{gm\ sec^2} \times \frac{5.97 \times 10^{27}\ gm}{(6.37 \times 10^8)^2\ cm^2}$$

$$= 980 \frac{cm}{sec^2} = 32.2 \frac{ft}{sec^2}.$$

The second point involves the law of action and reaction. Although the sun and earth exert the same number of dynes of gravitational force on each other, the acceleration of the earth by the sun is one-third of a million times the acceleration of the sun by the earth. This quantity is simply the mass ratio of sun to earth.

Given the laws of motion and gravitation, it is now possible by the process of deduction, of reasoning from the general to the particular, to ask not only whether Galileo's results on falling bodies are in conformity with Newton's laws (and they are, as we have just seen), but also whether Kepler's results on planetary motions follow from them also. To answer this question, we have to utilize the calculus, a discipline which was discovered independently by Leibniz and Newton. With the aid of this mathematical technique of reasoning, Newton succeeded in showing that Kepler's three laws of planetary motion are *necessary consequences* of his laws of motion and gravitation. Here is unity in variety: the motion of the apple and the ball, of the artillery shell and Saturn. All can be accounted for, and indeed predicted in advance, from Newton's laws.

8. Generalizing Kepler's Laws

IN THE PROCESS of deducing Kepler's empirical results from his own laws, Newton discovered two important generalizations of the Keplerian laws. The first law of Kepler is now amended to state that the orbit of a body around the sun is a *conic section*. The conic sections are the class of two-dimensional curves obtained by slicing a cone with a plane. Imagine an inverted paper cone, as in Fig. 7.8:1, slashed through in various ways. A slash perpendicular to the axis of the cone yields a circular cut; a tilted slash gives an ellipse. If a plane cut has the same pitch as the side of the cone, the resulting curve never closes at the lower end; it is a parabola. An even steeper slash yields another type of open curve, a hyperbola. Finally, it is possible to lay a plane tangent to the cone so that the intersection is a straight line. As we saw in Chapter 3, the eccentricity of a circle is 0, and that of an ellipse lies between 0 and 1. The eccentricity of a parabola is precisely 1, and that of a hyperbola exceeds 1.

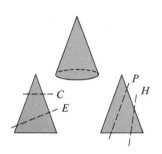

Fig. 7.8:1. The conic sections. Cut *C* gives a circle, *E* an ellipse, *P* a parabola, and *H* a hyperbola.

To clarify the various possible types of orbits in the gravitational field of the sun, imagine a number of objects lying at a fixed distance from the sun, say 1 a.u., and shot in a direction at right angles to the sun, as illustrated in Fig. 7.8:2. The first object is shot at zero speed; thus it is at rest relative to the sun. Its subsequent orbit is a straight line, ever-accelerating until it strikes the sun in about 65 days. The second object is shot at 2 mi/sec; its orbit is an ellipse of high eccentricity, with 1 a.u. the aphelion distance, and the major axis is the line passing from the original shooting point through the sun; at the perihelion point it clears the solar surface by a small margin. The details of its orbit and that of other objects are given in Table 7.8:1. The third object is shot at 10 mi/sec; its orbit is an ellipse of lower eccentricity, but with 1 a.u. again the aphelion distance. The perihelion distance of this object is 0.17 a.u. and thus its mean distance 0.59 a.u.; hence its

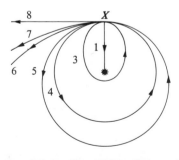

Fig. 7.8:2. The orbits of several objects shot from point *X* one astronomical unit from the sun.

orbital period is longer than that of object 2 but shorter than the earth's. The fourth object is shot at right angles to the sun at the so-called circular velocity, which may be deduced from Newton's work to be

$$v_{\text{circ}}^2 = \frac{GM}{D},$$

where M is the mass of the gravitating body and D the distance of the

TABLE 7.8:1. Orbital Characteristics of Bodies Projected at Right Angles to Sun from 1 A.U. at Various Speeds

Object number	1	2	3	4	5	6	7	8
Velocity of projection (mi/sec)	0	2	10	18.5	20	26.2	30	∞
Orbital shape	line	ellipse	ellipse	circle	ellipse	parabola	hyperbola	line
Eccentricity	1.00	0.99	0.71	0.00	0.17	1.00	1.63	∞
Perihelion distance (a.u.)	0.00	0.06	0.17	1.00	1.00	1.00	1.00	1.00
Perihelion velocity (mi/sec)	380[a]	320	59	18.5	20.0	26.2	30.0	∞
Aphelion distance (a.u.)	1.00	1.00	1.00	1.00	1.40	∞	∞	∞
Aphelion velocity (mi/sec)	0.0	2.0	10.0	18.5	14.3	0.0[b]	14.6[b]	∞[b]
Mean distance (a.u.)	0.50	0.50+	0.59	1.00	1.20	∞	∞	∞
Orbital period (yr)	0.35[c]	0.36	0.45	1.00	1.32	∞	∞	∞

[a] Velocity at instant the object strikes the solar surface.
[b] The "ultimate" speed when the object gets arbitrarily far from the sun.
[c] The Keplerian orbital period; actually the object will strike the sun in half this time and be destroyed.

circling particle from M. Now, for the sun, $M = 2.00 \times 10^{33}$ gm, and 1 a.u. $= 1.50 \times 10^{13}$ cm. Hence

$$v_{\text{circ}}^2 = 6.67 \times 10^{-8}\ \frac{\text{cm}^3}{\text{gm sec}^2} \times \frac{2.00 \times 10^{33}\ \text{gm}}{1.50 \times 10^{13}\ \text{cm}}$$

$$= 8.90 \times 10^{12}\ \frac{\text{cm}^2}{\text{sec}^2}.$$

Therefore

$$v_{\text{circ}} = 2.98 \times 10^6\ \frac{\text{cm}}{\text{sec}} = 29.8\ \frac{\text{km}}{\text{sec}} = 18.5\ \frac{\text{mi}}{\text{sec}}.$$

This is the same as the earth's average velocity as it moves in its nearly circular orbit around the sun. Our fourth object therefore has a circular orbit, with the sun at its center.

Let us shoot the fifth object at a speed of 20 mi/sec; it moves in a bigger orbit, with 1 a.u. now the perihelion distance; the major axis of the orbit again passes through the projection point and the focal sun; the path is an ellipse with eccentricity 0.17. For faster and faster velocities of projection we get a series of ever larger and more eccentric ellipses, until finally we reach a shooting speed for the sixth object that is $\sqrt{2}$ times the circular velocity. In our particular example this is 26.2 mi/sec. This orbit is a parabola, with $e = 1$, and the object moves on a one-way path to infinity. Although eternally decelerated by the solar gravitation, the speed of this object is just enough so that it moves farther and farther from the sun, ultimately of course escaping from the solar system. The speed required for a body to move in a parabolic orbit at distance D from a body of mass M is given by

$$v_{\mathrm{par}}^2 = \frac{2GM}{D}.$$

Since this *parabolic velocity* is also the minimum speed necessary to escape permanently from a point at distance D from body M, it is also called the *escape velocity*.

Let us next shoot our seventh object at 30 mi/sec; it moves on an even more open orbit, with perihelion distance again 1 a.u.; this orbit is hyperbolic with eccentricity 1.63. Finally, imagine shooting an object at right angles to the sun at infinite speed. At infinite speed it takes no time at all to get arbitrarily far from the sun; the sun's gravitation has no time, so to speak, to affect the orbit of the object. Our eighth object thus moves in a straight line, with infinite eccentricity, but again with perihelion distance 1 a.u. This final example is beyond the possibility of experience, since the velocity of light is the greatest possible speed of anything passing the sun. The prediction of Newtonian theory is that a corpuscle of light passing the sun moves in a hyperbolic path of enormous eccentricity. Its path is very nearly straight, but it curves ever so slightly on passing near the sun. At 1 a.u. the deflection is only about 0.004″.

It should be stressed that the example under discussion is merely one specific application of orbit theory. A second instructive application is the shooting of missiles horizontally at different speeds from atop a tall tower on earth. At zero speed an object falls in a straight line to the ground. At greater speed it arcs out along part of an ellipse. At the circular speed, given by $v_{\mathrm{circ}}^2 = GM_E/R_E = 5$ mi/sec, it circles the earth continually once every 84 minutes, if we disregard air resistance. The escape velocity of the earth is 7 mi/sec, and a missile shot at this speed moves indefinitely away from the earth in a parabolic orbit, soon coming under the dominant gravitational control of the sun.

Although for simplicity we have restricted our attention to shooting in a direction at right angles to the center of the attracting body, it is possible to solve the more general problem of finding the orbit when shooting from any point at any speed in any direction. Given the starting position and velocity vector of a particle relative to a large mass, Newtonian theory permits one to compute the orbit of the particle and its position and velocity at any moment in the past or future.

Newton's second generalization of Kepler's laws concerns the harmonic law. Kepler's formula was $P^2 = ka^3$; Newton found the value of k. Since the law of gravitation is the keystone of planetary theory, one might expect that the period of time it takes for one object to move around another would depend in some way on their distance apart, the masses involved, and the constant of gravitation. This expectation is fulfilled, for the complete statement of Kepler's third law is

$$P^2 = \frac{4\pi^2 a^3}{G(M_1 + M_2)}.$$

Here P is the orbital period, a the semimajor axis of the orbit of mass M_2 around mass M_1 (or M_1 around M_2). Notice that the period depends not only on a, as Kepler found, but also on another variable, the sum of the masses of the two bodies. In his studies correlating P and a for the planets, Kepler could not be aware of the existence of another variable, because the sum $M_1 + M_2$, sun plus planet, was very nearly constant from one application to another. Even for the most massive planet, the sum of sun plus Jupiter is only 0.1 percent greater than the solar mass itself.

Newton's modification of Kepler's third law is of crucial importance, for it permits us to find masses once we have observed periods and mean distances. The sun's mass can be deduced from the orbital size and period of a planet or asteroid; the mass of a planet can be found if we know the orbital size and period of its satellites. Strictly speaking, we find only the sum of two masses, but in most cases the small body is negligibly light compared with the parent about which it moves. It is even possible to deduce the masses of distant orbiting double stars, as we shall see later.

One deduction we can make from this more general formula is that the orbital period of a marble around the sun, if its mean distance is 1 a.u., is longer than one year, because the combined mass of sun plus marble is less than that of sun plus earth; the gravitational bond is weaker. But the marble's period is not much greater than the earth's; it is 1 year plus 47 seconds. Alternatively, if a second marble has a period of precisely 1 year, its mean distance from the sun is less than 1 a.u.—about 90 miles less.

9. Orbits of the Planets

As WE HAVE seen, if the position and velocity vector of a planet relative to the sun are known at any instant, it is possible to calculate all the characteristics of its orbit. Now, these characteristics are constant in time, apart from disturbing gravitational pulls by other planets, and can be specified completely by a set of six quantities called the *orbital elements*. First, two numbers are needed in order to specify the orientation of the orbital plane relative to some standard plane, which is usually taken as the earth's orbit plane. The arc *VN* in Fig. 7.9:1, measured east along the ecliptic from the vernal equinox, *V*, to the *ascending node, N*, is called the *longitude of the node*; the angle between the earth's orbital plane and the planet's is the *inclination, i*. Next, one quantity is needed to orient the actual orbit within its plane, and for this a line is drawn from the sun along the major axis through

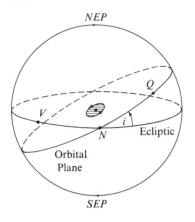

NEP

Q

V

N   Ecliptic

i

Orbital
Plane

SEP

Fig. 7.9:1. As seen from the sun, a planet moves along a great circle among the stars. The spatial orientation of the orbital plane is given by two numbers, the arc VN and the angle i. The orientation of the ellipse in this plane is given by the arc NQ; as seen from the sun, the planet at its perihelion passage is at point Q among the stars.

the planet's perihelion point and is projected onto the celestial sphere at point Q. The arc NQ is called the *argument of perihelion*. Two more quantities are required to specify the intrinsic characteristics of the orbit; its size is given by the *semimajor axis*, a, and its shape by the *eccentricity*, e. Finally a sixth quantity is needed to specify the actual location of the planet on its orbital track at some fixed time. This may be given, for example, by the *time of perihelion passage*; the year and date and time of any passage will do, since others follow at successive intervals one period apart.

The more revealing orbital elements of the planets are given, along with other data, in Table 8.10:1 (p. 205). Briefly, the planetary orbits are all nearly circular, with eccentricities less than 0.25; except for Mercury and Pluto, they are all less than 0.10. As we have seen, the orbits are also nearly in the same plane, with inclinations less than 20°; again excepting Mercury and Pluto, they are all less than 5°. The mean distances of the planets increase crudely in geometric progression; a planet's distance from the sun averages 1.7 times the distance of its next inner neighbor. These three general characteristics of the planetary orbits are not in any sense *required* by Kepler's laws; instead they are consequences of the mode of formation of the solar system.

10. The Problem of Many Bodies

WE HAVE BEEN dealing with the problem of two objects moving around one another. Actually, the task of keeping precise track of a planet, Venus for example, and of predicting its future positions must take account of the fact that Venus is simultaneously experiencing the gravitational forces of the sun, all of her sister planets, the myriad asteroids, and so on. Because the sun is overwhelmingly more massive than the other bodies of the solar system, the wandering of Venus from its elliptical orbit around the sun is small; the perturbing pulls of the other planets are relatively feeble. Extensive developments in celestial mechanics since Newton's time have made it possible to compute these perturbations with high accuracy. The triumphant discovery of Neptune is a fine example of such calculations as we shall see in Chapter 8. But in spite of such computations, no complete solution exists for the motion of ten bodies relative to each other—nor even for the motion of three bodies. The fact that each body exerts a continually changing gravitational force on all of the others renders the mathematical difficulties prohibitively great. Indeed, somebody has said that planets are far more clever than astronomers: the planet can solve, without any effort whatever, its problem of how to move; the astronomer cannot.

11. Einstein and Relativity

THE NEWTONIAN theory of planetary motions remained unchallenged until the present century, which has seen the creation of

Einstein's more general theory of gravitation, the *general theory of relativity*. The underlying idea of this theory is that we can measure the motion of an object only *relative* to other objects, and that there is no such thing as *absolute* motion of a body relative to "space." There is no such thing as absolute rest. In addition to the necessity of framing physical laws so that no place or motion is more exalted than any other, it was essential that formulation of the general theory of relativity be such that its predictions for most observable phenomena in the solar system agree closely with those of Newtonian gravitation. For after all, the Newtonian theory has been extremely successful.

The resulting theory was given by Einstein in 1917, and the differences between it and Newton's are appreciable only for objects in very rapid relative motion. In the realm of orbit theory only two observational tests for the Einstein theory have been devised. First, the line joining the sun and a planet's perihelion should slowly rotate eastward; the perihelion direction Q of Fig. 7.9:1 should move slowly rather than point toward a fixed place among the stars. The faster-moving planets are predicted to show the greatest effect, and the calculated time for Mercury's perihelion direction to make one full turn is three million years. More precisely, Einstein's predicted angular rate is 43.2" per century. The observed rate exceeds 500" per century, but nearly all of this is accounted for by the perturbing gravitational forces of other planets on Mercury. The remaining amount, accurately found by observation and fretted over for a long time, is 42.6" ± 0.9" per century. Before the advent of relativity theory, the misbehavior of Mercury was variously attributed to the effect of an undiscovered intra-Mercurial planet or to the fact that gravitational force might be inversely proportional to a power of the distance a shade different from 2. Once relativity was formulated, however, the fine agreement of the Einstein prediction with the observed rate of advance of Mercury's perihelion afforded good evidence of the validity of the new theory.

The second deduction concerning orbit theory that is different in Newton's and Einstein's formulations is the gravitational deflection of light, described in Chapter 6. Starlight passing close to the solar surface should change course by 1.75" according to Einstein's theory, and only half as much according to Newton's. Although eclipse measurements of this effect are difficult, the evidence points fairly closely to an observed deflection in the neighborhood of 1.75".

Thus the general theory of relativity has given us a new and superior theory of gravitation. Its impact on cosmology is great, but on planetary motions it is relatively minor, but nevertheless significant. We have witnessed in this chapter a continual interplay for over two thousand years between the observed facts of planetary motion and the theories developed to account for them and to predict new facts. As the observations have improved, they have demanded better and more all-encompassing theories. We have seen the underlying axioms of various planetary theories, from the Eudoxian spheres onward, fall flat from the punches by fresh facts. We cannot therefore assume that today's theories will stand up eternally.

12. The Solar System Seen from the Sun

AN OBSERVER located at the center of the solar system would see the planets moving always eastward on or near the ecliptic, Mercury moving about 4° per day and Pluto only about 15° per decade. Any closer planet would overtake and pass any more distant planet once each synodic period. With two exceptions, the closer a planet the brighter it would appear. The observer would need a moderate-sized telescope to see 14th-magnitude Pluto, binoculars to detect 8th-magnitude Neptune, and sharp eyesight to find 6th-magnitude Uranus. The other planets would be very bright, with Venus the brightest of all. Although Mercury is closer to the sun than Venus, its smaller size and low albedo would conspire to make it fainter than Venus; similarly, Mars would be fainter than Jupiter. Mercury and the earth would be about equally bright, but substantially fainter than Venus; the earth would be the prettier spectacle, with its moon as bright as Saturn swinging 18′ from side to side every month. No other satellite of the solar system could be seen without telescopic aid.

13. The Solar System Seen from Pluto's Distance

FROM A POINT in the main plane of the solar system 40 a.u. away from the sun, the planets would alternately swing from one side of the sun to the other, fluctuating in brightness as they passed through their several phases. The sun itself would be less than one-thousandth as bright as seen from the earth, but nevertheless hundreds of times as bright as the full moon seen from the earth. The sun from 40 a.u. would have an angular diameter of less than 1′ and therefore could not be resolved as a disc. Ranging from one side to the other of this bright star, Mercury would never get farther than 0.6° from the sun and never be brighter than about 5th magnitude. The earth would on occasion get as far as 1.5° from the sun; at its brightest it would resemble a star of middling brightness. Giant Jupiter would sometimes attain about the same brightness, swinging alternately up to 7.4° from the sun. From 40 a.u. the planets are scarcely the spectacle that would be seen from the sun or that we actually witness from the earth.

PRINCIPLES OF INTERPLANETARY FLIGHT

14. Man-made Satellites and Planets

ON OCTOBER 4, 1957, Russia launched the first man-made satellite, named Sputnik I or, more technically, 1957 Alpha; Sputnik II, or 1957 Beta, followed a month later. The first successful launching by the United States occurred on January 31, 1958; this object was Explorer I, or 1958 Alpha. Since that time a host of satellites of varying kinds has been placed in orbit around the earth; the moon was hit for the first time by a Russian satellite in the autumn of 1959. Also in 1959 the Russians and later the Americans shot space probes away from the earth into orbits around the sun; these craft were and are the first man-made planets. The first manned orbital flight was launched from the Soviet Union in the spring of 1961, and the first orbiting American astronaut circled the earth three times early in 1962. Mariner II, or 1962 Alpha Rho, was the first probe to make a successful fly-by past another planet, moving near Venus in December, 1962. During the first 5 years of the space age the number of successful launchings was 80. Of this total, 44 earth satellites and 9 space probes were sent up by the United States and 25 earth satellites and 2 space probes by the Soviet Union. As these early years passed, the Greek alphabet became inadequate, and since the beginning of 1963 the sequential designations are 1963–1, 1963–2, and so on.

15. Space Travel and Other Kinds of Travel

Now THAT WE have studied the theory of planetary motion under gravitation, let us study some of the problems of flight beyond the earth.

To keep a motorboat, automobile, or bicycle going, one must continually use power. Otherwise the retarding forces of friction will soon decelerate the vehicle until it comes to rest. Travel in space, however, is fundamentally different from the kinds of travel we are used to here on earth. Instead of a continual application of power, one uses powered flight briefly in order to accelerate the vehicle to some required starting velocity. Then Kepler's laws of planetary motion govern the rest of the flight, even if it is to last indefinitely long. It is well to recall the implication of Newton's first law: motion rather than rest is the natural state of affairs in the universe.

Achievement of the necessary starting speed is a major and difficult technological problem, and requires the use of multistage rockets to accelerate the vehicle from zero speed on the ground to several miles per second at the injection point, the point at which the vehicle is on its own in a natural orbit. During the period of acceleration, which lasts only a few minutes, the vehicle and its rockets must increase their speed while moving through a near-vacuum. Because, in the absence of air, conventional propellers will not do the job, use is made of the jet principle. Imagine for simplicity that you are riding in a vessel that is far from any star and at rest relative to the stars. If you now throw from the vessel a shoe of mass M_1 at speed v_1, the remainder of the vessel, of mass M_2, must acquire some velocity, v_2, in the direction opposite the shoe, because the center of mass of the two bodies must remain at rest. This requirement gives us the law of *conservation of linear momentum*. The momentum of an object is the product of its mass and its velocity, and the law says that the total linear momentum of an isolated system does not change. In our example, then, the vessel had zero momentum before the shoe was ejected. After ejection the momentum of the shoe plus the rest of the vessel must therefore still be zero. It follows that

$$M_1 v_1 + M_2 v_2 = 0.$$

Solving this formula for the rebound velocity of the vessel, we find that

$$v_2 = -\frac{M_1 v_1}{M_2}.$$

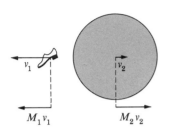

Fig. 7.15:1. Illustration of the conservation of momentum.

Thus the rebound velocity of the massive vessel is much less than the speed of the light shoe, and the minus sign indicates that the velocity is oppositely directed to that of the shoe. See Fig. 7.1£:1 for the momentum and velocity vectors of the two objects.

Throwing shoes out of the vessel is both inefficient and expensive. It is preferable to eject a large amount of mass at very high velocity, and this is achieved by the rocket engines. Each molecule of escaping gas gives the vessel a minute bit of recoil speed in the opposite direction. The combined effect of all such molecules over a period of a few minutes gives the vessel a continuous acceleration up to the required injection velocity. At the injection point power is cut; the vessel at this instant has a perfectly definite position and velocity vector relative to the center of the earth, and thus its orbit in the gravitational field of the earth is predetermined.

Achievement of a high injection velocity is no easy feat. For example, if the rocket engine is designed so that the fuel can be ejected as fast as 2 mi/sec, then to accelerate to 5 mi/sec about 90 percent of the take-off mass must be fuel, leaving only 10 percent for the rockets and pay-load. To accelerate to 7 mi/sec requires that 97 percent of the take-off mass be fuel. These stringent demands account for the use of multi-stage rockets hitched together in tandem. As each stage is exhausted of fuel it detaches and falls to earth, avoiding the necessity of dragging excess mass to the injection point. The final payload mass, the mass of the satellite and its instruments, is therefore but a small fraction of the take-off mass.

16. Orbits Relative to the Center of the Earth

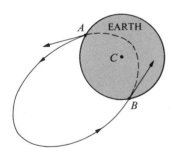

Fig. 7.16:1. A body shot from *A* at 6 mi/sec and at an angle of 45° from the vertical will land later at point *B* at 6 mi/sec and at an angle of 45° from the vertical.

WE SAW IN Section 8 that a bullet shot horizontally from a tower at various speeds moves in one of the conic sections. The minimum speed required for the bullet to orbit clear of the earth is the earth's circular velocity, 5 mi/sec, whereas the minimum needed to escape the earth is the earth's parabolic velocity, 7 mi/sec. A bullet shot in a direction other than the horizontal cannot be at its perigee at the time of firing. Hence, if its velocity is less than 7 mi/sec, it must necessarily reintersect the earth, as shown in Fig. 7.16:1. Its crash velocity will be the same as its muzzle velocity. The requirements for placing a man-made satellite into successful orbit around the earth are therefore that the injection velocity vector lie between 5 mi/sec and 7 mi/sec and also be directed parallel to the earth's surface. In practice it is desirable to launch vertically so as to overcome the resistance of the lower atmosphere as economically as possible. The satellite and rocket assembly, while still under power, then changes course gradually until it is moving horizontally 100 or more miles above the ground. It is usually turned in an easterly direction to take advantage of the rotational speed of the earth of nearly 1000 miles per hour. Still under power, the vehicle accelerates to a shade more than 5 miles per second at the injection point. In accordance with the principles set forth in Section 8, the now-free satellite has an orbit whose perigee is near the injection point, 100 or more miles above the surface. The orbital eccentricity is usually rather small, and thus apogee is several hundred or even a few thousand miles above ground. The center of the earth is of course at one focus of the elliptical path. A typical orbital period is somewhat longer than 100 minutes. The orbital inclination, the angle between the orbital plane and the earth's equator, equals the latitude of the injection point if the injection velocity is directed eastward. Variations are possible; for example, a polar orbit can be achieved by firing northward or southward (actually a bit west of north or south to counteract the earth's eastward rotation).

17. Observing Earth Satellites

WE MAY IMAGINE, for now, that the orbit of a satellite lies in a fixed plane in space. If the satellite could be watched from the center of the earth, it would sweep out a fixed great-circle path among the stars every orbital period. Observed from a point on the surface, however, things are quite different. Because of the earth's daily rotation, any given city comes under the satellite's orbital ring only twice a day at most. If we plot on a terrestrial globe the successive northeast-bound equator crossings of a two-hour satellite, they will occur 30° farther west in longitude each time, because the earth in two hours rotates 30° eastward under the orbit. Imagine that the satellite leaves a bright trail so that its orbit is a luminous ring in space. In Fig. 7.17:1 notice that an observer whose latitude (north *or* south) is equal to the inclination of the orbit must pass under the orbit ring once a day. Any observer closer to the equator must pass under the ring twice a day. Any observer closer to the north or south pole never passes under the orbit. Thus conditions for viewing a satellite can be favorable only twice a day. Even so, the satellite *itself* may be anywhere on its ring when the ring is over a specific observer's head. In general, then, the closest approach of the actual satellite to the observer will occur up to an hour before or after the moment when the ring is overhead. If before, the satellite will cross the sky to the east of the observer, since he has not yet come under the ring. If after, it will cross the western sky.

A second factor governing observations of satellites is their closeness to the earth. A distant object—the sun, any planet, or any given star—is in the long run above the horizon half of the time and below it half of the time, apart from minor refraction effects. But a close object is above the horizon much less than half of the time. Imagine an object placed 100 miles above ground at some randomly selected longitude and latitude. As can be inferred from Fig. 7.17:2, the chance that this object is above *your* horizon is very slim. Calculation shows the chance to be less than one part in two thousand.

A third factor in visibility is the size of the satellite. The amount of sunlight it can reflect is proportional to its surface area. Thus only large objects, such as the final-stage rocket of Sputnik I or the Echo I

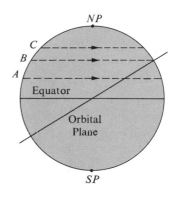

Fig. 7.17:1. Observer *B*, at a latitude equal to the inclination of the satellite's orbit, is carried under the orbit ring once a day by the earth's rotation. Observer *A* passes under the ring twice a day, and *C* never passes under it.

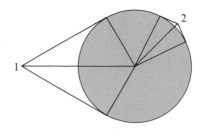

Fig. 7.17:2. A high object, like 1, can be seen from a large fraction of the earth's surface. A lower object, like 2, can be seen from only a limited area.

PLANETARY MOTIONS

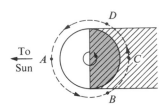

Fig. 7.17:3. At *A* and *C* a satellite cannot be seen, but at *B* and *D* it is visible because it is in sunlight while the observer beneath is in darkness.

balloon, can be seen with the unaided eye. Tracking faint satellites must be left either to high-speed telescopic cameras or to directive radio antennas which pick up the radio signals transmitted from the satellite.

Even if a big satellite happens to be crossing directly overhead, the chances are good that it cannot be seen. If it is daytime, the sky will drown the light from the satellite just as it does the stars. If it is near midnight, on the other hand, the satellite is in the earth's shadow and thus reflects no sunlight. Figure 7.17:3 shows that only in evening and dawn twilight can a close satellite be seen. The sky is adequately dark where the observer is standing, but the sun is still shining on the satellite.

Given that all the requisite conditions are fulfilled, a satellite resembles a star or meteor. Its angular motion is more rapid than that of a star but slower than that of a meteor. On occasion it resembles a high-flying distant jet airplane at night. If the satellite is not spherical, its rotation every few seconds will present alternately different amounts of reflecting surface to the observer. It therefore varies in brightness every few seconds during the few minutes it takes to cross the observer's sky.

Fig. 7.17:4. Track of the carrier of Sputnik III against the stars. The brightest star is Vega, and Epsilon Lyrae is resolved as a double star very close to the track. The periodic fading of Sputnik's trail is caused by the spin of the carrier. The more frequent breaks are produced by a rotating blade in front of the camera that chops the light every second and thus allows the angular rate of the object to be calculated. (*Dominion Astrophysical Observatory, Victoria, Canada*)

18. Orbit Perturbations

THE ORBITAL characteristics of a close satellite differ in three major ways from the simple results of the two-body problem. Two effects arise from the fact that the satellite is feeling the gravitational attraction of a nonspherical earth. If the earth were spherically symmetric and without an atmosphere, the six orbital elements of the satellite would be fixed. Actually, however, some of them change with time. The oblateness produces two effects. The first is the *regression of the nodes.* If the orbital ring is observed from the center of the earth, the points where the ring intersects the celestial equator move steadily westward, completing one circuit every few months for a typical satellite. The motion is reminiscent of the precession of the earth's equinoxes. Because of the regression the times of day a given city moves under the orbital ring get earlier by about 15 minutes a day.

A second effect is the *motion of perigee.* We saw earlier that the major axis of Mercury rotates slowly in its orbital plane as a consequence of planetary perturbations and relativity effects. The oblateness of the earth produces the same effect on close satellites. The perigee direction sweeps slowly around the orbital ring; the angular rate and sense of motion depends on the inclination of the orbit. The perigees of the early high-inclination Russian satellites regressed slowly westward; those of the early low-inclination United States satellites advanced more rapidly eastward, completing a cycle about every three months. Whatever the rate and direction, the perigee spends half its time above the northern hemisphere and half above the southern. If a satellite is observed crossing overhead when it is near the perigee of its orbit, it is as close to the ground as possible. Furthermore, by the law of areas its speed is a maximum. For both of these reasons its angular speed across the sky is as fast as possible, and therefore it may be visible for only a minute or two. If some weeks or months later, when perigee has moved through 180°, the satellite is watched by the same observer when near its apogee, it is as far above the earth as possible and its speed is a minimum. Its angular motion across the sky is leisurely, and it may be in sight for ten minutes or so.

If the earth had no atmosphere, regression of the nodes and motion of perigee would be the only major perturbations of the orbit. It is well known, however, that close satellites crash to the earth after a time. The agency responsible is the atmosphere. As the satellite moves along, even in the ultrararefied high atmosphere, it encounters a multitude of air molecules during each second of its flight. It sweeps clean each second a thin tube several miles in length. The molecules are batted in all directions at a speed of several miles per second. The satellite thus gives momentum to the air molecules and is continually robbed of momentum itself. This drag effect is not uniform around the elliptical orbit because the air density is halved with every few miles increase of height. Virtually all of the drag, or momentum loss, occurs where the number of molecules to be pushed aside is greatest, at perigee. Imagine, then, what happens to the orbit of a satellite that slams through perigee and suffers a small decrease in momentum and thus velocity. In terms of what we learned in Section 8 and with the aid of Fig. 7.18:1, it is clear that the new orbit will have a smaller eccentricity and a smaller semimajor axis. The continual result of ten or twelve

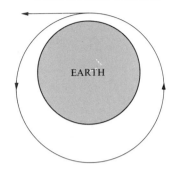

Fig. 7.18:1. Two successive orbits, showing the effect of air drag on the path of a close earth satellite. The velocity is reduced a bit at each perihelion passage, decreasing both the semimajor axis and the eccentricity.

Fig. 7.18:2. One of the Vanguard satellites. Vanguard I, launched on March 17, 1958, was the first object whose perturbations argued that the density of the highest atmosphere fluctuates dramatically. (*National Aeronautics and Space Administration*)

perigee passages a day is that the orbit steadily gets rounder and smaller. Ultimately, the satellite spirals into thicker atmospheric layers where it finally fragments into a shower of luminous parts that fall like meteorites or are consumed like meteors. The life expectancy of a satellite depends critically on its perigee height: the higher it is the less air encountered. The lifetimes of some of the early satellites were only a few months. Vanguard I, however, with an initial perigee height of 405 miles, is expected to stay aloft for a century or more. Precise tracking of a satellite and calculation of the rate at which its period decreases can lead to an indirect determination of the air density at the height of perigee. In this way previous estimates of air density at great heights have been revised sharply upward.

19. Voyage to the Moon

ALTHOUGH A comfortable manned trip to the moon is some time away, it is instructive to utilize what we have learned to reflect on a few aspects of such a voyage. On take-off under power the acceleration of the ship is quite rapid. To achieve an injection speed of nearly 7 miles per second in just a few minutes under power demands an average acceleration several times as great as the acceleration of gravity, g_E. A passenger's weight is several times its normal value and he is pressed strongly to the rear of the ship. After power is cut at the injection point, the ship moves in a natural Keplerian orbit with the center of the earth at one focus. The passenger's weight does not return to its normal value but to zero. The gravitational force exerted on him by the earth is still moderately strong, and because of his acceleration he moves in a given orbit. But his ship, being at the same position in space, is accelerated by the earth in exactly the same amount and direction. Since both the passenger and the ship left the injection point with precisely the same velocity vector, their orbits are identical. In his new abode, therefore, the passenger is freely afloat; *relative to his surroundings*, he is motionless and unaccelerated. The situation is the same for a person unlucky enough to be in an elevator when the cable snaps. Both fall at the same ever-increasing rate; relative to the car, the person is freely afloat for a few seconds—until the inevitable crash.

The duration of the one-way trip to the moon can be found from Kepler's third law. If we assume perigee at the earth's distance and apogee at the moon's distance, then

$$a = \tfrac{1}{2}(4000 \text{ mi} + 240,000 \text{ mi}) = 122,000 \text{ mi}.$$

The resulting period is ten days, and thus the one-way trip takes five days. Actually, the injection or perigee velocity needed to reach the moon is only about 1 percent less than the escape velocity of 7 miles per second. If we depart with this slight extra velocity on a parabolic path, the one-way trip time is cut down to only two days. Clearly, travel times are extremely sensitive to starting velocities.

The view from a porthole a few hours after injection is spectacular, with the sky black and the earth now filling much less than half of the celestial sphere, its phase dependent on where the sun lies. On the illuminated surface the oceans and continents are outlined where they are not overlain by brilliant white clouds. The whole disk becomes slowly but steadily smaller as the ship speeds away.

Meanwhile, life aboard is complicated by weightlessness. A man who finds himself unable to reach any wall or surface can only "land" if he removes a shoe and throws it in the direction opposite to the point toward which he wants to go. Or, if he prefers, he can accelerate himself slowly by breaststroking through the air of the cabin. The coffee break is not complex when one eats the doughnut (apart from floating crumbs). But drinking the coffee is an unnerving experience, for the liquid does not flow out of the cup; a straw is essential.

During the majority of the flight the ship's speed is continually decreasing because of the earth's gravitational back-pull. Its motion is much like that of a vertically thrown ball before it reaches peak height. As the trip nears completion, however, the gravitational pull of the moon becomes steadily stronger, until it is greater than the earth's. We can find the *neutral point*, where the two forces just balance, by equating the two gravitational forces, as diagrammed in Fig. 7.19:1.

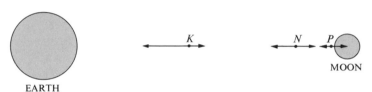

EARTH

Fig. 7.19:1. At K the earth's pull exceeds the moon's; at P the opposite is true. The pulls are equal and opposite at the neutral point, N.

Applying the law of gravitation successively to the earth's effect on particle m and to the moon's effect on it, we find that the neutral point lies on the line joining earth and moon such that

$$\frac{GM_E m}{D_E^2} = \frac{GM_M m}{D_M^2}.$$

Canceling and rearranging, we have

$$\frac{D_E^2}{D_M^2} = \frac{M_E}{M_M} \cong 80.$$

Thus $D_E \cong 9 D_M$, and the neutral point is 90 percent of the way to the moon.

It is now time to ready the ship for landing on the moon. If nothing is done, it will land at approximately the moon's escape velocity, 1.5 mi/sec, a far too vigorous impact for comfort or even survival. Instead, the ship is first oriented with its nose away from the moon. During the flight it was irrelevant in what direction the ship's axis pointed, or indeed whether the ship was spinning. But now, invoking the law of conservation of angular momentum and turning a flywheel around an appropriate axis (or briefly using appropriate small steering jets), the ship is rotated around its center of mass so that its nose points upward. Then, at a suitable time, the main engines blast fuel (and hence momentum) *downward* and the ship is thereby accelerated *upward*.

Thus the downward velocity is reduced. The ship literally sets itself down on its own gases, and if things go well, the landing need not be a rough one. It is interesting to note that it takes just as much fuel to land on the moon as it does to take off from the moon.

The return trip from this forbidding world follows the same sequence in reverse, with the exception that on arrival near the earth fuel may be conserved by utilizing the natural braking effect of the earth's atmosphere. A series of passes through the outer atmosphere will, as we saw in Section 18, decrease the ship's momentum. Ultimately, the rocket engines are used to bring the ship down, nose up, for a gentle landing.

20. Flight to the Planets

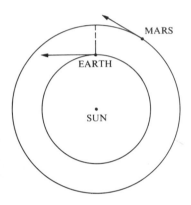

Fig. 7.20:1. A straight-line flight from earth to Mars is not economical from the point of view of fuel consumption.

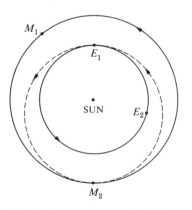

Fig. 7.20:2. A tangential flight to Mars. At take-off the two planets are at E_1 and M_1; at arrival they have moved to E_2 and M_2.

FOR TRIPS farther afield the gravitational field of the sun controls the orbital path. The ship is accelerated so that at the injection point it has some hyperbolic velocity faster than 7 mi/sec. In a day or so it is far enough from the earth so that the sun's force on it exceeds the earth's; it goes on to move in a Keplerian orbit around the sun. Let us now find an appropriate kind of orbit for a specific flight, to Mars for example. It may at first seem logical to choose the path so that the distance to be traveled is as short as possible, as shown in Fig. 7.20:1. Note, however, that to get the ship headed straight away from the sun would require counteracting the earth's 18.5 mi/sec orbital speed and also acquiring some outward velocity. If, on arrival near Mars, a landing is contemplated, it would be necessary to add 15 mi/sec in order to be running parallel to Mars in its orbit. The fuel requirements for such great velocity changes are impossibly high by conventional methods of space flight; keeping the total necessary velocity change to a minimum must therefore govern our choice of flight path.

Because the planetary orbits are nearly circular, nearly in the same plane, and described in the same direction, it is possible to select a very economical orbit—one that is tangent both to the earth's orbit and to that of Mars. If for simplicity we imagine the two planetary orbits to be precisely circular and in the same plane, then, as shown in Fig. 7.20:2, a ship may leave the earth's vicinity at a speed in excess of 18.5 mi/sec and move out on an ellipse of moderate eccentricity, reaching the vicinity of Mars at a speed not much different from that of the planet itself. The perihelion is 1 a.u. and the aphelion equals the distance of Mars from the sun, or 1.52 a.u. Accordingly, the semimajor axis of this orbit is 1.26 a.u. It follows that the sidereal period is 17 months and the one-way trip $8\frac{1}{2}$ months. The projection velocity necessary to achieve this orbit is 20.4 mi/sec, and therefore only about 2 mi/sec needs to be added to the earth's circular velocity to fly to Mars along this orbit. If a rocket leaves the injection point at 7.3 mi/sec on a hyperbolic orbit, it will still be moving some 2 mi/sec relative to the earth when it is indefinitely far away. Therefore if the rocket is shot in the direction of the earth's motion it will soon come under solar control and move out to the Martian orbit. On arrival at its aphelion its velocity is about 10 percent less than that of Mars. The speed of Mars is 15 mi/sec, and thus the velocity of the rocket *relative* to Mars is less than 2 mi/sec, a reasonably small value for attempting a landing.

A major disadvantage of the tangential orbit is that it can be carried out only at certain times. If a shot is tried on a random date, Mars will in all probability not be at the ship's aphelion point but somewhere else in its orbit. If Mars is not at the rendezvous, the ship will of course return to intersect the earth's orbit in another $8\frac{1}{2}$ months, but the earth will not be there to meet it either. Only once every synodic period is the time correct for departure. The time for departure from the earth is about 3 months before Mars comes to opposition, and the time to leave Mars is about $5\frac{1}{2}$ months before the earth is at inferior conjunction. An expedition following the tangential orbit would have to wait on Mars for more than 15 months before returning.

If navigational fixes during the flight indicate it is necessary to change course, use is made of steering jets at the side of the ship. The conservation of linear momentum demands that if fuel is ejected on one side the ship acquires a rebound velocity in the opposite direction. When the new velocity vector is added to the original velocity, the direction of travel is slightly altered and the craft moves along a somewhat different Keplerian orbit.

Tangential trips to planets other than Mars are also feasible. The one-way trip to Mercury lasts only $3\frac{1}{2}$ months, and to get to Pluto at 40 a.u. requires 43 years. But to go beyond the solar system a ship must leave the earth's vicinity on a hyperbolic orbit around the sun, with speed greater than 26 mi/sec, as we saw in Section 8. At 30 mi/sec from 1 a.u. a ship would have an ultimate recessional speed from the sun of about 15 mi/sec. At this rate it would take the ship about 50,000 years to travel as far as the nearest star.

PROBLEMS

1. What are the major observed features of planetary motions?

2. (a) How do the fundamental assumptions of the Copernican theory compare with those of the Ptolemaic theory? (b) How do those of Keplerian theory compare with those of the Copernican theory?

3. What phases can (a) Mercury and (b) Mars have in the Ptolemaic system? In the Copernican system?

4. To establish his third law, Kepler needed to know both the sidereal period and the semimajor axis of each of the planets then known. (a) Suggest one way in which he could deduce the sidereal period of a planet. (b) Explain how he found the semimajor axis of Mars in astronomical units.

5. (a) Compute the mean distance of an object from the sun if its orbital period is 1000 years. (b) Compute the orbital period of another object if its perihelion distance is 6 a.u. and its aphelion distance is 16 a.u.

6. (a) If Venus lies at maximum elongation east of the sun and is then in Gemini, in what constellation is it at the next maximum easterly elongation 584 days later? (b) In what constellation does the sun lie on these two occasions?

7. What is the synodic period of the earth as seen from Mars? Of Venus as seen from Mars?

8. The acceleration of the earth by the sun is about 0.6 cm/sec². (a) Compute the force exerted by the sun on the earth. (b) Compute the force exerted by the earth on the sun. (c) Compute the acceleration of Venus by the sun.

9. Describe and sketch roughly the orbits of objects that are shot horizontally from atop a tall tower on the earth's surface at the following speeds: 0 mi/sec, 2 mi/sec, 5 mi/sec, 6 mi/sec, 7 mi/sec, 10 mi/sec, 186,300 mi/sec. Ignore effects of the atmosphere, the earth's rotation, and the gravitational attractions of bodies beyond the earth.

10. (a) How is it possible to deduce the mass of Jupiter with the help of observations of one of Jupiter's satellites? (b) What quantities must be known before the mass can be found?

11. Define the six elements of a planet's orbit.

12. Suppose you are motionless in the center of a spherical spacecraft of radius 50 feet and that you throw a shoe $\frac{1}{50}$ as massive as yourself at a speed of 20 ft/sec. Where and when and at what speed will you contact the inner surface of the spacecraft?

13. For what two reasons is the angular velocity of an earth satellite greater if you observe it near its perigee than if you observe it several weeks later near its apogee?

14. A spherical comet one mile in diameter and made of ices has a mass of about 2×10^{15} gm; the sun's mass is 2×10^{33} gm. When the comet is 1 a.u. from the sun, how far is the neutral point of the pair of bodies from the center of the comet? From its surface?

15. (a) How frequently does the right time occur for leaving the earth on the tangential orbit to Saturn? (b) How long does such a voyage take?

8

THE PRINCIPAL
PLANETS

W<small>E</small> have studied the physical characteristics and motions of one planet—the earth—in Chapters 2 and 3. And in the last chapter we analyzed in a general way the motions of the planets. Let us turn now to the characteristics of individual planets, moving from Mercury out to Pluto. The orbital elements of a planet are determined by calculation from a series of observations of its changing place in the sky, whereas the rotational characteristics are determined either directly from telescopic observation or indirectly from observations of the Doppler effect in the spectrum of the planet. As to the over-all physical characteristics of a planet, its mass is determined from observations of its satellites and from application of Kepler's third law as amended by Newton; the mass of a moonless planet can be established only by delicate observations of the amount by which it perturbs the solar orbit of another planet. The diameter of a planet is deduced from its measured angular diameter at a certain time and its distance from the earth at that same time. The mean density follows on dividing mass by volume. Furthermore, once mass and radius are known, we can calculate the velocity of escape and the surface gravity of the planet. The shape of a planet, as indicated by its oblateness, may be determined directly by precise measurement at the telescope. The external features of a planet, such as albedo, surface temperature, topographic nature, and atmospheric characteristics, are chiefly deduced from telescopic observations by eye, by photography, or by spectroscopy.

& Rotation 88 days

THE TERRESTRIAL PLANETS

1. Mercury

WITH MEAN distance only 0.39 a.u., the innermost planet Mercury moves around the sun swiftly, once every 88 days. Its synodic period is just under four months, so that on the average it spends eight weeks as a morning planet and then eight as an evening planet. Although at times it rivals Sirius in brightness, only a small percentage of people ever see elusive Mercury. Even at maximum elongation it can lie only 28° from the sun, and thus it is partly drowned either in twilight or in the murk of low altitudes. Telescopically, the most successful observations of Mercury have been made in the daytime.

Besides being the closest and fastest-moving of the nine principal planets, Mercury ranks second to Pluto in eccentricity and inclination. The relatively eccentric orbit, with $e = 0.21$, means that some elongations are more favorable than others. When maximum elongation coincides with aphelion, Mercury is 28° from the sun; when with perihelion only 18°. The high inclination of 7° does not really make Mercury a renegade, for the linear distance that it moves above and below the main plane of the solar system is not exceptional. If the inclination of the orbit were zero, Mercury would cross, or *transit*, the sun's disk at every inferior conjunction. Actually, such transits occur either 7 or 13 years apart, with Mercury a "new" black telescopic dot slowly passing westerly across the bright face of the sun. Both of the inferior planets pass through phases like the moon, once each synodic period. Mercury and Venus differ from the moon, however, because at new phase they are close and thus angularly large, whereas at full they are passing superior conjunction and are at maximum distance and minimum angular diameter. Mercury's angular diameter varies by a factor of three.

Although it is extremely difficult to observe surface details on Mercury, most observers agree that the faint dark markings on the planet comprise an unchanging map from year to year and that the various aspects of the map we see indicate that the rotational period of Mercury is the same as its orbital period. The innermost planet is therefore tidally coupled to the sun, just as is the moon to the earth.

Mercury has no satellites, and therefore its mass is difficult to determine accurately. From disturbances of the motions of other planets, the mass is found to be about 5 percent of the earth's. With a diameter of 3000 miles, the smallest among the nine principal planets, the mean density of Mercury is about 5 gm/cm³. What polar flattening there may be is below the limit of detection, as we should expect for a planet that rotates so slowly. The apparent constancy of the darkish areas and the moonlike low albedo of only 0.07 indicate that we look directly down on a darkish surface, possibly composed of rugged solidified lava. Indeed, Mercury is in many respects similar to our moon in structural characteristics. Also like the moon, it has no appreciable atmosphere.

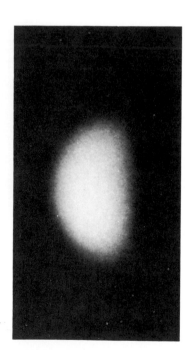

Fig. 8.1:1. Mercury in the gibbous phase, photographed with the 24-inch refractor. (*Lowell Observatory photograph*)

With its low escape velocity and its closeness to the sun, any original atmosphere would have rapidly escaped from the planet, except possibly for the relatively massive slow-moving molecules.

Being substantially closer to the sun than we are, a unit area at the noon-point on Mercury receives nearly seven times as much solar energy as a corresponding area on earth. With no appreciable protective atmosphere, the noon temperature at perihelion measures nearly 800°F. And because Mercury keeps the same face toward the sun, no relief can be hoped for by waiting until nightfall. The temperature at the midnight-point is extremely low, in all likelihood near absolute zero at −460°F. The innermost planet thus bears the added distinction of having both the hottest and coldest locales in the solar system.

DAY 800°F
NIGHT(−)460°F

2. Venus

APART FROM the sun and moon, Venus is the brightest object in the sky, delivering up to 13 times as much light to us as does Sirius. With mean distance 0.72 a.u., its sidereal period is 225 days. Because its orbit is not very far inside the earth's, Venus has the relatively long synodic period of 584 days. Thus it is an evening planet for nearly ten months; then it moves past inferior conjunction into the morning sky for nearly ten months. At maximum elongation Venus is about 48° from the sun and therefore at this time sets or rises at least three hours after or before the sun. Its brilliance is so great that one can easily see Venus in full daylight, providing it is not too close to the sun in the sky. Unless one knows within fairly narrow limits in what direction to look, Venus is hard to spot in the daytime, but once found, it is a wonder how it could ever be missed.

Venus goes through phases like the moon and Mercury, but with a period of 584 days. Recall that Galileo's discovery of the Venusian phases was crucial in dooming the Ptolemaic system. While changing phases, the angular diameter of Venus varies by a large factor; at inferior conjunction the planet comes closer to us than does any other principal planet, 26 million miles, whereas at superior conjunction it is 160 million miles away; accordingly, its angular diameter varies by a factor of 6. Venus does not attain maximum brilliancy when closest, for it is then in the new phase; nor does it in the full phase, for it is then far away and angularly small. Five weeks before and after inferior conjunction, when the phase is changing at a rate that just offsets the rate of change of angular size, Venus reaches greatest brightness. When near inferior conjunction, Venus offers the best planetary target for radar signals. In early 1958 the first radar contact was established, with a round-trip signal time of about five minutes. Combining the precise time with the velocity of light gives the distance to Venus in miles. Since the distance to Venus in astronomical units is also known, this type of experiment affords a very accurate determination of the length of the astronomical unit. Powerful radars operated by the Lincoln Laboratory of the Massachusetts Institute of Technology and the Jet Propulsion Laboratory of the California Institute of Technology yielded in 1962 a new value of 92,955,700 miles for the astronomical unit. These determinations are accurate to within a few hundred miles, and thus radar and Venus have served to increase about a hundredfold the precision of our knowledge of this fundamental unit of length.

With an eccentricity of only 0.007, Venus has the most nearly circular orbit of all the planets. Her orbital inclination is 3.4°, and transits of the sun are rare events. The most recent transits of Venus occurred in 1874 and 1882; the next ones are scheduled for 2004 and 2012. Observation of the times of beginning and end of such a transit from different points on earth affords another method of deducing the distance of the earth from the sun. But the observations are difficult and subject to error, and the results are of only historical interest today.

Although the spin or rotational period of every other planet is now known, that of Venus has defied astronomers for a long time, in spite of the fact that Venus comes closer to us than does any other principal planet. Because it is eternally cloud-covered, no fixed surface point can be followed telescopically. And yet indirect evidence has gradually accumulated. Venus cannot be spinning at a very large angular rate or it would show a measurable oblateness. Some years ago it was found specifically that the rotational period cannot be less than two or three weeks; otherwise the Doppler effect in the Venusian spectrum would reveal a detectable difference in the radial velocity of one side of the planet's disk as compared with that of the opposite side. A slow rotation is also in conformity with the expected effect of solar tidal forces: Mercury is strongly affected and is tidally coupled to the sun, whereas the earth is affected least of the three inner planets and is not tidally coupled. It has for some time seemed doubtful that Venus is fully locked to the sun and therefore rotating every 225 days, because temperature measurements show that the atmosphere of the dark side is not much cooler than that of the bright side. The sun is the supplier of the energy that maintains atmospheric molecules aloft; if it never shone on one hemisphere of the planet, the temperature there would presumably be far lower than observed. Again, high-powered radars, with their capacity to measure Doppler shifts with extreme precision, have come to the rescue. The period of rotation of Venus as deduced from radar observations is greater than 100 days, and the most probable value in early 1963 is about 250 days in the retrograde direction.

The gross physical characteristics of Venus make it a twin of the earth. Its diameter is 7700 miles, only slightly less than the earth's. Although Venus has no satellites, its mass has been found by two different methods. One calculation is based on the small modifications in the orbits of other bodies that are caused by the gravitational effect of Venus. A second was made possible on December 14, 1962, when Mariner II approached to within 25,000 miles of the center of Venus. The probe changed course as a consequence of the close approach, and the amount of the change depended, among other factors, on the mass of Venus. The mass of the planet is 81 percent of the earth's, and its average density is close to 5 gm/cm³.

Fig. 8.2:1. Mariner II at Cape Kennedy. (*National Aeronautics and Space Administration*)

Despite the over-all similarity of the two planets, there are many characteristics of Venus that contrast strongly with those of the earth. Mariner II was equipped to detect any strong magnetic field associated with Venus, but none was found. If there is one, it is very much weaker than the earth's. The surface of the planet is totally enshrouded by highly reflecting yellowish-white clouds, giving Venus an albedo of 0.60, the highest of any planet. From just over 20,000 miles above the

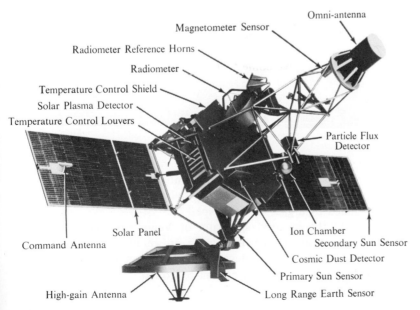

Fig. 8.2:2. A schematic diagram of Mariner II, showing the many kinds of equipment carried to Venus. (*National Aeronautics and Space Administration*)

THE PRINCIPAL PLANETS

surface Mariner II was unable to record any breaks in the cloud or to glimpse any solid surface. Faintish dark patches are seen occasionally with earthbound telescopes, and ultraviolet photographs reveal a more or less banded structure that may be evidence of trade-wind belts in the atmosphere. Additional evidence that Venus has an atmosphere is that very near to inferior conjunction the planet is seen as a ring of light rather than as a thin crescent. This effect is caused by the scattering of sunlight by molecules in the Venusian atmosphere. In 1959 a rare occultation occurred when Venus passed in front of Regu-

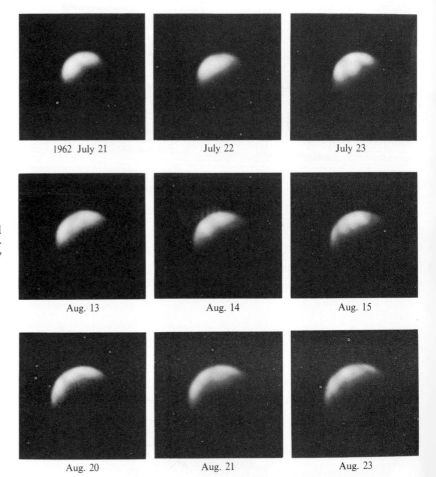

Fig. 8.2:3. Venus photographed in ultraviolet light with the 120-inch reflector. (*Lick Observatory photographs*)

1962 July 21   July 22   July 23

Aug. 13   Aug. 14   Aug. 15

Aug. 20   Aug. 21   Aug. 23

lus. The star's brightness diminished and its light path was refracted when near the planet's disk, as expected when the foreground object is surrounded by a gaseous envelope.

Studies of the infrared spectrum of Venus revealed in 1932 that the upper atmospheric levels contain an amount of carbon dioxide hundreds of times greater than that in our own atmosphere. And in 1959, as a result of observations made from a manned balloon, water vapor was reported. No traces of oxygen have been found, however.

Measurements in the infrared part of the spectrum show that the temperature in the higher layers of the Venus atmosphere is about −100°F both day and night. Radio radiation from Venus was first detected in 1956 and since that time has been studied often. The intensity of the received radiation at centimeter wavelengths indicates a temperature in the lower atmosphere of about 600°F. Early analysis of the information sent from Mariner II suggests that the solid surface may be as hot as 800°F. Because of its smaller distance from the sun, a unit area on Venus receives on the average twice as much solar energy as does a unit area on the earth. But this difference is not by itself

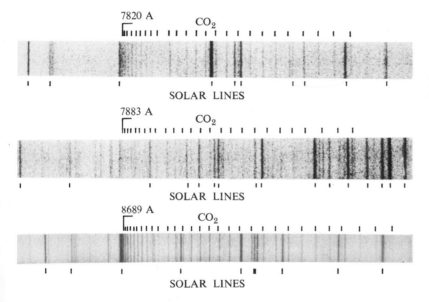

Fig. 8.2:4. The thumbprint of carbon dioxide on the spectrum of Venus. Above each spectrum are marked the features that originate in the Venusian atmosphere; below are marked the lines that originate in the sun. Photographed with the 74-inch telescope. (*Mount Stromlo Observatory*)

enough to explain such a high temperature. The heat content of the Venusian atmosphere is enhanced by the *greenhouse effect*: carbon dioxide and water vapor do not obstruct the ultraviolet and visual light of the sun from penetrating downward through the atmosphere, but the reradiation of the planet in the infrared is absorbed on the way upward. Thus heat energy tends to be held in as in a greenhouse. This effect also occurs in the terrestrial atmosphere, although in a different fashion because of the different molecular composition. At the high temperature of Venus water vapor cannot condense and collect into oceans; and without liquid water plant life does not emerge. On the earth, plants deplete the carbon dioxide of the atmosphere and return oxygen to it. Evidently no such process can occur on Venus, and carbon dioxide remains an important component of its atmosphere.

3. Earth

WE HAVE ALREADY dealt at length with our own planet. Third in distance from the sun, the earth is the largest of the terrestrial planets by a slight margin, but it ranks only fifth in size among the nine principal planets. Perhaps the major distinction of the earth is its ability to support life; its distance from its parent star means that the flux of sunshine is neither impossibly high nor impossibly low, and its size enables it to retain a reasonable atmosphere. Although planetary

Fig. 8.3:1. Part of the earth photographed from space by Tiros III. The major feature is a spiraling tropical storm centered over the Caribbean north of Venezuela. (*National Aeronautics and Space Administration*)

systems associated with other stars may abound in our galaxy, the happy and judicious combination of the proper distance and proper size to permit animal life is doubtless a rare one; it happens only once in our own solar system.

4. Mars

AS THE OUTERMOST of the terrestrial planets, ruddy Mars sweeps around the sun every 687 days at a mean distance of 1.52 a.u. Although its orbital plane is inclined by less than 2° to our own, the orbital eccentricity of Mars is relatively large, 0.09. Unlike the inferior planets, which never attain a large angle from the sun, the superior planets reach opposition once every synodic period. At this time they are both closest to us and in the full phase; on both counts Mars is then brightest as seen from the earth. Moreover, it can then be observed all night, for it is rising at sunset and setting at dawn. The synodic period of Mars is 780 days, longest among the planets, and thus this planet is best observed at intervals of 2 years plus 50 days. Some Martian oppositions are more favorable than others because of the orbital eccentricity, as shown in Fig. 8.4:1. At the opposition in early September 1956, Mars was close to its perihelion point and only 35 million miles away. At the next opposition, in November 1958, Mars was substantially farther from the earth, about 45 million miles. When an opposition occurs with Mars near its aphelion, the distance is 63 million miles and conditions are not very favorable for observing the planet. The next close opposition will occur in mid-August 1971. When Mars is at conjunction and therefore in full phase beyond the sun, its angular diameter is very small, only about one-seventh its angular diameter at a favorable opposition. Unlike Mercury and Venus, the superior

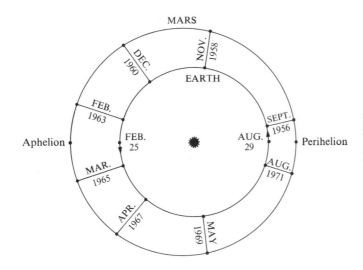

Fig. 8.4:1. Oppositions of Mars from 1956 to 1971. An opposition that occurs near August 29 is particularly favorable because Mars is then near its perihelion.

planets do not go through all phases each synodic period, although Mars on occasion is noticeably gibbous in shape, about like the moon three days before or after the full phase.

The rotational period of Mars can be established with high precision, since the distinctive surface features are not often obliterated by atmospheric phenomena. The period is known to ± 0.01 second; its approximate value is $24^h 37^m$, a bit longer than our own day. The angle between the Martian equator and orbit plane is $25°$, very similar to the earth's obliquity of $23\frac{1}{2}°$; seasonal effects like ours may therefore be anticipated. The axis of rotation points to within a few degrees of Deneb, which is therefore the Martian north star.

The polar flattening of the planet is appreciable because of the relatively rapid rotation. Direct telescopic measurements of the angular polar and equatorial diameters show that the flattening is about one part in 80. Alternatively, since Mars has a close satellite, the oblateness gives rise to a rather rapid regression of the nodes of its orbit, an effect we studied in the last chapter in connection with the orbits of earth satellites. Observation of this effect permits us to deduce that the Martian oblateness is only about one part in 200, much less than that indicated by the telescopic measurements. Perhaps the discrepancy can be accounted for by the fact that the telescopic angular measurements refer to the Martian atmosphere, which is warmer and thus more distended in the equatorial latitudes than in the polar latitudes.

The diameter of Mars is 4200 miles, slightly more than half that of the earth. Here is a provocative departure from the steadily increasing sizes we have so far seen on moving out from the sun. The mass of Mars may be computed from Kepler's third law after observations of either one of its two satellites; it is 11 percent of the earth's. Its mean density is 4 gm/cm³, comparable with the densities of the other terrestrial planets.

The presence of an atmosphere on Mars can be established in a variety of ways. The most direct, perhaps, is the occasional detection of clouds forming and drifting slowly across the surface. Additional

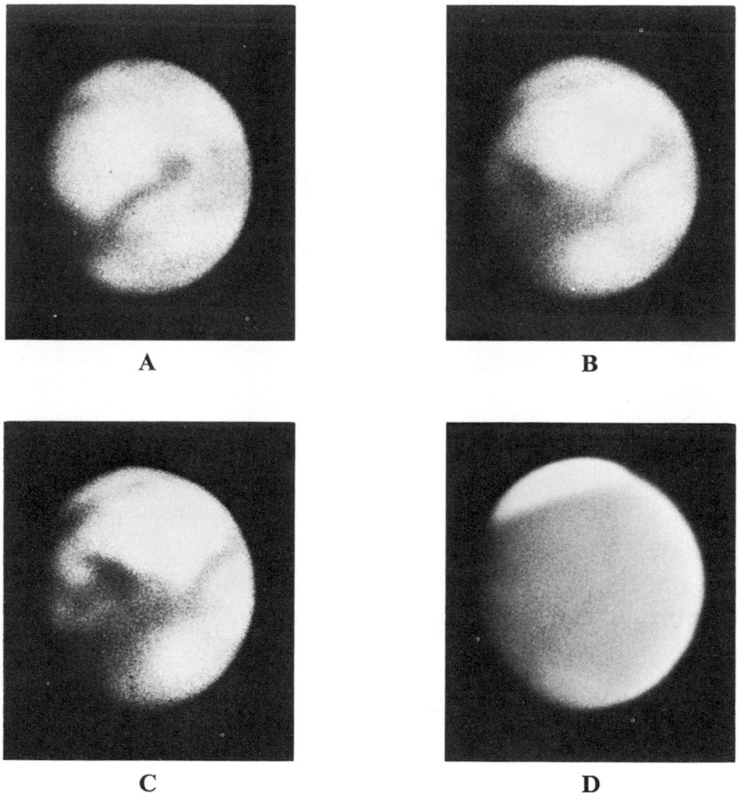

Fig. 8.4:2. Photographs A, B, and C show the rotation of Mars and were taken in red light. Photograph D was taken in violet light and shows the polar cap clearly. (*Mount Wilson and Palomar Observatories photographs*)

A   B

C   D

proof is afforded by spectral studies of the planet. Like Venus, Mars is known to have carbon dioxide in its atmosphere, about twice as much as in our own atmosphere, and perhaps substantially more. On the other hand, repeated unsuccessful searches have established that free oxygen cannot be more than 1 percent as abundant in the Martian atmosphere. Water vapor in low abundance appears to have been first detected with certainty in 1963, on spectra made at the Mount Wilson and Palomar Observatories. Because of the relatively low escape velocity of Mars, 3 mi/sec, it is certain that such light gases as hydrogen and helium cannot be retained. The only strong prospect for inclusion in the list of atmospheric elements is nitrogen, and estimates have been made that nitrogen accounts for as much as 98 percent of the Martian atmosphere. It is not possible to check this expectation observationally from the earth's surface because the spectrum of nitrogen lies in the ultraviolet. The atmospheric pressure at the surface of Mars is only 8 percent of its value on the earth, and possibly even less. But because on Mars it tapers off more gradually with height, the pressure on both planets is estimated to be the same at an altitude of about 11 miles. In addition to its gaseous component, the Martian atmosphere contains a more or less permanent concentration of fine-grained matter that results in a bluish haze. Also, yellow clouds occasionally cover much of the surface; they are presumably sandstorms blown aloft by the winds.

Many measurements have been made to find the surface temperature of Mars. At the equator it attains 70°F at perihelion and 30°F at aphelion. In midlatitudes temperatures range from 70°F to 30°F in the summer and from −20°F to −60°F in the winter. Near the poles the range is from 10°F to 50°F in the warmer months and from −150°F to −110°F in the colder months. Radio radiation by Mars, first detected in 1956, indicates an over-all average temperature near −70°F. As on the earth, the time of Martian perihelion nearly coincides with the beginning of summer in the southern hemisphere and aphelion with the beginning of winter there. Because of the greater orbital eccentricity of Mars, the southern seasons and temperatures are somewhat more extreme than the northern.

The surface features of Mars are of great interest, for on no other planet but the earth can we examine the ground in any detail. The albedo of Mars is intermediate between that of Mercury and the earth, about 0.15, and the general color is distinctly reddish. Viewed through the telescope, about 70 percent of the Martian surface is reddish or yellowish in hue, and the location of these bright areas is permanent. It is likely that this majority of the planet's surface area is sandy desert country, although just what kind of mineral predominates we do not know. The yellow clouds sometimes observed appear to be stirred up by winds blowing across the dry deserts, and the fact that no high mountains are known on Mars indicates that erosion by wind and sand may have played a major role in molding the surface we see today.

The most prominent features of the surface are the brilliant white polar caps. Their changing size offers striking testimony to the existence of seasons on Mars. At the end of winter in a given hemisphere the cloak of white may extend halfway from pole to equator. By the middle of spring the white area is shrinking rapidly toward the pole, until in summer there is scarcely any cap left. Near the beginning of autumn a tenuous shifting veil appears, whitish but with lower albedo than the springtime cap; the veil perseveres through late winter, when the brighter cap reappears. The sequence of events is reversed in the two hemispheres, and the shrinkage and growth of the southern cap is somewhat the more exaggerated, as would be expected from the greater severity of the seasons there. The receding polar caps of springtime are composed of water frozen out of the atmosphere in the form of snow or, more probably, hoarfrost; the overlying whitish curtain of autumn and winter is probably an obscuring cloud cover. At one time it was

THE PRINCIPAL PLANETS

thought that the surface polar caps were dry ice—solidified carbon dioxide. But the infrared reflection spectrum of the caps is unlike that of dry ice; instead it resembles that of snow or frost. Moreover, at the surface pressure of Mars it is much too warm, even at the poles, for carbon dioxide to exist in the solid state. What is more, it is now known that the atmosphere contains gaseous water vapor. Thus the aqueous composition of the caps seems definitely established. The thickness of

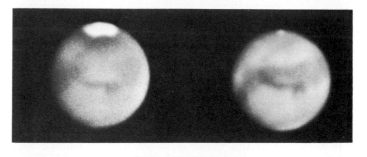

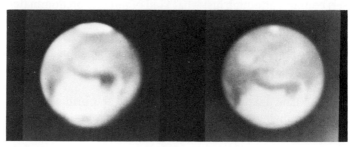

Fig. 8.4:3. Three pairs of photographs showing how the southern polar cap shrinks between spring and summer in the southern hemisphere of Mars. If dates like those of our northern hemisphere are assigned to the Martian southern hemisphere, the top pair shows conditions as of April 7 and then on June 29. Dates of the central pair are May 10 and July 31, and those of the bottom pair are April 29 and July 10. (*Photographs by E. C. Slipher, Lowell Observatory*)

the caps, however, cannot be great, for if it were they could not come close to evaporating in the summer. And spectrum analysis shows that the gaseous water vapor content must be very low, even though the major part of a winter polar cap must be transported through the atmosphere during the spring to form the cap of the other hemisphere. The polar caps are probably only a fraction of an inch thick. While the cap is receding toward the pole, a darkish fringe some hundreds of miles in width follows the cap; it is most prominent in spring when melting or evaporation of the frost is most rapid. With the prevailing conditions most of the snow of the polar caps sublimes directly into gaseous water vapor in the atmosphere. The receding darkish belt may be slightly moist ground due to the temporarily increased atmospheric humidity in these regions.

In addition to the variable polar caps and the permanent reddish deserts, there are dark areas on the Martian surface, found chiefly in the tropical latitudes. These grayish markings are relatively stable in location and shape, thus belonging to the surface rather than to the atmosphere, but they are not stable in reflectivity. The dark areas vary with the Martian seasons, those in a given hemisphere being darkest gray and most striking in the spring but fading in the fall. There has been great controversy among observers as to the color of the dark areas and the seasonal changes of color, with various hues of green being most frequently suggested. But there is no doubt about the seasonal changes in albedo.

The cyclic changes in the dark areas have usually been interpreted as being caused by the seasonal growth and decay of vegetation, and recent supporting evidence is that the reflection spectrum of the dark areas agrees with that of terrestrial lichens and mosses. More luxuriant plants could not withstand the rigors of life on Mars. An alternative hypothesis which accounts for the bizarre shapes of a number of these areas suggests that they arise from volcanic ash borne by the prevailing winds and deposited over a sizable area downwind from an active volcano. The changes in these dark areas are rooted in the seasonal variations of the strength and pattern of the Martian trade winds.

In 1877 Giovanni Schiaparelli announced that a number of "canali," channels or streaks, cross the reddish areas of Mars. Fine-structured features on a planet are extremely difficult to detect because of turbulence in our own atmosphere, and it is natural that there has been wide disagreement among observational astronomers about the nature of the finest details detectable on the Martian surface. Some have never seen these fine dark lines; others have mapped them and also found dark spots or oases at their intersections. Schiaparelli's label was unhappily translated as "canals," carrying the implication that these structures were products of intelligent life.

Granted for the moment that the canals do exist and are indeed straight, one can weave a wonderful tale: Mars has very little water, and yet the men of Mars must have water. But the water supply is limited; and what little there is lies in the polar caps where it is too cold to live. The Martians naturally choose to live in the tropics; they therefore build a complex of canals to bring water from the poles to the equator. But why build canals so wide? For the minimum resolvable Martian detail as observed telescopically from the earth is about 20 miles. Well, these lines are not the canals themselves, but vegetation growing under irrigation in reclaimed desert extending 10 miles on either side of the canals. The story reads well and logically; its chief difficulty is in its premise that canals exist and are straight. Photography from space probes will some day settle the point; as of 1963 the community of opinion is that there are myriad small-scale dark features on Mars, that they are distributed quite naturally, and that the human eye

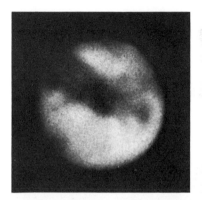

Fig. 8.4:4. Photograph and drawing of Mars at the same time, during the opposition of 1926. (*Lick Observatory photographs*)

and mind subconsciously join random dots into networks of lines—giving rise to the picture of a canal-crossed Mars.

Apart from the earth, Mars probably provides a better abode for life than any planet in the solar system. Even so, the prospect is not pleasant: atmospheric pressure much lower than atop Mount Everest, average temperature very low, a desert-like surface in most places, with occasionally vigorous sandstorms. The existence of some vegetation, of hardy type, appears probable. But aside from the possibility of lichens and mosses, there is no evidence for the presence on Mars of less hardy flora or of any kind of fauna—including man.

Accompanying Mars in its journey around the sun are two tiny satellites, Phobos and Deimos, discovered in 1877 by Asaph Hall at the U.S. Naval Observatory. The orbits of both are nearly circular, described in the usual easterly direction, and nearly in the plane of the Martian equator. Phobos is closer to its parent than any other known natural satellite, 5800 miles from the center of Mars and thus only 3700 miles above the surface. Since its orbital period of 7^h39^m is much less than the rotational period of Mars, Phobos rises in the west and sets in the east. The regression of its nodes about every two years permits computation of the polar flattening of Mars. Deimos is farther from its parent, and its orbital period of 30^h18^m is so close to the rotational period of Mars that it crosses the meridian at any point on Mars only once every five Martian days. Both satellites are too small to be resolved as disks even by large telescopes; their sizes can be estimated approximately, however, from their brightness. Deimos sends us only about one-millionth as much reflected sunlight as does Mars. If we assume the albedos to be the same, the area of Deimos is thus only one-millionth that of Mars, and the ratio of their radii or diameters is the square root of this, or one-thousandth. Deimos is accordingly only some 4 miles in diameter. If our assumption about the albedo is wrong by a factor of 2, for example, the estimated diameter is wrong only by a factor of $\sqrt{2}$. Phobos is somewhat larger, perhaps 8 or 10 miles in diameter. Seen from the Martian surface, Phobos would at most be one-third the angular diameter of our moon seen from the earth, and not nearly as bright. Deimos would be a starlike object, much fainter, but nevertheless somewhat brighter than Venus seen from the earth. There is some evidence that the orbital period of Phobos is decreasing with time, reminiscent of the behavior of close earth satellites. The effect could be caused by atmospheric drag, although it is hard to imagine an atmosphere dense enough to exert appreciable effect on a body of such large mass.

THE JOVIAN PLANETS

5. Jupiter

BEYOND THE great gap where the asteroids roam moves the largest planet of the solar system. With mean distance 5.2 a.u., more than three times that of Mars, Jupiter's orbital period is just under 12 years. It has a synodic period of 399 days, and successive oppositions occur one constellation further east along the zodiac. The orbital eccentricity and inclination are typically small, 0.05 and 1.3° respectively. Jupiter is yellowish in color and brighter than any planet except Venus or occasionally Mars; at opposition its angular diameter is nearly 1′. The oblateness of the planet is 1/15, large enough to be noticeable at the telescope. The rapid rotation implied by this flattening is confirmed by measurement of cloud features in its atmosphere; with a period of less than 10 hours, Jupiter spins faster than any other principal planet. Unlike anything we have encountered thus far, however, the deduced rotational period depends on the feature observed. A great equatorial belt, between latitudes 10°N and 10°S, has a rotational period of about 9^h50^m, while other parts of the planet have periods of about 9^h55^m, with the northern hemisphere turning slightly more slowly than the southern. The equatorial region thus comprises a vast current moving east at about 250 miles per hour relative to the rest of the clouds. The rotational axis is tipped only 3° to the perpendicular of the orbital plane, so that seasonal effects are negligibly small.

The equatorial diameter of Jupiter is 89,000 miles, about 11 times that of the earth, whereas the mass, established from observations of the Jovian satellites, is 318 times that of the earth but only about one-thousandth that of the sun. Although small compared with the sun,

Fig. 8.5:1. Jupiter, photographed in red light with the 200-inch telescope. Note the polar flattening. The largest satellite, Ganymede, is at the upper right, and its shadow is cast on the planet. (*Mount Wilson and Palomar Observatories photograph*)

Jupiter is more than twice as massive as all the other planets put together. Like the other outer planets, its average density is relatively low, only 1.3 times that of water. Thus the internal structure of Jupiter is very different from the earth's, for a good share of the outer layers of the planet must be of substantially lower density than water to offset a high-density central core. An earlier opinion was that a rocky metallic core is surrounded by a thick shell of compressed ices, which in turn is overlain by an extensive shell of lower density. The outermost parts of this final shell comprise the gaseous atmosphere, but not very far beneath the outermost clouds the material is solidified by the pressure of the overlying layers. More recent calculations, however, support the idea that Jupiter's over-all composition is similar to the sun's, chiefly hydrogen with some helium, and that hydrogen far inside the planet is solid and of very high density owing to the enormous compression at these deep layers.

Two gases, methane (CH_4) and ammonia (NH_3), have been definitely identified in the spectrum of Jupiter, and the presence of molecular hydrogen (H_2) has been suggested. Thus, whether or not the whole of Jupiter is chiefly composed of hydrogen atoms, the known molecules of the atmosphere certainly are. Evidence obtained during the 1952 occultation of a star by Jupiter has established indirectly that the dominant components of the outer atmosphere are helium and molecular hydrogen. The temperature of the planetary atmosphere is somewhere in the vicinity of $-200°F$, which means that it is "hot" enough for hydrogen, helium, and methane to be in the gaseous state. The ammonia, however, is largely in the solid state, with only enough in the vapor state to make its marks on the spectrum.

The shifting clouds of Jupiter are believed to be composed of tiny ammonia crystals afloat in the gaseous atmosphere. A telescopic view of the planet shows the striking banded structure of the clouds, with alternate light and dark bands running fairly parallel to the equator. Jovian meteorology, like the earth's, is demonstrably affected both by rotation and by the different solar heating at different latitudes. The darker bands are thought to be clouds riding lower in the atmosphere than the brighter cloud belts. Unquestionably, the most celebrated feature observed on Jupiter is the Great Red Spot, which has been known for over a century and perhaps for nearly three centuries. It is an oval spot centered near latitude 20° or 25°S, with an area a few times greater than the entire surface area of the earth, and participating in the rotation of the planet. Sometimes it is invisible, but its location is marked by a gouge in the adjacent bands of cloud. At its most conspicuous it has been called "brick-red" and "pale carrot," although "slightly pinkish" would probably be more apt. One suggestion is that the Great Red Spot originates in some deep-seated volcanic disturbance that sends fine-grained material into the clouds, but the rotational period of the Spot has varied slightly over the years, causing it to drift erratically many hundreds of degrees of longitude one way or the other from any possible "fixed" point on the solid planet beneath.

Radio radiation from Jupiter was discovered in 1955. The most intense components are found at the longer wavelengths and are quite variable with time. The signals are intermittent bursts lasting for a second or so, the group of bursts lasting about an hour. They reveal a longer periodicity equal to the rotational period of the nonequatorial portions of Jupiter's surface, thus apparently occurring on localized parts of the planet. The period of rotation is very well defined at $9^h55^m31^s$, but the cause of this very energetic static on meter wavelengths is unknown. At centimeter wavelengths Jupiter radiates much less strongly and like a well-behaved body whose temperature is near

−200°F. At intermediate wavelengths the radio radiation from the giant planet is probably emitted by charged particles that are far above the surface and are running back and forth in a cage created by a reasonably strong Jovian magnetic field.

Not only is Jupiter the biggest and most massive planet, but it has the largest satellite system as well. Twelve moons are known in all, of which the four bright ones were found by Galileo in 1610 and four of the faint ones by Seth Nicholson during the present century at the Mount Wilson Observatory. The four Galilean satellites range in period from less than 2 days to nearly 17 days; they are designated by Roman numerals, starting with the innermost. Their orbits are almost precisely circular and in the plane of the Jovian equator. The brightest, III, would be an easy object for the unaided eye if it were not always within

Fig. 8.5:2. Venus in conjunction with Jupiter and the Galilean satellites, 1916. (*Yerkes Observatory photograph*)

6′ of its overwhelmingly bright parent. It is the largest of the lot, slightly exceeding Mercury in diameter; and its mass, determined from its disturbances of the orbits of the other satellites, is about twice as great as the moon's. The other three Galilean satellites are generally similar to III, but somewhat smaller and lighter. Each of the four varies slightly in brightness with a period equal to its orbital revolution; it is therefore clear that each is tidally coupled to parent Jupiter.

The four great satellites showed Galileo and Kepler a solar system in miniature, and in addition their behavior gave the earliest indication that the velocity of light is not infinite. The seventeenth-century Danish astronomer Olaus Roemer found that the orbital periods of the satellites varied rhythmically every synodic period of 399 days, being longer than average when Jupiter was 90° or so east of the sun and setting near midnight, but shorter than average when Jupiter was west of the sun and rising about midnight. In 1675 he interpreted this curious effect as being caused by the finite speed of light. While a Jovian satellite circles once, the earth moves from *A* to *B* in Fig. 8.5:3; its observed period is too long because the second light signal has to travel a greater distance than the first. A few months later the motion of the earth from *C* to *D* causes an apparent diminution of period. Roemer thus simultaneously established the finite velocity of light and gave the earliest proof that the earth revolves around the sun. Today, knowing the velocity of light with high precision and using the phenomena of Jupiter's satellites to determine the time light takes to cross the earth's

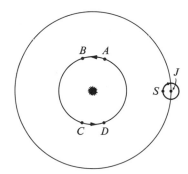

Fig. 8.5:3. The orbital period of a Jovian satellite serves as an impartial clock. Its orbital period as observed from the moving earth varies slightly during the year because the velocity of light is finite.

orbit (about 16 minutes), we can deduce the length of the astronomical unit with fair precision.

Because the Galilean satellites, Jupiter, and the earth all move in very nearly the same plane, we can witness an entertaining variety of transits and occultations of these satellites in a telescope of fairly small size. When Jupiter is 90° east of the sun, for example, as in Fig. 8.5:4,

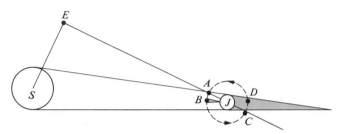

Fig. 8.5:4. Observing the satellites of Jupiter.

and a satellite is at *A*, we see it as a bright dot in *transit* across the Jovian disc. Later, at *B*, the satellite is still bright but clear of the planet, while its shadow moves across Jupiter as a black dot; this is a *shadow transit*. At *C* the satellite is in *occultation* behind Jupiter. Finally, at *D*, it is clear of the planet but experiences an *eclipse* in Jupiter's shadow and is thus invisible to us for a time.

Of the eight faint satellites, one moves very close to Jupiter with an orbital period of only half a day. Three of the remainder form a group having orbital periods of about eight months, and the outer four are so far from Jupiter that they take roughly two years to move around it. The eccentricities and inclinations of these four outermost satellites are moderately large and are variable because of the very strong perturbing force of the sun. Moreover, they have retrograde orbits, something we have not previously encountered in the solar system. Although it has been suggested that some of them may be asteroids that Jupiter has stolen away from the sun, it is also possible that these outer moons have accompanied Jupiter since the formative days of the solar system and that their strange orbits result from conditions existing at that early time.

6. Saturn

NEARLY TWICE as far from the sun as Jupiter, Saturn, the ringed planet, moves around the sun at a mean distance of 9.5 a.u. once every 29.5 years, in an orbit with eccentricity 0.06 and inclined 2.5° to that of the earth. Its synodic period is 378 days, exceeding the year by less than two weeks. Saturn is yellowish in color and, although never rivaling Sirius, is always among the brightest objects in the sky; it is the outermost of the planets known in ancient times.

Saturn spins on its axis every 10^h14^m, with variations reminiscent of Jupiter's. The Doppler effect shows a somewhat longer period of rotation at the higher latitudes. The equatorial plane is inclined to the orbital plane by some 27°, a bit more than for the earth and Mars. A consequence of the rapid rotation is the marked flattening of the planet; the ellipticity, easily noticed at the telescope, measures one part in 10 and is more pronounced than for any other planet.

Saturn's equatorial diameter is 74,000 miles and its mass, found from the satellite family, is 95 times that of the earth, but only 30 percent of Jupiter's. The mean density sets a record among the planets: only 0.7 times that of water. The internal structure of Saturn resembles that of Jupiter, the dominant constituent probably being solid hydrogen. Saturn's atmosphere shows methane and ammonia in its spectrum, but the amount of ammonia gas is much less than on Jupiter. Because of its greater distance from the sun, Saturn's atmosphere is colder,

Fig. 8.6:1. Saturn and its ring system, photographed with the 100-inch reflector. (*Mount Wilson and Palomar Observatories photograph*)

so that more of the ammonia is in the frozen crystal form. The planet has dark and light cloud bands, preventing us from seeing any sort of solid surface. Temperature measurements, including radio observations, indicate a value near $-250°F$.

Although similar to Jupiter in most characteristics, Saturn is unique among the planets in possessing a ring. Surrounding the planet and concentric with it is an extensive but very thin discoidal structure, lying precisely in the plane of Saturn's equator. Its shape is similar to that of a deflated inner tube. Galileo had noticed that the image of Saturn was unusual in shape, with ears; the ringed nature of the append-age was discovered later in the seventeenth century by the Dutch scientist Christian Huygens. Not long afterward Giovanni Cassini found a circular black gap in the disk, and other less prominent divisions have been reported since. If we were to take a trip outward from the center of Saturn in the equatorial plane, we would leave the cloud tops of the planet itself after traveling 37,000 miles; 7000 miles beyond we would enter the innermost parts of the ring. This region is sometimes called the *dusky ring* because of its dimness as viewed from the earth. Some 12,000 miles farther we would enter the middle or *bright ring*; after 16,000 more miles we would come to Cassini's division, 3000 miles wide. The final leg of our trip, through the *outer ring*, would

THE PRINCIPAL PLANETS

Fig. 8.6:2. Saturn at opposite places in its orbit every 15 years. At these times the rings are most open; at intermediate times they are seen edge-on.

Fig. 8.6:3. Photographs showing various aspects of Saturn and its ring system. (*Photographs by E. C. Slipher, Lowell Observatory*)

consume about 10,500 miles. The total radius of the ring system is thus about 85,500 miles, or 2.3 times the equatorial radius of Saturn.

Because the ring system maintains the same plane in space as Saturn sweeps around the sun, we in the inner part of the solar system sometimes see the northern side of the planet, and sometimes the southern, as shown in Fig. 8.6:2. Every 15 years the time is right to observe the rings edge-on, and at these times the ring system appears telescopically as an extremely thin line. It is estimated that the structure is less than 10 miles thick, and is perhaps only a few inches thick. Even if we adopt the larger figure, the ratio of thickness to over-all diameter, 10 mi/ 171,000 mi = 1/17,100, is several times smaller than the ratio of thickness to length for a sheet of typewriter paper. The material of the ring reflects sunlight well, and when the system is widest open it is nearly twice as bright as Saturn itself. When edge-on to the earth, however, the ring contributes scarcely any light. Therefore Saturn's brilliance as seen by the unaided eye varies periodically every 15 years.

The ring is not solid, for on occasion background stars can be seen through it, the diminution of the starlight varying as Saturn and ring spend several hours crossing in front of the star. Doppler measurements of the speed of the ring material show that the inner parts move at higher speed than the outer parts, quite unlike the behavior of a rotating solid disk. Moreover, the measured speeds are in accordance with Kepler's third law, showing that the ring system is composed of a swarm of individual particles, each one of which has a circular orbit in the plane of Saturn's equator. Because of our great distance from the scene, we witness it as a continuous sheet, just as we do the Milky Way or a plume of smoke. The sizes of these individual moonlets cannot of course be directly measured, but the reflection spectrum of the rings suggests that the particles are tiny crystals of snow or ice.

It is likely that the ring is material which, at the time of Saturn's formation, had no chance of agglomerating to become an ordinary satellite. The tidal force exerted by a parent planet decreases as the inverse cube of the distance from the planet. Thus Saturn's tidal force is weak at a large distance and is unable to prevent material from drifting together to form a normal satellite. But inside a spherical zone with radius about 2.5 times that of the parent planet, the tidal force exceeds the mutual gravitational attractive force of two moonlets in contact, thus preventing them from staying together. The outermost parts of the ring system are at 2.3 Saturn-radii from the center of the planet, whereas the innermost normal satellite, Mimas, is at 3.2 Saturn-radii, affording a quantitative foundation for the validity of these ideas.

The precise circularity of the orbits and their extreme confinement to the equatorial plane are probably explained by mutual collisions of the particles. If, long ago, individual orbits were inclined, then ultimately each upbound particle would run into a downbound particle, on the average reducing the orbital inclinations. If the orbits were at one time eccentric, each outbound particle would finally hit an inbound one, on the average reducing the eccentricities. When the process had continued for a sufficiently long time, the state of affairs would become much as we see it today. The varying brightness of the ring with distance from the planet indicates differences in the number density of particles. The variations result from two principal effects: the original distribution of the material and the perturbing effects of Saturn's satellites. The period of a particle in Cassini's division is one-half that of Mimas, one-third that of Saturn's second satellite, and one-fourth that of the third; the effect of the satellites is to remove objects moving in this zone and to place them into orbits of a different size. Other less pronounced gaps in the ring system correspond to other simple fractions of the orbital periods of the inner satellites.

Saturn has nine known satellites, of which Titan is by far the largest. Sixth in distance from the planet, Titan has an orbital period of about 15 days and is approximately the size of Mercury. It is massive enough and far enough from the sun to retain an atmosphere; and observation has indeed established the presence of methane in the spectrum of Titan. Out to Titan, the satellite orbits are nearly circular and nearly in the plane of Saturn's equator and ring system. Further out the regularity is less, culminating in a retrograde orbit with period 1.5 years for the most remote satellite, Phoebe. Several of the satellites vary cyclically in brightness, indicating that they, like the moon, are tidally coupled to their parent. The most extreme variation is that of the eighth satellite, Iapetus, whose brightness and hence albedo varies by a factor of 5; one side of its surface thus differs rather drastically from the other.

7. Uranus

UNLIKE THE planets we have considered up to this point, the three outer planets have become known only in recent times. The first and innermost of the discovered planets is Uranus, found by the great English astronomer William Herschel in 1781. Off and on for about a century prior to this time various people had observed and recorded Uranus as a star; indeed it is just comfortably visible to the unaided eye. Herschel was the first to notice, with his 7-inch reflector, that it looked distinctly different from a star; and its subsequent slow motion against the stellar background soon established it as a member of the solar system. Twice as far from the sun as Saturn, Uranus has a sidereal period of 84 years and a synodic period of 369 days. The orbital semimajor axis is 19.2 a.u., eccentricity 0.05, and inclination 0.8°. The rotational period, established by the Doppler effect in the spectrum and confirmed by small periodic changes in brightness, is about 10^h49^m. The attendant oblateness is hard to measure because of the great distance of Uranus, but is approximately 1/15. The equator of the planet is inclined 98° to the plane of its orbit; viewed from far north of the solar system, Uranus would therefore be spinning in the retrograde or clockwise sense. Because the inclination is not far from 90°, the sun is on occasion nearly overhead at the north pole of Uranus; 42 years later it is almost in the zenith at the south pole.

The diameter of Uranus is about 30,000 miles, intermediate between the terrestrial planets and Jupiter and Saturn. With a mass nearly 15 times the earth's, the mean density of Uranus is 1.3 gm/cm^3, the same as Jupiter's. The spectrum of Uranus shows the presence of methane and of molecular hydrogen. Ammonia has not been detected; it would be almost entirely frozen out at such a great distance from the sun. It is likely that we see only the top of a cloudy atmosphere, as on Jupiter and Saturn. Presumably, too, the outer planets contain much hydrogen inside as well as at their visible cloudy surfaces.

Uranus has five known satellites, the most recently discovered one, Miranda, having been found by Gerard Kuiper in 1948. The orbital periods of the satellites range from 1.4 days to 13.5 days. They com-

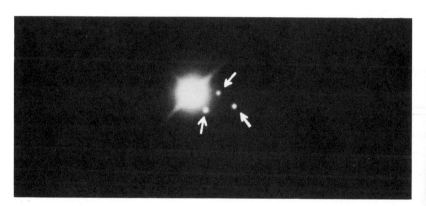

Fig. 8.7:1. Uranus and three of its satellites, photographed with the 120-inch reflector. (*Lick Observatory photograph*)

prise a beautifully regular system in that their circular orbits are in the equatorial plane of their parent and they are thus all inclined 98° to the orbital plane of Uranus. Since the satellites are very faint, their estimated diameters average only a few hundred miles.

8. Neptune

THE DISCOVERY of Neptune in 1846 was a major triumph of mathematical astronomy. After the discovery of Uranus and the subsequent uncovering of many prior observations of that planet, it was found that no given orbit would quite satisfy all of the observed positions of the planet, even when the disturbing gravitational effects of Jupiter and Saturn were accounted for. Uranus simply did not move quite as it was supposed to during the early years of the nineteenth century. Some astronomers thought there might be a defect in Newton's law of gravitation, but it occurred to two young men, John Couch Adams in England and Urbain Leverrier in France, that another unknown planet might be responsible for pulling Uranus off course. Unknown to one another, both men labored long to calculate how massive such a planet must be and approximately where and how it must be moving in order to explain the divergence of Uranus from its predicted track. Although Adams completed his work earlier, the Astronomer Royal of England pigeonholed his request that a telescopic search be made in a given small area of the sky. Ultimately, the Astronomer Royal asked an astronomer at Cambridge to make the search; the latter complied and actually saw Neptune, but without knowing until much later that the object was an intruder among the stars. On the continent Leverrier completed his theoretical work and sent his prediction to Johann Galle in Berlin, who found eighth-magnitude Neptune that night in less than an hour's time and within one degree of its predicted place in Aquarius. Leverrier and Adams share the honors of this celebrated discovery.

Neptune's mean distance from the sun is 30.1 a.u., and its orbital period is 165 years. Its orbit is inclined 1.8° to the plane of the earth's, with eccentricity only 0.009. The planet spins every 16 hours, as established from the Doppler effect in the spectrum; the angle between its equator and orbit is about 30°. The disk of the planet is too small for the oblateness to be measured, but the motion of the nodes of Neptune's inner satellite shows that the oblateness is intermediate in amount—less than that of the other Jovian planets but greater than that of any of the terrestrial planets. The mass of Neptune is known both from its perturbation of Uranus and from its own two satellites; it is 17 times that of the earth. Its diameter is about 28,000 miles, and its mean density thus about 2.2 gm/cm³. Physically, Neptune is a twin to Uranus. Its atmosphere contains methane in large abundance. It probably resembles Uranus internally also.

Two known satellites circuit Neptune. Triton is the brighter and was discovered by the English astronomer William Lassell a few weeks after Galle's first look at the planet. Triton moves around its parent in the retrograde direction every six days; it is about the size of the moon. Nereid was discovered by Kuiper in 1949; it is much smaller and its motion is direct, with orbital period 359 days. Nereid is distinguished by having an orbital eccentricity of 0.76, the largest of any known satellite in the solar system.

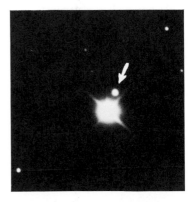

Fig. 8.8:1. Neptune and Triton, photographed with the 120-inch telescope. (*Lick Observatory photograph*)

THE ENIGMATIC PLANET

9. Pluto

THE OUTERMOST known planet was discovered in 1930 by C. W. Tombaugh at the Lowell Observatory, culminating a long photographic search. Many years previously, Percival Lowell had studied the slight divergences between the observed and predicted motions of Uranus and Neptune and had calculated where the unknown mass responsible for these effects might be found. More than two decades later, after Lowell's death, the elusive planet was located in Gemini, not very far from the predicted position.

Pluto's mean distance from the sun is 39.5 a.u., and its orbital period is 248 years. Its orbit is inclined by 17°, setting a record for the nine principal planets. Its eccentricity also sets a record at 0.25; at aphelion Pluto is nearly 50 a.u. from the sun, whereas at perihelion it is slightly closer to the sun than Neptune is. There is no present danger of the two planets colliding, however, for because of Pluto's large inclination the orbital rings are at no point closer than 2.6 a.u. The enigmatic planet varies slightly in brightness; its rotational period has accordingly been established at 6.4 days, which is far longer than any of the other outer planets.

The diameter of Pluto is exceedingly difficult to measure because of its great distance from the earth. Its size probably lies between that of Mercury and Mars, with a diameter near 3600 miles. Based on its gravitational disturbances of the other distant planets, its mass was at one time estimated as about equal to the earth's. But this value, coupled with the small diameter, implies that the mean density of Pluto is

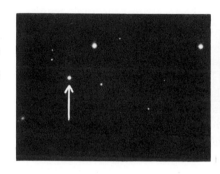

Fig. 8.9:1. The motion of Pluto in 24 hours, recorded by the 200-inch Hale telescope. (*Mount Wilson and Palomar Observatories photographs*)

about five times that of lead. More probably the mass is much less than the earth's. Neither surface details, atmospheric gases, nor satellites have been observed.

Pluto differs drastically from the Jovian planets: it is far smaller and slower in rotation than any body beyond the asteroid belt. The uniqueness of its orbital path, approaching Neptune's orbit on occasion, has given rise to the idea that Pluto at one time was a satellite of Neptune. Both its small size and the long length of its day confirm the suspicion that Pluto was once a comrade of Triton and Nereid.

Fig. 8.9:2. Small sections of the plates on which C. W. Tombaugh discovered Pluto. The left photograph was made on January 23, 1930, and the right photograph six months later. (*Lowell Observatory photographs*)

PLANETARY DATA

TABLE 8.10:1 presents some of the orbital characteristics and physical characteristics of the nine principal planets. Mean distances, periods, and synodic periods are rounded off to three-figure accuracy; eccentricities are given to the nearest thousandth and inclinations to the nearest tenth of a degree. Most of these values are known with far greater precision than listed here. Planetary diameters are given in terms of the earth's diameter as a standard. Masses are also given with reference to the earth's mass as a standard. The two unknowns in the table are the mass of Pluto and the rotational period of Venus. The latter probably lies near 250 days. If we assume the mean density of Pluto to be 4 gm/cm^3, which is typical of small planets and big satellites, the mass of Pluto can be estimated to be about 0.07 of the earth's.

TABLE 8.10:1.   The Principal Planets

Symbols at the head of each successive column are: a, mean distance from the sun in astronomical units; P, orbital period in years; P_{syn}, synodic period in days; e, eccentricity of orbit; i, inclination of orbit to plane of ecliptic; D, equatorial diameter in terms of the earth's; M, mass in terms of the earth's; P_{rot}, rotational period.

Name	a	P	P_{syn}	e	i	D	M	P_{rot}
Mercury	0.387	0.241	116	0.206	7.0°	0.38	0.054	88.0^d
Venus	0.723	0.615	584	0.007	3.4°	0.97	0.81	250^d?
Earth	1.00	1.00	—	0.017	—	1.00	1.00	23.9^h
Mars	1.52	1.88	780	0.093	1.9°	0.53	0.11	24.6^h
Jupiter	5.20	11.9	399	0.048	1.3°	11.2	318	9.8^h
Saturn	9.55	29.5	378	0.056	2.5°	9.47	95	10.2^h
Uranus	19.20	84.0	370	0.047	0.8°	3.75	15	10.8^h
Neptune	30.09	165	367	0.009	1.8°	3.50	17	15.7^h
Pluto	39.5	248	367	0.247	17.1°	0.45	0.07?	6.4^d

TABLE 8.11:1 contains a few data on the 31 known natural satellites. The mean distances from the parent planet and the orbital periods are given to two-figure accuracy only. The diameters of the larger satellites are deduced from measurements of angular diameter made with large telescopes. The estimates for the smaller ones are uncertain; each value is computed from the measured amount of sunlight that the satellite reflects to the earth and from some assumption as to its albedo. The faint satellites of Jupiter are designated by Roman numerals in order of discovery; in the table they are listed in order of increasing distance from their parent planet.

TABLE 8.11:1. The Natural Satellites

Symbols at the head of each successive column are: a, mean distance from the parent planet in thousands of miles; P, orbital period in days; D, diameter in miles.

Name	a	P	D
EARTH			
Moon	240	27	2200
MARS			
Phobos	5.8	0.32	10 $\pm$
Deimos	15	1.3	5 $\pm$
JUPITER			
V	110	0.5	100 $\pm$
I—Io	260	1.8	2100
II—Europa	420	3.6	1800
III—Ganymede	670	7.2	3100
IV—Callisto	1200	17	2900
VI	7100	250	70 $\pm$
VII	7400	260	20 $\pm$
X	7400	260	10 $\pm$
XII	13000	630	10 $\pm$
XI	14000	700	10 $\pm$
VIII	15000	740	20 $\pm$
IX	15000	760	10 $\pm$
SATURN			
Mimas	120	0.94	300 $\pm$
Enceladus	150	1.4	400 $\pm$
Tethys	180	1.9	700
Dione	230	2.7	800
Rhea	330	4.5	1100
Titan	760	16	3100
Hyperion	920	21	200 $\pm$
Iapetus	2200	79	700
Phoebe	8000	550	200 $\pm$
URANUS			
Miranda	81	1.4	100 $\pm$
Ariel	120	2.5	400 $\pm$
Umbriel	170	4.1	200 $\pm$
Titania	270	8.7	600 $\pm$
Oberon	360	13	500 $\pm$
NEPTUNE			
Triton	220	5.9	2500
Nereid	3400	360	200 $\pm$

PROBLEMS

1. Compute the perihelion distance of Mercury in miles. What is the angular diameter of the sun as seen from that point (recall that it is 32′ when viewed from 1 a.u.)?

2. Why is Venus brightest when it is neither at full phase nor at its closest approach to the earth?

3. Suppose an inferior planet like Venus has an infinite rotational period. Show with the help of a sketch that it appears to be rotating as observed from the earth at the time of inferior conjunction. Which limb is approaching us and which is receding?

4. Compare the distance of Mars and its relative brightness as seen from earth when at conjunction and at opposition. Assume that Mars lies at mean distance from the sun on each occasion, and recall that the intensity of a light source varies as the inverse square of its distance from the observer.

5. If we assume the albedo of Deimos to be the same as that of Mars, the estimated diameter of Deimos is about 4 miles. Supposing instead that Deimos has an albedo of 1.0, what is its calculated diameter?

6. Why are the Martian seasons more severe in the southern hemisphere than in the northern?

7. Dicuss the evidence that Mars has an atmosphere.

8. How many earths could fit into the volume occupied by Jupiter?

9. (a) Sketch the relative locations of sun, Venus, earth, and moon on an occasion when an observer on Venus could see each of the following: eclipse of moon by earth, occultation of moon by earth, shadow transit of moon, transit of moon. (b) About how often would a shadow transit of the moon be detectable telescopically from Venus?

10. Give the evidence that Saturn's ring system is not a continuous solid.

11. Uranus and Neptune are often called twins. What are some differences between them?

12. What is the evidence suggesting that Pluto may once have been a satellite belonging to Neptune?

13. Compare the satellite families and the nature of the atmospheres of the nine principal planets.

14. Describe several methods of determining the length of the astronomical unit.

9

ASTEROIDS, COMETS, AND METEORS

IN addition to the central sun and the nine principal planets with their moons, many other bodies roam the solar system. The asteroids, or minor planets, move chiefly in the great gap between Mars and Jupiter. The comets move throughout the solar system, but are prominent only when near the sun and therefore near us. Meteors, or shooting stars, become visible only on impact with our upper atmosphere, but they can reveal where they have been in space before being annihilated at the earth. In addition to these phenomena, there is the all-pervasive but tenuous interplanetary medium, about which much remains to be learned. We turn now to a study of these various topics, to the story of the less massive things in our system.

ASTEROIDS

1. Discovery and Names

THE MINOR planets are so small and distant that they nearly always appear starlike in the telescope—thus the name "asteroids" for these objects. The first of these little bodies was discovered on the first night of the nineteenth century, January 1, 1801, by the Italian astronomer, Giuseppi Piazzi, and was named Ceres. Apart from its faintness, this new object very nicely filled in the puzzling and long-known gap between Mars and Jupiter. Three other asteroids were discovered in the next half-dozen years, but no additional ones were then found for nearly four decades. With the advent of photography and wide-angle telescopes, many thousands of asteroids have been found since the turn of the century. A guided long-exposure photograph of a star field shows the distant stars as dots, but if any moderately bright asteroids are in the field, they easily reveal themselves because their images are short trails. The typical angular rate of motion of an asteroid at opposition is about 0.5′ per hour in the retrograde direction.

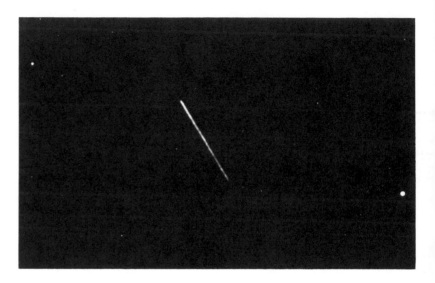

Fig. 9.1:1. The trail of Eros photographed by G. Van Biesbroeck with the 40-inch refractor. (*Yerkes Observatory photograph*)

Once the orbit of an asteroid is established, it is assigned a number; more than 1600 have been so designated. The discoverer has the option of naming the body; the earlier asteroids have mythological names, but these were soon exhausted. A few examples from the list are 1 Ceres, 151 Abundantia, 334 Chicago, 616 Elly, 1010 Marlene, 1383 Limburgia, and 1589 Fanatica. A few discoverers have not exercised their options, and these asteroids are simply referred to by their numbers.

2. Numbers and Orbits

ONLY ONE asteroid, 4 Vesta, is visible to the unaided eye, but some tens of thousands have been found on photographs, of which a much smaller number have known orbits. Probably 100,000 of these small bodies are within reach of present-day telescopes. The orbits of the known asteroids are chiefly confined to the zone between Mars and Jupiter, although some move outside that region. The average mean distance of the thousand or so biggest asteroids is 2.9 a.u. from the sun, and half of these have mean distances within $\frac{1}{4}$ a.u. of this average. A typical orbital period is therefore 5 years. The inclinations average about 10° and the eccentricities about 0.15. The region of space through which most asteroids roam is a doughnut-shaped volume centered on the sun and lying in the plane defined by the orbits of the principal planets. But there are some extreme exceptions: tiny Icarus at perihelion is only 0.23 a.u. from the sun and thus inside Mercury's orbit, whereas Hidalgo at aphelion is at 9.6 a.u., beyond Saturn. In spite of some highly inclined and highly eccentric orbits, however, not a single asteroid moves around the sun in a retrograde orbit. As in Saturn's ring system, there are vacancies at orbital periods that are simple fractions of Jupiter's period, for the repeated gravitational pull of the giant planet in the same direction moves any chance interloper out of these narrow zones, which are called *Kirkwood's gaps*.

3. Trojans

A DOZEN or more asteroids move so that they lie approximately at the vertex of an equilateral triangle whose other vertices are Jupiter and the sun and whose plane is that of the Jovian orbit. They are about equally divided between vanguards of Jupiter, leading by 60°, and rearguards, following by 60°. Achilles, found early in the present century, was the first discovered of the Trojan group. Long before, the French mathematician Joseph Lagrange had studied the problem of three bodies and demonstrated that any small body originally located in such a position would stay permanently in the same vicinity, providing no other gravitational disturbances interfered. Here is a most interesting example of a physical and mathematical theory preceding rather than following the observed facts, *confirmed by* the discovery of Trojans rather than devised to *account for* them.

4. Close Approaches to the Earth

ONCE IN A WHILE a relatively long asteroid trail is unexpectedly found on a photograph of a star field. The immediate implication is that the body in question, since it has moved through an appreciable angle in only an hour or so, is passing relatively close to the earth. Although no such object is known to have approached us nearer than the moon, Hermes came within half a million miles in 1937. Several other asteroids have also passed within a few million miles. These bodies were relatively faint, their diameters being estimated at about a mile. Such diminutive objects can of course be discovered only when relatively near the earth, although they are undoubtedly to be found throughout the asteroid belt. Even the close ones may not be discovered because the whole sky cannot be eternally patrolled by telescopic cameras. If, as a crude example, we estimate that one such small asteroid comes within a million miles of us each year, then the chance that any particular one will strike the earth is the ratio of the area of a circle with radius equal to the earth's (4000 miles) to that of a circle one million miles in radius. This chance is only about 1/60,000, so that such impacts would occur on the average once every 60,000 years. However, because our statistical data on close-approaching asteroids are very incomplete, this example has no necessary ring of authenticity.

5. Eros

KNOWN SINCE 1898, 433 Eros has an orbit with semimajor axis 1.5 a.u. and period 1.8 years. Its orbit is eccentric enough so that at a favorable opposition it can approach the earth within about 14,000,000 miles. At the approach in 1931 many observatories cooperated in photographing Eros; with a substantial base line between observatories, triangulation yielded an accurate distance to Eros. Comparison with the known orbit and hence known distance from the earth in astronomical units allowed yet another determination of the mean distance of the earth from the sun, accurate to perhaps ± 0.1 percent.

6. Sizes, Rotations, and Shapes

THE DIAMETER of Ceres, the largest asteroid, is 480 miles; altogether there are only 3 asteroids with diameters greater than 200 miles. A survey at the Yerkes and McDonald Observatories has shown that there are about 15 asteroids with diameters in the 100–200-mile range, some 100 in the 50–100-mile range, perhaps 400 in the 25–50-mile range, and roughly 2500 in the 12.5–25-mile range. The numbers continue to increase for the smaller sizes, but of course the discovery of very small asteroids is incomplete. Despite the rapid increase in numbers, most of the mass of asteroidal material is contained in the larger bodies, with the largest three asteroids probably containing more than half the combined mass of the entire belt.

The rotational period of an asteroid may be deduced after its light curve has been determined photoelectrically at the telescope, provided the asteroid is either spotted or nonspherical so that its brightness varies periodically. Rotational periods found in this way range from about 5 hours to perhaps 18 hours. Detailed studies of the light curves indicate that most of the light variation is caused by deviations from sphericity rather than by spottedness. An observer on the earth now sees more reflecting area, later less, as with nonspherical man-made satellites. The largest asteroids do not vary in brightness very greatly, suggesting that they are not far from spherical. Little Eros, however, on occasion changes in brightness by a factor of 4 in a few hours. Actual observations at the 1931 close approach established that Eros is roughly rod-shaped with a length of some 14 miles and a thickness of about 4 miles, rotating every 5^h16^m around an axis nearly perpendicular to its long dimension. When seen end-on, therefore, it reflects much less light to us than when seen broadside. Other small asteroids behave in more or less the same fashion; it is thus probable that many are rough-shaped, jagged fragments.

7. Origin

THE FACT that the larger asteroids are fairly spherical and many if not all of the small ones are irregular in shape lends credence to the idea that the solar system originally contained one or two dozen nearly spherical large asteroids moving around the sun in much the same kinds of orbits we see today. Although at any instant it is unlikely that any two of the orbit rings intersect, these light bodies are rather strongly affected by the gravitational pull of Jupiter; the eccentricities and inclinations change as the ages pass. Once in a great while, therefore, the orbit rings of two asteroids may intersect; should both of the bodies happen to be at the intersection at the same time, a collision will occur. Statistical calculation shows that in the history of the solar system it is highly probable that at least one such pair of big asteroids has collided.

The resultant jagged fragments of the collision leave the scene with various relative velocities, like a clay pigeon being shot in flight. Each fragment takes up its new orbit around the sun; the eccentricities and inclinations of some of the new orbits will be larger than those of the original colliding bodies. Moreover, when larger masses are fragmented into many smaller ones, the smaller ones collide with one another more frequently; these yield still smaller fragments, which in turn collide even more often. The picture emerges, then, of an asteroid belt in which a few large nearly spherical asteroids roam around without much prospect of damage; the small bodies they inevitably encounter are not energetic enough to break up their big fellows. The smaller fragments are, however, more likely to collide with other small ones and break up. There is thus a continuing pulverizing action, and we should expect to find asteroids of all different sizes, from the few large undamaged ones to very small bodies. The smallest discoverable asteroids are those that pass near enough to the earth to be modestly bright, and they are about a mile in diameter. But is there evidence of even smaller asteroidal bodies? We shall see later in this chapter that there is: it is likely that meteorites, the small bodies that penetrate the earth's atmosphere and strike the ground or ocean, are nothing other than ultrasmall asteroids.

COMETS

8. Appearance

Now AND THEN an impressive comet visits the neighborhood of the earth, usually appearing unheralded at an unexpected time and in an unexpected part of the sky. A typical visit lasts a few weeks or months and then the comet is gone. These bodies derive their name from the Latin *cometes*, meaning "long-haired"; and a look at a bright one tells why: surrounding a brilliant and almost stellar *nucleus* is a roundish fuzzy *coma* of light, and away from the coma stretches a less luminous *tail*, often many degrees in length. In earlier times comets were regarded as omens of death or disaster, for their nature was unknown and the unknown is feared. The opinion prevailed that they were things of the atmosphere, until Tycho Brahe's studies of the comet of 1577 established that its path through the stars was essentially the same as seen from various parts of Europe and thus that it was more distant than the moon. It is universally agreed today that comets, like planets and asteroids, are objects of the solar system.

9. Discovery and Names

AT THE PRESENT time an average of about ten comets are discovered each year, sometimes by amateur hunters who sweep the skies with small wide-angle telescopes, alert for any new fuzzy patch in the sky, but more often by astronomers who are examining a celestial photograph made for some different reason. Most comets are very faint at best; only about one a year is visible to the unaided eye as a dim patch of light. Perhaps once every five years a fairly conspicuous comet appears, and once or twice a century a comet outshines all celestial bodies except the sun and moon and is visible even in daylight.

These bodies are often named for their discoverers, such as Comet Arend-Roland, or for those who have done significant research on the object, such as Halley's Comet. Newly discovered comets are tempo-

Fig. 9.9:1. Comet Arend-Roland on April 25, 1957. (*Lick Observatory photograph*)

rarily designated in the order of discovery, 1956a being the first comet found in that year and Comet Arend-Roland being called 1956h. The final designation is in order of perihelion passage; thus Morehouse's Comet is also known as Comet 1908 III, because it was the third known comet to pass perihelion that year.

10. Parabolic Orbits

THE MAJORITY of newly discovered comets have nearly parabolic orbits; about three-fourths have eccentricities between 0.99 and 1.01. We shall soon see that a number of cometary orbits differ distinctively from the parabolic shape, but let us deal first with the more typical comets. Because of the law of areas, a body in a near-parabolic orbit sweeps through perihelion at great speed; for a perihelion distance of 1 a.u. the speed is 26 mi/sec, and for Comet 1882 II, which passed within 300,000 miles of the sun's surface, the perihelion speed was close to 300 mi/sec. Because of such high speeds and also because comets usually spend a good share of their visit in the daytime sky, it is sometimes difficult to obtain an adequate number of positional observations. Futhermore, the near-perihelion path of a high-eccentricity ellipse, of a parabola, and of a low-eccentricity hyperbola are very similar in shape.

It has nevertheless been established without doubt that some cometary orbits are definitely elliptical and others are certainly slightly hyperbolic. At first it would appear that the latter must be visitors from interstellar space, but closer study reveals that every known hyperbolic comet was previously in an elongated elliptical orbit. Before discovery each of these objects was perturbed by passing too close to one of the planets, usually Jupiter, and thrown into a one-way orbit, thus destined to leave the solar system for good. Thus, although comets are on occasion ejected *into* interstellar space, there is no known case of a capture *from* interstellar space. All of the many hundreds of known comets are or at one time were members of our planetary system.

The orbits of the nearly parabolic comets differ from those of the planets in another important way: they are inclined at all possible angles to the main plane of the solar system. Therefore about half of these objects move along retrograde paths. Not only are the orbital planes oriented at random, but also the high eccentricities indicate that the orbits are extremely large, with periods of thousands or millions of years. In such extremely elongated ellipses, the law of areas dictates that each comet spend the great majority of its time near aphelion, much too far away to be detected from the earth. The comets we are able to see, within only a few astronomical units of the sun, seem to represent but an infinitesimal fraction of a vast spherical cloud of such bodies extending tens or hundreds of thousands of astronomical units out from the sun.

11. The Pull of Jupiter

THE NEAR-parabolic comets all have periods that are longer than the millennia during which men have been recording events in the sky; each of the comets has been seen at only one passage. By contrast, somewhat over 40 comets have been observed at two or more perihelion passages; their periods are all less than two centuries, and the last 200 years is the approximate interval during which good records have been kept. They are referred to as the *periodic comets*. Their orbital planes are not at all distributed at random; among them only two are in retrograde motion, whereas three-quarters of them are inclined by less than 30° to the plane of the planets. This remarkable difference from the near-parabolic comets is elucidated when we notice that the orbital rings of many periodic comets come close to the orbit of massive Jupiter. On occasion, therefore, Jupiter and comet approach one another closely and the cometary orbit is modified by the gravitational attraction of the giant planet. We may imagine that all known comets at one time had long-period, near-parabolic orbits. A small number of those visiting the planetary realm passed close to Jupiter; some of them were perturbed into hyperbolic orbits and left the system; others had their periods greatly reduced and later made many more close approaches to Jupiter. Thus our most massive brother planet appears to have been responsible for many of the periodic comets, although the outer Jovian planets have had a minor effect too. Naturally, if Jupiter has been pulling comets into the inner parts of the solar system for several billion years, we would expect the evening sky to be ablaze with hundreds of short-period comets. It is not, however, and it is necessary to seek for competing processes that remove comets from membership in the solar system. Perturbation into a hyperbolic orbit is one such process; in addition, some comets are known to have disintegrated or evaporated, as we shall see later.

Of all the periodic comets known, Encke's Comet has the shortest known period, 3.3 years. With eccentricity 0.85, inclination 12°, and perihelion distance inside Mercury at 0.34 a.u., this comet has been observed at more than 40 returns to perihelion. The brightest of the periodic comets is Halley's. Its average period is 77 years, although the individual returns to perihelion have varied over a range of 5 years

Fig. 9.11:1. Halley's Comet, photographed from Honolulu on May 12 and May 15, 1910. (*Mount Wilson and Palomar Observatories photographs*)

because of planetary perturbations; it has eccentricity 0.97, inclination 162°, and perihelion distance 0.59 a.u. Records have been found for every return visit of this most celebrated comet since 240 B.C.; the first record goes back to 467 B.C. Halley's name is given to it because he was the first to establish that comets may return periodically; he noted the great similarity in the orbits of the bright comets in 1682, 1607, and 1531. The most recent visit of Halley's Comet was in 1910, and in 1948 it passed aphelion beyond Neptune; its next visit is scheduled for 1986.

12. Comet Groups

IN ADDITION to single comets, a few dozen small groups of comets are known, with two to six members in each. All of the members of any group have remarkably similar orbits, but the members cannot be the same comet periodically returning because they do not reappear at fixed intervals. The most celebrated example is the group of 1668, 1843, 1880, 1882, 1887, 1945, and 1963; the orbits are too similar to have arisen by chance. It seems certain this group long ago broke into fragments, each subsequently moving in a slightly different orbit and period, gradually separating from one another. This particular group has an unusually small perihelion distance, less than one solar diameter, and the 1882 member, which was visible in daylight, broke into four fragments which drifted slowly apart from one another while receding from the sun. Presumably these will some day reappear as four new comets. A close approach to the sun is not prerequisite to such subdivision of cometary nuclei; other comet groups are known which never approach the sun closer than 1 a.u.

13. Sizes and Masses

A BRIGHT comet is more voluminous than anything in the solar system. The roughly spherical coma is about the size of Jupiter on the average; in some comets it is only as large as the earth but in others is as large as the sun. Moreover, the diameter of a typical coma changes with distance from the sun. Small when far away, it attains maximum size at about 1 a.u. and then apparently diminishes again if perihelion is inside the earth's orbit. The central bright condensation of the coma is roughly 1000 miles in diameter, but the nucleus proper is estimated to be only 1 to 10 miles in diameter. The tail of a bright comet, on the other hand, stretches for 10 to 100 million miles out from the coma, an enormous fan-shaped appendage.

Although occupying an enormous amount of space, a comet has very little mass. Some have come near the earth and other planets, their motions being measurably perturbed by the planets. By contrast, however, no comet has ever perturbed a planetary orbit by any measurable amount. If a comet were very massive and came close to the earth, it would for example change the length of the year by changing our orbital period. Since no such modification has been observed, the mass of a typical comet must be less than 1/10,000 that of the earth. At its last visit, Halley's Comet passed directly between the sun and the earth, and nothing was seen against the solar disk. This negative result means that the comet is essentially transparent and that the nucleus of Halley's Comet is less than 50 miles in diameter. It seems likely that virtually all of the mass of a comet is in a small nucleus, with a mass no more than one-billionth that of the earth, and probably less. Thus these bodies are light but voluminous, and their average densities accordingly are extremely low. They are far more vacuous than the inside of a windbag.

14. The Stuff in a Comet

SINCE STARS are visible through the tail and even through the coma of a comet, it is clear that most of the volume is occupied by small, finely divided matter. Spectral studies reveal that a comet puts its own peculiar stamp on top of the solar spectrum; the latter shows

ASTEROIDS, COMETS, AND
METEORS

that comets shine in part by reflection of sunlight from small particles. In addition, however, the bright bands in a cometary spectrum show the presence of various kinds of individual molecules, such as C_2, CN, OH, NH, CH, CO^+, and N_2^+. These are all two-atom molecules composed of one or more of the relatively abundant elements hydrogen, carbon, nitrogen, and oxygen. They emit light as a consequence of absorbing radiation from the sun. A few metals, such as sodium, iron, nickel, and chromium, have also been detected in the spectra of comets near perihelion.

15. Comet Tails

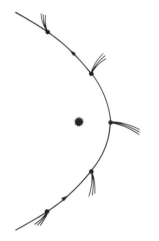

Fig. 9.15:1. The tail of a comet points generally away from the sun.

THE STRIKING feature of the tail of a comet is that it points generally away from the sun, as illustrated in Fig. 9.15:1. When the body is moving in toward perihelion, the tail follows more or less behind the coma, but at closest approach it is running beside the coma. By the time the comet is leaving the solar vicinity the tail leads the rest. Not only in this respect is the behavior of a cometary tail unlike that of a dog, but in addition the material of the tail moves continually outward from the coma. Photographs of bright knots and patches from night to night show that any given feature moves more or less rapidly away from the nucleus; thus the maintenance of a tail requires continual replenishment from the main body of the comet. It is further known that bright comets do not have tails except when they are within 2 or 3 a.u. of the sun.

The observed facts suggest strongly that the sun is completely responsible for the phenomenon of cometary tails and that something repels the particles away from the sun. Two agencies are responsible. (1) The radiant energy of the sun impacting on a particle exerts an outward force on it. If the particle is small enough, about 1/100,000 inch in diameter, this *radiation pressure* overbalances the attractive gravitational force exerted by the sun on the particle, and the particle leaves the solar system on a hyperbolic orbit. (2) Clouds of charged

Fig. 9.15:2. Four views of Brooks's Comet. Note especially the fine details of the tail in the October pictures. (*Yerkes Observatory photographs*)

atomic particles erupt from the sun, chiefly in directions not far from the plane of the planetary orbits. These clouds travel outward at speeds of hundreds or even thousands of miles per second and are responsible, among other things, for the auroras of our upper atmosphere. The rate of such solar outbursts varies with time, and the direction of ejection also changes from day to day. The outbound solar corpuscles interact with the charged particles of the coma and drag them away from the sun. Grossly but not in detail, the situation is similar to smoke driven downwind. A smoke particle emerging from a chimney is bombarded by air molecules whose average velocity vector is that of the wind, and the particle very soon is moving with the air. The interaction of charged solar and cometary molecules, on the other hand, is electrical in nature, and the details are not fully understood. It is certain, however, that both radiation pressure and *corpuscular pressure* play roles in producing cometary tails. The latter is responsible for some of the irregularities in their behavior.

16. The Nucleus

IT IS POSSIBLE to understand much of the perplexing behavior of comets in terms of the theory of Fred Whipple at the Harvard College Observatory. The typical nucleus of a near-parabolic comet is a small body, perhaps 1 to 10 miles in diameter, largely composed of various ices, such as water, ammonia, methane, and carbon dioxide. Mixed in with this conglomerate is a small proportion of metallic or stony lumps. As the nucleus moves in toward perihelion, the increasing solar radiation melts and evaporates some of the surface ices into the space surrounding the nucleus, and breaks the H_2O, NH_3, CH_4, and CO_2 into less complex molecules whose thumbprints we see in the cometary spectrum. These molecules and other small bits of matter comprise the coma, which travels along with the nucleus. Radiation and corpuscular pressure continually drive some of this material away to form the tail. Whipple suggests that the rocky and metallic nodules insulate the ices well beneath the surface, so that only about 1 percent or 0.1 percent of the nuclear mass is blown away at each perihelion passage. Some of this heat may be trapped for a time, later causing the explosive jets of material that are sometimes observed issuing from the nucleus.

17. Life Expectancy of a Comet

COMETS THAT never visit the inner solar system can survive indefinitely, for at great distances their ices will not melt. But the near-parabolic comets we see have perihelion distances averaging only about 1 a.u.; and since these comets lose part of their masses at each approach to the sun, they cannot survive more than a hundred or a thousand perihelion passages. At each return more of the surface ices evaporate; as time goes by, the nucleus will thus have an increasingly large percentage of its mass in the form of stony and metallic chunks which can survive the heat of the sun. Ultimately, there will be scarcely any meltable ices left, so that a comet which has made thousands of passes close to the sun should not have a large coma or appreciable tail.

ASTEROIDS, COMETS, AND
METEORS

Observation of the short-period comets shows that they are indeed devoid of tails; some look almost stellar in appearance. This evidence supports the thesis that most short-period comets have lost much of their mass and are gradually becoming swarms of stony and metallic fragments.

Although comets cannot withstand too many trips around the sun, we nevertheless still see them. It would at first seem that all comets ought to have been ruined by the sun during the past five billion years. The only explanation of how comets can still appear is that there is a continuing source of supply, that new ones appear at more or less the same rate that old ones fade away. To explain the origin of new comets, eruptions from the sun or from Jupiter have been suggested in the past. It seems likely, however, that there is a vast spherical reservoir extending 100,000 a.u. or more from the sun and containing many billions of comets. Every century we witness only an infinitesimal fraction of them—those few that happen to be diverted by the perturbations of passing stars into near-parabolic orbits with small perihelion distances.

METEORS

18. Frequency and Nature

ON A NIGHT when the sky is clear and dark, one can see five or ten shooting stars every hour. Each one looks like a star racing across the celestial sphere at a high angular rate and burning out a second or so after the start of its flight. Some of these meteors are brighter than others and leave temporary, faintly luminous wakes behind them; on very rare occasions an ultrabright *fireball* arcs across the sky, illuminating the whole landscape. The rapid angular motion of all these objects argues that they are relatively close to us, and triangulation of meteors from two points apart has established that they are indeed plunging into our upper atmosphere at the instant we see them.

Fig. 9.18:1. A meteor trail at the right and the Pleiades star cluster at the left. (*Yerkes Observatory photograph*)

An average meteor is a small, loosely bound aggregate of stony or dust-like grains, having a mass of roughly a gram, a density about one-tenth that of water, and a diameter of a fraction of an inch. This fragile flake pursues its own orbit around the sun until finally it and the earth reach the same place at the same time. The incoming flake first encounters, at a speed of many miles per second, the molecules of our upper atmosphere; surface atoms are knocked off the individual grains of dust, and collisions of these atoms with each other and with those of the air result in the emission of the light we see. The traveling zone of disturbed and emitting atoms is much larger than the meteor itself, probably many feet in diameter; it becomes visible to us at the level where the atmospheric density is sufficiently great to produce light that can be seen from the earth, 60 or 70 miles away. By the time the meteor has penetrated another 10 or 20 miles down through the atmospheric barrage, it has been consumed and burns out, thoroughly shattered and shredded into individual atoms and molecules and other microscopic bits. Fainter and smaller meteors die out about 50 miles above ground, whereas the brighter and larger ones survive down to 40 miles or so. Only the very rare larger objects, roughly the size of a basketball or larger, can survive the entire flight and reach the ground; these are the *meteorites*.

Other things being equal, the luminosity of a meteoric body is proportional to its mass; thus the meteorites are the brightest category. Somewhat smaller in size are the fireballs. Then come the far more frequent ordinary meteors, ranging in diameter down to a small fraction of an inch for the faintest ones that can be seen with the unaided eye. Even fainter objects are often seen through the telescope, at random times, dashing instantaneously across the field of view. A single observer can of course survey only a minute part of the earth's entire atmosphere, and when account is taken of this, the total number of meteors that it would be possible to see each day is estimated at about 100 million. Since most of them are small, however, their combined mass is only a few tons. The total mass of tiny telescopic meteors and even smaller specks is enormous; the combined daily mass accretion from them may amount to thousands of tons.

19. Techniques of Observation

To SEEK AN answer to what meteors are, it is necessary to gather statistics on where they come from, on the nature of their orbits before they end their days in our atmosphere. We saw in Chapter 7 that, if we know both the position and the velocity vector of a particle at a given moment, it is possible to calculate the characteristics of its orbit around the sun. Now, for any meteor we can observe, the spatial position is easy to establish, for it is simply the position of the earth in its orbit at that instant. Obtaining the amount and direction of the meteor's velocity, however, is more difficult.

One excellent method is that of double-station photography, in which by means of two wide-angle telescopic cameras, stationed 20 or 30 miles apart and aimed at a common volume of the upper atmosphere, synchronized time exposures are made. If the trail of a bright meteor occurs on both developed photographs, the three-dimensional track can be established by triangulation, as shown in Fig. 9.19:2. The beginning of the trail lies at a certain point among the stars, A', as

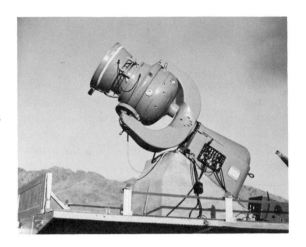

Fig. 9.19:1. A super-Schmidt meteor camera especially designed for recording the tracks of meteors across the sky. (*Harvard College Observatory photograph*)

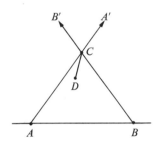

Fig. 9.19:2. Photographs of a meteor trial from stations A and B provide information for computing the three-dimensional track CD.

photographed at A; on the second photograph it is in the direction of B'; the spatial location of the beginning of the trail is thus at point C. Similarly, the end of the trail is found to be at D. In this way the *direction* from which the meteor came, the so-called *radiant*, is deduced. The *speed* may be found by spinning a propeller-like object in front of the camera at a known rate, interrupting the incident light 100 times per second, for example. The image of the meteor will thus be a long interrupted streak; from the measured angular separation of the breaks in the streak, the angular velocity can be calculated. Then, from the known distance to any point on the trail, the speed in miles per second may be found. Thus all the required information is at hand, and once the minor influence of the earth's own gravitational field is taken into account, the solar orbit of the meteor can be computed.

A second excellent method, developed since World War II primarily in England and Canada, is that of radar. Hundreds of times a second pulses of radio energy are bounced off the traveling cloud of ionized atoms surrounding an incoming mcteor, thereby giving a record of the distance of the meteor from the radar set at each instant of its flight. Simultaneous radar observations from three different stations allow the orbit to be calculated. Because these studies can be made by day or night, in fair weather or foul, they have amplified the knowledge that can be accumulated at visual wavelengths only on nights that are clear. A great merit of the technique is that radar can detect incoming particles far too small to be seen by the unaided eye or to be studied successfully with the telescope.

A third type of research employs sensitive detectors aboard rockets and earth satellites. A microphone, for example, counts the number of impacts of microparticles that strike with different values of momentum. Such spacecraft have sampled objects of very small mass—in the range

10^{-6} gram to about 10^{-10} gram. The diameters of these tiny meteors range from about 0.01 inch down to substantially less than 0.001 inch. In spite of the smallness of the individual particles, it appears definite that their great abundance more than makes up for individual size and that the solid matter collected by the earth is chiefly of this kind.

20. Speeds and Orbits

A PARTICLE belonging to the solar system and striking the earth must hit at a speed between 7 mi/sec and 45 mi/sec. The smaller figure is simply the escape velocity of the earth; a meteor striking at that speed started its fall at some distance from the earth but originally was at rest relative to it. The maximum figure is for a particle moving around the sun in a parabolic orbit in the plane of the earth's orbit, but in the retrograde direction. Its velocity is 26 mi/sec in one direction, the earth's is 18.5 mi/sec in the opposite direction; thus the particle moves toward the earth at a relative speed of 44.5 mi/sec, as in Fig. 9.20:1. The earth's own gravitational pull increases this relative velocity slightly, to 45 mi/sec. Of the thousands of meteors recorded by photography and radar, no velocity definitely outside these limits has been found, and the average arrival speed is close to 20 mi/sec. In particular, no hyperbolic velocities are yet known, and thus meteors are members of the solar system rather than visitors from interstellar space.

The luminosity of a meteor is proportional not only to its mass but also to the square of its velocity on entering the atmosphere. Accordingly, flakes of a given mass are brighter the faster they are moving. Alternatively, for a given luminosity the faster meteors are of lower mass. Also, the smaller flakes are known to be more abundant in space, as is attested by the fact that more naked-eye meteors are seen per hour in the predawn hours than in the premidnight hours. Before sunrise we are on the forward side of the moving earth, as shown in Fig. 9.20:2, and experiencing fast head-on collisions; at sunset and in early evening we experience only the slower overtaking collisions. Thus, if two small meteors have the same mass, the one striking after sunset has low velocity and may be too faint to see, whereas the one striking before dawn is fast-moving and substantially brighter. This diurnal effect means that we see three or four times as many meteors before dawn as after evening twilight.

The average meteors we have been considering are called *sporadic*, because they appear at scattered times and places in the sky. Analysis of the photographic and radar records of many sporadic meteors shows that their orbits around the sun are all elliptical, and that the orbits are inclined at all angles to the plane of the ecliptic. More specifically, those sporadic meteors having retrograde motion show a definite tendency toward very long-period near-parabolic orbits, in planes inclined at random. Those having direct motion, on the other hand, tend to have low inclinations, less extreme eccentricities, and fairly short periods. These results are reminiscent of the characteristics of cometary orbits.

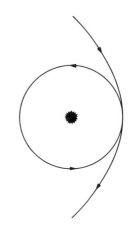

Fig. 9.20:1. A parabolic meteor may have a velocity relative to the earth as great as 45 mi/sec.

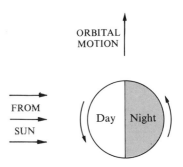

Fig. 9.20:2. After sunset an observer is on the trailing part of the earth; before dawn he is on the leading side and sees more meteors.

ASTEROIDS, COMETS, AND
METEORS

21. Meteors in Showers

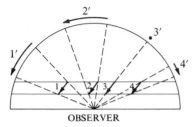

Fig. 9.21:1. Four shower meteors arriving at different times but on parallel paths. The apparent arcs on the celestial sphere are shown; they appear to radiate from point 3′ among the stars.

ON OCCASION we see substantially more than the usual five or ten sporadic meteors per hour. Every year for a few evenings before or after August 12 one can count perhaps 50 meteors per hour after midnight. On the evening of November 12, 1833, a blizzard of meteors was observed, falling at the rate of some 100,000 per hour. Not only are such *meteor showers* characterized by large numbers, but each of the meteors in a particular shower moves outward from a definite point among the stars, the shower *radiant*. Thus the August meteors are called the Perseids, because their paths, when plotted on a celestial globe, radiate out from a point or small area in the northern part of the constellation Perseus. Meteors like those of 1833 are the Leonids, because their paths emanate from a point in the sickle of Leo the Lion.

The fact that shower meteors appear to radiate from a point argues that their paths in space are parallel to one another. When a squadron of airplanes, flying in echelon, moves in from a distance, the individual planes appear to radiate out from a common point; in three-dimensional space we know that their paths must be parallel to one another if they are to stay in formation. Figure 9.21:1 shows this perspective effect, and it also indicates that the angular length of the path of a shower meteor depends on its angular distance from the radiant point. In particular, a temporary nonmoving glow at the radiant itself is a meteor heading directly toward the observer.

TABLE 9.21:1. The Major Nighttime Meteor Showers

Shower Name	Dates	Approximate Radiant		Hourly Rate[a]	Associated Comet
Quadrantids	Jan. 3 ± 1	15^h20^m	50°	50	?
Lyrids	Apr. 21 ± 1	18 10	32	5	1861 I
Eta Aquarids	May 5 ± 5	22 30	0	20	Halley
Delta Aquarids	July 28 ± 8	22 40	−17	20	?
Perseids	Aug. 12 ± 3	3 10	57	50	1862 III
Draconids	Oct. 10 ± 1	17 50	56	0[b]	Giacobini-Zinner
Orionids	Oct. 21 ± 3	6 10	15	20	Halley
Taurids	Nov. 7 ± 20	3 40	17	5	Encke
Leonids	Nov. 16 ± 2	10 00	22	5[b]	1866 I
Geminids	Dec. 13 ± 3	7 30	32	50	?
Ursids	Dec. 22 ± 1	14 30	76	15	Tuttle

[a] The listed rate is approximate only. It is an indication of the maximum number of shower meteors seen per hour by an observer with the radiant overhead on a clear moonless night.

[b] These entries are rates for typical years; great displays of Draconids and Leonids have been witnessed in certain years.

22. The Origin of Showers

COMPARED WITH the random times and radiants of the sporadic meteors, the shower meteors show a peculiarly strong organizational pattern, all members of any one shower moving in common orbits. About a century ago it was recognized that the Leonid meteors all move in paths similar to the orbit of Comet 1866 I and that the annual Perseids mimic the orbital elements of Comet 1862 III. Since then about a dozen meteor showers have been identified with known comets. A number of additional showers are known, although their associated comets are not. In recent years several daytime showers have been discovered by radar techniques.

It is certain that a shower occurs when the earth moves across a stream of meteoric flakes that once belonged to the parent comet. These particles were ejected from the cometary nucleus near the time of some previous perihelion passage, as a consequence of the solar forces described in Section 15. Because their velocities of ejection were small, they moved slowly away from the nucleus and are now moving around the sun in individual orbits that do not differ much from that of their parent comet. Each fleck is some miles from its nearest neighbor, although traveling along a nearly parallel track; when the earth crosses this stream we witness a meteor shower.

It may at first seem strange that we know many hundreds of comets but only about 20 meteor showers, for, if these ideas are correct, each comet with small enough perihelion distance for discovery should be damaged enough by the sun to yield a meteor stream. Very probably this is true, but only those few comets whose orbit rings intersect or come close to the earth's ring can give rise to showers; the particles in streams associated with other comets cannot hit the earth.

23. Old and New Showers

ON AUGUST 12 of each year the earth returns to the same point in space and crosses the orbit of Comet 1862 III. With an orbital period of about 110 years, the comet itself spends most of its time far from the sun and is undetectable from the earth. Nevertheless, every 110 years at perihelion passage the surface layers of its icy nucleus are melted and evaporated, and some of the stony or dust-like nonvolatile specks are ejected. Because the new velocity vector of the speck differs slightly from that of the parent comet and because the repulsive effect of the sun on it is much greater, the speck moves in a somewhat different orbit, most probably with a longer period. Let us assume that one of these specks has a period one year longer than the comet's; then from the formula for synodic periods that was discussed in Chapter 7, the speck will lose one lap in about 12,000 years. Quite generally, the stream of ejected meteoric flakes will gradually spread out over a great volume of space shaped like an elliptical doughnut. Each year for a few days around August 12 the earth crosses through this region and encounters some of the objects moving along it, as shown in Fig. 9.23:1. Thus the annual Perseid shower is relatively old.

ASTEROIDS, COMETS, AND
METEORS

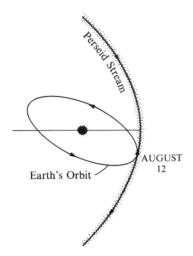

Fig. 9.23:1. Looking down on a plan view of the Perseid meteor stream from a point roughly in the direction of Arcturus. The earth's orbit is seen in projection as an elongated ellipse, and the earth itself crosses the center of the stream every August 12.

Although a few of the mid-November Leonids can be seen each year, spectacular showers like that of 1833 occur only once every 33 years, and even they have ceased since 1866 because planetary perturbations have altered the orbits. But records back to about A.D. 900 have established the 33-year periodicity without doubt. The material responsible for these great showers is bunched, moving along behind the parent comet; not enough time has elapsed for the flakes to have spread around the entire orbit. They were ejected at more recent perihelion passages than the material responsible for the much weaker annual Leonid shower. Thus every 33 years the earth collided with many more particles than usual.

On October 9, 1933, an intense shower was observed in Europe; this was the Draconids, whose parent is Comet Giacobini-Zinner with orbital period 6.6 years. At that time the earth was crossing some 150 million miles behind the comet. In October 1939 the earth reached the intersection point well ahead of the comet and in 1940 well behind it, and no showers were seen. On October 10, 1946, however, the earth cut through only two weeks behind the comet and another fine shower was detected. In 1959 we reached the intersection about six weeks before the comet and no shower was seen. Thus the Draconid shower is relatively young, in the sense that its material is strongly bunched behind the nucleus and has not had time to spread far along the orbit.

A meteor stream cannot survive forever, of course, because of the effects of solar corpuscular pressure and radiation pressure and also because of planetary perturbations. The path of one fragile particle is modified differently from that of another one. The long-run effect is a change from organization to chaos; ultimately, the meteor stream of today will be dispersed into the unrecognizable tangle of tomorrow. Similarly, the meteor streams of yesterday are scattered beyond recognition today; the sporadic meteors we see today almost certainly belonged to meteor streams in the past and even earlier belonged to the conglomerate nucleus of a comet.

24. Meteorites

A FEW TIMES a day, perhaps five or ten, the earth is bombarded by a body large enough to survive its journey through the atmosphere and hit the surface. These visitors from space are the meteorites, and their preatmospheric sizes are probably bigger than a basketball. A meteorite is so massive that its brilliance while plunging through the upper atmosphere is enormous—perhaps as great as the moon's; and sharp noises are often heard some seconds later. The brightness dies away while the meteorite is still some 10 miles above ground, indicating that its velocity has been decreased greatly by air drag. Accordingly, most meteorites only dent the ground or bury themselves a few feet below the surface. Annually, about half a dozen meteorites are seen to fall, and are tracked down and recovered. Even if found right away, however, a meteorite is not too hot to handle; the great heating from the atmospheric plunge is a surface effect only, and most of the skin materia sparks off and joins the surrounding disturbed air. The final remaining surface usually is a thin dark glossy shell, the material having fused briefly and then cooled and solidified rapidly at the end of its journey.

Fig. 9.24:1. A meteorite from the Arizona crater. (*Yerkes Observatory photograph*)

25. Structure and Composition of Meteorites

THE TOTAL number of known meteorites is about 1500, and many of them have been analyzed by chemists and mineralogists. One major result of such analyses is the discovery that these extraterrestrial bodies are composed of the same kinds of atoms we find on earth, attesting to the uniformity of nature in the small. With respect to large-scale structure, however, there are important differences among meteorites. About 3 percent of those recovered are composed almost entirely of two metals: iron and nickel. The nickel content varies from 5 percent in some metallic meteorites to 20 percent in others. A second group are the stony metallic meteorites, containing roughly equal amounts of iron-nickel and silicates. The third and most abundant group consists of the stony meteorites; silicon and oxygen account for the majority of the material in these objects, as in the rocks of the earth's crust. But in contrast with our crust, stony meteorites are relatively deficient in aluminum and relatively rich in iron, nickel, and magnesium. As in the metallic meteorites, the nickel content of stony meteorites averages about 10 percent of the total iron-nickel content. Inside a stone these metals occur as grains and chips here and there throughout the volume. Although one meteorite may differ in composition from the next, there is little doubt that we are dealing with a sequence of bodies which originated under rather similar conditions. We shall return soon to the problem of the origin of meteorites.

Many attempts have been made to establish the ages of meteorites by the methods of radioactive dating. The measurements deal with

ASTEROIDS, COMETS, AND
METEORS

exceedingly minute quantities of material, and various age estimates range from tens of millions to several billions of years. Based on the fact that one isotope of potassium decays into argon, recent measurements of some stony meteorites have yielded time estimates of between 4 and 5 billion years since the solidification of these bodies, estimates which are in accord with those of the age of the earth's solid crust.

26. Siberia, Arizona, and Quebec

LARGE meteorites, although rare, are extremely destructive. In 1908 an ultrabright object crossed the sky and struck ground in central Siberia, laying waste to a region nearly 100 miles in diameter. The forests of the area were laid flat by the blast, individual trees as much as 20 miles away being knocked radially outward from the scene of the hit. Windows were shattered by the impact; smoke rose many miles into the atmosphere. Exploration of this isolated region many years later revealed a number of conical craters up to 150 feet in diameter, indicating that a cluster of bodies had hit the earth. In 1947 another large meteoritic body, rivaling the sun in brightness, struck in eastern Siberia, gouging more than 100 pits over an elliptical area some 3 miles long and 1 mile wide. The individual craters are as much as 30 feet deep and 90 feet across. Several tons of iron fragments were collected in the area, and it is likely that the preatmospheric mass of both of these great meteorites was around 100 tons.

On an extensive plain in Arizona there is a nearly circular crater with diameter 4000 feet, surrounded by a circular hill rising more than 100 feet above the level of the surroundings. The depth of the crater, measured from the top of the rim to the floor, is 600 feet. The cross section is shown in Fig. 9.26:1. Rocky and metallic fragments of assorted sizes lie here and there up to several miles from the crater itself. Holes have been drilled in several places and rich iron-nickel material was finally encountered some 1400 feet beneath the south rim of the crater. The impacting body approached from slightly west of north and from a large zenith distance. The Arizona crater is not a recent addition by ordinary standards, although it is very recent com-

Fig. 9.26:1. Cross section of the Arizona meteorite crater.

Fig. 9.26:2. The Arizona meteorite crater from the air. (*Yerkes Observatory photograph*)

pared with the age of the earth; most estimates are in the tens of thousands of years.

In 1950 a circular, water-filled crater was discovered in northern Quebec. Although no meteorites have been found in the vicinity, its general similarity to the Arizona crater and the lack of any past crater-producing volcanic activity in the area suggest that the Quebec crater is meteoric in origin. With a diameter of 2 miles, a rim 500 feet above the surrounding country, and a lake 800 feet deep, this crater is the largest known on the earth.

Studies of the Siberia, Arizona, Quebec, and a few other known meteorite craters show the same general characteristics: nearly circular shape, a central depression, and a surrounding uplifted rim. Usually, telltale iron-nickel material is found in the vicinity. The earth evidently is struck a few times a day by small meteorites, a few times each century by objects as large as the Siberian falls, and even more rarely by bodies large enough to make the Arizona or Quebec craters. The fact that some meteorites hit in groups whereas others hit singly suggests that some meteorites break into fragments while plummeting through the atmosphere. From the total number of group hits and single hits every century, it is possible to estimate crudely what percentage of the earth's surface will be scarred with craters after a few billion years. Such calculations reveal that the earth's surface should be badly scarred after such a long bombardment. That we do not find many craters must mean that the forces of erosion gradually obliterate fresh craters. Only the relatively recent ones are still in evidence. But if we turn our instruments to the moon, we find tens or even hundreds of thousands of craters larger than the Arizona crater. There, where there is no atmosphere, the forces of erosion are not at work and the records of history are therefore not lost. The remarkable similarity in structure of lunar and terrestrial craters suggests that they originated in the same way, by meteoritic bombardment. And, in view of the excessively littered surface of the moon, it is likely that the rate of bombardment was greater in the past than it is today.

27. Where Meteorites Come From

VERY LITTLE precise information is available on the orbits of meteorites, for they fall only rarely, chiefly in the oceans or on land that is far away from any trained observer. The information at hand indicates that meteorites tend to have direct orbits of low inclination. From this information alone, these bodies may be associated either with short-period comets or with asteroids. Looking further, however, we find that no meteorite or bright fireball has ever been seen during a meteor shower. It appears fairly certain, therefore, that meteor streams contain only the small stuff that can be evaporated from the parent comet by solar effects. Thus it is doubtful that comets produce the typical meteorites. Turning to the asteroids, we have already found that many of them are ragged-shaped fragments. It appears that meteorites may be asteroids—the relatively small but abundant chips that are products of the collision and fragmentation of the material that once belonged to one or more pairs of large spherical asteroids. Supporting evidence for this view is the gradation in composition of meteorites; the denser metallic meteorites may once have been in the central core of one of the parent asteroids, the stony metallic meteorites at an intermediate depth, and the stony meteorites not far from the surface. At the time of collision and disruption, objects with a broad range of size and chemical composition were released to pursue their individual paths around the sun, and we still encounter a few thousand of them every year as we annually sweep clean a ring-shaped volume of space.

28. The Origin of Sporadic Meteors

ALTHOUGH nothing final can be said, it appears fairly certain that meteorites and fireballs, objects much brighter than Venus when transiting our atmosphere, are small asteroidal fragments. On the other hand, meteors in showers are definitely from comets. Finally, what is the origin of the countless sporadic meteors that collide with us each day? Photographic and radar records give no certain evidence that any are interstellar. From their orbital characteristics, it appears that they too are associated with comets and asteroids. The evidence cited in Section 20 shows nearly perfect agreement with what we should expect if the sporadic meteors are members of old and dispersed meteor streams, if the flakes with randomly inclined near-parabolic orbits are exmembers of one of the long-period comets, and if those with direct and low-inclination orbits of short period are exmembers of one of the Jupiter-made short-period comets. Although some of the sporadic meteors, particularly the brighter ones, may be small asteroidal chips, the overwhelming majority seem to be cometary in origin.

INTERPLANETARY MATTER

29. Zodiacal Light and the Counterglow

FROM THE tropics one can see after evening twilight a milky wedge of light pointing up the western sky along the ecliptic. Before dawn a similar subluminous cone stretches up the eastern sky, its axis also coincident with the ecliptic. In midnorthern latitudes this *zodiacal light* is rarely conspicuous, being dimmed by the murk of low altitudes; it is best seen when the ecliptic lies nearly perpendicular to the horizon—after sundown in late winter and early spring and before sunrise in late summer and early autumn. At large angular distances from the sun the zodiacal light is much fainter, although keen-eyed observers have followed it fully around the zodiacal belt. At the point opposite the sun the light broadens into a slightly brighter, nearly circular patch known as the *counterglow* or *gegenschein*; even in the best of skies on a moonless night the counterglow eludes most who hunt for it.

The spectrum of the zodiacal light is similar to that of the sun, indicating that most of the glow is sunlight reflected by very small particles. The shape of the belt shows that the particles are distributed in a lens-shaped cloud which is centered on the sun. The main plane coincides with that of the planetary orbits, and the cloud extends well beyond the earth, although it decreases in number of flakes per unit volume with increasing distance from the sun.

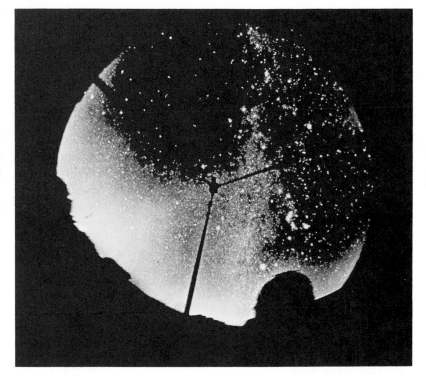

Fig. 9.29:1. Part of the Milky Way, and also the zodiacal light near the horizon, photographed with the 140° camera. (*Yerkes Observatory photograph*)

30. Interpreting the Zodiacal Light

THE SPECKS comprising the zodiacal light are not very large, or we should have continual and spectacular meteor displays in our atmosphere. Nor are they extremely small, or they would be immediately blasted out of the solar system by the radiation and corpuscular pressure of the sun. A typical diameter is perhaps 0.001 inch. The comets, particularly the low-inclination short-period ones, are probably chiefly responsible for the particles, although asteroidal chips may contribute somewhat to the flattened cloud. Earlier we concluded that the sporadic meteors are dominantly small particles that long ago belonged to a comet; most of these smaller micrometeoric specks probably have the same origin.

A major question to be faced is this: if comets have been generously contributing tiny flakes to the zodiacal cloud for billions of years, why by this time is not the sky sufficiently filled with grains to be as bright as the rings of Saturn? Clearly, the older particles must be removed from the solar system at roughly the same rate that cometary ejection provides new ones, as with the water in the Mississippi River. There are several possible mechanisms for getting rid of such particles.

Fig. 9.30:1. *Above:* The velocity vector A/M of an outbound solar atom as seen by a moving meteoric flake. *Below:* The outward component of the corpuscular force reduces the net gravitational attraction; the other component of the corpuscular force acts as a headwind.

One is solar pressure, but these flakes are too large to be pushed out of the solar system by the sun. Another is collisions with planets, but the planets capture only a tiny fraction of the zodiacal cloud. The dominant process of removal appears to be a slow spiraling of these particles into the sun, similar in some ways to the spiraling of a man-made satellite into the earth. The time required for one of these small stony or dust-like flakes to spiral from 1 a.u. into a point where solar heat will vaporize it is some thousands of years. Solar pressure, disturbing the pure elliptical orbit under gravitation, is responsible for the effect. For simplicity, let us think of how a stream of atoms emanating from the sun will influence the motion of a micrometeor in a circular orbit. Figure 9.30:1 shows the velocity vectors M/S of a meteor around the sun, A/S of the fast-moving atoms out from the sun, and the resultant A/M of the atoms relative to the moving micrometeor. The impacting atoms exert a force on the particle that is chiefly directed outward from the sun but slightly opposes the motion of the particle. The micrometeor is thus bucking a slight headwind; it is big enough so that the sunward-directed gravitational force overbalances the *outward* component of the atomic wind, as shown in Fig. 9.30:1. But there is nothing to compensate for the *headwind* component. Thus, like the man-made satellites, this drag effect forces the particles to spiral closer and closer into the sun to their inevitable doom. Lost to the zodiacal cloud, they are replaced by fresh micrometeors ejected by comets.

31. Interpreting the Counterglow

WHY THERE should be a faint patch of light at the antisolar point is not certain. If the micrometeoric bodies composing the counterglow are outside the earth's shadow, they are of course in full phase and reflecting more light than their neighbors in other directions. But only if they have exceedingly ragged surfaces will they reflect substantially more light than their counterparts some degrees away. An alternative possibility is that the earth has a tail like that of a comet, caused by solar pressure; looking at such a tail end-on, we would see a faint circular patch.

32. Other Interplanetary Material

IN ADDITION to the micrometeoric particles of the zodiacal cloud, there is strong evidence that a tenuous gas pervades interplanetary space, denser near the sun and more rarefied far from the sun. Studies of comet tails, of the aurora borealis, and of the sun all agree that clouds of charged atomic particles—ions and electrons—erupt from the sun and move out into space at high speed. These findings have been confirmed and extended by space probes. At the time of a major eruption there may be as many as a million atoms per cubic inch at 1 a.u. from the sun, moving outward at 1000 mi/sec or more. A more normal minimum value is perhaps a few hundred atoms per cubic inch, moving away from the sun at about 200 mi/sec.

It is instructive to think of this tenuous expanding gas as the extreme outer atmosphere of the sun, extending outward from the gaseous solar corona seen at a total solar eclipse. For every atom leaving the solar system on a hyperbolic orbit another one is ejected from the sun. Thus there emerges a picture of the interplanetary spaces being traversed by solar radiation moving outward at 186,000 mi/sec and also by a tenuous and gusty wind of atoms blowing at hundreds or thousands of miles per second away from the sun. Here and there are ultrasmall cometary particles that are driven out of the solar system by these forces, because the hold of solar gravitation on them is not strong enough to prevent their escape. The larger meteoric bits, conversely, react by slowly spiraling in toward the sun until they evaporate at a few million miles and join the interplanetary gas. Only large bodies can survive these forces for millions and billions of years. In particular, planet Earth moves serenely around the sun almost completely oblivious of them.

PROBLEMS

1. (a) Give an orbital period, semimajor axis, eccentricity, and inclination for the orbit of a typical asteroid. (b) What would be a typical synodic period for an asteroid?

2. How has it been possible to establish the period of rotation of certain asteroids, even though they cannot be resolved by telescopes?

3. Compute the escape velocity from an asteroid that is spherical in shape, with mean density the same as the earth's, and with a diameter of 0.8 mile (1/10,000 the diameter of the earth).

4. (a) Contrast the size and shape of the regions in which the near-parabolic comets and the periodic comets move. (b) Account for the small inclination of the orbit of a typical periodic comet.

5. How do we know that a comet has a mass much smaller than that of the earth?

6. Explain the forces that cause a comet tail to stretch away from the sun.

7. List the names of the major categories of meteoric objects that are incident on the earth or its atmosphere, and describe the various techniques by which these bodies can be studied.

8. The escape velocity of Venus is 6.4 mi/sec and her orbital velocity is about 21.8 mi/sec. What are the minimum and maximum possible speeds of solar system meteors about to crash on Venus?

9. Why are some meteor showers seen every year and others seen much less frequently?

10. For what reasons do we believe that meteorites are small asteroids?

11. Explain why sunlight incident on a small particle in an essentially circular orbit causes the particle to spiral slowly in toward the sun.

12. What is the zodiacal light and how do we believe it is replenished?

13. Mention some of the known characteristics of the interplanetary gas.

10

THE SOLAR SYSTEM:
ORIGIN AND EVOLUTION

Now that we have studied the solar system as it is today, let us examine the challenging problem of its birth and development. The question of how our planetary system came into being is an extremely difficult one to answer, for the story goes back many thousands of times as far into the past as the whole of human history. Indeed, the only framework within which we can even attempt to reconstruct the far past is the simple faith that the physical laws we know today are the same as those that were operative yesterday. If we dare not assume, for example, that the law of gravitation has been valid for billions of years, we cannot even begin to probe the past. Let us adopt this faith, look at the solar system we know today, and see if it is possible to make some intelligent guesses about its origin.

1. Age of the System

WE HAVE already seen that the earth and meteorites are roughly 5 billion years old, as evidenced by studies of radioactive decay. On the basis that meteorites are tiny asteroids, we infer a common age for the planets. When we later turn to study the stars and our Milky Way galaxy, we shall find from the theory of stellar evolution that many stars are also about 5 billion years old. The sun, in particular, is approximately this age, and thus, from evidence of a quite different sort, our parent star is found to be about as old as its attendant bodies. From all the clues we have, it is highly probable that the solar system came into

2. Is Ours the Only Planetary System?

being as a single event, during a time interval that was short compared with its present age.

WE CAN sometimes learn more about ourselves by studying other people and their successes and failures. Similarly, we could learn more about our own solar system if we could locate and study other such systems, looking for similarities and differences and trying to find whether planetary systems surround most other stars, very few other stars, or no other stars. Until 1963, however, no other planetary systems had been found, and so this route of inquiry seemed to lead down a dead-end road. Astronomers realized, of course, that the lack of other planetary systems was only apparent, and not necessarily real. Imagine, for example, that the 200-inch telescope were transported out into space 4 light-years to the vicinity of the nearest star, Alpha Centauri, and pointed back at the solar system. The sun would be one of the brightest stars, but its largest attendant, Jupiter, would be near the marginal faintness detectable with a 200-inch aperture, and lying at most only 4″ away from the glare of its parent. It is little wonder that we have not yet found planets in other systems by their reflected light, although observations with special equipment from above the earth's atmosphere may sometime in the future yield positive results.

In 1963 Peter van de Kamp of the Sproul Observatory announced his discovery that Barnard's Star has a very small oscillatory motion as it moves slowly across the celestial sphere. The effect is so tiny that measurements had to be made on more than 2000 photographs taken over a quarter of a century. The 24-year oscillation is caused by the orbital motion of Barnard's Star around the common center of mass of the star and a low-mass companion. The deduced mass of the invisible partner is only 1.5 times that of Jupiter and the average separation of the two bodies is about 4 a.u. Thus for the first time there is strong evidence for a body of planetary mass in an orbit of typical size around another star. Although it may be foolhardy to generalize from only one case, it is worth noting that Barnard's Star is the second closest known and that its motion has been studied very extensively and carefully. The implication is clear: many if not most stars may be expected to have planetary partners.

Another approach, initiated by Kuiper, is to think of the solar system as a sort of double star, composed of the sun and Jupiter. Jupiter's mass is too small for it to be a star, but it nevertheless contains most of the material of the solar system that is not in the sun. If we now study other stars, it turns out that less than half of the stars are isolated in space; most belong to teams of two or three or more. It is possible to determine the masses of the stars in a pair, as we shall see in Chapter 14; and when the mass ratios are computed, it is found that in most pairs both of the member stars have roughly the same mass. But about 20 percent of the pairs have one massive star attended by a second star that is less than 10 percent as massive. From the trend of the numbers it appears that one star out of every hundred or a thousand may be attended by one or more planets. Since there are 100 billion stars in our galaxy, these figures imply that there are between 100 million and a billion planetary systems in the Milky Way system, even though the astronomer can point out to a doubting Thomas just one beyond our own. Thus, although we cannot yet study many other systems in order to learn more about our own, it appears likely that the processes giving rise to planetary systems are not ultrarare and freakish, but relatively common.

LET US RETURN to our own solar system and see what must be accounted for by a successful theory of origin. (1) We want to know how the sun formed, but since this is a problem common to all stars, we shall consider star formation in detail later. (2) We must explain why the planetary orbits are nearly in the same plane, described in the same direction, and nearly circular in shape. Kepler's laws require of course that the orbits be conic sections but not at all that they should be nearly circular and nearly in the same plane. We also want to know why the distances of the planets from the sun increase more or less in geometric progression, why there is a rather uniform run in planetary diameters, and why most planets rotate in the same direction that they revolve around the sun. (3) Some of the satellite systems are beautifully regular, but perhaps a dozen satellites have orbits with appreciable eccentricities and inclinations, with half a dozen in retrograde motion. These features, along with the existence of a twin planet, earth-moon, need explaining. (4) Why is the zone between Mars and Jupiter littered with asteroids instead of being occupied by a single planet? (5) We must inquire how and where the comets were born, for their near-parabolic, randomly inclined orbits differ drastically from those of the planets. Let us examine several hypotheses of the origin of the solar system to see whether they can account for these special properties, especially for the near-circular low-inclination orbits of the principal planets.

3. Special Properties of Our System

ASSUME THAT small solid planets wander among the stars and that on occasion our particular star, the sun, passes close to such a body and captures it. This notion may be entertaining, but it is not correct. In the first place, the orbital planes of such bodies would be inclined at all angles. In the second place the orbits would all be hyperbolic; a planet moving in from interstellar space would have its direction of motion altered by the gravitational force of the sun but would leave the solar system again at greater than the escape velocity. Thus the random-capture hypothesis fails badly on the first two tests asked of it, so let us turn elsewhere.

4. The Random-Capture Hypothesis

OF THE MANY hypotheses of origin that have been put forward, those deserving serious attention are rooted in one of two fundamental ideas. Historically, the first idea was that the solar system was born

5. The Encounter Hypothesis

THE SOLAR SYSTEM:
ORIGIN AND EVOLUTION

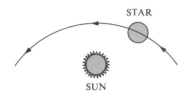

STAR

SUN

Fig. 10.5:1. The hyperbolic path of another star around the sun.

from a great cloud of gaseous or gaseous-dusty matter; we shall return to this idea presently. The second fundamental idea, first put forward at the turn of the twentieth century, is that the solar system is a product of a past close approach of the sun and another star. The various versions of origin based on this idea may be called *encounter hypotheses*, although an actual collision is not necessarily required. Imagine a star approaching the general vicinity of the sun but not aimed to hit it directly. If for simplicity we imagine the sun at rest, the second star would move around the sun on a hyperbolic path, as indicated in Fig. 10.5:1. If the perihelion distance were small enough, each star would raise great tides on the other one, both on the facing side and far side of each. The tidal forces would be so strong that great ribbons of gas would be torn off each star. As the stars later receded, some of the material would fall back into each, and some would be left in permanent orbits around each star. The moving gas would condense into small solids, which in turn would collide, cohere, and sweep up material ahead of themselves, and eventually grow into planets. The encounter hypothesis thus explains why the planets have orbits in nearly the same plane and described in the same direction, for this is the orbital plane and sense of motion of the visiting star. The nearly circular orbits were originally quite eccentric but were gradually rounded out as the planets plowed through the remaining interplanetary gas that never joined a planet.

Despite the prettiness of this picture, there are several major difficulties with the encounter hypothesis. (1) The rarefied hot gases in the filaments will disperse rather than condense into solids, and the dispersion would be aided by the tidal forces of the sun. (2) Unless the perihelion distance were only a few solar-radii, the mutual tide-raising forces would not be strong enough to eject material from the stars. But if we grant such a close approach, it is then impossible for the visiting star to give the planetary material enough angular momentum to get it out to the present large distances of the planets. Although not fatal, two additional objections may be mentioned. (1) Since the visiting star may have passed by at any time, the planets can be any age younger than the stars. As we have seen, however, the planets are about as old as the sun and most other stars. (2) It is extremely improbable that the sun has ever come very close to another star. Even though 100 billion stars move around among one another in our galaxy, the chance is less than one in a thousand that any other star has passed as close as Pluto to the sun; it is less than one in a million that any other star has come within a few solar-radii of the sun during the past 5 billion years. This argument of course does not prove anything, but it does instill confidence that a tidal origin for the solar system is exceedingly improbable.

6. The Nebular Hypothesis

THE OTHER fundamental idea at the root of hypotheses of origin was first proposed by the German philosopher Immanuel Kant in 1755 and again some 40 years later by the French mathematician and astronomer Pierre Laplace. According to this theory, there was, to begin with, a gaseous *nebula*, or cloud, as large as the solar system and in slow rotation. The mutual gravitational forces of all its parts on one another pulled the mass together, the majority going to make up the sun. As the remainder contracted, it necessarily rotated faster and faster, because its angular momentum had to stay constant. Because of the interplay of gravitational force and centripetal force, the mass flattened to a disk and equatorial rings of gas were successively ejected as their velocities increased beyond the escape velocity. These rings later condensed to form the planets, and a repetition of the process produced the satellite families.

Laplace's theory held sway for many years, but during the past century several objections have been leveled against it. For one thing, the sun should have the majority of the angular momentum of the solar system, whereas it actually has only $\frac{1}{200}$ of the total. In addition, one wonders why the material shed as individual rings rather than seeping off continually. As with the encounter hypotheses, there is the difficulty of getting the rarefied gas atoms to collect into solids instead of dispersing into space.

In recent years evidence has accumulated that stars have been and still are being born in great but tenuous clouds of interstellar gas and dust. There lingers no doubt, therefore, that the starting point of the nebular hypothesis is the correct one for the majority of stars. Now it also seems that many planetary systems may exist, and thus that planet formation has occurred frequently and naturally. It is reasonable to expect, therefore, that a planetary system may also be formed from a large mass of interstellar matter, even though the original form of Laplace's theory is no longer tenable. Several interesting modifications of the nebular hypothesis have been proposed in the past two decades, and we shall examine one of them—Kuiper's protoplanet hypothesis— in some detail.

7. The Protoplanet Hypothesis

ACCORDING to the protoplanet hypothesis, the solar system began as a rarefied and cool fragment of gas and dust particles, of the same chemical composition as the sun. This mass was remote from other similar ones and from pre-existing stars. It was perhaps 100 a.u. in diameter and inevitably had some net angular momentum. About 95 percent of the mass collapsed gravitationally at ever-increasing speed, becoming the young cool sun, red in color and perhaps as big as Mercury's orbit. The remaining 5 percent, the outlying part of the initial fragment, contracted in response to its own gravitational force and that of the sun. But the more the contraction proceeded, the faster was the angular rate of spin, until finally no further shrinkage was possible in the equatorial plane of rotation. The nebula continued collapsing vertically, however, until it was a flat circular disk, prevented from greater flattening by the expansive pressure force of the gas itself. The general sequence of events is pictured in Fig. 10.7:1. The final wheel of gas and dust was some 30 a.u. in radius, but its thickness was

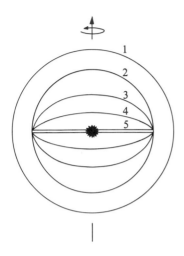

Fig. 10.7:1. Successive stages in the contraction of the solar nebula, with the rotation axis vertical. The first stage is a very slowly turning sphere; the final stage is a rapidly revolving disk.

only a fraction of an astronomical unit. The material in the wheel revolved around the cool red sun according to Kepler's laws.

The flattening solar nebula was a turbulent and churning medium, with eddies forming here and there. As the great cloud contracted, a given mass occupied a smaller and smaller volume of space, and therefore the *average* density of the nebula increased with time. Superposed on this increase was a continuous forming and dissolving of denser-than-average eddies. At a certain stage one of these whirls, for the first time, became dense enough to hold together. The mutual gravitational attraction of all its particles on one another was now strong enough so that the eddy would neither spontaneously dissolve nor be disrupted by solar tidal forces. Here was the first protoplanet, a large mass of gas and dust moving in a Keplerian orbit and sweeping additional interplanetary material into itself. Other protoplanets formed too, and any that formed in the same ring combined with the others in that ring, the whole moving in a new orbit that tended to be more circular. Ultimately, there were eight protoplanets, each one many times as large and massive as its present adult product.

Because the early sun was cool and because the dusty interplanetary matter acted as a fairly efficient smoke screen, no protoplanet saw much sunshine. It was thus very cold throughout much of the solar nebula, a condition that favored the condensation of gaseous molecules into bits of water ice, ammonia ice, methane ice, and other solid flakes. A protoplanet may be pictured as a complex mélange whose mass, like the sun's, was 99 percent hydrogen and helium, with lesser but important amounts of ices, silicates, and metals. It slowly contracted, the denser elements such as iron and nickel tending to bypass the lighter components and drift to the center, leaving silicates and ices farther from the core, with an extensive envelope of low-mass helium and hydrogen.

All the protoplanets were initially so large that they were tidally coupled to the sun, rotating once for each revolution. As they contracted, however, the law of conservation of angular momentum dictated that they spin at a greater angular rate. Thus most planets became uncoupled from the sun, and instead of spinning easterly once each revolution, they spun easterly at a faster rate. The end result of this process is in accord with our knowledge of present-day planetary rotations, except for Mercury, which is most strongly affected by solar tides and thus still keeps its same face toward the sun, for Venus, whose slow rotation may be retrograde, and for Uranus, whose 98° inclination remains unaccounted for.

The approximate geometrical progression in the distances of the planets from the sun resulted chiefly from the density of material in the solar nebula at various distances from the sun. Presumably the sun either swallowed or repelled much of the nebular material in the inner part of the flat cloud, and thus the density of building material there was low. With increasing distance the density increased, reaching a peak between the present distances of Jupiter and Saturn, and then decreasing again out to 30 a.u. or more. In the outer solar nebula, where the tidal force of the sun was weak, large protoplanets could form, the largest of all being proto-Jupiter and proto-Saturn, each with an initial mass of about 1.5 percent of the sun's. Farther out, proto-Uranus and proto-Neptune were even less inhibited by solar tides from being larger in diameter, but because there was less sweep-up material available in the outer part of the nebula, their masses were each only about 0.5 percent of the sun's. The inner protoplanets were prevented from being large because of the greater tidal forces near the sun. Nor could they become very massive because of lack of material. Since the sizes of these giant disks increased with distance from the sun, the spacings between them also increased outward; otherwise they would have collided before one synodic period had elapsed. The mean distances of today's planets are very likely about the same as those of the original eddies out of which they formed, accounting for the geometrical progression we witness today.

During the tens of millions of years that the protoplanets were contracting, the giant red sun was slowly contracting too, somehow transferring angular momentum to outlying material. As the contraction continued, the surface temperature of the sun steadily increased and the energy output similarly increased, until after 100 million years the central parts of the sun were hot and dense enough to begin to burn by hydrogen fusion; at this stage the sun was much like the sun of today, some 5 billion years later. Thus, after an interval of only about 2 percent of its present age, the sun was radiating and also erupting atomic clouds vigorously enough to force most of the remaining gaseous and dusty interplanetary material out of the solar system. But once the material that did not join a protoplanet was blown away, the smoke screen was gone and the space between the planets became transparent; the enormous planetary atmospheres then felt the full heating effect of the sun. All but one-thousandth of proto-Earth's material escaped, chiefly the light atoms of hydrogen and helium, leaving today's earth extremely deficient in the two chemical elements that make up 99 percent of the mass of the sun. Farther out, proto-Jupiter lost only about 95 percent of its original mass, for the solar heating was less and the escape velocity of the dwindling planet remained high. Thus present-day Jupiter contains much more hydrogen and helium than does the earth, although it is deficient in these atoms when compared with the sun.

8. The Origin of Satellites

DURING THE contraction of each outer protoplanet, a flattened disk of gas and dust developed in its equatorial plane. In this plane a family of protosatellites was formed, each member moving in a circular orbit around its parent protoplanet. In miniature, the process is similar to the earlier formation of the protoplanets themselves. Later these condensations contracted to become the small satellites we know today. It is conceivable that our own moon was formed in the same way, but it seems far more probable that the moon was a separate small protoplanet that was captured but not absorbed by the earth. For unlike most satellites, the moon's orbit is nearly in the same plane as that of the planetary orbits rather than that of the parent planet's equator.

Mercury and Venus, being nearer the sun, were dominated by solar tidal forces, and their rotations never speeded up enough to spill out satellite-building material at their equators. Similarly, the proto-satellites of the solar system never could flatten enough to produce subsatellites, for they were under the strong tidal control of their parent planets. As we have seen, all satellites for which we have data are tidally coupled to their parents; presumably they always have been so coupled and thus, like Mercury and Venus, could not produce small partners in their equatorial planes.

A dozen satellites have orbits that are appreciably eccentric and inclined, with half of them moving in retrograde orbits about their parent planets. Their orbits differ radically from the circular coplanar paths of most satellites. In the past it has often been suggested that these unconventional bodies were captured asteroids. Within the frame-work of the protoplanet hypothesis, however, a satellite of this sort was probably originally born rather far out in the equatorial plane of its parent protoplanet. As the protoplanet lost mass, its gravitational hold on the satellite weakened, so that it spiraled out to greater and greater distances from its parent. Ultimately, the sun stole it away. But after one or more synodic periods the satellite may have been recaptured on passing through the protoplanet's extensive atmosphere, moving in a new orbit quite different from its original circular equatorial path.

9. The Origin of Asteroids

THE SIZES of today's planets increase more or less steadily from Mercury out to Jupiter and then decrease more or less steadily out to Neptune. The notable exceptions are Mars, which has only about half the earth's diameter, and the asteroids, which are exceedingly small. These deficiencies in size are perhaps explained by the disturbing gravitational effects of proto-Jupiter, which formed early and thereafter prohibited the formation of any large protoplanet in the asteroid zone. Only a number of smaller bodies could form in the presence of such strong tidal forces. The statistics on today's asteroids are consistent with the picture of an original group of small spherical planets, with one or more pairs later colliding and producing the fragmented asteroids and the meteorites.

10. The Origin of Comets

AS WE LEARNED in the last chapter, the comets we see are probably supplied to the inner solar system from a vast spherical reservoir extend-ing halfway to the nearest stars. The perturbations by such stars serve to divert a few of these small icy spheres every century into near-parabolic orbits. Since the comets are known to be members of the solar system and thus were presumably formed in the flat solar nebula a few billion years ago, along with planets, satellites, and asteroids, we must ask why they are now in a great spherical space instead of a small flat one. According to the protoplanet hypothesis, these small icy bodies were formed in the outer tenuous part of the flat solar nebula, beyond Neptune and out to some 50 a.u. They were of various sizes, but none could grow very large because there was not enough building material available. Pluto, after being released from contracting proto-Neptune into its eccentric and inclined orbit, swept throughout the zone of comet birth and eventually came close enough to each comet to change its orbit. The orbit may have been modified enough so that the comet was later influenced by Neptune or Uranus, and so on. The general effect was a loosening up of the original ring-shaped volume occupied by the comets until it became a great sphere. In the process many comets were lost to the solar system, and many more were doomed if they came too close to the sun; the trillion or so survivors now occupy the great spherical reservoir.

11. The Future of the System

AS FAR AS we know, the planetary orbits have been stable for billions of years. Although solar radiation and corpuscular pressure decrease the mean distance of a planet from the sun by a minute amount every million years, this effect is more than compensated for by the loosening gravitational hold of the sun as it steadily loses mass. It is doubtful, however, that the planets' orbital sizes will increase as much as 1 percent during the bright phase of the sun's life. Satellites and asteroids will not be much affected either. Only the supply of comets will dwindle, but the reservoir is so full that the drain-off will not be serious.

The chief producer of change in the future will be the sun. Since its initial contraction it has not changed very much, but in another few billion years it will begin to grow bigger, redder, and more luminous, becoming a giant red star, emitting perhaps 100 times as much energy as today, perhaps engulfing Mercury, and certainly altering atmospheric and surface conditions on the various planets. The intensity of sunshine at Saturn, for example, will then be as great as it is at the earth today. After that time the sun will shrink, become bluer, and finally less and less luminous. Ultimately getting dimmer and dimmer, it will evolve into a fading white dwarf star. Atmospheric and surface conditions on the planets will then undergo a reversal. From the earth, a hypothetical and very cold person will then witness the sun as a white stellar point, brilliant compared with other stars but only 1/10,000 as bright as today, and too small to be seen as a disk. No planet will be visible to the unaided eye, for the source of planetary light, the feeble sun, will be too dim. Comets will shine only when they chance to pass very close to the small sun. The moon, although still going through phases, will be very pale. The planetary system 10 billion years from now will be a chilling and forbidding place as our star emits less and less radiation. But the sun will remain the gravitational master of the system, for its mass will not be much less than it is today. Thus, although the heat will be off, at least we will not be turned out of our home—the solar system.

PROBLEMS

1. What evidence is there that most bodies of the solar system came into being at approximately the same time—some 5 billion years ago?

2. Give some of the over-all features of the solar system that must be accounted for by any successful theory of origin of the system.

3. What are some objections to the random-capture hypothesis about the formation of the solar system?

4. What are some objections to the encounter hypothesis about the formation of the solar system?

5. Describe the original nature of the solar nebula according to the protoplanet hypothesis.

6. List the changing physical conditions of a protoplanet from birth to achievement of planetary status.

7. What are the reasons, according to the protoplanet hypothesis, that most planets rotate in the same direction that they revolve in their orbits?

8. Mercury, Venus, and the natural satellites have slow rotations and also have no smaller bodies orbiting around them. Why?

9. The gross characteristics of the orbit of Halley's Comet have probably changed markedly from the comet's birth through the billions of years until today. Describe a reasonable sequence of such changes and the forces that may have produced them.

10. It is likely that the sun during its future evolution will at one time emit 100 times as much radiation as it does now and much later only 1/10,000 as much as now. At what distances would one have to be from the sun on those two occasions to receive as much solar radiant energy as we do now on the earth?

11

ATOMS, RADIATION, AND SPECTRA

O F THE KNOWN matter in the universe, less than one part in a thousand is in the solid or liquid state. The overwhelming majority of atoms are members of gases; and thus, if we are to understand the behavior of the sun, the stars, and the tenuous interstellar matter, we need to probe the fundamental properties of gases. To obtain as vivid a picture as we can, we shall look first at the *kinetic theory of gases*, which treats of the relationships among such familiar properties as pressure, density, and temperature. Although a brilliant construction, the kinetic theory does not deal with the fact that gases radiate, emitting light, radio radiation, and so on. Since we know the stars only from the radiant energy they send us, we shall next turn to the *laws of radiation* to discover how much energy is emitted by the stars and how this energy is distributed over the different parts of the spectrum. The radiation laws, in turn, are concerned with idealized bodies, bodies that are simpler than the stars. We shall then need to recognize that radiation is actually emitted and absorbed by the individual atoms that comprise a gas. To see how these processes work, we shall look at the rudiments of *atomic structure* and study the arrangement of those elementary particles which comprise every atom. Then we shall move on to a few results of the *quantum theory*, which describes the radiation of atoms. Finally, with the help of all this knowledge, we shall see how the *spectrum* of a star, obtained at the telescope, can reveal to us a tremendous wealth of information about the composition and physical conditions of that star.

GASES

1. Sun and Stars as Spheres of Gas

A TYPICAL star is a massive sphere of hot gas, of essentially constant size from one century to the next. Such a star is in *equilibrium*. If gravitation were suddenly turned off, the moving atoms in the sphere would fly away from each other and disperse. On the other hand, if the chaotic motions of the atoms could suddenly be stopped, the star

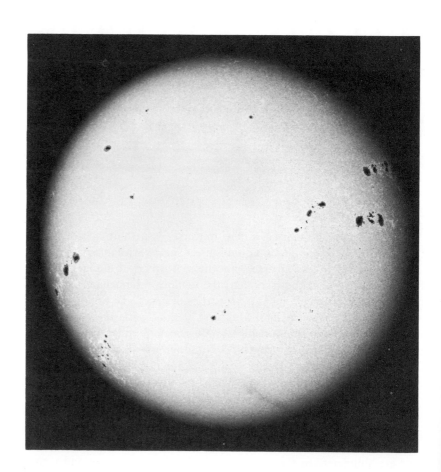

Fig. 11.1:1. The sun, a great sphere of gas in equilibrium. (*Mount Wilson and Palomar Observatories photograph*)

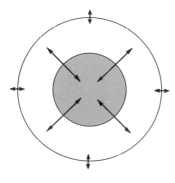

Fig. 11.1:2. A star in equilibrium. At any distance from the center the inward gravitational force is opposed by an equal outward pressure force.

would rapidly collapse because of the mutual gravitational attractive pull of every pair of atoms. If a star is to be in equilibrium, then at each spherical layer inside it the inward-directed gravitation force must be exactly balanced by the outward-directed pressure force, as shown in Fig. 11.1:2. If some demon should artificially stretch or squeeze such a star, these opposing forces would temporarily be forced out of balance. The star would respond by shrinking or swelling, readjusting its structure until it was in equilibrium once again.

IN THE KINETIC theory we imagine any cubic inch of a gas to consist of myriads of infinitesimal spheres, or atoms, dashing in all directions and colliding frequently with each other. The average distance between atoms is much greater than their own diameters, so that the fraction of space occupied by these tiny balls is very small. For example, a cubic inch of air under normal conditions contains 4×10^{20} particles. A typical atom travels at an average speed of 1600 ft/sec, about the length of a par-five golf hole. But because its average journey between collisions, or *mean free path*, is only three-millionths of an inch, its direction of motion is changed very frequently and it thus does not move far from its former location. Dividing the average speed by the mean free path, we find that the *collision frequency* is 6 billion per second for each atom. The individual particles are only about 10^{-8} inch in diameter, so that even though ordinary air contains 4×10^{20} of them in each cubic inch, they occupy less than one-thousandth of the available room.

To picture a gas, let us imagine a perfectly smooth square table edged with a rim. On it we place many similar marbles and set them moving in various directions at various speeds; once started, they are assumed to move indefinitely because there is no friction. Watching any one marble, we find that it collides frequently with others and moves in a random zigzag path. At one time its speed is nearly zero, and later, as a result of a particular sequence of collisions, its speed is well above the average. Statistically, however, its long-run average speed is found to be a definite constant amount and is the same as that of every other marble on the table. Since the marbles are all similar, there is no reason why the speed of one marble should be faster or slower than that of another. This average velocity, v, is one of the essential physical characteristics of our particular group of marbles. More generally, the average *kinetic energy*, or energy of motion, of any marble is a constant quantity; the kinetic energy of a body is $\frac{1}{2}mv^2$, where v is its speed and m is its mass.

Now, in the kinetic theory of gases the average kinetic energy per atom at any one instant is proportional to the *temperature* of the gas, reckoned from absolute zero. Thus the "temperature" of the zigzagging marbles is a perfectly definite quantity. If at a certain instant we double the speed of each marble, its kinetic energy is quadrupled and the "temperature" of the group is thus quadrupled. If later we suddenly stop each particle, the kinetic energy becomes zero and so does the temperature. In picturing a gas, it is useful to remember that temperature (more specifically, *kinetic temperature*) is simply a measure of the average speed of its member atoms in their chaotic random dance.

In our previous discussions we have usually expressed temperature in degrees Fahrenheit. In dealing with the physical nature of the sun and stars, it is far simpler to work with absolute temperature, which is expressed in degrees Kelvin. The scale of absolute temperature is the same as the centigrade scale, in which the span between the freezing point of water and the boiling point of water is 100°. The zero point of the absolute system is the state in which the kinetic energy of the atoms is zero; they would thus be motionless, and there can be nothing "colder." This state lies 273° (more accurately 273.16°) below the freezing point of water. In the three systems—absolute, centigrade, and Fahrenheit—absolute zero lies at 0°K, −273°C, and −460°F. The freezing point of water lies at 273°K, 0°C, and 32°F. The boiling point of water lies at 373°K, 100°C, and 212°F. Now let us leave the concept and definitions of temperature and return to our model.

Another characteristic of our group of similar marbles is their *number density*. On our two-dimensional table the number density is the total number of marbles divided by the area of the table. For example, there may be 50 marbles per square foot. If we double the total number, we double the number density, providing the size of the table has not been changed. Actual gases occupy three-dimensional space, of course, so that for them the number density must be expressed as a number per unit volume. Thus air at the earth's surface contains 4×10^{20} molecules per cubic inch and at an altitude of $3\frac{1}{2}$ miles only 2×10^{20} per cubic inch. For simplicity, the scientist usually prefers to work in metric units, and since there are $(2.54)^3$ or 16.4 cubic centimeters in one cubic inch, the number density of air molecules near sea level is about 3×10^{19} per cubic centimeter.

Any given marble on our rimmed table hits the rim occasionally and is reflected off again. The successive impacts of various marbles on the rim exert an average force on it; the measure of this force is the *pressure* of the group of marbles. The pressure is the same at all points on the rim and indeed at every point on any imaginary obstacle one might place on the table.

Now let us put all the marbles on one half of the table and separate them by a barrier from the empty half; their average velocity is to remain as before. In so doing we have doubled the number density but have not changed the temperature. Each atom now collides with the rim twice as frequently and the pressure is therefore doubled. Thus the pressure of a gas is proportional to the number density of its atoms. If the barrier is now removed, the marbles immediately move into the empty half and the pressure returns to its original value.

Next let us double the speed of each marble. Now collisions with the rim are twice as frequent and the force of each impact is doubled. The pressure is thereby increased by a factor of 4. If instead we triple the speed, the pressure increases ninefold. Quite generally, the pressure is proportional to the square of the average speed of the marbles and thus to the average kinetic energy or temperature. The pressure of a gas is thus proportional to the product of its density and temperature.

Another experiment we can try is to put slow-moving blue marbles on one half of the table and fast-moving red ones on the other half. When the barrier is removed, the marbles immediately diffuse into one another and become a mixture. Furthermore, because of collisions the faster red marbles tend to be slowed down and lose kinetic energy to the blue ones, which in turn are speeded up. Soon the average kinetic energy of each type is the same. This experiment shows how actual gases diffuse rapidly into one another and how hot and cool gases interpenetrating one another come to a common temperature.

Finally, imagine a mixture composed of marbles and more massive billiard balls. Because of their greater inertia, the billiard balls are not as much affected by collisions as are the lighter marbles. Their average speed is substantially less. The principle involved here is the *equipartition of energy*; in a mixture of gases the average kinetic energy of each kind of atom is the same, equally divided. Thus, since $\frac{1}{2}mv^2$ is the same for each type of particle, the light ones move faster. This principle accounts for the deficiency of hydrogen and helium in the earth's atmosphere. These atoms are so light that their speeds are high and they can readily escape from the earth.

At any instant the individual velocities of the particles in a single gas, hydrogen for example, differ greatly from one another. But statistically they follow a perfectly definite law. Most atoms at any given time are moving with speeds near the average; a few have higher or lower speeds. Figure 11.2:1 is a plot of the relative numbers of atoms with various speeds in terms of the most frequent speed. Unlike the speeds, the *directions* in which the atoms move show no preference; at any instant as many are moving in one direction as in any other direction.

In summary, the kinetic temperature of a gas measures the average kinetic energy of all the particles in it. At any instant the individual velocities and individual kinetic energies vary over a wide range, but the average is a perfectly definite quantity. If the gas is a mixture of particles of different masses, the average speed of the lighter atoms is greater than that of the heavier ones. Another fundamental property of a gas is the number density of its component atoms. The pressure of a gas is the force it exerts on a unit area of the container which holds it; it is proportional to number density and temperature. Pressure is also a measure of the kinetic energy per unit volume of a gas.

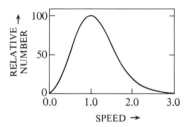

Fig. 11.2:1. The speeds of the individual atoms in a gas cluster around the most frequent speed. At any one instant less than one atom in a thousand is traveling faster than three times the most frequent speed.

RADIATION

3. The Nature of Radiation

ALTHOUGH THE sun and typical stars comprise hosts of atoms rushing about on zigzagging paths, and although there is a perfectly definite pressure, density, and temperature at each point inside them, the kinetic theory does not tell us how much and what kind of light they emit into space. Let us next turn, therefore, to the topic of radiation. In general, radiation may be thought of as energy moving from one place to another, such as heat emitted by a radiator or light moving through space from Vega to the earth. We are not now dealing with moving *matter* but with moving *energy*; and radiation in fact *is* a form of energy.

4. Waves and the Speed of Light

SOMETIMES it is instructive to think of radiation as consisting of moving waves. For example, when a stone is dropped into a calm pond, a series of circular waves moves outward away from the point where the stone was dropped. Similarly, when a red bulb is snapped on and off, a group of waves spreads outward in spheres at high speed away from the bulb. The speed of these waves, if they are moving in a vacuum, is always the same, and is of course the velocity of light, 186,300 mi/sec. When moving through a material medium, such as the earth's atmosphere or a lens, waves move slowly and are refracted and dispersed, as we saw in Chapter 5. But in a vacuum, where no matter is present, electromagnetic waves of all kinds move at precisely the same speed.

5. Wavelength and Frequency

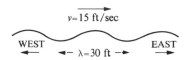

Fig. 11.5:1. The wavelength of an ocean wave.

IMAGINE THAT a series of ocean waves is traveling eastward at a velocity, v, of 15 ft/sec, and that the crest of each wave is a straight line running north and south. The distance from crest to crest or from trough to trough between successive waves is the *wavelength*, which is symbolized by λ. Suppose, for example, that in Fig. 11.5:1 the wavelength is 30 feet. The *frequency* of the wave, f, is the number of wave crests passing a fixed point per unit of time, or the number of times per second a floating chip bobs up and down. The general relationship between frequency and wavelength is given by

$$\text{Frequency} = \frac{\text{Wave velocity}}{\text{Wavelength}}.$$

In our specific example the frequency is

$$f = \frac{v}{\lambda} = \frac{15 \text{ ft/sec}}{30 \text{ ft}} = \frac{1}{2 \text{ sec}}.$$

Thus the chip moving up and down completes one cycle every 2 seconds; the frequency is said to be one-half per second.

The same relationship holds for radiation moving in a vacuum, but with the simplification that the wave velocity is the constant c, the speed of light. Thus the wavelength of red light is about 3×10^{-5} inch or 7×10^{-5} centimeter. Since the speed of light expressed in centimeters per second is 3×10^{10}, the frequency of vibration of red light is about 4×10^{14} per second. A radio station broadcasting at 1000 kilocycles per second or 10^6 vibrations per second is emitting radiant energy whose wavelength is 30,000 centimeters or about 1000 feet.

6. The Spectrum of Radiation

WE SAW IN Chapter 2 that the electromagnetic spectrum is not confined to the rainbow colors detectable by the unaided eye. In order of increasing frequency (decreasing wavelength), the broad bands of the spectrum are radio, infrared, visual, ultraviolet, X-ray, and gamma-ray. Waves of these different frequencies all move at the velocity of light in a vacuum; the only thing that differentiates one from another is the frequency or wavelength.

7. The Doppler Effect

A PRINCIPLE of crucial importance in astronomy was discovered by the Austrian physicist Christian Doppler in the midnineteenth century. Imagine that you are at anchor in the ocean waves described in Section 5, with the boat pitching up and down once every 2 seconds. Tiring of this, you haul up the anchor and motor westward *into* the waves. You now meet the waves more frequently, perhaps every $1\frac{1}{2}$ seconds; thus the measured time between wave crests is now less and the frequency greater because of your motion into the waves. Annoyed by the more frequent pitching, you now turn around and motor eastward *with* the waves. The waves now overtake you less frequently, perhaps only every $2\frac{1}{2}$ seconds; as far as you are now concerned, the frequency is less than before.

In the same fashion, sound waves change in apparent frequency. When the source and listener are approaching each other the pitch of the note is of higher frequency; when they are receding the pitch is lowered. When a car with a jammed horn comes along the road, the pitch is a given note as the car approaches, and then as it passes and begins to recede, the pitch rapidly drops down. The same phenomenon holds for radiation: the light from an approaching star is received by us at a higher frequency than its frequency at the source; that from a receding star is shifted to a lower frequency. The quantitative expression for the Doppler effect is

$$\frac{\text{Change of frequency}}{\text{Frequency}} = \frac{\text{Change of wavelength}}{\text{Wavelength}} = \frac{\text{Radial velocity}}{\text{Velocity of light}}.$$

The *radial velocity* of any two objects is the rate of change of the distance between them. Figure 11.7:1 illustrates the radial velocity of two automobiles at several instants of time. Both cars are traveling at 50 mi/hr, with A southbound and reaching the intersection before B, which is eastbound. At time 1 the cars are at $A1$ and $B1$ and their rate of approach must be found by adding that part of each car's velocity vector which lies along the line joining them. In this particular instance the radial velocity is -68 mi/hr at time 1, the negative sign being used because the cars are approaching one another. At time 2, with car A at the intersection, the radial velocity is -50 mi/hr; at time 3, with car B at the intersection, it is $+50$ mi/hr; at time 4 it is $+68$ mi/hr. At the instant of closest approach, halfway between times 2 and 3, the cars are neither approaching nor receding from one another; the radial velocity is then zero.

If the spectrogram of a star is obtained, and if also the spectrum of a motionless laboratory source of light is photographed on the same photographic plate, the spectral lines of the star will all be shifted relative to their laboratory wavelengths, each in an amount proportional

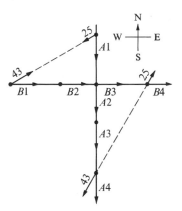

Fig. 11.7:1. Dots indicate four successive locations of cars A and B, each traveling at 50 mi/hr. The radial velocity on the four occasions is given in the text.

to the laboratory wavelength itself. For example, if the stellar lines are displaced to the short-wave or violet side of the laboratory lines by one part in 10 thousand, then the radial velocity of the star is

$$\text{Radial velocity} = -\frac{1}{10,000} \times \text{Velocity of light}$$

$$= -18.6 \text{ mi/sec.}$$

Fig. 11.7:2. Illustration of the Doppler effect in stellar spectra. Spectra ($\lambda4200$ A to $\lambda4300$ A) of the constant velocity star Arcturus taken about six months apart. **(a)** July 1, 1939; measured velocity $+18$ km/sec. **(b)** Jan. 19, 1940; measured velocity -32 km/sec. The velocity difference of 50 km/sec is entirely due to the orbital velocity of the earth. (*Mount Wilson and Palomar Observatories photograph*)

By convention, the negative sign refers to an approaching source, the positive sign to one that is receding.

8. The Laws of Radiation

LET US NEXT inquire how much energy is radiated at each wavelength by a so-called *black body*, which is the name given to a perfect absorber and emitter of radiation. To gain a definite picture, imagine an enclosure whose walls, kept at a definite temperature T, absorb and re-emit all of the radiant energy that is incident on them. Then in the wall make a small hole which will let radiation emerge from the enclosure. If spectra of the emerging light are recorded for a variety of different temperatures, two effects are noticed.

(1) The higher the temperature inside the enclosure the bluer the color of the emerging radiation, and the lower the temperature the redder the color, until at absolute zero the color would be "black" because there would be no radiation at all. Quantitatively, the wavelength at which a black body emits the greatest amount of energy is inversely proportional to its absolute temperature; this relationship is known as *Wien's law*. If we designate the wavelength of maximum emission by λ_{max}, then Wien's law states that

$$\lambda_{max} = \frac{0.29 \text{ cm degree}}{T}.$$

Here λ_{max} is in centimeters and T is in degrees absolute. The sun, although not a perfect black body, may be used as an example. Its surface temperature is about 5800°K, and thus $\lambda_{max} = 5.0 \times 10^{-5}$ cm. This wavelength is in the middle part of the visual spectrum, accounting for the yellowish color of the sun. A star like Rigel, with twice the surface temperature of the sun, has a radiation peak at only half the wavelength; its color is thus white or bluish-white. A star like Betelgeuse is cooler than the sun and thus is reddish in color.

(2) The higher the temperature inside the enclosure the greater the amount of radiant energy emerging through the hole. The specific relationship is known as *Stefan's law*, which states that

$$Q = AT^4.$$

In this formula Q stands for the total radiant energy at all wavelengths emitted in all directions in one second by one square centimeter of the surface of a black body, and T is the absolute temperature of the body. The constant of proportionality is

$$A = 5.7 \times 10^{-5} \frac{\text{erg}}{\text{cm}^2 \text{ sec degree}^4}.$$

Substituting 5800° in the equation for Stefan's law, we find that a square centimeter at the sun's surface emits in one second about 6×10^{10} ergs of radiant energy. This quantity is roughly equal to the kinetic energy of a brick when it hits the ground after being dropped from the top of a tall skyscraper. A star like Rigel, which has twice the surface temperature of the sun, emits not twice but 2^4, or 16, times as much radiant energy per second from a unit area of its surface as does the sun. Thus the hotter a black body of given size, the shorter the wavelength at which it radiates the most energy and the greater the total amount radiated at all frequencies.

9. Planck Curves

THE COMPLETE solution to the problem of how much energy a black body emits at every wavelength was solved by the German physicist Max Planck around 1900. The resulting equation is rather complex, and we shall not set it down here. Instead, let us examine the curves of Fig. 11.9:1, which are plotted from Planck's equation for black bodies at several different radiation temperatures. The horizontal scale is in wavelength units, and the vertical scale is radiant energy

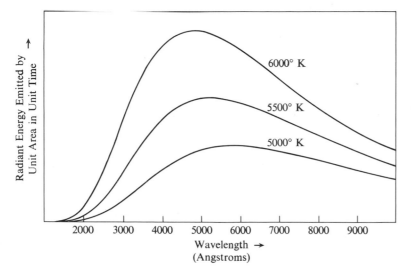

Fig. 11.9:1. Planck curves for bodies at different radiation temperatures.

output. Notice that the *peak* of any curve for a hotter body lies at a *shorter* wavelength than it does on the curve for any colder body, as stated in Wien's law. Also notice that every point on the hotter curve lies above its counterpart (at the same wavelength) on the cooler curve. The total area under any curve represents the total energy output at all wavelengths; it is found to be proportional to the fourth power of the temperature, as it should be according to Stefan's law.

If the sun and stars were ideal radiators, their spectra would be perfectly smooth or continuous, like the Planck curves. In actuality, the spectrum of a typical star consists of a fairly smooth continuum of light at all visual wavelengths, but superimposed on this structure is a host of dark lines. In order to understand why these lines appear, we must leave the Planck curves and delve into the problem of atomic structure.

THE STRUCTURE OF ATOMS

10. The Chemical Elements

ALL MATTER is composed of atoms, the fundamental building blocks of the material universe. There are 92 different kinds of atoms or chemical elements found in nature, ranging from the simplest and lightest, hydrogen, to massive uranium. A few other heavier elements can be produced inside stars under natural circumstances or can be made artificially in high-energy accelerators; these transuranic atoms are radioactive and decay into something else in a relatively short time. The total number of known and named chemical elements has passed the 100 mark.

11. Molecules and Mixtures

WHEN CONDITIONS are right and the temperature is not high, individual atoms of various kinds can bond together to form molecules. Every molecule of water comprises two hydrogen atoms and one oxygen atom and its symbol is H_2O; similarly, carbon monoxide is CO, for each molecule consists of one carbon atom and one oxygen atom. An example of a more complex molecule is cane sugar, $C_{12}H_{22}O_{11}$. If any one of these substances is in the pure form, then each one of its molecules is like every other one, and the collection is called a *chemical compound*. More complicated than a compound is a *mixture*, which comprises individual atoms or molecules in arbitrary proportions. Air, for example, is a mixture chiefly of N_2 molecules and O_2 molecules, together with minor amounts of argon atoms, CO_2 molecules, and other substances. In addition, a variable percentage of H_2O molecules is present.

A star is a mixture, since it is composed of a variety of substances. But because it is hot throughout, at best only a few of the more strongly bonded kinds of molecules can withstand the rigor of continued violent collisions. Most stellar matter is thus in the atomic form. Let us therefore turn away from jamming atoms together to make molecules and look at the structure of the atom itself.

12. The Fundamental Particles

ALTHOUGH THE name "atom" derives from the Greek *atomos*, meaning "indivisible," any one of these tiny building blocks is actually composed of a number of even more fundamental particles: *protons*, *neutrons*, and *electrons*. Providing the analogy is not carried too far, an atom may conveniently be pictured as a miniature solar system; at its center is a relatively massive and compact *nucleus* consisting of protons and neutrons. Moving around the nucleus is a cloud of very light electrons. The radius of this electron cloud, although minute by ordinary standards, is roughly 10 thousand times as great as that of the nucleus. These figures stand in about the same ratio as the semimajor axis of Pluto's orbit to the radius of the central sun itself.

13. Nuclei and Isotopes

EACH PROTON carries one unit of positive electric charge and has a mass of 1.67×10^{-24} gram. Each neutron has a zero charge and a mass very nearly equal to that of the proton. Any possible kind of atomic nucleus can be characterized by two distinct numbers: one that tells the amount of its electric charge and another that tells its mass. The first of these is the *atomic number* and uniquely identifies the chemical element in question. Hydrogen has atomic number 1 and thus the nucleus of each hydrogen atom has one unit of positive charge, or one proton; uranium has atomic number 92 and hence any atom of uranium has 92 protons. The second number is the *mass number* and indicates the total number of protons and neutrons in the nucleus. For example, ordinary hydrogen has mass number 1 and thus contains one proton and no neutrons. An ordinary uranium atom has mass number 238; since it must contain 92 protons to be uranium, it has to contain 146 neutrons so that the total number of nuclear particles will add up to 238. In principle, then, each chemical element, such as tin with atomic number 50, can exist with different mass numbers. The different types of tin or any other kind of atom are its *isotopes*. More abundant than other sorts of tin atoms is the isotope with mass number 120. Each such atom thus contains 70 neutrons. Several other isotopes of tin are known, however, with mass numbers 118, 116, 119, and so on. Only a limited number of the possible isotopes of an element are stable; for such atoms as beryllium, aluminum, and gold, only one stable isotope is known; tin, on the other hand, has ten known stable isotopes. An isotope is designated by writing the atomic number as a subscript, followed by the chemical symbol, followed by a superscript giving the mass number. Thus $_1H^1$ represents ordinary hydrogen, $_2He^4$ ordinary helium, $_{92}U^{238}$ ordinary uranium, whereas $_{50}Sn^{120}$ and $_{50}Sn^{118}$ are two of the isotopes of tin.

14. Electrons and Ions

ALTHOUGH WE shall deal more with atomic nuclei later on, we shall here consider their attendant outer electrons, upon which the

TABLE 11.13:1. The Chemical Elements [a]

Name	Symbol	A	M	Name	Symbol	A	M
Hydrogen	H	1	1	Iodine	I	53	127
Helium	He	2	4	Xenon	Xe	54	132
Lithium	Li	3	7	Cesium	Cs	55	133
Beryllium	Be	4	9	Barium	Ba	56	138
Boron	B	5	11	Lanthanum	La	57	139
Carbon	C	6	12	Cerium	Ce	58	140
Nitrogen	N	7	14	Praseodymium	Pr	59	141
Oxygen	O	8	16	Neodymium	Nd	60	142
Fluorine	F	9	19	Promethium	Pm	61	147
Neon	Ne	10	20	Samarium	Sm	62	152
Sodium	Na	11	23	Europium	Eu	63	153
Magnesium	Mg	12	24	Gadolinium	Gd	64	158
Aluminum	Al	13	27	Terbium	Tb	65	159
Silicon	Si	14	28	Dysprosium	Dy	66	164
Phosphorus	P	15	31	Holmium	Ho	67	165
Sulphur	S	16	32	Erbium	Er	68	166
Chlorine	Cl	17	35	Thulium	Tm	69	169
Argon	Ar	18	40	Ytterbium	Yb	70	174
Potassium	K	19	39	Lutecium	Lu	71	175
Calcium	Ca	20	40	Hafnium	Hf	72	180
Scandium	Sc	21	45	Tantalum	Ta	73	181
Titanium	Ti	22	48	Tungsten	W	74	184
Vanadium	V	23	51	Rhenium	Re	75	187
Chromium	Cr	24	52	Osmium	Os	76	192
Manganese	Mn	25	55	Iridium	Ir	77	193
Iron	Fe	26	56	Platinum	Pt	78	195
Cobalt	Co	27	59	Gold	Au	79	197
Nickel	Ni	28	58	Mercury	Hg	80	202
Copper	Cu	29	63	Thallium	Tl	81	205
Zinc	Zn	30	64	Lead	Pb	82	208
Gallium	Ga	31	69	Bismuth	Bi	83	209
Germanium	Ge	32	74	Polonium	Po	84	210
Arsenic	As	33	75	Astatine	At	85	210
Selenium	Se	34	80	Radon	Rn	86	222
Bromine	Br	35	79	Francium	Fr	87	223
Krypton	Kr	36	84	Radium	Ra	88	226
Rubidium	Rb	37	85	Actinium	Ac	89	227
Strontium	Sr	38	88	Thorium	Th	90	232
Yttrium	Y	39	89	Protactinium	Pa	91	231
Zirconium	Zr	40	90	Uranium	U	92	238
Niobium	Nb	41	93	Neptunium	Np	93	237
Molybdenum	Mo	42	98	Plutonium	Pu	94	242
Technetium	Tc	43	99	Americium	Am	95	243
Ruthenium	Ru	44	102	Curium	Cm	96	247
Rhodium	Rh	45	103	Berkelium	Bk	97	249
Palladium	Pd	46	106	Californium	Cf	98	251
Silver	Ag	47	107	Einsteinium	Es	99	254
Cadmium	Cd	48	114	Fermium	Fm	100	253
Indium	In	49	115	Mendelevium	Md	101	256
Tin	Sn	50	120	Nobelium	No	102	254
Antimony	Sb	51	121	Lawrencium	Lw	103	257
Tellurium	Te	52	130				

[a] The column headed A gives the atomic number. The column headed M gives the mass number of the most abundant isotope of each element, except for atomic number 84 and above, for which the mass number of the most stable isotope is given.

ordinary radiation as well as the chemical properties of atoms depend. Each electron carries one unit of negative electric charge and has a mass of 9.11×10^{-28} gram. Thus the charge of the electron is of opposite sign but of the same amount as that of the proton. The mass of an electron, however, is only 1/1840 that of the proton, roughly comparable with the ratio of Jupiter's mass to that of the sun. When an atom is in its electrically *neutral* state, it must have as many outer negative electrons as nuclear positive protons so that its net charge is zero. Hence the atomic number of a chemical element tells not only the number of protons per atom, but also the number of electrons associated with the nucleus of a neutral atom of that element. A neutral atom of the ordinary isotope of hydrogen therefore consists of one proton, no neutrons, and one electron. The electron may be thought of moving in a two-body orbit around the proton because of the *electrostatic* force of attraction exerted by the massive proton on the light electron. The electrostatic force of attraction between two particles of opposite charge is an inverse-square law, like gravitation, but it is proportional to the product of the two charges, rather than to the two masses as in gravitation. For a proton–electron pair the electrostatic force is about 10^{39} times as strong as the gravitational attraction. Thus a neutral hydrogen atom may be pictured as a relatively massive central proton around which an electron circles rapidly, held in its orbit by the electrostatic pull of the proton.

Under conditions of very high temperature most of the atoms in a gas will be lacking one or more of their normal complement of electrons. The electrons may, for example, be knocked away from their parents as a result of the energetic collisions of the fast-moving atoms. Atoms without their full complement of electrons are called *ions*, and a gas in such a state is said to be *ionized*. A gas of neutral hydrogen is designated H I; a gas of ionized hydrogen H II. Neutral helium is labeled He I, helium with one of its electrons missing is said to be singly ionized and is labeled He II, and helium with both of its electrons missing is doubly ionized and is labeled He III. Similarly, Fe XIV refers to iron with 13 of its 26 electrons detached. A fully ionized atom is a bare, positively charged nucleus with no electrons at all; a few such are H II, He III, and Fe XXVII.

A cool neutral hydrogen gas may be pictured as a host of similar neutral hydrogen atoms moving about at random and colliding with one another, although not energetically enough for any appreciable number of outer electrons to be knocked away from their parent protons. A hot, fully ionized hydrogen gas, on the other hand, is a mélange of free electrons rushing around at high speed among the protons, but no particular electron belongs for long to any given proton. Each particle of the gas is charged, although the gas as a whole is neutral. Although there is a force of attraction between the members of every proton–electron pair, any electron that should, in response to this force, chance to combine with a proton is very soon set free as a result of a vigorous atomic collision. Thus at a high enough temperature only a minute fraction of all the atoms will at any instant be neutral;

for all practical purposes the gas is fully ionized. It is useful to remember that in this ionized hydrogen gas, as always, the average kinetic energy of the free electrons and free protons is the same; therefore, since the electron is only 1/1840 as massive as the proton, the average speed of the free electrons is $\sqrt{1840}$ or 43 times as great as that of the protons.

Returning to atoms that have electrons moving around them, we find that the electrons do not reside at haphazard distances from their parent nuclei but rather in shells of various sizes. The innermost, or first, shell may contain no more that $2 \times (1)^2$ or 2 electrons; the second shell at most $2 \times (2)^2$ or 8, and so on. Thus the one electron of hydrogen is normally in the first shell and both electrons of neutral helium are also there. The neutral lithium atom, with three electrons, has two filling up the first shell and the third one is relegated to the outer second shell. Atoms having all their shells filled are complete structures; they are sufficient unto themselves and must be battered with exceptional vigor to become ionized. They are the inert gases, of which the two lightest are helium (atomic number 2) and neon (atomic number 10). Atoms such as lithium (atomic number 3) and sodium (atomic number 11) have, when neutral, a lonesome electron moving in an outer shell and will become ionized at much lower temperatures. The properties of a given kind of chemical element at ordinary temperatures depend intimately on the number of electrons present in the outermost occupied shell.

THE BIRTH AND DEATH OF LIGHT

15. Photons

IN DEALING with radiation, it is often convenient to set aside the notion of waves temporarily and to substitute a picture of light or other radiant energy as a stream of essentially massless corpuscles or parcels of energy. One of these corpuscles is called a *photon* or a *quantum*, and the study of the interaction of photons with matter is a part of the *quantum theory*, proposed by Planck about 1900. One photon differs from another only in its energy; all photons move at the same velocity, c, the same quantity we earlier found for the velocity of electromagnetic waves in a vacuum. A fundamental rule enunciated by Planck is that the energy of a photon is proportional to its frequency, and frequency is here defined precisely as in Section 5. The relating equation is

$$E = hf,$$

where E is the energy of a photon, f its frequency, and h Planck's constant. The numerical value of this fundamental constant of nature is $h = 6.62 \times 10^{-27}$ erg sec. Earlier we saw that the frequency of red light is about 4×10^{14} per second. In our present picture, then, a single photon of red light has

$$E = 6.62 \times 10^{-27} \text{ erg sec} \times \frac{4 \times 10^{14}}{\text{sec}} = 2.6 \times 10^{-12} \text{ erg.}$$

If, for concreteness, we think of the sun in terms of the quantum picture, we envisage each patch of the solar surface emitting an enormous number of photons in all directions every second, each one characterized by a given frequency, or wavelength, and moving at the speed of light in a given direction. The relative number of photons at each energy is such that the spectrum of sunlight is approximately that of a black body at 5800°K. The *intensity* of sunshine depends on the number of solar photons striking the eye each second. In the corpuscular picture a distant star is faint because only relatively few of its photons hit the eye each second, whereas the sun is bright because the number is large.

16. Emission and Absorption

THUS FAR we have dealt separately with matter in the form of atoms and radiant energy in the form of photons. Let us now weld these concepts together with the statement that whenever a change occurs in the internal structure or energy of an atom, a photon of radiation is either produced or consumed. Alternatively stated, whenever an atom produces, or *emits*, a photon of radiation, it loses a bit of energy; because of the law of conservation of energy, the state of this atom must change so that its new energy is less by an amount equal to the energy of the departing photon. Whenever an atom consumes, or *absorbs*, a photon from outside, on the other hand, it has gained energy and its structure must change so that its new energy is greater by an amount equal to that of the incident photon.

Imagine a hydrogen gas that is neither very hot nor very cool. At any instant most of the atoms are neutral, each with one electron circling the nucleus and neither emitting nor absorbing light. But all is not quiet; since the temperature is not zero, atoms are moving and thus colliding with one another, in accord with kinetic theory. Also, many photons are flying around in accord with the laws of radiation. First, suppose one atom receives some energy from another one as the result of a collision; this energy may be used to send the electron out to a bigger shell or orbit of higher energy. Second, an atom may absorb a photon from those that are flying around and use this energy to put its electron in a bigger orbit; the absorbed photon exists no more. Whichever the method, the atom is said to be *excited*. Once excited, however, an inverse process occurs; after about 10^{-8} second the electron jumps *spontaneously* down to a smaller orbit of lower energy, the excess energy, E, being emitted in a random direction as a photon of energy E and hence frequency f, governed by the Planck formula, $E = hf$. Thus the myriad atoms of hydrogen are continually emitting and absorbing photons of radiation, and if the temperature and number density of the gas are constant at all points and times, the processes are in balance and at each frequency the number of photons flying about is the same at all points and times. That is, the *spectrum* of the radiation, as recorded any place by a hypothetical spectrograph, would always look the same.

ATOMS, RADIATION, AND
SPECTRA

17. Bohr and the Hydrogen Atom

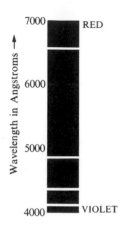

Wavelength in Angstroms →

7000 — RED

6000

5000

4000 — VIOLET

Fig. 11.17:1. The bright lines of hydrogen in the visual part of the spectrum.

WE MUST next account for the fact that the spectrum of a hot and rarefied gas is not continuous like that of the black bodies shown in Fig. 11.9:1, but is instead a series of sharp bright lines separated by broad dark spaces. In particular, the spectrum of hydrogen in the visual range of wavelengths shows bright lines, as indicated in Fig. 11.17:1. Two things are evident from the illustration. (1) In a rarefied gas, whose atoms of course are not crowded close together, the photons emitted are of certain definite wavelengths or energies and no others. We have already seen that a black body radiates energy at *all* wavelengths of the spectrum; a rarefied gas, on the other hand, does not. Crudely, one may think of the difference as akin to the places where boats may ply; in the oceans they can be anywhere, but on a continent they are highly restricted and can only be on rivers or lakes, because land surfaces are forbidden territory. (2) The spacings between the spectral lines of hydrogen are by no means random but get closer and closer toward the violet end of the spectrum, coalescing beyond the left edge of the diagram. Johann Balmer in 1885 found an empirical formula for the wavelengths of all these lines, which is

$$\frac{\lambda}{\lambda_0} = \frac{1}{\left(\frac{1}{2^2} - \frac{1}{n^2}\right)},$$

where the constant λ_0 is a fixed wavelength of 9.12×10^{-6} cm. To avoid repeated use of negative exponents, it is convenient here to introduce the Angstrom unit of length; it is defined by $1 \text{ A} = 10^{-8}$ cm. Hence $\lambda_0 = 912$ A, a wavelength in the ultraviolet part of the spectrum whose significance we shall see presently. When $n = 3$, the above formula gives $\lambda = (36/5)\lambda_0 = 6563$ A, which is the observed wavelength of the red line of hydrogen. When $n = 4$, $\lambda = (16/3)\lambda_0 = 4861$ A, the blue line of hydrogen. Successively setting $n = 5, 6, 7$, and so on, and calculating each wavelength, we find precise agreement with the observed spectral pattern. When n gets very large, $1/n^2$ is very small and thus successive lines are very close together. The limiting value of the series of lines comes where n is infinite and thus $1/n^2 = 0$. Here, then, $\lambda = 4\lambda_0 = 3646$ A. This whole series of spectral lines is called the *Balmer series*, and the minimum wavelength at 3646 A is called the *Balmer limit*; the red line ($n = 3$) is known as Hα, the blue line as Hβ, and so on.

Other series of hydrogen lines have been discovered experimentally, and they can all be represented by the formula

$$\frac{\lambda}{\lambda_0} = \frac{1}{\left(\frac{1}{m^2} - \frac{1}{n^2}\right)},$$

where m is an integer and n is some integer greater than m. When $m = 2$, we have the Balmer series already described. When $m = 1$, we have a series of wavelengths in the ultraviolet ranging from 1216 A when $n = 2$ to 912 A when n is infinite. This series has been observed in the spectrum of rarefied hydrogen in the laboratory and is called the *Lyman series*. The wavelength of 912 A where the Lyman lines coalesce is the *Lyman limit*; the line at 1216 A is Lα, the next is Lβ, and so on. The *Paschen series* of spectral lines corresponds to $m = 3$, and these lines lie in the infrared between 18751 A, when $n = 4$, and 8863 A for the *Paschen limit*. The *Brackett series*, for $m = 4$, lies even further in the infrared.

Thus the wavelengths of all the spectral lines of hydrogen can be represented by one empirical formula. The discovery of this empirical formula is reminiscent of the achievement of Kepler in establishing his harmonic law. The first correct theory accounting for the Balmer formula was worked out by the Danish physicist Niels Bohr in 1913. His achievement in finding the deeper significance of the relationship in terms of fundamental physical quantities is similar to the deductive work of Newton on planetary motions. Bohr started with Coulomb's law of electrostatic attraction, which states that opposite electric charges exert forces on each other that vary inversely as the square of the distance between them. A consequence of this law, as we have seen, is that the negative electron moves in an orbit around the positive nucleus. To account for the sharp lines in the hydrogen spectrum, Bohr added two new axioms. (1) The electron cannot move in any orbit whatever, but only at certain definite distances from the proton. More precisely, this axiom states that the angular momentum of the electron must be an integral multiple of $h/2\pi$, where h is Planck's constant. (2) When an atom emits or absorbs radiant energy, this energy is in the form of a single photon of energy $E = hf$. And because of the law of conservation of energy, the energy of the atom changes by exactly this amount.

It follows from the first axiom concerning angular momentum that the radii of the allowed orbits increase as the squares of the integers; if the innermost is of unit radius, then the next is four times as large, the next nine, and so on. The *energy* of the atom is a minimum when the electron is in the innermost orbit and greater as it is farther out. Suppose an electron jumps spontaneously from outer shell n to an inner shell m. Then it is a consequence of Bohr's work that the energy *difference* between these orbits is proportional to

$$\frac{1}{m^2} - \frac{1}{n^2}.$$

This quantity must equal the energy of the outgoing photon, which is

$$hf = \frac{hc}{\lambda}.$$

Thus the Bohr theory predicts a formula the same as that of Balmer's empirical equation, or

$$\lambda \propto \frac{1}{\dfrac{1}{m^2} - \dfrac{1}{n^2}}.$$

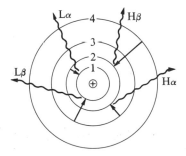

Fig. 11.17:2. Some possible events that can occur in a hydrogen atom. Each straight arrow represents a downward electron jump and the attendant wavy arrow represents the simultaneous emission of a photon of radiation. (Not drawn to scale.)

Moreover, the constant of proportionality is given in terms of three fundamental constants: the mass of the electron, its electric charge, and Planck's constant. When evaluated numerically, the constant is $\lambda_0 = 912$ A, which is in agreement with the empirical determination of Balmer three decades earlier.

Thus there emerges a picture of an electron jumping from some definite outer orbit down to another inner orbit, accompanied by the emission of a photon of perfectly definite wavelength. Another electron jumps from an inner orbit to an outer orbit only if the atom receives from outside a perfectly definite amount of energy and no other. Figure 11.17:2 shows schematically the different shells or orbits for hydrogen. Whenever an electron spontaneously jumps from any outer orbit down to orbit 1, a photon of the Lyman series is emitted. A jump from 2 to 1 produces a quantum of Lα at 1216 A, from 3 to 1 a quantum of Lβ at 1026 A, and from a shell far out to 1 a quantum near 912 A. The Balmer series represents all transitions down to orbit 2. A jump from 3 to 2 is accompanied by a quantum of Hα in the red, from 4 to 2 a quantum of Hβ in the blue, and so on.

18. Excitation

UNDER QUIESCENT conditions the electrons of most atoms in a hydrogen gas will be moving in the innermost orbit, of radius 5×10^{-9} cm = 0.5 A. This innermost orbit is the so-called *ground state*. When the electron is circling in any outer orbit, the atom is in an *excited state*; and from this outer orbit the electron usually makes an immediate transition or series of transitions down to the ground state, accompanied by the emission of one or more photons. For example, if an electron is in the fourth orbit, it may take a variety of routes down to the first orbit: a direct jump $4 \rightarrow 1$ is accompanied by the emission of a photon of Lγ; a jump $4 \rightarrow 2$ followed by $2 \rightarrow 1$ is accompanied by a photon of Hβ and another of Lα; other routes are also possible. The relative numbers of atoms which at any instant have their electrons in various orbits depend on the temperature. If the gas is cool, an excited atom is a rarity; even at the temperature of the solar surface only four out of every billion atoms on the average have their electrons in the second orbit at any one instant. At a temperature of 50,000°K, however, the vigor of collisions and the copious supply of photons flying about mean that there is one atom with an electron in the second orbit for every three atoms with their electrons in the ground state.

19. Ionization

IF A HYDROGEN gas is both extremely hot and of low density, most of its atoms will be superexcited, or *ionized*. An atom in the ground state is likely to receive enough energy from collision with another atom or by absorbing an energetic ultraviolet photon so that the orbital electron is completely ejected from the atom. For the hydrogen atom this energy corresponds to a photon with $\lambda = 912$ A. The higher the temperature the greater the proportion of atoms that are ionized. Thus among the neutral atoms run free electrons and free protons, the protons seeking to capture free electrons and become neutral once again. If the gas is of low density, there simply are not many free electrons to be found; once ionized, a hydrogen atom will tend to stay that way. Therefore both high temperature *and* low density favor ionization.

Unlike the definite transitions between electron orbits which are responsible for photons of definite wavelengths, transitions between the neutral state and the ionized state involve radiation that is not thus restricted. A hydrogen atom in the ground state may absorb a passing photon of *any* wavelength shorter than 912 A. The energy corresponding to 912 A is utilized to raise the electron from $n = 1$ to $n = \infty$; the balance is the kinetic energy of motion of the departing electron. For instance, if a photon of $\lambda = 800$ A is absorbed from the radiation field, the electron has enough energy to escape from the atom and also leave the vicinity with a speed of about 8×10^7 cm/sec. This speed is comparable to but somewhat less than the speed of an electron in the innermost orbit of a neutral hydrogen atom, which is 22×10^7 cm/sec, or 1400 mi/sec. In a similar way a free proton may attract and capture a passing electron, becoming a neutral atom. Accompanying this recombination is the emission of a photon of energy equal to the sum of the kinetic energy of the electron and the ionization energy of hydrogen. The visual spectrum of hot rarefied hydrogen thus not only shows the discrete lines of the Balmer series arising from jumps of various electrons from outer orbits down to the second orbit; in addition, to the violet side of the Balmer limit there is a faint *continuum* of radiation arising from all the ionized atoms which at that moment are regaining electrons via the route $n = \infty$ to $n = 2$. Similarly, there is a continuum of light to the high-energy side of the Lyman and other series.

20. Complex Atoms

OUR DISCUSSION thus far has stressed the behavior of hydrogen both because it is the simplest chemical element and because more than 90 percent of the atoms in the known universe are hydrogen. The spectra of other neutral elements are more complex. The Bohr theory has had to be changed and extended to cope with these heavier elements because they have more electrons, each one of which can occupy a number of possible orbits. The number of possible transitions and their energy differences is very large, and therefore the number of spectrum lines is likely to be great. In addition, the spectral pattern of a neutral atom, of oxygen for example, is quite different from that of singly ionized oxygen. The latter is different from the spectral pattern of doubly ionized oxygen, and so on. One simplification, however, is that of the *isoelectronic sequences.* Singly ionized helium has one electron and thus structurally resembles neutral hydrogen, apart from the fact that its nucleus of two protons exerts double the electrostatic force on the orbiting electron. The energy differences of the allowed transitions are four times as great as for hydrogen, and thus each line of the spectrum of singly ionized helium has four times the frequency, or one-fourth the wavelength, of the corresponding line in the hydrogen spectrum. We saw before that the Lyman limit of hydrogen occurs at $\lambda = 912$ A; the corresponding limit for He II is thus in the extreme ultraviolet at $\lambda = 228$ A. Similarly, Li III resembles H I, but each possible transition has an energy nine times the corresponding one for hydrogen.

SPECTRUM LINES

21. The Three Kinds of Spectra

LUMINOUS sources produce three different kinds of spectra: *continuous*, *emission*, and *absorption*. A continuous spectrum, in which light of all wavelengths is present, is given off by an incandescent solid, liquid, or dense gas. We have already seen that an ideal black body, for example a dense gas in a hot enclosure, emits radiation of all frequencies in accordance with the Planck curves for various temperatures. Such radiation is entirely independent of the kinds of atoms present in the gas.

An emission, or bright-line, spectrum is given off by a hot rarefied gas. Light of only selected wavelengths is present: at those definite wavelengths corresponding to allowed electron transitions and also in the bright continua as ions capture free electrons. We speak of emission "lines" because this is the shape of the images formed by the slit of the spectrograph; what we are referring to in using the term is radiation of a single wavelength. What the spectrograph is "seeing" at any given wavelength, Hα for example, is all of those particular photons which were produced by atoms whose electrons jumped from level 3 to 2 during the exposure and which were sent in the direction of the telescope objective.

Each stage of ionization of every chemical element has its own individual pattern of emission lines; this pattern, observed in the laboratory or worked out by computation, serves as a unique thumbprint when we come to study the composition of the stars.

It may seem curious that the continuous spectrum of a black body is independent of its composition, whereas that of a hot and rarefied gas is crucially dependent on what it consists of and also that the two types of spectra are so extremely different in appearance. Actually, there is a continuous gradation between the two types that depends on the density of the gas. In a rarefied hydrogen gas the atoms are relatively far apart and emit and absorb in accordance with the Bohr theory. In a gas of higher density the atoms are much closer together and thus the electrostatic force on an orbiting electron is modified continually and markedly as other particles pass near. Photons may be emitted at frequencies well away from the normal frequencies for an undisturbed atom. If the medium is dense enough, the sharp lines are completely smeared out and a continuous spectrum is produced. Although a person may walk resolutely in a given direction when he is alone, he is apt to find himself doing something quite different if he is part of a moving mob.

An absorption, or dark-line, spectrum is produced when a cooler and rarefied gas lies between the spectrograph and a hotter source of a continuous spectrum. The absorption spectrum of hydrogen, for example, is the reverse of its emission spectrum: light appears at all wavelengths *except* at the Balmer lines and in the Balmer continuum to the violet of 3646 A. Imagine rarefield hydrogen in front of a hotter and more distant black body. A photon with $\lambda = 5000$ A emitted by the black body will get through the rarefied hydrogen and reach the spectrograph, for there is no line in the hydrogen spectrum at this wavelength; hence no such photon can be absorbed. Another photon at $\lambda = 6563$ A emitted by the black body will probably not get through, for this is the wavelength of Hα. The photon will probably ram a hydrogen atom whose electron is in the second orbit; it will be absorbed, exciting the electron to the third orbit. About 10^{-8} second later the electron will jump from 3 to 1, emitting a photon of Lβ in a random direction, or from 3 to 2 and then 2 to 1, emitting Hα in some random direction and Lα in another random direction. Thus the overlying rarefied gas depletes the background continuous spectrum at just those wavelengths it can itself emit.

The spectra of the sun and most stars are absorption spectra, because a star is a sphere of hot gas whose temperature and density decrease with distance from the center. The deeper atmospheric layers from which photons reach us are relatively dense and hot and give a continuous spectrum; just above them are cooler and more rarefied strata where the atoms absorb those photons coming up from below that they are permitted to absorb by the rules of the quantum theory. The absorption spectrum of a star is a complicated superposition of dark lines formed by many different elements in various stages of ionization. The lines that appear prominently depend of course on the kinds of atoms present, but they also depend strongly on the temperature of the star's atmosphere and on its density.

22. Molecular Bands

COOLER STARS display broad *bands* as well as lines in their spectra. In such stars the collisions of particles are not excessively violent and a few kinds of two-atom molecules can survive the buffeting without being dissociated into individual atoms. Just as atoms can be excited or ionized, so can molecules. But here the number of permitted energy changes is enormous, for not only may the electrons make transitions, but the two atoms of a molecule may vibrate toward and away from each other in a variety of ways and they may rotate around each other with various energies. What was a single atomic line in the spectrum of an atom is, in a molecule, a system of bands. The bands of molecules such as CN, CO, C_2, and TiO are prominent in the spectra of some of the cooler stars.

From our studies of spectra it is clear that spectroscopy is a difficult and complicated business. Nevertheless, since the spectrum of a celestial source depends on a host of physical characteristics of that source, it is equally clear that we can work from the observed spectrum of a star and discover indirectly a wealth of fundamental information about it.

PROBLEMS

1. At any point well inside the sun, the gaseous matter in a small cube is pushed or pulled by various forces. But there can be no net force exerted on the cube or it would start to move. Describe the forces involved.

2. Although a molecule of N_2 in air at room temperature moves a total distance of about 1600 feet every second, it is most likely to be only a quarter of an inch from its starting point after one second of flight. Explain this fact qualitatively in terms of the kinetic picture.

3. The relationships between Fahrenheit, centigrade, and absolute temperatures are: $T_F = 1.8T_C + 32 = 1.8T_K - 460$ and $T_K = T_C + 273$. (a) What are the centigrade and absolute temperatures in a room at 70°F? (b) The solar surface is at temperature about 5800°K. Express this temperature in centigrade and Fahrenheit measure.

4. Gas B has twice the number density of gas A and is at temperature 1200°K. Gas A is at 400°K. Compare the pressure of the two gases.

5. The unit of energy in the cgs system is the erg; it is the energy expended in exerting a force of 1 dyne through a distance of 1 centimeter. Thus 1 erg = 1 dyne cm = 1 gm cm^2 sec^{-2}. In a hot gas of hydrogen and helium the average speed of the hydrogen atoms is 10^6 cm/sec (about 6 mi/sec). (a) Given that the mass of a hydrogen atom is 1.7×10^{-24} gm, what is the average kinetic energy of a hydrogen atom in ergs? (b) What is the average speed of a helium atom in this gas, given that its mass is four times that of a hydrogen atom?

6. What is the wavelength corresponding to a UHF television station operating on a frequency of 500 megacycles per second (500 million cycles per second)?

7. A spectral line normally at a wavelength of 4861 A is shifted by the Doppler effect toward the violet by an amount 0.32 A. What is the radial velocity of the source?

8. The surface temperature of Procyon is about 7000°K. (a) What is the approximate wavelength of maximum emission? (b) At what rate is energy emitted by a square centimeter at the surface of Procyon?

9. Give the number of protons, neutrons, and electrons in one atom of each of the following, taking the mass number of the most abundant isotope in each case from Table 11.13:1: neutral hydrogen, doubly ionized helium, Ca II, Fe XIV, completely ionized gold.

10. What else happens in a neutral hydrogen atom when each of the following electron jumps occurs: orbit 4 to 2, orbit 3 to 5, orbit 1 to 2, orbit 3 to 2 to 1?

11. A proton captures a passing electron on orbit 4, then the electron spontaneously jumps down to orbit 3, and then it jumps directly to the ground state. In what part of the spectrum is each of the resulting photons emitted?

12. Distinguish between the three fundamental kinds of spectra and the kinds of situations in which each type is produced.

12

THE SUN

STUDY OF THE sun provides a bridge between our exploration of the solar system and of the distant stars and galaxies. From our local point of view, the sun, containing nearly all the mass of our system, serves to bind it together gravitationally. Moreover, its radiant energy is the source of virtually all of our energy resources here on the earth; we receive more than 100 million times as much light from the sun as from all the other stars combined. From the point of view of a student of the stars, however, the sun is important because it is the only star, among 100 billion in our galaxy, whose surface can be examined; all the other stars are point sources even at the focus of the largest telescope.

1. Distance to the Sun

BEFORE WE can make appreciable progress in establishing the overall physical characteristics of the sun, it is necessary to find its mean distance from the earth. As we have seen, the length of the astronomical unit may be established by several techniques. For example, the orbital velocity of the earth may be established from the aberration of starlight or from the annual change of the Doppler shift in the spectra of a star. Combining the average velocity with the earth's orbital period gives the sought-for result. More accurately, triangulation of a close-approaching planet or asteroid from a number of observatories or radar observations of a close-approaching planet will yield the distance to the object in miles. If the orbital characteristics are also known, Kepler's third law and the relative positions of sun, earth, and object give the distance in astronomical units. Comparing the two provides the value of the astronomical unit, which is 93,000,000 miles, or 150,000,000 kilometers. More precisely, as we saw in Chapter 8, Section 2, powerful radars reflecting energy from Venus have given us an estimate of 92,955,700 miles. In cgs units

$$1 \text{ a.u.} = (1.495977 \pm 0.000005) \times 10^{13} \text{ cm}.$$

MAJOR PHYSICAL CHARACTERISTICS

2. Size and Shape

THE ANGULAR diameter of the sun can be measured precisely, and is known to within $\pm 0.01''$. When the sun is at mean distance, its angular diameter is $32.0'$; when we combine this with the distance, as we did with the moon, we find the linear diameter of the sun to be 865,000 miles, or 109 times that of our earth. Measurements of the angular diameter of the sun at various orientations give identical results, providing the effects of atmospheric refraction are taken into account. Therefore the sun shows no equatorial bulge and may be regarded as spherical in shape. The observed globular shape accords with expectation because the sun rotates very slowly.

3. Mass and Density

THE MASS OF a star is perhaps its most fundamental characteristic and at the same time is a quantity very difficult if not impossible to determine. Finding the mass of the sun, however, is not very taxing. In Chapter 7 we saw that Newton's form of Kepler's third law is

$$P^2 = \frac{4\pi^2 a^3}{G(M_1 + M_2)}.$$

In applying this formula to the sun and earth, we know from other studies all quantities except M_1 and M_2. Thus

$$M_1 + M_2 = \frac{4\pi^2 a^3}{GP^2}$$

$$= \frac{4 \times (3.14)^2 \times (1.50 \times 10^{13})^3 \text{ cm}^3}{6.67 \times 10^{-8} \text{ gm}^{-1} \text{ cm}^3 \text{ sec}^{-2} \times (3.16 \times 10^7)^2 \text{ sec}^2}$$

$$= 2.0 \times 10^{33} \text{ gm}.$$

The combined mass of sun and earth therefore is 2.0×10^{33} grams. We found in Chapter 2 that the earth's mass is 6.0×10^{27} grams, or only three-millionths that of the sun. Hence the mass of the sun is

$$M_1 = 2.0 \times 10^{33} \text{ grams} - 0.000006 \times 10^{33} \text{ grams}$$

$$= 2.0 \times 10^{33} \text{ grams}.$$

Even when a, G, and P are inserted with their most accurately known values, the earth's mass makes no difference in the computation.

The mean density of the sun may be computed by dividing its mass by its spherical volume, which is 1.4×10^{33} cm³. The average density is thus 1.4 gm/cm³, about one-fourth that of the earth and close to that of Jupiter.

4. Surface Gravity and Escape Speed

THE ACCELERATION of gravity at the solar surface is 28 times its value at the earth's surface. If air resistance is ignored, we find that an object dropped from a 1000-foot skyscraper on the earth hits ground about 8 seconds later with a speed of about ½ mi/sec. If an object were dropped from the same height on the solar surface and were able to withstand the rigors of the hot gaseous climate, it would fall more than 10 miles in the same time, acquiring in 8 seconds a speed of fall of some 30 mi/sec. Just as we can compute the surface gravity of a spherical object once its mass and radius are known, so we can find its escape velocity. To leave the sun, an atom or other object must have a speed in excess of 380 mi/sec.

5. Rotation

THE PERIOD of the sun's rotation about its axis can be established by two independent methods. (1) Sunspots or other features parade across the sun's disk, as shown in Fig. 12.5:1. After its first appearance on the east limb, a very large sunspot will be near the center of the disk

← EAST

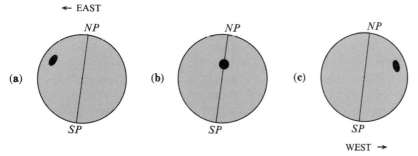

Fig. 12.5:1. A hypothetical sunspot rotating with the sun, shown in (a) four days before transit of the central meridian, in (b) at transit, and in (c) four days later.

WEST →

a week later, will disappear behind the west limb about two weeks later, and, if long-lived enough, will reappear at the east limb after 27 days. When we correct for the orbital motion of the earth, utilizing the formula for synodic period given in Chapter 7, we find that the true rotational period of the sun is 25 days. (2) When the slit of a

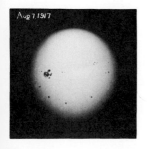 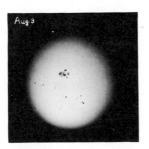  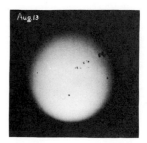

Fig. 12.5:2. The east-to-west motion of sunspots reveals the rotation of the sun. (*Yerkes Observatory photographs*)

THE SUN

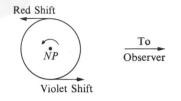

Red Shift

To Observer

Violet Shift

Fig. 12.5:3. The recessional speed at the west limb minus the approach speed at the east limb equals twice the rotational velocity.

spectrograph is trained on the east limb of the sun, the spectrum lines are shifted to the violet; at the west limb they are shifted to the red. The maximum observed difference in wavelength corresponds to a velocity difference of 2.5 mi/sec. As shown in Fig. 12.5:3, these observations indicate that the equatorial velocity of rotation is one-half of this amount. Given this speed and the circumference of the sun, the equatorial period of rotation again turns out to be 25 days. Studies of the sunspot parade allow us to establish not only the period but also the direction of the sun's axis of rotation: (1) the rotation is direct, like the planetary orbits, and (2) the equatorial plane of the sun is titled only 7° to the plane of the earth's orbit, reminding us of the low-inclination direct spins of most planets.

As with Jupiter, the rotational period of the sun depends on latitude. The period is a minimum, 25 days, at the solar equator. At latitude 30° in both hemispheres it is slightly over 26 days, and at latitude 45° the period is nearly 28 days. At polar latitudes there are no sunspots and the Doppler shifts are so small that the observations are difficult; rotational periods in excess of 30 days have been reported at the polar latitudes of the sun.

6. Luminosity and Surface Temperature

THE *luminosity*, or power output, of the sun is the total amount of radiant energy at all wavelengths emitted into space per unit time by the entire solar surface. To determine the solar luminosity, it is first necessary to establish the intensity or flux density of solar radiation at the earth's mean distance from the sun. From experimental measurement of the time taken for a pan of water exposed to the sun to increase its temperature by a given amount, it is possible to deduce the *solar constant*. Account must be taken of the facts that water is not a perfect absorber or black body and that the earth's atmosphere itself absorbs a good percentage of the incident solar radiation. The solar constant is the energy received per unit time from the overhead sun by unit area outside our atmosphere when the sun is at its mean distance. Its value is

$$1.37 \times 10^6 \text{ erg/cm}^2 \text{ sec,}$$

and appears to be constant to within 1 or 2 percent.

To find the luminosity of the sun, we must remember that the above figure refers to the rate of receipt of radiant energy on only one square centimeter at 1 a.u. from the sun. The total surface area of a sphere with radius r is $4\pi r^2$, and a sphere of radius 1 a.u. = 1.5×10^{13} cm thus has an area of

$$4 \times 3.14 \times 2.25 \times 10^{26} \text{ cm}^2 = 2.83 \times 10^{27} \text{ cm}^2.$$

The total solar energy flowing out in all directions over this sphere is therefore

$$1.37 \times 10^6 \frac{\text{erg}}{\text{cm}^2 \text{ sec}} \times 2.83 \times 10^{27} \text{ cm}^2 = 3.9 \times 10^{33} \frac{\text{erg.}}{\text{sec}}$$

And this is the total power output, or luminosity, of the sun.

The surface temperature of the sun may be established in a variety of ways. Knowing the radius of the sun, R, we can calculate its surface area, $4\pi R^2$. Dividing the luminosity by the surface area, we find the radiant energy emitted per unit area of surface. From Stefan's law, described in Chapter 11, we can then compute the black-body temperature of a sphere of solar size that emits the same total energy as the actual sun. The so-called *effective temperature* of the sun is found to be $5800°K$. Alternatively, we can examine the solar spectrum to see at what wavelength the continuous spectrum is most intense; Wien's law can then be applied to deduce a temperature, with results somewhat higher but not much different from $5800°K$. Finding which Planck curve best agrees with the observed spectral curve of the sun constitutes yet another way of estimating the temperature of the solar surface. The several results agree to within about $300°$; closer agreement cannot be expected because the sun's spectrum is masked by many thousands of absorption lines and is therefore not quite that of an ideal radiator.

7. Chemical Elements in the Sun

THE COMPOSITION of the sun is revealed by a comparison of its spectrum with the spectra of known elements obtained in the laboratory. More than 70 percent of the 92 naturally occurring elements have been found from the positions of their absorption lines in the solar spectrum. It is likely that all the elements are present, and indeed many thousands of solar absorption lines are still to be identified. Some elements such as radium and uranium are probably present in such minute quantities that they do not produce a detectable absorption spectrum; the chief lines in the spectra of other elements like chlorine and bromine are at wavelengths we cannot observe from the bottom of our absorbing atmosphere.

Studies of the relative abundance of the different chemical elements in the sun make use of the intensities of the various absorption lines. The darkness and breadth of a line is not solely a measure of the abundance of the particular atom, but also depends on the temperature and density at and near the solar surface. If, for example, the surface of a star has a temperature of $100,000°K$, nearly all of its hydrogen is ionized and so can produce no spectrum at all, even though hydrogen may abound there. Alternatively, the two absorption lines of ionized calcium in the violet are by far the strongest lines in the solar spectrum, even though only two atoms out of every million are calcium atoms. Conditions are just right, however, for an important percentage of these ionized calcium atoms to absorb photons coming up from below. When allowance is made for all of these effects, abundance studies show that at the solar surface about 90 percent of all atoms are hydrogen, 10 percent are helium, and only a tiny proportion are heavier elements. Confining our attention to the 6 most plentiful elements, for every 10,000 atoms of hydrogen there are about 1000 of helium, 6 of oxygen, 3 of nitrogen, 2 of carbon, and 1 of neon. The atomic abundances in other stars follow the same general pattern, and the enormous preponderance of the two lightest atoms must be accounted for in the story of the birth and evolution of stars.

THE QUIET SUN

8. The Observable Sun

LESS THAN one-billionth of the solar mass is accessible to observation; the vast majority lies beneath the surface and can be studied only indirectly. We shall return later to the nature of the solar interior, and here study those parts of the sun that we can observe directly: the visible surface, or *photosphere*, and the two layers of the atmosphere, the *chromosphere* and *corona*. The sun is in some ways a steady and

Fig. 12.8:1. The Robert R. McMath solar telescope at the Kitt Peak National Observatory, dedicated in November 1962. Sunlight is incident on an 80-inch plane mirror at the top of the structure, 100 feet above ground. There it is reflected down the polar axis and on through an inclined underground tunnel. About 500 feet from the upper plane mirror the sunlight strikes a 60-inch paraboloid of 300-foot focal length and is reflected back up the tunnel at a small angle from the polar axis. Near ground level it is then fed into powerful spectrographs. The image of the sun is about a yard in diameter. (*Kitt Peak National Observatory photograph*)

constant star, and in others is a variable and disturbed star. Let us first study the *quiet sun*, as evidenced by the ordinary solar features that are always present; later we shall look at the *active sun* and examine those more unusual features that are now conspicuously present and then perhaps totally absent.

9. The Photosphere

THE APPARENTLY sharp surface of the sun is the photosphere, and from this region is emitted nearly all of the sunlight we see. Actually, the photosphere is not a sharp surface like that of a billiard ball, but is rather a relatively thin spherical shell 200 or 300 miles thick and without definite boundaries. Photons emitted beneath the photosphere are stopped and thus cannot emerge into space, and above the photosphere the rate at which the rarefied atmospheric gases emit photons is very low. Therefore the vast majority of the solar photons that reach us are launched from a shell whose thickness is less than one-thousandth the radius of the sun. Compare the sun with a distant thick cloud: the space between you and the cloud is relatively transparent or you could not see it; the cloud itself is foggy or opaque, for no light from the sky beyond nor any light from deep inside the cloud can reach you; only light from a thin layer near the surface of the cloud reaches your eye and thus you are able to "see" its geometrical outline. Just as the myriad water droplets in a cloud or fog reduce the distance you can see into it, so the hot photospheric gases are quite opaque.

Physical conditions vary markedly in the photospheric layer, with both temperature and density decreasing with increasing distance from the center of the sun. A typical temperature is 6000°K and a typical density is about one-thousandth that of air. A majority of the radiation emitted in this layer and in an outward direction is able to penetrate the nearly transparent outer atmosphere of the sun and pass into space. About 10 percent of the emerging radiation is stopped; this fraction of the upward-moving photons is absorbed by atoms in the upper part of the photospheric shell and even higher. Thus are produced the 20,000 or more absorption lines in the solar spectrum.

10. Limb-Darkening

As FIG. 12.10:1 shows, the center of the sun's disk is brighter than places near the edge, or *limb*, of the sun. Not only does the brightness decrease toward the limb, but the color of the solar surface becomes

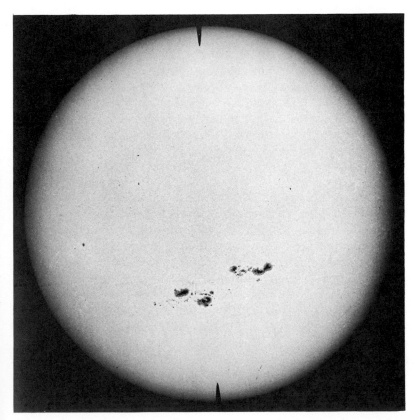

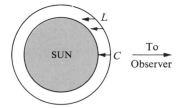

Fig. 12.10:1. Photograph of the sun showing limb-darkening and the granular structure of the solar surface. (*Mount Wilson and Palomar Observatories photograph*)

redder. These effects are explained when we remember that we are looking at an opaque medium into which we can see only a given distance, as on a foggy day. When, as indicated in Fig. 12.10:2, we look at the center of the disk, we are looking to a greater depth, where the temperature is higher; when we look at a point near the limb,

Fig. 12.10:2. When from afar we examine *C*, the center of the solar disk, we see deeper and hotter layers than when we examine *L*, near the limb.

we look along a slanting path and the radiation reaching us is emitted from higher and therefore cooler levels. Thus Stefan's and Wien's laws tell us that the brightness will be less and the color redder at the outer parts of the disk.

11. Granulation

Fig. 12.11:1. The granulated solar surface, photographed by a balloon telescope. (*Project Stratoscope of Princeton University, sponsored by the Office of Naval Research, the National Science Foundation, and the National Aeronautics and Space Administration*)

HIGH-RESOLUTION photographs of the sun, exposed when our atmospheric seeing is excellent or from high-flying balloons, show that the normal solar surface is mottled with fine-scale, bright *granules* or *rice grains*. They are irregular or polygonal in shape, with average diameters of a few hundred miles or less and with temperatures about 100°K greater than their darker surroundings. At any instant the granules cover about one-third of the solar surface. Figure 12.11:1 shows a photograph of a small part of the sun made from an unmanned balloon. Comparison of photographs made in rapid succession shows that a typical granule lasts only about three minutes. Thus the fine detail of the quiet solar surface changes rather completely every ten minutes or so. Radial velocity measurements suggest that a typical bright granule is moving upward in the photosphere at something like 1 mi/sec. The granules may be interpreted as turbulent blobs or cells of heated gas rising from the hotter invisible layers beneath the photosphere, while the darker and cooler gas between the granules is sinking. At any time there is as much gaseous matter rising as is falling. But more energy rises than falls; this process of *convection* is the likely means by which most of the energy coming up from the solar interior is transported for the final part of its trip to the surface, before emerging at the photosphere.

12. The Chromosphere

ABOVE THE top of the photosphere, which is the level of the visible limb of the sun, lies the tenuous and nearly transparent innermost layer of the solar atmosphere, the chromosphere. Its lower and denser part extends upward about 2500 miles, and the top of the upper chromosphere merges gradually with the corona some 13,000 miles above the photosphere. The chromosphere may be observed visually for a brief time at a total eclipse of the sun. At the instant the last photospheric light is covered by the moon, a thin crescent of red light can be seen; it lasts for a few seconds and is then itself covered, leaving only the pale white outer corona. The thin red arc then reappears for a few seconds, followed by the end of totality. This colored light originates in the lower chromosphere. When a thin objective prism is placed in front of the lens of a telescopic camera, the chromospheric crescent is dispersed into a series of arcs, each at a separate wavelength. Figure 12.12:1 shows this flash spectrum, so-called because it lasts but a few

Fig. 12.12:1. A flash spectrum of the sun made in 1900. (*Yerkes Observatory photograph*)

seconds. The flash spectrum of the chromosphere is an emission spectrum, as would be expected from a hot rarefied gas. Detailed studies show it to be nearly a reversal of the ordinary absorption spectrum of the photosphere, although there are more emission lines arising from ionized metals and there is even a line of ionized helium. These spectral lines must and do originate in regions where the density is lower and the temperature is higher than in the photosphere. The integrated light of the chromosphere looks red because the Hα line at 6563 A contributes a good share of the total light of all the emission lines.

The kinetic temperature at the top of the photosphere is about 4500°K, less than in any other layer of the sun. Moving out through the lower chromosphere, the density decreases rapidly, and the temperature rises until at 2500 miles it has increased to perhaps 6000°K. Farther out the density continues to decline, and the kinetic temperature rises sharply, attaining 1,000,000°K at the top of the chromosphere and base of the corona, 13,000 miles up. We shall look at the evidence for this high temperature when we study the corona. At this level, which lies only 3 percent of the solar radius above the top of the photosphere, the gas density is less than one-millionth of its value at the base of the chromosphere. The chromosphere is thus rather sharply divided into two zones: the layer below 2500 miles is cool and the hydrogen is nearly all neutral, but above a narrow transition zone the gas is hot and the hydrogen is almost completely ionized.

13. Spicules

PERMANENT features of the chromosphere are the bright short-lived jets, or *spicules*, rising above the lower chromosphere and seen on photographs of the solar limb, as in Fig. 12.13:1. They are best observed

Fig. 12.13:1. Spicules at the limb of the sun, photographed at Sunspot, N. Mex. (*Sacramento Peak Observatory, Air Force Cambridge Research Laboratories*)

when one uses a filter which tunes out the whole spectrum except for the Hα line. These hydrogen-emitting spikes are visible on the average up to 5000 miles above the photosphere; they last about 2 minutes and radial velocity measurements show up-and-down motions of 10 to 15 mi/sec. The spicules are present on all parts of the limb at all times, and at any moment there are at least 100,000 of them on the solar surface. They may be related to the short-lived granules of the photosphere, and they are probably an important factor in the transportation of energy upward to keep the corona heated to 1,000,000°K.

14. The Corona

THE OUTER solar atmosphere, the corona, extends outward from the top of the chromosphere and is normally seen only at the time of a total solar eclipse. When the photosphere and chromosphere are fully blocked by the moon, the corona appears as a pale white halo, with total light about the same as that of the full moon. The surface brightness of the innermost coronal regions is one-millionth that of the solar disk, but it falls off with distance until at two solar radii from the center of the sun it is only 1 percent as bright. The normally quiet corona is not ring-shaped, but, as seen in Fig. 6.28:3, shows extended streamers stretching outward in the equatorial regions and shorter rays or tufts in the polar regions. These nonsymmetrical features probably have some connection with the weak magnetic field of the sun.

Early studies of the corona were confined to the fleeting moments of total eclipses of the sun, so that in the course of a century only about an hour of observing time was available—most of it in remote parts of the earth. Since the invention of the *coronagraph* in 1930 by Bernard Lyot of the Paris Observatory, it has been possible to observe the corona at other times. Coronagraphs are installed on mountains at high altitudes above most of the atmosphere so that the surface brightness of the daylight sky is reduced below that of the corona. The essential feature of such an instrument is that it successfully eclipses the main disk of the sun and permits only the outer solar atmosphere to be photographed. The objective lens focuses the main body of the sun onto an occulting disk that reflects its light out of the way. The lens must be optically perfect; a tiny bubble in the glass could scatter enough unwanted sunlight onto the feeble image of the corona to overwhelm it. The coronal light passes around the occulting disk and is sent by an auxiliary lens behind the disk to the camera lens and then to the photographic film. In addition to a wealth of coronagraphic studies in the visual part of the spectrum, many studies of the outermost solar atmosphere have been made with radio telescopes, as we shall see in the next section. Among the most impressive results of all these observations are the visual spectra of various parts of the corona. Its lower parts have a pure continuous spectrum which resembles that of the photosphere, except that the dark absorption lines do not appear. In the middle corona about 30 emission lines appear superposed on the continuous spectrum. Because none of these lines occurs at the same wavelength as any photospheric absorption line, it was once thought that a new chemical element, named coronium, occurred in the solar atmosphere. Finally, the spectrum of the outer corona is similar to that of the solar disk: a background continuum of light crossed by hosts of absorption lines.

Let us interpret this sequence of spectral changes as we move outward through the corona. Because the solar atmosphere is of low density and high temperature, nearly all the atoms are ionized. Thus many free electrons are running to and fro. Now, free electrons scatter light that is incident on them, reminding us of the molecules of the earth's atmosphere whose scattered sunlight is responsible for the blue sky. Unlike molecules, however, electrons scatter light of all wavelengths equally well and thus behave more like the particles in a puff of smoke or cloud of dust. The light of the inner corona consists of photons that left the photosphere in some other direction but were scattered by free electrons in the inner corona and headed toward the observer. But if electron scattering is responsible, we are entitled to expect that the spectrum of this light should be a carbon copy of that of the disk. Actually, we have seen that the absorption lines are missing. The explanation is found in the Doppler effect: because the electrons are moving at high speeds, light from the photosphere is not only scattered but shifted to the violet and red by randomly moving electrons, and thus the absorption lines are filled in with light from adjacent wavelengths. In order for the absorption lines to be so completely smeared out, the average speed of the coronal electrons must be several thousand miles per second. In other words, missing absorption lines establish that the kinetic temperature of the corona is 1,000,000°K or more.

The emission lines superposed on the continuum must arise, of course, from a rarefied gas whose atoms have electrons jumping from outer orbits to inner orbits. The actual identification of these lines was not achieved until 1940. Instead of being due to coronium or some other new chemical element, they arise from transitions in highly ionized atoms of familiar elements. The most intense of these lines, in the green part of the spectrum at 5303 A, is due to Fe XIV (iron with 13 of its normal complement of 26 electrons missing); the next strongest line, in the infrared, arises from Fe XIII. Other stages of ionization of iron have been identified, as well as highly ionized argon, calcium, nickel, and other elements. The vigor of collision necessary to strip these atoms of so many electrons argues once again for a temperature of around 1,000,000°K. At such a high kinetic temperature the random velocities of even the heavy atoms are high; therefore at any instant in any small volume some of the emitting atoms will be approaching the observer fast, some will be receding fast, and others will have zero radial velocity. Because of the Doppler effect, we should expect each emission line to be broadened, with light on the violet side of the line having been emitted by approaching atoms and that on the red side by receding atoms. The measured line-widths of about 1 A give a third independent estimate that the coronal kinetic temperature is about 1,000,000°K.

At one million miles from the center of the sun there are only about 10^5 atoms per cubic centimeter, although the temperature remains high. From here outward the dominant coronal light shows an absorption spectrum. This outer contribution cannot arise solely from electron scattering because the solar absorption lines are not smeared out. Rather it arises chiefly from the scattering of sunlight by tiny interplanetary particles in the innermost parts of the solar system. In Chapter 9 we saw that the zodiacal light was produced largely by cometary debris scattering sunlight. The outer faint corona is thus considered the innermost part of the zodiacal cloud.

The unexpectedly high temperature of the corona is a *kinetic temperature*; it refers to the average kinetic energy of motion of the atoms and electrons there. The *radiation temperature* is much lower. Imagine a tiny test sphere placed one million miles from the center of the sun. Only an insignificant fraction of the radiation falling on it would originate in the tenuous corona; all but about one-millionth would come from the 5800°K photosphere, and the body would attain an equilibrium temperature of only 2700°K, radiating like a black body at this temperature. Although it has not been difficult to determine these two different kinds of temperature, it has not been fully possible to explain *why* the kinetic temperature of the corona is 1,000,000°K. It appears likely that the energy required to keep the corona heated is brought up from below by the continually intruding chromospheric spicules. The spicules, in turn, seem to be related to the granules of the photosphere.

Whatever the explanation of coronal heating may be, it is certain that at 1,000,000°K the average velocity of a proton is 100 mi/sec and that of an electron 4000 mi/sec. Since the escape velocity of the sun is 380 mi/sec, it would seem that the negative electrons would soon escape into space, leaving a positively charged corona of protons. However, the faster outbound electrons attract the slow protons upward electrostatically, while the lower protons decelerate the fast electrons, with the result that equal numbers leave the sun together. The only particles that can escape are those in the tenuous outer corona where the number density is very low and thus the mean free path very large. The estimated rate of loss from the quiet corona into space is roughly 10^{33} protons and electrons per second, and thus, since there are about 10^{41} of them in the corona at any one time, an average member spends about 10^8 seconds, or a few years, there. Like a head of hair or the tail of a comet, the corona continually replenishes itself. The destiny of the escaping corpuscles is not necessarily escape into interstellar space, for they may collide with one another or with cometary particles. Rather, it seems likely that the corona of ionized hydrogen extends outward on and on, with lower and lower density but not much lower kinetic temperature. As the earth itself orbits around the sun, it is moving through an ultrararefied medium of hot ionized hydrogen. As we have seen, space probes have found that at 1 a.u. from the sun there are normally about 10 outbound coronal corpuscles per cubic ‾entimeter. Their kinetic temperature is roughly 100,000°K. In addition, the earth is buffeting its way through faster and denser outbound proton–electron streams from the disturbed sun and through the cometary dust particles of the zodiacal cloud.

SINCE THE 1940s radio telescopes operating at various frequencies have been able to detect radio radiation emitted by the sun. Much of the radiation so recorded is from the active, or disturbed, sun. But at any given frequency there is a minimum base level below which the solar radio output never falls. At the highest frequencies accessible through our earth's atmosphere, about 50,000 mc/sec (1 mc/sec = 1 megacycle per second = 10^6 cycles per second = 10^6/sec), the sun delivers radio energy to us equal to that from an ideal black body the same size as the sun and at a temperature of 6000°K. Thus the *apparent temperature* of the sun at 50,000 mc/sec is 6000°K. At lower frequencies the apparent temperature is higher: at 1000 mc/sec it is 100,000°K, and at 100 mc/sec it is 1,000,000°K. These temperatures span the same range as those determined in the visual part of the solar spectrum: 6000°K in the photosphere and 1,000,000°K in the corona. Evidently, radio radiation from the sun originates at different levels in the solar atmosphere.

This expectation is beautifully confirmed by theory. In a hot ionized region radiation of all wavelengths is emitted, but only waves of frequency higher than a certain critical value can get through the gas, and the critical value depends only on the number density of free electrons. Near the photosphere there are so many electrons per unit volume that only ultrahigh frquencies can emerge; thus at 50,000 mc/sec the solar radio radiation has the characteristics of its place of origin, or a temperature of 6000°K. In the corona, where the electron density is much lower, long-wave radiation is able to emerge; the radiation we receive is thus characteristic of the corona, and the measured apparent temperature is 1,000,000°K. The validity of these ideas has been checked at total solar eclipses. At ultrahigh frequencies, just as at visual wavelengths, the radiation received is reduced to almost nothing at totality, showing that the bulk of it is emitted near the photosphere. At low frequencies, however, the diminution at totality is only partial, proving, as shown in Fig. 12.15:1, that the radiation at these frequencies originates in the corona. A hypothetical observer with radio eyes tuned to a low frequency would see a sun of much larger angular diameter than $\frac{1}{2}°$.

Fig. 12.15:1. At a total solar eclipse the high-frequency radio radiation originating near the photosphere is blocked by the lunar disk, while only the central part of the low-frequency coronal radio emission is stopped by the moon.

THE ACTIVE SUN

SUPERPOSED on the quiet constant sun are several kinds of transitory phenomena, which occur at various levels in the solar atmosphere and which are observed by a number of different techniques. These phenomena are generally associated with one another and break out in a localized position on the solar surface, which is called a *center of activity.* The most readily observed type of activity is the large sunspot, with an average lifetime of a few days. But other associated phenomena may last for several solar rotations, and therefore those connected with a given center of activity vary periodically every 27 days as recorded from the earth.

17. Sunspots

BLACK BLEMISHES on the solar disk were reported in pretelescopic times and were noted by Galileo in 1610. Although at first thought to be inferior planets or other bodies transiting the sun, sunspots have long been known to reside on the actual solar surface. A spot first appears among the bright photospheric granules as a black pore, perhaps 1000 miles in diameter. The majority do not grow very much, lasting less than a day. A typical large spot, however, lives about a week; and occasional very large sunspots, dwarfing the earth in size, may survive one or more rotations of the sun before dying out. The central part of a spot is a fairly well-defined black umbra and seems to be a shallow depression in the photosphere. Surrounding the umbra is a less dark penumbra, averaging about five times the area of the umbra and marked by radial granulation. Sunspots usually occur in pairs or groups, with the western, or leading, member frequently dominant in size. Spots and spot groups do not appear in the polar regions of the sun, being almost always found closer to the solar equator than latitude 45°. They also tend to avoid a narrow belt around the equator.

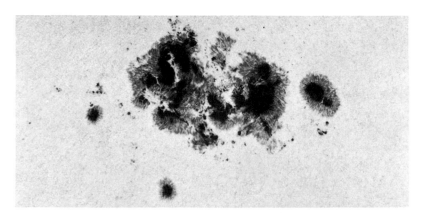

Fig. 12.17:1. A large sunspot group photographed on May 17, 1951. (*Mount Wilson and Palomar Observatories photograph*)

The umbra of a spot appears black only by contrast with the intense surrounding photosphere. Spectral studies show that certain hardy molecules exist in the umbra but not in the hotter photosphere. The deduced temperature of a sunspot is near 4500°K, as compared with about 6000°K for the photosphere. Because sunspots are relatively cool, they are sometimes referred to as solar refrigerators. Nevertheless, black as the umbrae appear on photographs, the average light we receive from those present on the disk is several times the light of the full moon. Detailed Doppler studies show that the sunspot gases at lower levels flow radially outward at 1 to 2 mi/sec, while at higher levels there is a compensating inflow. Associated with sunspots are localized but strong magnetic fields, ranging in strength up to 10,000 times that of the earth's general magnetic field. When emitting atoms are in a region permeated by a magnetic field, certain spectral lines are split into several separate components at slightly different wavelengths. This splitting is called the *Zeeman effect*; it was first noticed in the spectra of sunspots early in this century by George Ellery Hale, the solar astronomer for whom the 200-inch telescope is named. In addition to measuring the field strengths of spots and finding them correlated with spot diameters, Hale showed that the magnetic polarity of the dominant spot in a pair or group is opposite to that of the smaller spots.

18. The Sunspot Cycle

THE NUMBER of spots or spot groups on the sun varies from one year to the next, with a rise and fall whose average duration is 11 years, as shown in Fig. 12.18:1. At a typical sunspot minimum there are only three or four spots on the sun, and in some cases none at all. At an average sunspot maximum there are perhaps one hundred spots on the visible disk, most of them clustered together in about ten spot groups. When a new cycle begins, a few spots and groups break out near latitude 30° in both hemispheres. As time goes by, the dying spots are replaced by more and more fresh spots at lower latitudes. After about 4 years sunspot maximum occurs, at which time the average spot latitude is 15°. After maximum the number of spots and groups declines slowly and their average latitude continues to migrate toward the solar equator. About 7 years after maximum there are just a few spots near latitude 8° in both hemispheres, and usually before they fade away a few new ones break out at higher latitudes, signaling the start of a new 11-year cycle. In Fig. 12.18:2 the latitude and time are plotted for the sunspots of one cycle.

We saw before that the magnetic polarity of the big leader spot in a pair or group is opposite to that of the smaller spots. When studies are continued for a whole cycle, it is found that the leader spots in one hemisphere have one polarity and those in the other have the opposite polarity. During the following cycle the situation is reversed as shown in Fig. 12.18:3. The magnetic observations thus indicate that the fundamental periodicity of the sunspot cycle is 22 years, although it remains the custom to speak of the 11-year cycle.

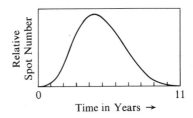

Fig. **12.18:1.** Relative numbers of sunspots for an average cycle. Time is reckoned from sunspot minimum.

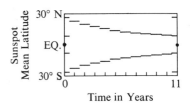

Fig. **12.18:2.** The average latitude of sunspots decreases during the cycle.

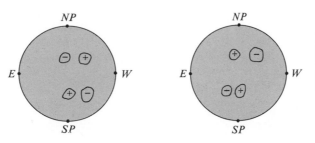

Fig. **12.18:3.** Polarities of sunspots are opposite in the two hemispheres. In the following cycle, at the right, the situation is reversed.

19. Faculae

PHOTOGRAPHS of the sun often reveal bright granulated patches surrounding sunspots near the edge of the solar disk. These regions, several times the area of their companion spots, are called *faculae*, Latin for "small torches." Their average lifetime is about two weeks. The birth of a facula as a tiny bright spot usually forewarns us that about a day later a sunspot will appear there. Although some days later a typical spot group has died away, the center of activity persists. The facular area goes on increasing in size, not dissolving away until a later time. These luminous clouds are not much hotter than the photosphere and therefore cannot be seen near the center of the disk on ordinary photographs; they show up only near the limb where the photospheric light is dimmer.

They are beautifully revealed by monochromatic photographs, however. By filtering out all incoming sunlight except for a tiny wavelength interval at the red absorption line of hydrogen, we eliminate all of the light of the continuum that originates in the photosphere and study the structure of the chromospheric levels. Such photographs are known as *spectroheliograms* and can be made by using a monochromatic filter which admits only the light of a single absorption line—usually hydrogen or ionized calcium. An alternative method, long known, utilizes the spectrograph: light from a thin slice of the sun is admitted through the slit and then dispersed by a prism; a second slit admits only the light of the selected absorption line onto a photograph plate, yielding a picture in monochromatic light of this thin slice of the sun.

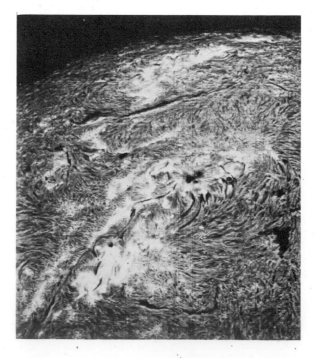

Fig. 12.19:1. An Hα spectroheliogram of part of the sun, May 4; 1958. (*Mount Wilson and Palomar Observatories photograph*)

By proper manipulation of the instrument and the plate, the adjacent slice is photographed. Thus a picture of the solar disk is built up strip by strip. Figure 12.19:1 shows how very different the sun looks in monochromatic light.

20. Flares

ONCE IN a while a localized patch in a center of activity suddenly brightens in a few minutes and then dies away after an hour or so. These chromospheric *flares* generally occur near the center of a group of sunspots; they are always associated with faculae, and 99 percent of

 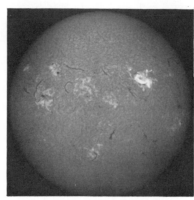

 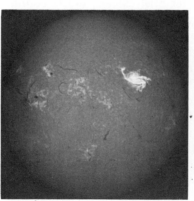 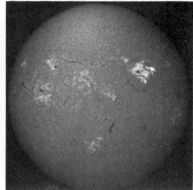

Fig. 12.20:1. Evolution of a solar flare, July 16, 1959, photographed in Hα light. Exposures were made at 21ʰ18ᵐ, 21ʰ26ᵐ, 21ʰ33ᵐ, 22ʰ05ᵐ, and 23ʰ05ᵐ U.T. Note the relative permanence of the dark filaments and bright faculae as compared with the rapid growth and dissolution of the flare. (*The McMath-Hulbert Observatory, The University of Michigan*)

them occur near a sunspot. At an average sunspot maximum they erupt at a rate of five or ten a day. Flares are only rarely seen in white light but are extremely prominent in Hα and Ca II photographs. They are sometimes detected at the limb of the sun, and such observations reveal that flares rise to an average height of about 10,000 miles at speeds up to hundreds of miles per second. These short-lived but vigorous bursts of light are accompanied by intense radiations in the X-ray, ultraviolet, and radio parts of the spectrum, and they seem to be the birthplaces of the corpuscular clouds of atoms ejected by the disturbed sun.

Fig. 12.20:2. The McMath-Hulbert Observatory at Lake Angelus, near Pontiac, Mich. The two towers house instrumentation for observing the sun. (*The McMath-Hulbert Observatory, The University of Michigan*)

21. Filaments or Prominences

MONOCHROMATIC photographs taken during the younger life of a center of activity show one or more dark, narrow, serpentine streaks near the sunspots and faculae. Although many of these *filaments* die after brief careers, others continue to develop for many months and can be seen long after the associated spots and even the faculae disappear. When seen at the edge of the sun, filaments are bright and red; they are then called *prominences*. Because they are relatively long-lived phenomena, they can be followed for several solar rotations and their three-dimensional structure can be inferred. Only about 3000 miles thick, these curtain-shaped masses of gas stretch well up into the corona, to 20,000 or 50,000 miles. Their lengths increase with time until after the associated faculae have disappeared, exceeding 100,000 miles. Distended by the differential rotation of the sun, a well-developed filament is stretched out in a nearly east-west direction. Although a majority of filaments stay in the vicinity of the centers of activity where they first appeared, some wander poleward before ultimately disappearing. At the time of sunspot maximum there is also a maximum of such polar prominences and filaments. Both types, low-latitude as well as polar, are much cooler than the surrounding coronal gases but at the same time about a hundred times as dense. Motion pictures of prominences, when projected at several hundred times the rate at which the frames were exposed, show that downward motions predominate. As with water in the earth's atmosphere, the rising motions are not normally visible whereas the falling rain is readily seen.

Of all the visible phenomena connected with a center of activity, the filaments or prominences live for the longest time. But even more persistent is the magnetic field. First detectable about a day before the first bright facular dot and a few days before the first sunspot pore, the associated magnetic field increases rather rapidly in strength. Later

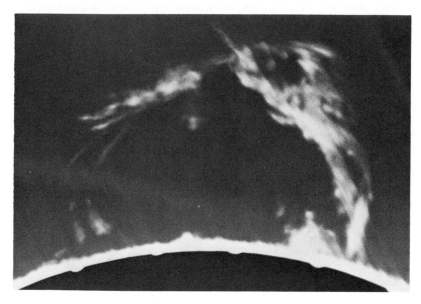

Fig. 12.21:1. A prominence photographed in the violet light of the K line of ionized calcium at 3934 A. (*Mount Wilson and Palomar Observatories photograph*)

it declines, but if the associated spot group was a large one, the magnetic field can still be observed five or ten solar rotations later, even after the filaments have dissolved.

22. Coronal Condensations

HIGH IN the corona above a center of activity are localized regions that are denser and perhaps hotter than the quiet surrounding regions; they are called *coronal condensations*. Their development resembles that of the facular areas beneath them, brightening and then later decreasing in intensity. We saw in Fig. 6.28:3 that the quiet corona, when observed at eclipses near a sunspot minimum, is elongated in the equatorial latitudes. The active corona, however, is nearly circular in shape, with streamers projecting out at all latitudes. There is thus no doubt that the coronal structure correlates closely with solar activity. The circularity is accounted for by the fact that at sunspot maximum there are a maximum of polar prominences as well as lower-latitude centers of activity. Thus the corona is active at all latitudes.

Fig. 12.22:1. The corona of the sun, photographed from Chile during the total eclipse of October 12, 1958. The shape of the corona is characteristic of the years near sunspot maximum. (*Photograph by Fernando L. de Romana of Arequipa, Peru*)

23. The Active Radio Sun

Fig. 12.23:1. The 4-foot Canadian radio telescope which from 1947 to 1963 recorded the daily intensity of solar radio radiation at a wavelength of 10.7 cm. (*Photograph courtesy of the National Research Council of Canada*)

SUPERPOSED on the radio radiation of the normal quiet sun is a variety of types of radio emission. One type shows a clear 27-day variability that correlates with individual centers of activity. This slow-varying emission rises at its maximum to roughly twice that of the quiet sun and endures, apart from the 27-day periodicity, for 3 or 4 months. Studies at solar eclipses indicate that the radiation originates in coronal condensations above the facular area of an activity center. Over and above this enhanced radiation are occasional *noise storms*, lasting for hours or even days. The intensity of such storms ranges up to a hundred times that of the quiet sun and fluctuates from moment to moment. Noise storms are also coronal features and correlate strongly with large sunspots or spot groups on the photosphere below them.

Among other radio phenomena, the most spectacular are the great *outbursts* whose energy output increases thousands of times in a few seconds. A typical outburst lasts for several minutes at a very high level; one recorded in Australia in 1947 emitted briefly some 10^7 times as much radio radiation as the quiet sun. Studies at different frequencies reveal that the higher frequencies are received from an outburst a few minutes before the lower frequencies arrive. As we saw in Section 15, the higher frequencies are emitted from the low chromosphere and the lower ones can originate only in the corona. From the measured delay, the radiation must come from a disturbance that rises at about 1000 mi/sec through the solar atmosphere. These outbursts are associated with large and vigorous solar flares, and we therefore suppose that a high-speed cloud of atoms, when launched from the scene of a flare, moves rapidly outward, exciting radio radiation from higher and higher layers as the seconds pass. Those outbound atoms that survive their fast trip through the corona and escape from the sun at 1000 mi/sec take about a day to travel 1 a.u. We have already seen that there is excellent additional evidence for corpuscular clouds leaving the sun at approximately this velocity.

Fig. 12.23:2. *Above*: A hydrogen spectroheliogram of the sun on April 21, 1961. *Below*: A drift curve of the sun on the same date, made with a radio interferometer operating at 10.7 cm. The lower envelope of the curve shows the intensity of the quiet sun; the humps are produced in the bright active regions. The radio peak just to the left of the east limb is caused by a center of activity about to rotate into veiw. (*Photograph courtesy of the National Research Council of Canada*)

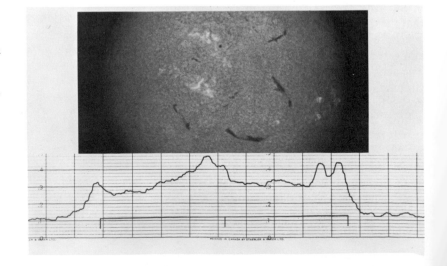

Much of our consideration of the active sun has been descriptive rather than interpretive. Our own star, the only one we can watch in detail, exhibits a great diversity of phenomena during its busier times. But, although most of its antics correlate with one another and follow the 27-day rotational periodicity and the 11-year cycle of activity centers, we still cannot explain the solar variability. We know many of the symptoms, but we do not understand the disease.

SOLAR ACTIVITY AND THE EARTH

24. Immediate Effects

WHEN A large flare bursts forth on the sun, much energetic ultraviolet radiation is emitted. Incident on the upper atmosphere of our daytime hemisphere, these photons ionize a substantial number of nitrogen and oxygen molecules about 50 miles above the surface. Now, normal long-distance radio communication depends on reflecting signals from permanent ionized layers at much higher levels. The ultraviolet photons arriving from a flare create this new and lower barrier, thereby disrupting long-range communications. Since the ultraviolet and visual photons travel at the same speed, the speed of light, the occurrence of a visual flare and a terrestrial radio fade-out are simultaneous. After an hour or so, the flare subsides, the free electrons at an altitude of 50 miles are able to rejoin their parent molecules, and communications return to normal. A second phenomenon that coincides with solar flares is a temporary variation in the earth's magnetic field, lasting for perhaps an hour and confined to the daytime hemisphere. Since a magnetic field is a consequence of circulating electric charge, it appears likely that the increased ionization at a height of 50 miles during a solar flare leads to increased electric currents and thus to temporary changes in the measured magnetic field strength.

25. Delayed Effects

ABOUT A day after the occurrence of a large solar flare near the center of the solar disk, several terrestrial effects are noted: worldwide disturbances of radio communications lasting for a few days, world-wide fluctuations in the magnetic field known as *magnetic storms*, and auroras at high latitudes in the nighttime hemisphere. These commotions are triggered by the arrival of gas clouds which have erupted with solar flares and have moved at about 1000 mi/sec outward from the sun. Chiefly protons and electrons, these tenuous and extended clouds cannot be seen directly. On approaching the earth, however, the positive protons and negative electrons are guided differently by the earth's magnetic field and a circulating electric current is set to flowing around the earth. This change modifies both the normal state of ionization of the upper atmosphere and the normal magnetic field strength. Furthermore, the solar charged particles interacting with the earth's magnetic field affect most strongly those belts on earth located some 20° or 25° from the magnetic poles, accounting for the predominance of auroras in those zones. Spectra of the auroras have revealed Doppler shifts of the Hα emission line corresponding to velocities of approach in the range from a few hundred to a few thousand miles per second along the lines of force of the earth's magnetic field. Thus, although the details of these delayed effects are not understood, the Doppler observations of the aurora and the one-day time delay of these upheavals afford evidence that solar corpuscular clouds are responsible.

Fig. 12.25:1. A view of the aurora borealis, seen from Alaska. (*Photograph by Dr. Victor Hessler*)

The frequency of occurrence of these terrestrial effects, both immediate and delayed, follows the 11-year sunspot cycle. At spot minimum there are few or no centers of activity and thus flares are infrequent. A few years later, at spot maximum, many flares break out in centers of activity and therefore the associated terrestrial disturbances occur more frequently.

HOW THE SUN KEEPS SHINING

26. The Solar Interior

OUR STUDIES of the sun have thus far been confined to the infinitesimal fraction that is visible to us. But to learn what our star is and how it keeps going, we must try by some indirect means to deduce its inner nature. As a starting point for examining the solar interior, we have at our disposal two different kinds of information: the results of astronomical observation and the results of physical theory. From astronomical observation we know that the sun is a sphere in equilibrium, neither contracting nor expanding, nor changing its light from one century to the next. We have also learned three of its fundamental over-all characteristics: mass, radius, and luminosity. Finally, spectral studies of the outer layers suggest, but do not prove, that the sun may be composed chiefly of hydrogen, with a minor percentage of helium and a pinch of heavier elements. Next, we may assume that the laws of physics are obeyed at each point inside the sun and that therefore we can utilize the results of gravitational theory, kinetic theory, radiation theory, atomic physics, and nuclear physics, where they are relevant to our problem. A great simplification is the spherical shape of the sun: the numerical values of density and temperature in the sun depend only on distance from the center and not on latitude and longitude.

One specific example of the physical rules that can be applied to the sun is that of mechanical equilibrium: at every point in the interior the weight of all upper layers squeezing down must be precisely balanced by the expansive force of all the hot lower layers. If such a balance did not exist, the solar gases would expand or contract until equilibrium was restored, much as a squeezed balloon returns to the spherical shape when left alone. A second example refers to the rate of flow of energy outward through the sun. We know that the sun radiates photons at the rate of 3.9×10^{33} erg/sec. Since the solar luminosity is not changing, energy must be produced or liberated at precisely this same rate inside the sun. For a room to stay at a constant temperature of 70°F in winter, the furnace must deliver heat at the same rate it is seeping out through the walls; in summer the air-conditioner must remove heat at the same rate it is seeping in through the walls from outside. In the sun this relationship must necessarily hold at all levels: the outward rate of flow across any spherical shell must equal the total rate of energy production inside that shell.

A third physical rule concerns the rate of decrease of temperature outward from the center of the sun. In general, energy flows from hotter places to cooler ones; in most layers of the sun the outward energy flow is carried by photons rather than by atoms. The rate of decrease of temperature with distance would be zero if there were no net outward flow of energy. But since there is a definite flow outward over each spherical shell, there must be a definite temperature gradient to maintain this flow. Furthermore, the solar interior is very foggy or opaque: photons are emitted, travel only a fraction of an inch, and are then absorbed. The greater the fogginess or opacity, the more the photons are obstructed. Therefore the temperature gradient must be steep enough to maintain the energy flow in spite of the obstructing atoms. Imagine a large table covered with marbles and suppose a painted red line divides the table in two. If the table is tilted slightly, marbles will cross the red line at a certain slow rate; if instead it is inclined at a large angle, the rate of flow across the red line will be faster. Similarly, the net outward flow of radiation is related to the steepness of the temperature gradient. Next, pound a number of nails halfway into the table and tilt it slightly as before; the flow of marbles is now slowed down because of their collisions with the nails. To maintain the original rate of flow across the red line, the table must be inclined at a larger angle. Similarly, the temperature gradient in the sun is greater the larger the obstructiveness or opacity of the solar matter.

When these various conditions and a number of others are cast into mathematical form, it is possible, although very difficult, to work out the model of any star. One crucial matter, to which we shall return presently, is the question of how the sun produces or liberates energy in its interior. Here let us refer to an important theorem about spherical stars in equilibrium: given the *mass* and *chemical composition* of a star, its entire structure is uniquely determined—its radius, its luminosity, and the variation of density and temperature with distance from the center to the surface. Another useful generality to remember is that the temperature and pressure must steadily decrease toward the surface. The temperature must decrease if energy is to flow outwards; the pressure must decrease because the weight of overlying layers is less and less the closer we get to the surface. Similarly, the density decreases toward the surface. A final general result about stellar interiors is that they are everywhere gaseous. Even though the central density of a star is very great, it is so hot that atoms are almost completely ionized. Because the tiny stripped atomic nuclei and free electrons therefore occupy only a small fraction of the available room, even at densities many times that of solid lead, such a medium is a gas.

Results on the interior structure of the sun are not final, but much is already known. The chemical composition is roughly the same inside as in the photosphere; the photospheric composition was discussed in Section 7. The central density of the sun is about 100 gm/cm^3, or some ten times that of lead, decreasing to about 1 gm/cm^3 halfway to the surface and of course to a very low value at the photosphere. Half of the sun's mass is confined to a sphere whose radius is only one-fourth the photospheric radius; about 95 percent of the solar material is closer to the center than to the surface. The temperature at the center is about 15×10^6°K, falling to some 3×10^6°K halfway to the surface and to 6000°K in the photosphere. The average temperature gradient is therefore approximately -35°K per mile. Virtually all of the energy is produced within half a solar radius from the center, and fully half is produced in the hot and dense region within one-tenth of a solar radius of the center. Thus only one-thousandth of the solar volume contributes 50 percent of the total energy liberated, or about 2×10^{33} erg/sec.

A consequence of the very high interior temperature is that the photons flying about are chiefly in the X-ray part of the spectrum, at wavelengths of only a few Angstroms. Toward the surface the temperature becomes lower and the Wien wavelength longer, until at the surface the typical photon leaving the sun is in the visual part of the spectrum. Thus as photons are continually emitted and reabsorbed, the energy working its way toward the surface is in the form of photons of longer and longer wavelengths. At any given point photons are traveling in all directions at the speed of light, but because of the high opacity no single photon moves very far. If the sun were transparent, a photon emitted at the center would reach the surface in 2.3 seconds; but because of the obstructiveness of solar matter, energy liberated near the center takes tens of thousands of years to reach the surface.

27. Energy Production

From the law of conservation of energy, we know that the energy radiated by the sun must be derived from some other form of energy. At one time it was thought that the kinetic energy of meteors falling into the sun might supply the requisite amount, but it is now clear that this mechanism is totally inadequate. Ordinary chemical combustion, as in a wood fire, will not work either. A lump of coal of solar size would liberate only enough radiant energy to match the solar output of a few thousand years. Geological evidence tells us, on the other hand, that the sun has shone steadily for hundreds of millions of years at least. Another possible source of energy is *gravitational contraction*. Just as an electron in an outer orbit has more potential energy than when in an inner orbit, so does a given mass have greater potential energy the larger it is. Therefore a shrinking sun will make energy available for radiation. Although gravitational contraction is indeed an important physical process in certain stages of the evolution of a star, it cannot serve as the energy supply for the present sun, for the available energy from this mechanism could keep the sun going for only a few tens of millions of years.

The actual energy source of the sun is the atom. Precise measurements of atomic masses show that the mass of a nucleus is slightly *less* than the sum of the mass of its constituent protons and neutrons. The deficiency represents the so-called *binding energy* of the nucleus and is the amount of energy that must be supplied from outside to break up the nucleus into its component parts. But how can we talk about mass and energy being equivalent to one another? Einstein, in developing the special theory of relativity, established the fundamental formula $E = mc^2$, where E is the energy of mass m and c is the constant velocity of light. We must now regard matter as a highly concentrated but tangible form of energy. Since c^2 is a large quantity, Einstein's equation indicates that a little bit of mass represents an enormous amount of energy. For example, the energy locked up in a one-pound mass is about equal to the daily dietetic requirements of the human race (3000 large calories per person for some 3 billion persons). Utilizing the formula $E = mc^2$ and substituting the mass deficiency of a particular nucleus for m, the binding energy of that nucleus can be computed. For a helium atom, for example, the combined mass of two free protons plus two free neutrons is 0.7 percent greater than the measured mass of a helium nucleus. The difference in mass when multiplied by c^2 gives a binding energy of 4.5×10^{-5} erg for the helium nucleus (see Fig. 12.27:1).

We have seen that energy is required to break up an atomic nucleus, but in the sun we need to get energy *out* of matter in order to supply the radiant energy required. There are two possibilities: *nuclear fission* and *nuclear fusion*. In nuclear fission a heavy nucleus such as uranium is bombarded and breaks into two lighter nuclei whose combined

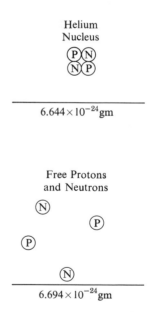

Fig. 12.27:1. The mass of a helium nucleus is less than the combined mass of its parts when they are free. The difference is proportional to the binding energy of the helium nucleus.

mass is less than that of the uranium nucleus; the balance is energy. Fission is not important in the sun, however, because of the extremely low abundance of heavy elements. In nuclear fusion, on the other hand, nuclei of low atomic number are built up when lighter particles combine with one another. And since energy has to be supplied to break up a nucleus, the inverse process of nuclear synthesis releases energy. Nuclear fusion therefore permits the sun to shine at the expense of its mass.

Departing from these generalities, let us inquire what is being fused into what? What kinds of atoms are the best candidates for supplying the enormous energy needed? (1) The only positive nuclei that can collide and join before being repelled electrically by one another are those with small charge or low atomic number. (2) The nuclei must be present in large numbers if adequate energy production is to be achieved. (3) The energy released per fusion ought to be relatively large. (4) If nuclei of a given element have been coming into being in the sun for hundreds of millions or even billions of years on end, they should be reasonably abundant by now. The only candidate, clearly, is hydrogen, with its end product being helium. Hydrogen nuclei have only one positive charge and they comprise most of the matter in the sun. The helium nuclei have a relatively high binding energy and are second in abundance to hydrogen. Thus the fundamental process by which the sun keeps radiating is the transmutation of hydrogen into helium. For each new helium atom that is formed, 4.5×10^{-5} erg of radiant energy is released. Since the luminosity of the sun is 3.8×10^{33} erg/sec, about 10^{38} fresh helium atoms are produced in the sun each second.

28. The Proton–Proton Reaction

THE SPECIFIC processes by which hydrogen is transmuted into helium inside stars are the *proton–proton reaction* and the *carbon–nitrogen cycle*. The latter is dominant in stars that are more massive than the sun; in the sun itself and in less massive stars the proton-proton reaction is the process responsible for most of the energy liberated. Deep down in the hot, dense core of the sun the particles rush around at high speeds and light atoms are completely ionized. Two protons may collide at a speed high enough to overcome their mutual electrostatic repulsion. When they are close enough together, about 10^{-13} cm, very strong binding forces overpower the force of electrostatic repulsion, and the two particles stick together as a new and heavier nucleus. The reaction is

$$_1H^1 + {}_1H^1 \rightarrow {}_1H^2 + {}_1e^0 + \text{neutrino},$$

the two protons forming a heavy isotope of hydrogen, $_1H^2$, consisting of one neutron and one proton. The excess charge flies off as a *positive* electron, or a *positron*. In addition, a neutral particle of ultrasmall mass, a *neutrino*, is emitted. A neutrino is so small that it can penetrate a wall of lead many light-years thick without being stopped. The neutrino emitted in the above reaction leaves the scene at the speed of light, emerges from the photosphere about two seconds later, and thus represents undetectable energy leaving the sun. The positron soon finds an opposite partner, an electron, and the two annihilate each other,

$$_1e^0 + {}_1e^0 \rightarrow \text{gamma ray}.$$

What was two particles is now an ultrahigh-energy photon of radiation. The heavy hydrogen atom later collides with another proton, with the reaction

$$_1H^2 + {}_1H^1 \rightarrow {}_2He^3 + \text{gamma ray}.$$

The result is one nucleus of the light isotope of helium and another photon of radiation. As a summary of all three of these reactions, the input is three protons and one electron, and the things produced are one light helium isotope, two gamma rays, and one neutrino. If there are *two* such series of reactions, the total input is now six protons and two electrons; the total outcome is two light helium nuclei, four photons, and two neutrinos. The final reaction in this sort of fusion is

$$_2He^3 + {}_2He^3 \rightarrow {}_2He^4 + {}_1H^1 + {}_1H^1 + \text{gamma ray}.$$

Thus the two light helium nuclei collide to yield a stable nucleus of ordinary helium, two fresh protons, and a photon. The total input for the entire sequence of reactions is therefore six protons and two electrons; the total output is one helium nucleus of $_2He^4$, two protons, five photons, and two neutrinos. The *net* result is that four protons and two electrons disappear and in their place are one helium nucleus, five quanta of radiation, and two neutrinos. The neutrinos carry away perhaps 5 percent of the released energy, but the quanta provide energy that will ultimately be radiated from the solar surface.

29. The Carbon–Nitrogen Cycle

IN MASSIVE stars and to a minor extent in the sun, energy is liberated by reactions involving protons with carbon and nitrogen. The specific reactions are

$$_6C^{12} + {}_1H^1 \rightarrow {}_7N^{13} + \text{gamma ray}$$

$$_7N^{13} \rightarrow {}_6C^{13} + {}_1e^0 + \text{neutrino}$$

$$_6C^{13} + {}_1H^1 \rightarrow {}_7N^{14} + \text{gamma ray}$$

$$_7N^{14} + {}_1H^1 \rightarrow {}_8O^{15} + \text{gamma ray}$$

$$_8O^{15} \rightarrow {}_7N^{15} + {}_1e^0 + \text{neutrino}$$

$$_7N^{15} + {}_1H^1 \rightarrow {}_6C^{12} + {}_2He^4 + \text{gamma ray}.$$

In this series of reactions the two positrons collide with two free electrons and both pairs are annihilated, with the production of two gamma rays. Therefore the total input in this series of reactions is one carbon nucleus, four protons, and two electrons; the total output is one carbon nucleus, one helium nucleus, six gamma rays, and two neutrinos. The *net* result is that four protons and two electrons are replaced by one helium nucleus, six quanta, and two neutrinos. As with the proton–proton reaction, the energy released per fusion is 4.5×10^{-5} erg. Of interest in the carbon–nitrogen cycle is the fact that a carbon atom reappears at the end of the cycle and can be used over and over again. Thus, although there is not much carbon compared with the helium in a star, its repeated use helps to make the cycle possible. The mass of the pots and pans in a kitchen is very small compared with the mass of food cooked in them in a period of a year, because they survive and can be used repeatedly. If, on the other hand, three aluminum pots had to be purchased per meal, eating would become prohibitively expensive.

30. Past and Future of the Sun

ALTHOUGH from one century to the next the solar interior changes scarcely at all, the long-term changes are profound. Born perhaps 5 billion years ago as a gravitationally contracting mass of tenuous gas, the sun shrank in size, radiating more and more as gravitational energy was freed. The interior density and temperature increased until conditions were extreme enough for nuclear reactions to begin. Early, at relatively low central temperatures, protons reacted with lithium, beryllium, and boron (with atomic numbers 3, 4, and 5) to produce isotopes of helium, thereby accounting for the extremely low abundance of these three elements in the present sun as compared with neighboring carbon, nitrogen, and oxygen. Later, when the temperature rose to millions of degrees, the proton–proton reaction began and continues today, the dominant energy-producing process in the life story of the sun.

Can this process continue forever? Let us see how long the sun can last if it continues to radiate with its present luminosity and consumes its entire mass. The sun radiates 3.9×10^{33} ergs/sec; dividing by $c^2 = 9.0 \times 10^{20}$ cm^2/sec^2, we find that the sun consumes its mass at a rate of 4.3×10^{12} gm/sec, or 4 million tons per second. Since the present mass of the sun is 2.0×10^{33} gm, its estimated life is the present mass divided by the rate of loss of mass:

$$\text{Life} = \frac{2.0 \times 10^{33} \text{ gm}}{4.3 \times 10^{12} \text{ gm/sec}} = 4.7 \times 10^{20} \text{ sec} = 1.5 \times 10^{13} \text{ yr.}$$

This estimate is about 3000 times the past life of the sun, and at first our star would seem to be in its infancy. We have erred badly in this computation, however, because we assumed *total* annihilation of the atoms in the sun. Actually, in the conversion of hydrogen to helium only 0.7 percent of the mass is converted into radiant energy; the rest becomes fresh helium. Further processes, such as the synthesis of carbon out of helium, can yield but a bit more. Thus our revised estimate is only 0.7 percent of the above time, or 10^{11} years. Finally, we must remember that only a minor part, possibly 10 percent, of the central solar mass is hot enough for the proton–proton cycle to operate. Our final guess is roughly 10^{10} years. The present sun is therefore a star of middling age.

The central parts of the sun are slowly getting richer in helium and poorer in hydrogen. Since the surface and central material do not circulate or mix with one another, the core will become purer and purer in helium content. In response to this change in chemical composition, the sun in a few billion years will probably begin to increase in size and luminosity at an accelerating rate and become a red giant star. Finally, the central temperature will be high enough for helium to fuse into heavier elements. The course of solar evolution will then be faster than it is today, and the sun will probably eventually decrease in size and increase in surface temperature. Ultimately, it will evolve into an ultradense, feebly luminous white dwarf star, with no thermonuclear resources left.

PROBLEMS

1. Give numerical values and units for each of the following characteristics of the sun: radius (in centimeters and in miles), mass (in grams and in terms of the earth's mass), average density, surface gravity, escape velocity, luminosity.

2. Describe two ways of finding the rotational period of the sun. What are the results of such investigations?

3. Describe two ways of determining the surface temperature of the sun.

4. (a) Why is the photosphere of finite thickness? (b) Why does the solar disk appear dimmer near the limb than at the center?

5. Explain why the inner corona shows a continuous spectrum and why the outer corona shows an absorption spectrum.

6. Although in many situations the kinetic temperature and the radiation temperature at a specific point are identical, they are not the same in the corona. Distinguish between the two kinds of temperature.

7. Give three kinds of evidence that indicate a kinetic temperature of about 10^{6}°K for the corona.

8. Discuss the nature of a typical large sunspot and its change with time.

9. Describe two techniques by which a solar astronomer can make a photograph of the sun in the light of Hα.

10. List the several types of solar activity that correlate with the sunspot cycle.

11. Discuss the several lines of evidence, cited in this chapter and in Chapter 9, which reveal that the sun ejects clouds of gaseous material at speeds of hundreds or thousands of miles per second and that some of these clouds strike our atmosphere.

12. Various physical concepts are utilized in deducing the nature of the solar interior. Qualitatively, what is meant by mechanical equilibrium? By energy production? By opacity? By temperature gradient?

13. Give a few numerical results on the physical conditions at various points inside the sun.

14. For what reasons is hydrogen an excellent prospect as a major supplier of energy in the core of the sun?

15. Review the various reactions in the proton–proton reaction and in the carbon–nitrogen cycle. In one complete reaction of each type, what disappears and what comes into being?

13

THE STARS: GEOMETRICAL AND RADIATIVE PROPERTIES

Having examined one star in detail, let us turn outward to study the host of others that dot the evening sky. Through most of history the stars were conceived as being attached to an enormous but finite crystalline sphere, and until Copernican times this sphere was imagined to turn once a day about the fixed and central earth. The view of Copernicus, however, was that the starry sphere is stationary and centered on the sun. In 1572 Tycho discovered a bright temporary star, a *nova*, in the constellation of Cassiopeia, dispelling the notion that the crystalline sphere is absolutely unchanging and eternal. Given the possibility of change, the Englishman Thomas Digges a few years later took the next conceptual step when he set forth the bold hypothesis that the stars lie at differing distances in infinite three-dimensional space rather than at the same distance on a sphere. His contemporary, the philosopher Giordano Bruno of Italy, went further: he supposed the stars to be other suns, to be circled by planets, and to be inhabited by people. For his rebellious notions and more especially for his heresy of equating nature and God, Bruno was burned at the stake in 1600. Ten years later Galileo turned his telescope to the Milky Way and discovered that this feebly luminous belt was composed of myriads of individual stars too faint to be seen with the unaided eye. In the latter part of the seventeenth century both Newton and Huygens tried to estimate the distance of the bright stars by comparing their light with that of the sun and assuming sun and stars to have identical luminosities. Their results hinted that the stars are exceedingly far away from us and therefore from one another: suns strewn at random in three-dimensional space.

But does the system of stars stretch infinitely far in all directions or, like a continent, is it bounded by shores? The first suggestion that our stellar system is finite in size seems to have been made by the English sailor and instrument-maker, Thomas Wright, in 1750. To him the circular belt of the Milky Way was evidence that our galaxy is an enormous congregation of stars occupying a disk-shaped volume of space, with the sun and solar system located at a point near the center of the disk. By this time telescopes had revealed a number of faint elliptical and spindle-shaped small patches in the sky, and Wright made the daring guess that these objects were other ultradistant stellar systems similar to our own flattened Milky Way of stars. These ideas were elaborated a few years later by the German philosopher Immanuel Kant, who called these dim objects island universes; today we call them galaxies.

Despite these several landmarks of speculative thought, the first stellar distances were not actually measured until 1838, by the German astronomer Bessel. Then and only then was it possible to compute the luminosities of these stars and to show that the sun's luminosity fitted nicely into their range. Meanwhile the nineteenth century saw the development of spectroscopy, and it was discovered that the complex spectrum of the sun was similar to that of many stars. The sun was finally and certainly established as a star. Not until the twentieth century were the speculations of Wright and Kant proved correct: in 1924 observational work with the 100-inch telescope on Mount Wilson showed that Wright's faint patches are indeed outside our own galaxy and are other galaxies comparable with our own.

Our study of the universe beyond the solar system begins with the stars. Later we shall be concerned with the over-all structure and behavior of their home and ours, the Milky Way galaxy. After that we shall look beyond to other galaxies and at their distribution and behavior in the physical universe. Returning to the stars themselves, our first task is to learn how stars are named and numbered, what things the astronomer can learn about a single normal star, and how he makes his measurements. Briefly, we can discover the *geometrical properties* of a star, such as position, velocity, and acceleration; and the *radiative properties*, such as brightness, color, spectral characteristics, and luminosity.

1. Name and Number

WE HAVE SEEN that the entire sky is divided into 88 regions, or constellations, and that each constellation is referred to by its Latin name, such as Capricornus the Goat, Equuleus the Little Horse, and Telescopium the Telescope. Many individual stars have been given Greek, Latin, or Arabic names, although only a few dozen are now commonly referred to by name. Sirius, the brightest star in the sky, comes from the Greek for "scorching"; Arcturus is the "guardian of the bear"; and Rigel is the Arabic for "foot" and marks the left foot of

Orion the Hunter. The usual way of referring to the brighter stars is by the lower-case letters of the Greek alphabet, followed by the genitive of the name of the parent constellation, as given in Table 4.17:1. Most stars visible to the unaided eye were designated in this fashion by Bayer around 1600, usually but not always in order of decreasing brightness. The letters and names of the Greek alphabet are given in Table 13.1:1. Thus Sirius is also α Canis Majoris, the

TABLE 13.1:1. The Greek Alphabet

α	Alpha	η	Eta	ν	Nu	τ	Tau
β	Beta	θ	Theta	ξ	Xi	υ	Upsilon
γ	Gamma	ι	Iota	o	Omicron	φ	Phi
δ	Delta	κ	Kappa	π	Pi	χ	Chi
ε	Epsilon	λ	Lambda	ρ	Rho	ψ	Psi
ζ	Zeta	μ	Mu	σ	Sigma	ω	Omega

brightest star of the Larger Dog; Arcturus is α Bootis; and Rigel is β Orionis (even though it is somewhat brighter than Betelgeuse, which is α Orionis). A number of fainter stars that had no Greek letter assigned were given numbers by the English astronomer John Flamsteed around 1700. Within each constellation these numbers are in order of increasing right ascension. For example, 61 Cygni is the first star whose distance was measured. Vast numbers of fainter stars are listed in various catalogues; even fainter ones can be identified by their right ascension and declination at some fixed time.

GEOMETRICAL PROPERTIES

To DEFINE the location of a star in three-dimensional space, astronomers must assign three numbers, or coordinates, to it. They usually use two angular coordinates to define the *direction* of the star, placing it at a unique location on the celestial sphere, and the third coordinate to define the *distance* of the star. The origin of coordinates is the sun. The two angular quantities normally used are right ascension and declination, although on occasion it is more convenient to use either ecliptic coordinates or galactic coordinates. These several systems were described in Chapter 4. Figure 13.2:1 shows the three coordinates of star *S*, with the sun located at *O* and the vernal equinox at *V*. The distance of the star is the length *OS*; the two angular coordinates are the right ascension, arc *VG* or angle *VOG*, and the declination, arc *GP* or angle *GOP*.

Granted that we know the right ascension and declination of many stars, can we obtain any general statistical information by confining our attention to the directions of stars alone, without any reference to their distances? Let us first plot the coordinates of the brightest hundred stars on a celestial globe and view the results. These stars are

2. Directions

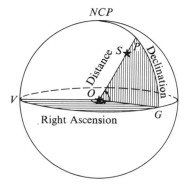

Fig. 13.2:1. The three spatial coordinates of a star.

found to be sprinkled pretty much at random; thus the brighter and presumably nearer stars lie in all directions from us, showing no preference for certain constellations. Next let us plot the coordinates of the brightest 100 million stars and survey the scene. Now something quite different appears: the density of points is about 30 times as great around the Milky Way circle as it is 90° away. Since the vast majority of these 100 million stars are very faint and far away, and since they *are* the

Fig. 13.2:2. *Left*: A 5-minute exposure of a 9° by 9° area of the north galactic polar region, made with a 4-inch Ross camera. The pole itself is above center and near the right edge of the photograph. *Right*: An identical exposure of the winter Milky Way in Auriga and Taurus, opposite the direction to the center of the galaxy. Note the greater density of stars. The galactic anticenter itself is at left center, very close to the margin. (*Photographs by Raymond E. White, University of Illinois Observatory*)

Milky Way, we are justified in favoring Wright's hypothesis of a flattened stellar system with the sun near its equatorial plane. This contrast between near and distant stars is analogous to an office worker on the tenth floor of a tall building: his nearest neighbors are above, below, beside, and in all directions from him, whereas the directions of the more numerous distant people in the city are pretty much confined to a narrow belt around his horizon. The English astronomer William Herschel, using coordinates and counts of stars alone, pioneered in making statistical studies of the sort we have sketched here, and his work was done before the distance of any star was known. We shall return to his studies in Chapter 20.

3. Distances

THE FUNDAMENTAL method of measuring the third coordinate of a star employs triangulation, using the earth's annual orbit as a base line. The general principle was described in Chapter 3, Section 21 and is illustrated here in Fig. 13.3:1. We are seeking the distance of a relatively nearby star, Q. When the earth is at E, the star is seen in one direction against the ultradistant galaxies; some six months later the earth is at E' and the star appears in a slightly different direction. This particular star is in the earth's extended orbital plane and thus lies at a point on the ecliptic; as viewed from the moving earth, it moves back and forth along a small arc of the ecliptic each year. Any nearby star not on the ecliptic executes a small annual ellipse against the distant background. These effects resemble the apparent motion of a nearby tree-leaf against a more distant building when the viewer's head is moved in a circle. Now, the angular semimajor axis of the star's ellipse is called its *parallax* or *annual parallax*, and is labeled p in Fig. 13.3:1. It is measured on photographs made at various times of the year. The angular separation of Q on exposures made at E and E', as shown in Fig. 13.3:2, is the angle $2p$. In other words, the parallax of a star is the maximum possible angle between the sun and the earth as viewed from the star.

What is the distance of a star whose parallax, for example, is $1''$? In Fig. 13.3:1 let $p = 1''$; ES is of course 1 a.u. Now, since the triangle EQS is always extremely long and thin, it is legitimate to use the same kind of proportionality that Eratosthenes used in measuring the size of the earth. Constructing a circle of radius QS around the star Q, we find that

$$\frac{ES}{1''} = \frac{2\pi \times QS}{360° \times \frac{60'}{1°} \times \frac{60''}{1'}} = \frac{6.28 \times QS}{1,296,000''}.$$

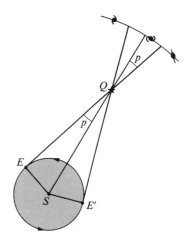

Fig. 13.3:1. The annual parallax of star Q is the angle p.

Solving for QS, we have

$$QS = 206,000 \times ES = 206,000 \text{ a.u.,}$$

if the parallax of a star is $1''$. This length is defined as the *parsec*, and we shall use it often; it is the distance of a star whose parallax is one second of arc. Another unit of length used by astronomers is the light-year, the distance traveled by light in a vacuum in one year. A light-year is about 6 trillion miles, but only about 1/3 parsec. The following relationships are important:

$$1 \text{ parsec} = 3.26 \text{ light-years} = 206,000 \text{ a.u.}$$

The general relationship between the measured parallax of a star and its computed distance is

$$D \text{ (in parsecs)} = \frac{1}{p \text{ (in seconds of arc)}}.$$

Thus a star with measured parallax $1''$ is 1 parsec away, in accordance with our definition of this unit of length. A star whose parallax is only $0.1''$ is 10 parsecs away; because of its greater distance, it makes a proportionately smaller annual ellipse against the background galaxies. Even a galaxy a million parsecs away goes through a small annual ellipse, but the semimajor axis of its ellipse, or parallax, is only $10^{-6}''$. Angles as small as this are much smaller than the most precise angular measurements we can make; thus these very distant objects form a practical background reference frame.

When several observatories determine the parallax of a given star, the average scatter of the separate measurements is about $\pm 0.005''$. This error is not important for the nearest stars, but if the measured parallax of a star is $p = 0.005'' \pm 0.005''$, its true parallax probably lies between $0.010''$ and $0.000''$ and thus its true distance probably lies between 100 parsecs and infinity. The method of annual parallaxes therefore gives reliable stellar distances only out to a few tens of parsecs.

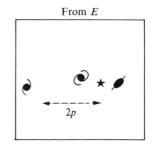

From E

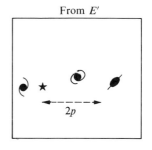

From E'

Fig. 13.3:2. Star Q photographed from opposite points of the earth's orbit.

We shall see later that there are many other methods of estimating great distances, but we should remember that nearly all of them are based ultimately on information supplied by the method of annual parallaxes as applied to the nearest several thousand stars.

The closest neighbor of our solar system is the triple star Alpha Centauri, deep in the southern celestial hemisphere. A bright first-magnitude star to the unaided eye, Alpha Centauri is resolved as a double star at the telescope, attended by a faint third star, Proxima, some 2° away from the other two. The parallax of the bright pair is 0.75″ and the distance therefore 1.3 parsecs; Proxima is about 1 percent closer and describes an orbit around the others every million years or so. The only other star closer than 2 parsecs is Barnard's Star, a faint object in Ophiuchus with a parallax of 0.55″ and accompanied by a recently-discovered planetary companion. The nearest stars are given in Table 13.3:1, which lists all known stars within 4 parsecs of the sun, as well as various kinds of information whose significance we shall examine later. Additional nearby stars will doubtless be found in the future, but they are so faint that they have not yet received adequate attention.

When we examine the nearest stars statistically, we can deduce an important fact. From Table 13.3:1 we find that there are 37 known stars closer than 4 parsecs, including 3 *unseen companions*. These 37 stars occupy a sphere whose radius is 4 parsecs and whose volume is thus about 270 cubic parsecs. The number density of stars in our part of the galaxy is therefore about *0.14 per cubic parsec*. When we notice the multiplicity of stars, 2 triplets and 9 pairs, we find that there are only 24 systems within 4 parsecs and therefore only *0.09 systems per cubic parsec*. The average distance between nearest neighboring systems is a bit greater than one parsec.

4. Proper Motions and Transverse Velocities

HAVING SEEN how to establish the position of a star, we next seek to measure its velocity, or rate of change of position with time. The first evidence that stars move at all was found by Halley in 1718. While comparing contemporary star charts with those of the Greeks, he noticed that several of the brighter stars had moved slightly from their earlier positions on the celestial sphere. The rate of change of direction of a star is called its *proper motion*, is symbolized by μ, and is expressed in seconds of arc per year. We measure the proper motion of a star by comparing two photographs of the same area taken some decades apart. Figure 13.4:1 shows schematically two photographs made 50 years apart. When they are superposed, it is seen that star A has moved appreciably in a west–northwest direction and star B a lesser amount in a southeast direction. When the lengths are measured and multiplied by the plate scale for the particular telescope, it is found, for example, that A has moved 63″ and B 34″ in this 50-year interval. Thus the proper motion of A is $\mu_A = 63″/50 \text{ yr} = 1.26″/\text{yr}$ and that of B is $\mu_B = 0.68″/\text{yr}$. To specify both direction *and* amount, it is customary to give separately the proper motion in right ascension and also that in

TABLE 13.3:1. The Nearest Stars

Name	p ('')	D (parsecs)	μ (''/yr)	v_T (mi/sec)	v_R (mi/sec)	v (mi/sec)	m_v	M_v	Sp
Sun							−26.7	4.9	G2
Proxima Centauri	0.762	1.3	3.85	15		21	11.0	15.4	M5e
Alpha Centauri A	0.751	1.3	3.68	14	−15	21	0.0	4.4	G2
Alpha Centauri B	0.751	1.3	3.68	14	−13	19	1.4	5.8	K5
*Barnard's Star	0.545	1.8	10.30	56	−67	87	9.5	13.2	M5
Wolf 359	0.421	2.4	4.84	34	+8	34	13.5	16.6	M6e
*Lalande 21185	0.398	2.5	4.78	35	−53	64	7.5	10.5	M2
Luyten 726–8 A	0.380	2.6	3.31	26	+18	32	12.5	15.4	M6e
Luyten 726–8 B	0.380	2.6	3.31	26			13.0	15.9	M6e
Sirius A	0.375	2.7	1.32	10	−5	11	−1.4	1.5	A1
Sirius B	0.375	2.7	1.32	10			8.5	11.4	wd
Ross 154	0.351	2.8	0.67	6	−2	6	10.6	13.3	M5e
Ross 248	0.316	3.2	1.58	14	−50	52	12.2	14.7	M6e
Epsilon Eridani	0.303	3.3	0.97	9	+9	13	3.7	6.1	K2
Ross 128	0.298	3.4	1.40	14	−8	16	11.1	13.5	M5
*61 Cygni A	0.293	3.4	5.22	52	−40	66	5.2	7.5	K6
61 Cygni B	0.293	3.4	5.22	52			6.0	8.3	K7
Luyten 789–6	0.292	3.4	3.27	33	−37	50	12.2	14.5	M6e
Procyon A	0.288	3.5	1.25	12	−2	12	0.3	2.6	F5
Procyon B	0.288	3.5	1.25	12			10.8	13.1	wd
Epsilon Indi	0.285	3.5	4.67	48	−25	54	4.7	7.0	K3
Cincinnati 2456 A	0.280	3.6	2.29	24	+1	24	8.9	11.1	M4
Cincinnati 2456 B	0.280	3.6	2.29	24	+9	26	9.7	11.9	M5
Groombridge 34 A	0.278	3.6	2.91	30	+9	31	8.0	10.2	M2e
Groombridge 34 B	0.278	3.6	2.91	30	+13	33	11.0	13.2	M4e
Tau Ceti	0.275	3.6	1.92	20	−10	22	3.5	5.7	G8
Lacaille 9352	0.273	3.7	6.87	73	+6	73	7.4	9.6	M2
Luyten's Star	0.263	3.8	3.73	42	+16	45	10.1	12.2	M4
Lacaille 8760	0.255	3.9	3.46	40	+14	42	6.8	8.8	M1
Kruger 60 A	0.253	4.0	0.87	10	−15	18	9.8	11.8	M4
Kruger 60 B	0.253	4.0	0.87	10	−17	20	11.4	13.4	M6
Kapteyn's Star	0.251	4.0	8.79	106	+150	184	9.2	11.2	M0
Ross 614 A	0.251	4.0	0.97	11	+15	19	11.3	13.3	M4
Ross 614 B	0.251	4.0	0.97	11			14.8	16.8	M6

NOTE: Stars or systems with an asterisk are accompanied by unseen companions (see Chapter 14, Section 5).

THE STARS: GEOMETRICAL,
RADIATIVE PROPERTIES

FEB. 17, 1911

FEB. 17, 1961

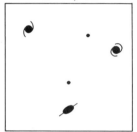

SUPERPOSED

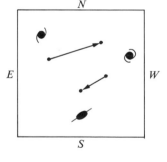

Fig. 13.4:1. Determination of the proper motions of two stars.

declination. The reason for photographing the stars on the same *date* of the year is to avoid the complication of annual parallax effects, for the earth is of course at the same point in its orbit on a given date each year and thus the star is at the same point in its parallactic ellipse. In general, a nearby star moves on a serpentine path because of the combination of its own motion relative to the sun and the earth's orbital motion; both the proper motion and the parallax of the star can be deduced from the nature of the path. Barnard's Star has the largest known proper motion, 10.3″ per year. Yet this rate is leisurely by ordinary standards, for it takes 350 years for Barnard's Star to move 1 degree of arc across the celestial sphere. Among the stars visible to the naked eye, 61 Cygni sets the record, with a proper motion of 5.2″/yr. This star was the first whose parallax was measured and is only 3.4 parsecs away. Of the first-magnitude stars, Alpha Centauri has the greatest proper motion, 3.7″/yr. It is no accident that the nearest stars have in general the greatest proper motions.

The *transverse velocity* of a star, v_T, is its speed at right angles to the line of sight, the sun being considered stationary. The transverse velocity of a star cannot be directly measured but must be computed from a knowledge of the distance and proper motion. Figure 13.4:3(a) shows two stars at the same distance but with different proper motions. Star 1 travels farther per year than star 2 and thus has the larger transverse velocity. The two stars in Fig. 13.4:3(b) have the same proper motion but are at different distances. Star 3 is farther away and therefore must travel more miles per year in order to describe angle μ. Hence the transverse velocity is proportional both to proper motion and distance. If the distance D is expressed in parsecs and the proper motion μ in seconds of arc per year, the transverse velocity of a star in miles per second is given by

$$v_T \text{ (mi/sec)} = 2.94D \text{ (parsecs)} \times \mu \text{ (″/yr)}.$$

The number 2.94 arises from the fact that we are using different units of velocity on the two sides of the formula. For rough computations it is simpler to use the approximation $v_T = 3D\mu$. As an example, suppose the parallax of a star is $p = 0.050″$ and its proper motion is 0.30″/yr. From the measured parallax, the distance is $D = 1/p = (1/0.05)$ parsecs = 20 parsecs. Therefore the transverse velocity is $v_T = (3 \times 20 \times 0.30)$ mi/sec = 18 mi/sec.

The fact that the nearest stars have on the average the largest *proper motions* arises simply from their proximity to us. If two jet planes are

Fig 13.4:2. In the interval between the two photographs Barnard's Star moved 3.7′ across the celestial sphere. *Left*: August 24, 1894; *right*: May 30, 1916. (*Yerkes Observatory photographs*)

flying overhead at 600 mi/hr, the plane 1000 feet up has a much greater angular velocity than the one 5 miles up, even though they have the same transverse velocity. Table 13.3:1 shows that the median transverse velocity of the nearest stars is about 25 mi/sec, whether we reckon with all the individual 33 stars or with the 23 systems, excluding the sun.

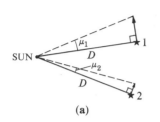

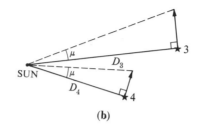

(a)   (b)

Fig. 13.4:3. In (a) star 1 has the larger transverse velocity and the larger proper motion. In (b) both stars have the same proper motion.

The median value of a quantity is the value possessed by the middle member; as many members have greater values as have lesser values. Thus the median distance of the 33 stars in the table is 3.4 parsecs, for Luyten 789–6 is the seventeenth in the list. Closer inspection of the list of transverse velocities shows a few runaway objects: Kapteyn's Star tops the list at 106 mi/sec. On the other hand, the most common transverse velocity is only about 15 mi/sec.

5. Radial Velocities

ALTHOUGH WE have just succeeded in finding the speed of a star across the face of the celestial sphere, we wish also to find its radial speed along the line of sight. In other words, we now seek to measure the *radial velocity*, v_R, of a star. We saw in Chapter 11 that the Doppler shift in the stellar spectrum is proportional to the radial velocity of the object. To date, the radial velocities of more than 15,000 stars have been measured and catalogued. Reference to the radial velocity column of Table 13.3:1 shows first that there are about as many approaching stars (negative v_R) as receding stars (positive v_R). If *all* the stars were approaching, we would be justified in forecasting that our neighborhood is collapsing; the figures suggest neither collapse nor expansion of the nearby stars. Next, the median radial speed, without regard to approach or recession, is about 15 mi/sec, with the most common value being near 10 mi/sec. As before, Kapteyn's Star is the fastest of the group.

6. Space Velocities

THE COMPLETE description of the velocity vector of a star relative to the sun specifies the direction of its motion and its speed. These quantities may be deduced from the direction and amount of its proper motion, its distance, and its radial velocity. Here we shall be concerned chiefly with the *space velocity*, or speed, of the star relative to the sun. The space velocity, v, may be determined with the help of Fig. 13.6:1 and the theorem of Pythagoras. The diagram shows a star approaching the sun with radial velocity v_R and moving at right angles to the line

3O8

THE STARS: GEOMETRICAL,
RADIATIVE PROPERTIES

SUN

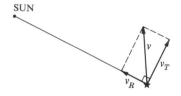

Fig. 13.6:1. The space velocity
of a star relative to the sun may
be computed when both the
transverse velocity and the
radial velocity are known.

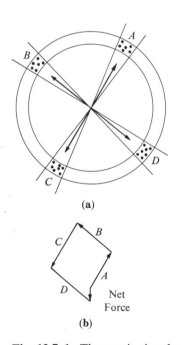

(a)

(b)

Fig. 13.7:1. The gravitational
force exerted on the sun by a
moderately distant star is
extremely weak; the net force
exerted by all of the stars is
even weaker.

of sight with transverse velocity v_T. On completion of the rectangle, the diagonal gives the total, or space, velocity, v. From the Pythagorean theorem for right triangles, the space velocity may then be found from the formula

$$v^2 = v_T^2 + v_R^2.$$

For example, if $v_T = 30$ mi/sec and $v_R = -18$ mi/sec, then

$$v^2 = 900 \text{ mi}^2/\text{sec}^2 + 324 \text{ mi}^2/\text{sec}^2 = 1224 \text{ mi}^2/\text{sec}^2.$$

When the square root is taken, the space velocity is $v = 35$ mi/sec. The space velocities in Table 13.3:1 were computed in this way. The median space velocity for the 23 systems (counting each pair and trio only once) is 32 mi/sec. Since Kapteyn's Star set the individual record for both transverse velocity and radial velocity, it necessarily has the highest space velocity of the group. Furthermore, the direction of its motion is chiefly radial, whereas that of a star like Lacaille 9352 is dominantly transverse. Both of these stars, along with Barnard's Star and 61 Cygni, are high-speed renegades; we shall interpret the significance of their high velocities later in conjunction with the general character of stellar motions in the galaxy.

7. Accelerations

HAVING examined the positions and velocities of stars, let us now see whether the stars are in accelerated motion, whether they change course and speed over the year. Actual observations of single stars from decade to decade have not revealed any measurable changes in their parallaxes, proper motions, or radial motions. The observed constancy of these quantities implies that any single star moves through space in a fixed direction at a constant speed, and is therefore not being accelerated.

Unaccelerated motion means that the stars obey Newton's first law of motion: no net force is being exerted on a star if it is moving in a straight line at constant speed. And indeed the force on and acceleration of any single star in our part of the Milky Way is very small, although certainly not zero. The only important force between stars is gravitational, but since the stars are very far apart and gravitational force decreases as the inverse square of the distance, the effect of a star on its nearest neighbor is extremely weak. The sun accelerates Proxima Centauri only about 10^{-11} as strongly as it accelerates the earth. As for the gravitational effect of more distant stars, let us think of the 400,000 stars lying between 10 and 100 parsecs from the sun. They pull on the sun (or on Proxima) in a stalemate tug of war. Statistically, for every star pulling in one way, there is another pulling in the opposite direction with the same strength. When the individual force vectors of these 400,000 stars are added together, their *net* pull is essentially zero. This effect is illustrated in Fig. 13.7:1(a), in which the pull of the six stars in volume A on the central star nearly cancels that of the seven stars in the equal and opposite volume C; the same is true for regions B and D. The *net* force is computed graphically in Fig. 13.7:1(b); it is of course very small.

Thus, because the mutual interaction between nearest neighbors is weak to begin with and also because the forces of more distant stars cancel each other, an isolated star pursues its course almost entirely oblivious of its surroundings. The major effect on the path of a star through space is the combined gravitational pull of the billions of very distant stars in the nuclear part of our galaxy, some 10,000 parsecs away. We shall deal with these large-scale effects in detail later. For now it is enough to note that when we examine the motion of a star relative to the center of our galaxy, we find that for every 2 million miles of travel its path curves only *one inch* towards the galactic nucleus. Little wonder that we have not yet observed any deviations from straight-line motion among the isolated stars.

8. The Solar Motion

WE HAVE seen that each star has its own constant space velocity relative to the sun—constant for at least centuries on end, as precisely as our measurements can tell. It is now in order, therefore, to ask how the sun itself moves through the nearby stars, for after all it is but one of them. Thus far we have *referred* stellar motions to the sun as a convenient standard of rest, much as a passenger on a cruise ship might consider a deck chair a stationary point of rest. Now we seek the *solar motion* relative to a more detached standard of rest defined by the stars themselves. If the solar system is indeed moving in a definite direction at a definite speed, we ought to be able to detect that motion by watching the stars *appear* to move in the opposite direction. Similarly, on a train we can infer that we are moving by watching the outside landscape wheel past in the opposite direction.

William Herschel discovered in 1783 that the sun is moving approximately toward Vega. At that time the proper motions of about a dozen stars were known, and when the position and proper motion vector of each star were plotted on a celestial globe and the results surveyed, the stars were found to be preferentially headed toward a point south of Orion. Herschel interpreted this effect as arising from the motion of the sun through these stars in the opposite direction, toward Vega. To simplify the picture, imagine looking out of a train window at nighttime lights here and there, as in Fig. 13.8:1. In 10 seconds the train moves from *A* to *B*. Lights 1 and 2, ahead and behind, do not change direction; their proper motion is zero. The other lights all have proper motions directed backwards; the angle described per unit time by a particular light is greater the less its distance from the train and the more nearly it is 90° from the direction the train is moving. Studies of the solar motion may be made in the same fashion, but there is the added complication that each of the stars has its own space velocity relative to the group as a whole. It is therefore essential to work statistically, using data for many stars. Such investigations do indeed show that the average proper motion of the stars in the Vega and in the Orion directions is nearly zero, whereas in the circular belt of the sky lying 90° from these two directions the average proper motion of a group of stars is a maximum and is directed away from Vega.

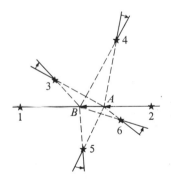

Fig. 13.8:1. The solar motion may be determined by analyzing either the proper motions or the radial velocities of the stars.

Additional and important evidence on solar motion can be obtained from the radial velocities of stars. Returning to Fig. 13.8:1, we find that light 1 ahead is approaching us with the speed of the train while light 2 is receding at the same speed. Lights at right angles *were* approaching and soon *will be* receding, but *now* they are neither approaching nor receding. Similarly, if we analyze the radial velocities of the thousand brightest stars, we find that the average radial velocity of the stars in Lyra and Hercules is about -12 mi/sec, the average for the stars in Orion, Lepus, and Columba is about $+12$ mi/sec, whereas the average in Pisces or Leo or other constellations 90° from the direction of solar motion is about zero. Thus the velocity vector of our star through the swarm and relative to that swarm is 12 mi/sec, or 4 a.u./yr, toward Vega.

When the space velocities of individual stars relative to the sun are corrected for our own motion, it is found that the stars in our part of the galaxy are moving something like the atoms in a gas at a given instant. (1) They are moving in essentially random directions; no heading is much more likely than any other one. (2) They are moving with a variety of speeds, but with a fairly well-defined average of about 15 mi/sec. Unlike the atoms of a gas, however, the stars do not collide with one another. Whereas the atoms in a cube of air occupy about 10^{-4} of the room available, the stars occupy only 10^{-21} of galactic space. The analogy with a gas must therefore not be stretched too far. Given that a star is moving in a random direction at 15 mi/sec, how long will it take to move a distance equal to that of its nearest neighbor, or about 1.3 parsecs? The answer is about 50,000 years. Thus in their wanderings the stars switch nearest neighbors every hundred thousand years or so; in a million years they will be thoroughly scrambled. Viewed another way, the constellations we study today will look rather different in the year 100,000 and very different in the year 1,000,000.

9. Statistical Distances

SUPPOSE THAT a star is at rest relative to the swarm of stars through which the sun is moving toward Vega at 12 mi/sec, and suppose further that its distance is too great to be measured reliably by the method of annual parallax. As seen from the moving sun, the star must be headed toward Orion at 12 mi/sec. In the particular example of star 1 in Fig. 13.9:1, the space velocity and the transverse velocity of the star are identical, 12 mi/sec. Measurement of the proper motion of the star then permits calculation of its distance. We solve the formula of Section 4 to find

$$D \text{ (parsecs)} = \frac{v_T \text{ (mi/sec)}}{3\mu \text{ ("/yr)}} = \frac{4}{\mu \text{ ("/yr)}}.$$

Here we are using as our base line the continuing straight-line motion of the sun rather than the annual orbit of the earth. By waiting long enough, therefore, we can use as long a base line as we wish. If, for example, star 1 has $\mu = 0.008''/yr$, its distance is then $D = (4/0.008)$ parsecs $= 500$ parsecs. Although in principle a beautiful method, we must remember that it rests on an unwarranted assumption, for a typical star has its *own* motion relative to the swarm. Star 2, for instance, has a velocity component toward Orion of 12 mi/sec due to the sun's motion and an extra 11 mi/sec due to its own velocity through the swarm. As we have seen, we cannot determine its motion unless we know its distance first. All is not lost, however, for again we can measure the *average* proper motion of a number of faint stars in a given constellation. The random velocities relative to the swarm will tend to cancel out, and we can then compute a reasonably reliable *average* distance to the group by using the formula given above.

To summarize the problem of finding stellar motions in our part of the galaxy: (1) We can determine the speed and direction of motion of any single star relative to the sun if we can measure its parallax, proper motion, and radial velocity. By combining parallax and proper motion, we can compute the transverse velocity of the star; combining this with the measured radial velocity gives us the space velocity of the star. (2) We can determine the speed and direction of our own star through the others by statistical studies of their proper motions and radial velocities; the sun is found to move at 12 mi/sec toward Vega. (3) We can subtract this velocity vector from the observed space velocity vector of each particular star. When the results are surveyed, the typical star is found to be moving through the swarm in a random direction at a speed not far from 15 mi/sec.

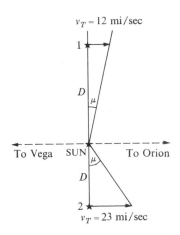

Fig. 13.9:1. Superposed on the random velocities of the stars is a reflex motion of 12 mi/sec arising from the sun's own motion through the group. The measured proper motion of a group of stars in a given constellation allows a rough estimate of their average distance.

RADIATIVE PROPERTIES

10. Apparent Magnitudes

THE BRIGHTNESS of a star is expressed in terms of its *apparent magnitude*. In the second century B.C., Hipparchus compiled a catalogue of about a thousand stars and assigned to each a number from 1 to 6 to indicate its relative brilliance. The first-magnitude stars were the brightest and the sixth-magnitude stars the faintest. With the advent of the telescope, even fainter stars were revealed, and the system was extended to higher numbers. The dimmer the star the larger, numerically, is its apparent magnitude. When actual measurements were made of the flux of radiation from a variety of stars, it was found that a first-magnitude star delivers about 100 times as much radiant energy to us as does a sixth-magnitude star, a fourth-magnitude star 100 times as much as one of the ninth magnitude, and so on. In the midnineteenth century the following definition of the magnitude scale was therefore adopted: *Two stars whose intensity ratio is 100 differ by exactly 5 magnitudes.* By *intensity* or *flux* we mean the radiant energy received from a source per unit time on unit area of a receiving device on the earth. Thus if star A is of magnitude 3.18 and star B is only $\frac{1}{100}$ as intense as A, its magnitude is 8.18. If star C is only $\frac{1}{100}$ as intense as B, its magnitude is 13.18. Now, A delivers 10,000 times as much radiation to us as does C; therefore a difference of $5 \times 2 = 10$ magnitudes corresponds to an intensity ratio of $(100)^2 = 10,000$.

Similarly, a magnitude difference of $5 \times 3 = 15$ corresponds to an intensity ratio of $(100)^3 = 1,000,000$; and a magnitude difference of 1 corresponds to an intensity ratio of $\sqrt[5]{100} = 2.512\ldots$. Table 13.10:1 shows the intensity ratios corresponding to various magnitude differences.

TABLE 13.10:1.
The System of Stellar Magnitudes

Magnitude Difference	Intensity Ratio	
0	$100^{0/5} =$	1
1	$100^{1/5} =$	2.5
2	$100^{2/5} =$	6.3
3	$100^{3/5} =$	16
4	$100^{4/5} =$	40
5	$100^{5/5} =$	100
6	$100^{6/5} =$	250
7	$100^{7/5} =$	630
$\cdot \quad \cdot \quad \cdot \quad \cdot$	$\cdot \quad \cdot \quad \cdot$	$\cdot \quad \cdot \quad \cdot$
10	$100^{10/5} =$	10,000
$\cdot \quad \cdot \quad \cdot \quad \cdot$	$\cdot \quad \cdot \quad \cdot$	$\cdot \quad \cdot$
15	$100^{15/5} =$	1,000,000
$\cdot \quad \cdot \quad \cdot \quad \cdot$	$\cdot \quad \cdot \quad \cdot$	$\cdot \quad \cdot \quad \cdot$

The magnitude system may seem needlessly complex, but it has a natural origin in that we respond logarithmically to external stimuli. Quantities that have a given *ratio* in nature are perceived by us as equal *differences*. A familiar example is the musical scale: when an octave is struck anywhere on the scale, the frequency of vibration of the higher note is double that of the lower one. For any pair of notes two octaves apart, the frequency of the higher one is $2^2 = 4$ times that of the lower. Three octaves corresponds to a frequency ratio of $2^3 = 8$, and so on.

We have defined the *scale* of magnitudes, but not the zero point. To fix a suitable zero point, we could adopt a variety of procedures. Just as 0°C is by convention the freezing point of water, we could, for example, agree that the bright star Betelgeuse has apparent magnitude 1.00. But Betelgeuse is an erratically variable star and thus not suitable. At the present time the assigned magnitudes of the naked-eye stars are consistent with the numbers given long ago by Hipparchus. But today's photoelectric measures enable us to establish intensity ratios with high precision and to find magnitude differences accurately to the nearest hundredth. The working zero point of the magnitude scale is at present *defined* by the self-consistent magnitudes of ten moderately bright, nonvariable stars scattered here and there over the celestial sphere; these stars are the so-called primary magnitude standards.

The brightest object in the sky is of course the sun, with magnitude -26.7; next comes the full moon at -12.7. Since the full moon is 14

TABLE 13.10:2.   The 30 Brightest Stars

Name	m_v	CI	Sp	p (")	D (parsecs)	μ ("/yr)	v_T (mi/sec)	v_R (mi/sec)	v (mi/sec)	M_v
Sun	−26.7	0.6	G2V							4.9
*Alpha Canis Majoris (Sirius)	−1.4	0.0	A1V	0.375	2.7	1.32	10	−5	11	1.5
Alpha Carinae (Canopus)	−0.7	0.2	F0Ia	0.018	60?	0.03		+13		−4
*Alpha Centauri	−0.3	0.7	G2V	0.751	1.3	3.68	14	−15	21	4.1
Alpha Bootis (Arcturus)	−0.1	1.2	K2III	0.090	11	2.28	75	−3	75	−0.3
Alpha Lyrae (Vega)	0.0	0.0	A0V	0.123	8.1	0.35	8	−9	12	0.5
*Alpha Aurigae (Capella)	0.1	0.8	G2III	0.073	14	0.44	18	+19	26	−0.6
*Beta Orionis (Rigel)	0.1 ± 0.1	0.0	B8Ia	−0.003		0.00		+13		
*Alpha Canis Minoris (Procyon)	0.3	0.4	F5IV	0.288	3.5	1.25	12	−2	12	2.6
Alpha Eridani (Achernar)	0.5	−0.2	B3V	0.023	40?	0.10		+12		−3
*Beta Centauri	0.7	−0.2	B0V	0.016	60?	0.04		−7		−3
*Alpha Orionis (Betelgeuse)	0.7 ±	1.9	M2Iab	0.005		0.03		+13		
Alpha Aquilae (Altair)	0.8	0.2	A7V	0.198	5.1	0.66	10	−16	19	2.3
*Alpha Tauri (Aldebaran)	0.9 ± 0.1	1.5	K5III	0.048	21	0.20	12	+34	36	−0.7
*Alpha Crucis	0.9	−0.2	B0V			0.04		−7		
*Alpha Scorpii (Antares)	1.0 ± 0.1	1.8	M1Ib	0.019	50?	0.03		−2		−3
*Alpha Virginis (Spica)	1.0 ± 0.1	−0.2	B1V	0.021	50?	0.05		+1		−2
Alpha Piscis Austrinus (Fomalhaut)	1.2	0.1	A3V	0.144	6.9	0.37	8	4	9	2.0
Beta Geminorum (Pollux)	1.2	1.0	K0III	0.093	11	0.63	20	+2	20	1.0
Alpha Cygni (Deneb)	1.3	0.1	A2Ia	−0.013		0.00		−3		
Beta Crucis	1.3	−0.2	B0IV			0.05		+12		
*Alpha Leonis (Regulus)	1.4	−0.1	B7V	0.039	26	0.25	19	+2	19	−0.6
*Epsilon Canis Majoris	1.5	−0.2	B2II			0.00		+17		
*Alpha Geminorum (Castor)	1.6	0.1	A1V	0.072	14	0.20	8	+4	9	0.9
*Lambda Scorpii	1.6	−0.2	B2IV			0.03		0		
Gamma Orionis (Bellatrix)	1.6	−0.2	B2III	0.026	40?	0.02		+11		−2
Beta Tauri	1.7	−0.1	B7III	0.018	60?	0.18		+5		−2
Beta Carinae	1.7	0.0	A0III	0.038	26	0.18	14	−3	14	
Gamma Crucis	1.7	1.5	M3II			0.27		+13		
Epsilon Orionis	1.7	−0.2	B0Ia	−0.007		0.00		+16		−0.4

NOTE: Stars with an asterisk are multiple. Their magnitudes and colors are for the combined light, but the spectral types, radial velocities, and space velocities are for the brighter components. Stars whose apparent magnitudes have the ± sign appended are variable in light. In particular, Betelgeuse varies erratically in magnitude.

313

magnitudes fainter than the sun, it delivers only about 1/400,000 as much radiant energy to us as does the sun. Next in order is Venus, with magnitude −4.2 at its brightest. The brightest star is Sirius, at −1.4, followed by the southern star Canopus, at −0.7. The 30 brightest stars, including the sun, are listed in order of increasing magnitude in Table 13.10:2, along with additional data. The annual parallaxes of these stars, where measured, are given in column 5, and the resulting distances in column 6. If the parallax of a star is less than 0.030″, the distance is doubtful and is given only to the nearest 10 parsecs, with a question mark. If the parallax is less than 0.010″, the distance is not given at all; indeed the appearance of 3 *negative* parallaxes in the list attests to the extreme difficulty of measuring displacements less than 0.010″. For stars whose parallaxes are less than 0.030″ no computed transverse velocities or space velocities are given. We shall refer to other data in the table later.

If we exclude the sun, we find from the table that there are two stars of magnitude −1 (between −1.5 and −0.5); they are Sirius and Canopus. There are 6 of magnitude 0 (between −0.5 and +0.5) and 13 of magnitude 1 (between +0.5 and +1.5). These 21 stars brighter than magnitude 1.5 are commonly called the first-magnitude stars. The approximate total numbers of stars in the sky brighter than certain magnitudes are given in Table 13.10:3. Because a person with

TABLE 13.10:3.   Counts of the Stars

Magnitude	Number Brighter	Magnitude	Number Brighter
−2.0	0	5.0	1,700
−1.0	1	6.0	4,900
0.0	4	7.0	15,000
1.0	14	10.0	350,000
2.0	40	15.0	37,000,000
3.0	150	20.0	1,200,000,000
4.0	540		

good eyesight can detect stars as faint as magnitude 6.2 or so, the total number of stars visible to the unaided eye is seen from the table to be about 6000. Note also the rapid increase in star numbers with increasing magnitude. This increase occurs because the fainter the stars we see the farther in space we look and the greater volume of space and number of stars we encompass. The numbers do not go on increasing indefinitely, however, for our galaxy is finite in size and contains a finite number of stars—about 100 billion. Although the brightest stars individually are quite striking, their small numbers mean that they do not contribute very much to the total light of all the stars. Stars near the 12th magnitude contribute most strongly to the total starlight, the larger number of such stars more than making up for the dimness of each individual. Fainter than 12th magnitude the number of stars does not increase fast enough to compensate for the decreasing intensity of each one, and the half-billion 20th-magnitude stars contribute a bit less to the total light than do the 20 brightest stars. The 2,500,000 12th-magnitude stars deliver 4 or 5 times as much light as either of these categories. The combined light of all stars excluding the sun is the same that we would receive from one star with apparent magnitude −6.7 or from 10 Venuses.

EARLY ESTIMATES of the apparent magnitudes of stars were made by eye, either unaided or at the eyepiece of a telescope. Now, the human eye is most responsive to light in the middle, or yellow-green, part of the spectrum. The magnitude of a star thus determined is m_v, the *visual magnitude*. With the advent of photography and its increasing astronomical use in the latter part of the nineteenth century, magnitudes were more and more often estimated by inspecting photographic plates rather than visually at the telescope. Because an untreated

11. Kinds of Magnitude; Stellar Colors

Fig. 13.11:1. Two photographs of the same star field, one in the blue and one in the yellow, adjusted so that most stars have images about the same size on each. Note, however, that the brightest star is conspicuously brighter on the right. (*Yerkes Observatory photographs*)

photographic emulsion is most responsive to light in the blue-violet part of the spectrum, a magnitude measured in this way is called m_p, the *photographic magnitude* of the star. For any given star, the two quantities m_v and m_p are likely to differ significantly from one another. For example, the bluish-white star Spica has $m_p = 0.8$ and $m_v = 1.0$, whereas the reddish star Antares has $m_p = 2.8$ and $m_v = 1.0$. The origin of these differences is the individual Planck curves of the two stars. Figure 13.11:2 shows the relative Planck curves for stars at 23,000°K, 5,800°K, and 3,400°K, corresponding approximately to Spica, the sun, and Antares. The distribution of their radiation with wavelength is very different, with the peak of Spica's curve in the ultraviolet and that of Antares in the infrared. The violet-sensitive photographic plate therefore responds relatively strongly to Spica but weakly to red Antares. The eye, on the other hand, takes relatively more note of the output of Antares than that of Spica.

The difference between the two kinds of magnitude is a sensitive and useful indicator of the surface temperature of the star in question. This quantity is called the *color index* of a star, *CI*, and is defined as

$$CI = m_p - m_v.$$

A white star with surface temperature 10,000°K, such as Vega, has by definition a color index of zero. Its photographic and visual magnitudes are therefore the same. Spica, bluish-white in color and very hot, has $CI = m_p - m_v = 0.8 - 1.0 = -0.2$, a slightly negative index. Antares, reddish in color and relatively cool, has $CI = 2.8 - 1.0 = 1.8$, a large positive index. The sun, intermediate in color and with surface temperature 5800°K, has $m_p = -26.1$, $m_v = -26.7$, and therefore $CI = +0.6$. If two photographs of the same area of the celestial sphere are made in succession with the same telescope, one with a blue filter in front of the plate and the other with a yellow filter to match the response of the eye, and if the exposure times are selected so that Vega and other stars with temperature 10,000°K look equally bright on the two plates, then every hotter star will look brighter on the first and every cooler star will look brighter on the second. The difference between the two magnitudes of each star is its color index.

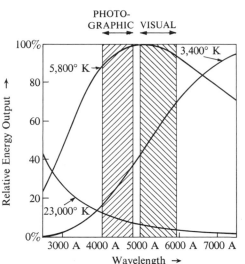

Fig. 13.11:2. Planck curves for three temperatures. Each curve is adjusted to peak at 100 percent, but only the curve for 5800°K has its maximum in the visual part of the spectrum.

Other kinds of magnitude may be found by turning to other parts of the spectrum. At visual or near-visual wavelengths a suitable filter in front of a photographic plate or photocell will yield ultraviolet magnitudes, red magnitudes, or infrared magnitudes. At radio wavelengths one radio telescope may be tuned to operate at 1000 mc/sec, another at 100 mc/sec, and so on; each one records the intensity and therefore the magnitude of celestial objects in a small band of the electromagnetic spectrum in the neighborhood of the wavelength on which it operates. Generally speaking, any nonvarying celestial source has a given intensity at each wavelength. Each kind of magnitude may be thought of as a measure of the height of the intensity curve at a given wavelength. A more fundamental kind of magnitude is the *bolometric magnitude* of a star, as measured with a bolometer. This device records radiant energy at *all* wavelengths of the spectrum, but because of its insensitivity and because of the complex absorption of incoming radiation by our atmosphere, bolometric magnitudes are usually found by computation from the known visual magnitude and Planck curve of a star. The zero point of this system is adjusted so that the bolometric magnitude and visual magnitude of the sun are equal.

12. Measuring Apparent Magnitudes

THE SIMPLEST and earliest measure of stellar intensity was a ranking in order. It is not a difficult matter, given a map of the United States, to rank the individual states approximately in order of decreasing area; errors may be made only when two states have nearly equal areas. Similarly, it is easy to note that Sirius is brighter than Rigel, which in turn is brighter than Betelgeuse, and so on. Here, however, we are not measuring magnitude differences *quantitatively*. Obtaining precise numerical results is important because the apparent magnitude of a star depends among other things on its distance, and we must always be alert for ways of finding distances of stars.

In principle, a simple method of measuring magnitudes is the following. With a given telescope and type of photographic plate, first make a one-minute exposure of a star field. Then move the telescope very slightly in declination and make a 100-minute exposure. The resulting plate will resemble Fig. 13.12:1, with two images for each star that is bright enough to be revealed on the short exposure. Now for any given star, the number of photons striking the plate during the second exposure is 100 times that during the first, giving a magnitude difference of 5. Next find any two stars where the short-exposure image of the first is exactly the same size as the long-exposure of the second. Since the plate has responded identically to both sources, the total radiant energy incident on the plate is the same. Because the first image was recorded in only $\frac{1}{100}$ the time of the second, the rate of arrival of energy per unit time, or intensity, of the first star is 100 times that of the second, and thus the stars differ by 5 magnitudes. By comparing all such pairs and also by ranking all the images of the long exposure, it is possible to establish approximate magnitudes for all the stars. In principle, this particular method is fine, although in practice it is liable to a number of errors and astronomers therefore usually employ more elaborate techniques.

Much more accurate magnitudes are found by using the photoelectric cell just behind the focus of a telescope. The telescope is pointed at a star and the photons arriving from the star pass through a small circular hole at the focal plane, on through a blue filter, and onto the cell. Their impact causes electrons to flow, and this electric current is proportional to the intensity of the star in the blue part of the spectrum. The current is read and recorded. Next the blue filter is replaced by a yellow filter and the new reading noted, after which the telescope is offset to blank sky and the yellow intensity of the little circle of sky is recorded. Then a blue reading of the sky is obtained. Now it is time to turn the telescope to another star and record its blue intensity,

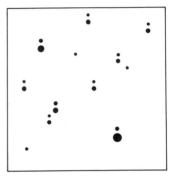

Fig. 13.12:1. Two exposures of the same star field on the same plate serve as data for estimating apparent magnitudes.

and so on. The sky readings are necessary because the background sky is not perfectly black: even on a perfect moonless night it is brightened weakly by permanent aurora in the atmosphere, zodiacal light, and scattered starlight. Thus to find the intensity of a star alone, we subtract the two readings (star + sky) − (sky) = star. The blue intensities may be converted to m_p and the yellow intensities to m_v by moving the telescope occasionally to measure one or more of the primary standard stars.

13. Absolute Magnitudes and Luminosities

ONE OF THE most important intrinsic characteristics of a star is its luminosity, or total radiant energy output per second. We have already seen that the luminosity of the sun is 4×10^{33} erg/sec, and that this quantity can be found only after measuring the flux, or intensity, of solar radiation incident on the earth and the distance of the earth from the sun. As with the sun, the intensity of a star or any other source depends on both its intrinsic luminosity *and* its distance from the observer. The oncoming high-beam headlights of a car get uncomfortably intense as the car approaches, since the luminosity, or wattage, of the bulbs is fixed but the distance is decreasing. Relief comes instantaneously when the lights are flicked to low-beam; the intensity is reduced by decreasing the wattage of the source at some fixed distance.

The astronomer's measure of stellar luminosity is *absolute magnitude*. The absolute magnitude of a star is defined as the apparent magnitude it would have if it were placed at the standard distance of 10 parsecs; it is symbolized by M. To find the absolute magnitude of a celestial object, we first measure its apparent magnitude, m, and its distance in parsecs, D. We then compute M from the formula

$$M = m + 5 - 5 \log D.$$

The logarithm, or log, of a number is the power to which we must raise 10 to obtain the number in question. A star 100 parsecs away, for example, has $D = 100 = 10^2$. Therefore from the definition log $D = 2$. Table 13.13:1 gives a few numbers whose logarithms are integral numbers, and we shall here restrict our attention to logarithms

TABLE 13.13:1. Selected Logarithms

Number	Logarithm
. . . .	
$0.001 = 10^{-3}$	−3
$0.01\ \ = 10^{-2}$	−2
$0.1\ \ \ = 10^{-1}$	−1
$1\ \ \ \ = 10^0$	0
$10\ \ \ = 10^1$	1
$100\ \ = 10^2$	2
$1000\ \ = 10^3$	3
. . . .	

of this kind. It should be noted, however, that all positive numbers have logarithms. For instance, $2 = 10^{0.30103\cdots}$; therefore log $2 = 0.30103\ldots$.

Imagine three faint stars of the sixth apparent magnitude, just visible to the unaided eye. Suppose the first star is 1 parsec from the sun. Then, from the formula,

$$M = 6 + 5 - 5 \log 1 = 6 + 5 - (5 \times 0) = 11.$$

The star has *mentally* been pushed out tenfold to 10 parsecs, and we therefore receive only $\frac{1}{100}$ as much radiation from it. A reduction in intensity by a factor of 100 corresponds to an increase in magnitude of 5. Thus the *absolute* magnitude of the star is 11. Suppose the second sixth-magnitude star is 10 parsecs away. Then we find

$$M = 6 + 5 - 5 \log 10 = 6 + 5 - (5 \times 1) = 6,$$

a result that makes sense; because this star is already at the standard distance, its apparent and absolute magnitudes must be equal. Finally, let the third sixth-magnitude star lie at 100 parsecs. Its absolute magnitude is

$$M = 6 + 5 - 5 \log 100 = 6 + 5 - (5 \times 2) = 1.$$

Thus, if brought in to 10 parsecs, this star would rank among the brightest stars; intrinsically, it is a luminous star.

Our earlier definition of the apparent magnitude scale was that a difference of apparent magnitude of 5 corresponds to an intensity ratio of 100. This system carries over for the absolute magnitude scale, so that a *difference of absolute magnitude of 5 corresponds to a luminosity ratio of 100*. Thus the first star in the above example has $M = 11$ and the second has $M = 6$. Since both are lined up at 10 parsecs, the distance effect is eliminated, and the luminosity of the second star is 100 times that of the first. Just as we have different kinds of apparent magnitudes, so we have different kinds of absolute magnitudes. The *photographic absolute magnitude* of a star is

$$M_p = m_p + 5 - 5 \log D,$$

and the *visual absolute magnitude* is

$$M_v = m_v + 5 - 5 \log D.$$

And if we construct a quantity analogous to our definition of color index, by taking the differences of the above two formulas, it follows that

$$M_p - M_v = (m_p + 5 - 5 \log D) - (m_v + 5 - 5 \log D)$$

$$= m_p - m_v = CI.$$

Therefore the color index of a star, which is the difference of its two *apparent* magnitudes, is also the difference of its two *absolute* magnitudes. We can thus deduce something *intrinsic* about the star, namely its surface temperature, without knowing its distance.

The visual absolute magnitudes of the nearest stars are given in Table 13.3:1 in the column headed M_v. Notice (1) that the sun ranks fourth in luminosity among the 34 entries, exceeded only by Sirius A, Procyon A, and Alpha Centauri A. Sirius is 3.4 absolute magnitudes brighter than the sun and thus radiates about 23 times as much energy into space. The feeblest emitter in the sample is Ross 614 B, 11.9 absolute magnitudes fainter than the sun; this star has a luminosity only 1/58,000 that of the sun. (2) If we divide the range of absolute magnitudes from 1.5 to 16.8 in two at $M_v = 9.15$, there are only 11 stars more luminous than this value but 23 less luminous, indicating that subluminous stars are the more abundant per unit volume. (3) The absolute magnitudes correlate with space velocities, in the sense that the most luminous stars in the table are relatively slow-moving, whereas a typical low-luminosity star has a higher space velocity. It may seem strange that the luminosity of a star should have anything to do with its speed, but recent advances in our understanding of stellar evolution and galactic structure explain the correlation; we shall consider it in Chapter 20.

Values of M_v are given for some of the brightest stars in Table 13.10:2. Where the distances are known with some precision, M_v is given to the nearest 0.1; for more distant stars it is given only to the nearest integral number; and for members of the most remote group it is not listed. The stars that make this list are either near and moderately luminous, like Sirius, Procyon, and Altair, or very far away and ultraluminous. Canopus, some nine absolute magnitudes brighter than the sun, radiates perhaps 4000 times as much energy as does the sun. Stars like Rigel, with a very bright apparent magnitude and an exceedingly large distance (and thus an unmeasurable annual parallax), are even more luminous. Although Arcturus is exceptionally fast, the space velocities of most of these very luminous stars are rather low, as we found for the more luminous stars within 4 parsecs.

The range in absolute magnitude among the known stars is from about $M_v = -9$ for the most luminous down to about $M_v = +19$ for van Biesbroeck's Star in Aquila. These figures are not to be considered final because all ultraluminous stars are too far away for reliable measurement of annual parallax and because very subluminous stars are too faint for easy discovery. Because its M_v is about 5, the sun stands in the middle of the range: the most luminous star is 14 absolute magnitudes brighter than or 400,000 times as luminous as the sun, and the sun in turn is 400,000 times as luminous as van Biesbroeck's Star. Thus one star with $M_v = -9$ radiates as much energy into space as $400,000 \times 400,000$, or 160 billion, stars with $M_v = +19$. Although the sun itself may seem a very average sort of star, standing right in the middle of the known range of absolute magnitudes, it is actually rather distinguished because there are so many more feeble stars than luminous ones. Its rank is fourth among the nearest 34 stars.

The number of stars per unit volume in each interval of absolute magnitude is called the stellar *luminosity function*. If we imagine a cube of space 100 parsecs on a side, located somewhere in our part of the

Milky Way galaxy, then the probable numbers of stars to be found inside this cube are shown in Table 13.13:2, for a few selected absolute magnitudes. The entry 0.05 means that there is a chance of only 0.05, or 5 percent, of finding even one star with $M_v = -5$ inside these million cubic parsecs. The run of the numbers shows how extremely abundant the subluminous stars are as compared with the

TABLE 13.13:2.
Selected Entries in the Luminosity Function

Absolute Magnitude	Probable Number
−5.5 to −4.5	0.05
−0.5 to +0.5	90
4.5 to 5.5	3,000
9.5 to 10.5	8,000
14.5 to 15.5	20,000

ultraluminous ones. But at magnitudes even fainter than $M_v = 15$ the number must somewhere begin to decline; otherwise we would be faced with the prospect of finding an infinite number of stars in a finite volume of space.

14. Stellar Spectra

THE SPECTRA of hundreds of thousands of stars have been photographed, the majority with an objective prism placed in front of the telescope objective, and a minority with greater dispersion by means of a slit spectrograph. These devices were described in Chapter 5, Section 16. When compared with one another, the spectra of stars can be

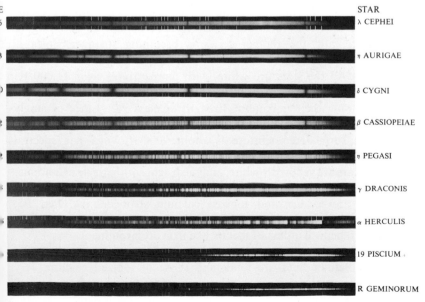

STAR

λ CEPHEI

η AURIGAE

δ CYGNI

β CASSIOPEIAE

η PEGASI

γ DRACONIS

α HERCULIS

19 PISCIUM

R GEMINORUM

Fig. 13.14:1. Examples of stellar spectra. Stars of the seven major classes are shown, as well as the N0 star 19 Piscium and the Se variable star R Geminorum with its emission lines. (*Mount Wilson and Palomar Observatories photographs*)

arranged in an orderly sequence, from rather simple spectra without many absorption lines at one end to very complex spectra with multitudes of absorption lines and bands at the other. The Harvard system of spectral classification was developed largely by Miss Annie Cannon at the Harvard College Observatory and is the one we use today. In this system the sequence is divided into seven major spectral classes of increasing complexity: O, B, A, F, G, K, and M. For finer gradation each major class is subdivided numerically, utilizing numbers from 0 to 9. Class O9 is followed by B0; class A1 is followed by A2; and M6 follows M5. In addition to these classes, several others are employed to include a few unusual stars: W, or Wolf-Rayet, stars are placed before the O stars, and they have emission lines in their spectra. Branching off from the latter part of the sequence are classes R, N, and S. The letter *e* following the class designation indicates that emission lines are also seen in the spectrum.

When stellar spectra were matched with laboratory spectra of the chemical elements, it was found that absorption lines of helium, for example, were prominent in B stars, of hydrogen in A stars, and ionized calcium in G stars. At first these striking differences were interpreted as indicating important variations in the chemical composition of the stars. But about 1920 the Indian physicist Megh Nad Saha, pioneer in developing the theory of atomic excitation and ionization, pointed the way to the correct interpretation: the spectral sequence is primarily a *temperature sequence*—the earlier the spectral type the greater the surface temperature; the later and more complex the spectral type the lower the temperature.

Stars of spectral class O5 have surface temperatures of about 50,000°K and are bluish-white in color. Characteristic absorption lines are those of ionized helium, and also multi-ionized nitrogen, oxygen, and silicon. The Balmer series of hydrogen appears, but it is weak.

Stars of class B0 are bluish-white, with temperatures near 25,000°K. Neutral helium lines are strong and ionized helium is no longer present. At B5 the temperature is 16,000°K, neutral helium is declining in prominence, and the Balmer series is becoming stronger. Spica is classified as B1 and Rigel as B8.

At class A0 the stars are white, with temperatures near 11,000°K. Helium lines no longer appear, but the hydrogen lines are very prominent, attaining their maximum strength at class A2. Lines of singly ionized calcium are detectable at class A0 and are stronger at class A5, where the surface temperature is about 9000°K. Vega has spectral class A0, Sirius A1, and Altair A7.

The F stars are yellowish-white, and the bright southern star Canopus, of class F0, has a temperature close to 7500°K. In these stars the hydrogen lines are weaker and ionized calcium stronger. At class F5, exemplified by Procyon, the temperature is about 6500°K and the many lines due to neutral atoms of metals like iron are prominent.

A star of class G0 is yellow and at a temperature near 6000°K. Here the Balmer lines are weak and those of ionized calcium very strong. The spectrum is crossed by hosts of lines arising from neutral metals. At this temperature a few hardy molecules are able to stay together; CN and CH put their imprint on the spectrum. The sun, Alpha Centauri, and Capella are G2 stars. At class G5 the surface temperature has decreased to about 5500°K, hydrogen lines are weaker, and the metallic lines and the molecular bands of CN and CH are more prominent than at G0.

At class K0 the color is orange and the temperature near 5000°K. Lines of ionized calcium are at maximum intensity, those of neutral metallic atoms are strong, and the molecular bands are more noticeable. Arcturus is a K2 star, and Aldebaran is classified as K5. Stars of the

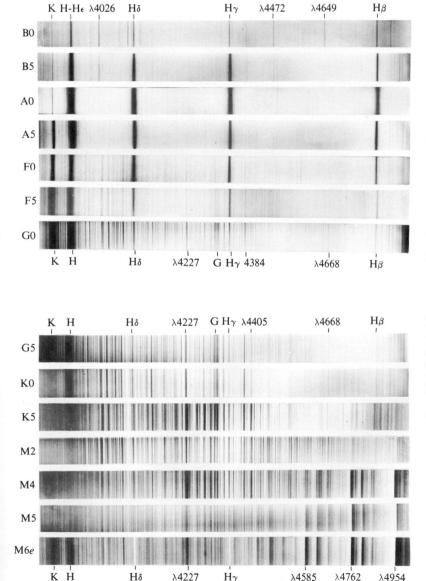

Fig. 13.14:2. Representative stellar spectra in the violet, obtained at the University of Michigan by W. C. Rufus and R. H. Curtiss. The Balmer series of hydrogen is conspicuous in the upper stars. The H and K lines at 3968 A and 3934 A are produced by Ca II, and the G band arises from the cyanogen molecule, CN. Other identifications are He I at 4026 A and 4472 A; O II at 4649 A; Ca I at 4227 A; Fe I at 4384 A, 4405 A, and 4668 A. In the cool M stars the violet edges of molecular TiO bands lie at 4585 A, 4762 A, and 4954 A. The M6e spectrum is that of the celebrated variable star Mira and features hydrogen emission lines. (*The Observatory of The University of Michigan*)

THE STARS: GEOMETRICAL,
RADIATIVE PROPERTIES

latter class have surface temperatures near 4200°K and the trend of increasing complexity continues in them.

At spectral class M0 the temperature is about 3500°K and the color red. The lines of neutral metal atoms are very intense and the lines of the Balmer series very weak. Bands of titanium oxide are visible in the spectra of these stars. Antares, class M1, and Betelgeuse, class M2, are examples of cool red stars. At spectral class M5 the surface temperature is only some 3000°K. Here the molecular bands of titanium oxide, TiO, are the characteristic features. Neutral calcium lines are very strong and ionized calcium and hydrogen lines weak. Proxima Centauri is of this class, but it also has emission lines in its spectrum; thus its designation is M5e. Inspection of Table 13.3:1 shows that a number of the subluminous red stars near the sun are of class M and also feature emission lines.

Only a few stars of the other classes are known. Those of classes R and N are called carbon stars; bands due to molecular carbon, C_2, and to CH and CN are strong, but the titanium oxide bands so promi-

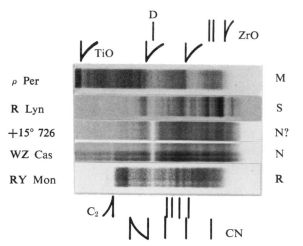

Fig. 13.14:3. Spectra of several red stars between 5400 A and 6600 A. (*From* An Atlas of Stellar Spectra, *by Morgan, Keenan, and Kellman, University of Chicago Press, 1943*; *Yerkes Observatory photographs*)

nent in M stars do not appear. These stars are very red in color. The S stars, also red, show bands of zirconium oxide, lanthanum oxide, and yttrium oxide (see Fig. 13.14:3). The atmospheres of these stars differ in chemical composition from those of normal ones. The W stars, with broad emission lines, are interpreted as having expanding envelopes of gas around them; we shall deal with these later.

Returning to the seven major spectral classes, O, B, A, F, G, K, M, let us interpret the sequence as a *temperature* sequence rather than as a *composition* sequence. Helium atoms require more energy to become excited or ionized than do hydrogen or metal atoms. Only in the hottest stars, at 50,000°K and class O, do we observe ionized helium. In the B stars it is too cool, and thus the vigor of atomic collisions too little, for helium to become ionized. Yet it is excited at these temperatures, and transitions in neutral helium are observed at 20,000°K. In even cooler stars only an insignificant fraction of helium is excited, so that not enough absorptions are occurring at any one time to make detectable absorption lines. Turning from helium to hydrogen, nearly all the hydrogen atoms are ionized at very high temperatures, whereas most are quiescent in the red stars. At 10,000°K conditions are most favorable for the electrons to be caught in the second orbit and excited to even higher orbits as they capture Balmer photons. At higher temperatures these lines are not prominent because of the high degree of ionization; at lower temperatures practically no hydrogen atoms are excited to the second orbit at any one moment. Finally, calcium atoms do not require much energy to become ionized. Only in the very coolest stars are lines of neutral calcium prominent; in stars like the sun most of the calcium atoms are ionized; in hotter stars they are multi-ionized. Thus the lines of Ca I are prominent in M stars and those of Ca II in the hotter G and K stars. The run of spectral classes therefore follows change of surface temperature; differences in chemical composition among the stars are of much less importance in interpreting the spectral sequence.

15. HR Diagrams

THUS FAR we have been able to isolate two intrinsic characteristics of a star. If the annual parallax and apparent magnitude are measured, then the absolute magnitude, or *luminosity*, can be computed. If either the color index or the spectral class is observed, then the *surface temperature* is known. In the early years of this century the Danish astronomer Ejnar Hertzsprung and the American astronomer Henry Norris Russell independently asked themselves whether these two quantities were correlated with each other. Any graph in which some measure of the luminosity of a star is plotted against some measure of its temperature is known in their honor as an HR diagram. For example, in Fig. 13.15:1 each point represents the location of one of the 33 nearby stars in Table 13.3:1 for which the data are known. A few

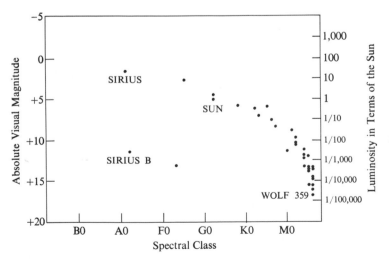

Fig. 13.15:1. The HR diagram for the nearest stars.

specific stars are labeled; the others can be identified by referring to the last two columns of the table.

The most striking feature of the diagram is that nearly all the stars lie within a narrow band running from upper left to lower right. This band is called the *main sequence* and the large majority of all stars are main-sequence stars. The diagram reveals a strong correlation between the surface temperature and the luminosity of main-sequence stars. In general, the higher the surface temperature the greater the rate at which energy pours into space from the stellar surface. The two nonconformists among the 33 stars of Fig. 13.15:1 are those whose spectra are marked "wd" in Table 13.3:1. Since their spectra differ from those of normal stars they have been placed horizontally according to their measured color indices: Sirius B is white and Procyon B yellowish-white. These stars are about ten magnitudes feebler than main-sequence stars of the same temperature and are *white dwarfs*—dwarfs because of their low luminosity and white because of their distinctly different color from the abundant *red dwarfs* like Wolf 359 at the bottom of the main sequence. Most white dwarfs are moderately hot and emit more energy from each unit area of surface than does the sun. Nevertheless, their *total* energy output is only a tiny fraction of the sun's. It is clear therefore that these stars must be very small in size.

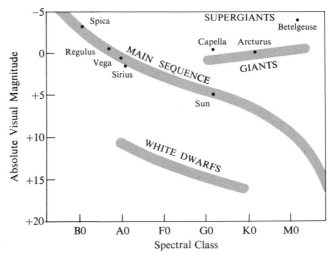

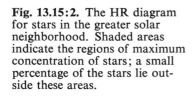

Fig. 13.15:2. The HR diagram for stars in the greater solar neighborhood. Shaded areas indicate the regions of maximum concentration of stars; a small percentage of the stars lie outside these areas.

Our sample of 33 stars embraces only the nearby objects and does not include any of the ultraluminous stars. When we extend our studies further afield to include a bigger sample, the HR diagram for stars in our part of the galaxy shows additional features. Figure 13.15:2 reveals that the main sequence continues to hotter and more luminous stars. There is also a concentration of bright yellow and red stars, called *giants* because of their excessive luminosity; Capella and Arcturus are examples. Even greater radiators are the *supergiants* scattered here and there near the top of the diagram. Betelgeuse is a red supergiant; it is cooler than the sun but of very much higher luminosity. In order to be so luminous, the red supergiants must have huge diameters.

Thus the stars in the greater solar neighborhood define four main groups in the HR diagram: supergiants, giants, main-sequence stars, and white dwarfs. Three points about the figure need emphasis. (1) The shaded parts show only where stars tend to congregate rather than where all stars must reside. (2) The number of stars per unit volume of space is not the same from point to point in the shaded areas: red dwarfs are the most abundant, white dwarfs follow, giants are spread sparsely in space, and supergiants are exceedingly few and far between. (3) Figure 13.15:2 includes only the kinds of stars we find in our part of the Milky Way galaxy. Recognition that the HR diagrams of other groups of stars may be distinctly different from the local HR diagram has spurred observational studies of star clusters and nearby galaxies since World War II. As we shall see, these studies have played a crucial role in enhancing our knowledge of stellar evolution—the story of the birth, life, and death of the stars.

16. Spectroscopic Absolute Magnitudes

A LOOK AT Fig. 13.15:2 reveals that at certain spectral classes, G5 for example, a star may belong to any one of the four main groups. We have already seen that when an astronomer empirically assigns a spectral class to a particular star, he is estimating the degree of complexity of its spectrum or, more specifically, the over-all average degree of ionization of the atoms in its atmosphere. If there is little ionization, the spectrum is complex, with hosts of lines arising from transitions in metal atoms. If most of the atoms are ionized, the spectrum is simpler because many lines arising from transitions in ionized atoms lie in the inaccessible ultraviolet part of the spectrum, leaving the visual spectrum less complicated. Let us ask if it is possible to tell *solely* from the spectrum of a star to which of the four main groups it belongs. What we shall need to do is look in detail at the behavior of spectral lines of specific chemical elements instead of getting a general impression of the appearance of the whole spectrum. Miss Antonia Maury at Harvard pointed the way to solving this problem; Walter Adams and Arnold Kohlschutter at Mount Wilson around 1915 showed how giants could be distinguished from main-sequence stars of the same spectral type; and around 1950 William Morgan of the Yerkes Observatory and Philip Keenan of the Perkins Observatory proposed a detailed scheme for classifying the stars both horizontally and vertically in the HR diagram.

To see how this classification is possible, recall from Chapter 11 that the percentage of atoms that are ionized in a gas depends on both the temperature and the density of the gas. High temperature and low density favor ionization; low temperature and high density favor neutrality. Now think of a supergiant and a main-sequence star both classified as G8. The supergiant is larger and its atmosphere is dis-

THE STARS: GEOMETRICAL,
RADIATIVE PROPERTIES

tended and of low density; the main-sequence star is smaller, with an atmosphere of relatively high density. To have the same average ionization and hence the same Harvard spectral class, the G8 supergiant must have a lower temperature than the G8 main-sequence star. The supergiant is the cooler by about 1000°K, and its atmosphere is more rarefied than that of the main-sequence star of the same spectral class. These differences affect the prominence of certain specific spectral

Fig. 13.16:1. High-dispersion spectra of three G8 stars recorded with the 120-inch telescope, showing details in the violet over a span of 70 A. Notice that ionized strontium is strongest in the Ib supergiant. (*Lick Observatory photographs*)

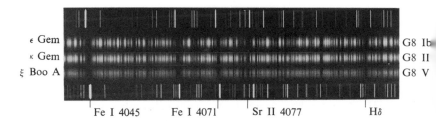

lines, those of ionized strontium for example being much more prominent in a G8 supergiant than in a G8 star of the main sequence. Although the spectra of these two stars look generally similar, a careful study of the relative prominence of certain spectral lines shows that there are real differences. For another example, we may compare the spectra of an A2 main-sequence star and an A2 supergiant. The

Fig 13.16:2 An objective prism plate of part of the Praesepe cluster, taken with the Curtis Schmidt telescope. The G0III and K0III stars are giants and the rest are main-sequence stars. The F2n star is so designated because of its notably diffuse lines. All marked stars belong to the cluster except for the F7 and F8 objects, which are closer to us. Classifications by W. P. Bidelman. (*The Observatory of The University of Michigan*)

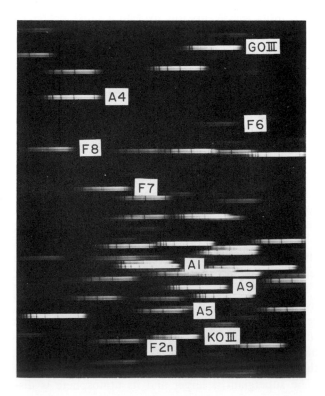

Balmer lines of hydrogen are at peak strength in the A2 main-sequence star but less prominent in the cooler supergiant, whereas lines of ionized iron are stronger in the low-density A2 supergiant.

From knowing the place of various stars in the HR diagram, it has become possible to correlate their luminosities with various *detailed* criteria in the spectra. This two-dimensional system of classifying spectra, the Morgan-Keenan, or MK, system, recognizes not only the ordinary spectral types but several luminosity classes as well. The most luminous supergiants such as Deneb and Rigel are called Ia, less luminous supergiants like Antares are Ib, bright giants like Epsilon Canis Majoris are of luminosity class II, and normal giants such as Arcturus and Capella are of class III. Lambda Scorpii lies between the giants and the main sequence; such stars are of luminosity class IV and are called subgiants. Main-sequence stars like Sirius and the sun are of class V. The spectral classes and luminosity classes of the brightest stars are given in Table 13.10:2. Less luminous than main-sequence stars are the subdwarfs, sd, exemplified in Fig. 13.15:1 by Kapteyn's runaway star at spectral class M0. Least luminous at a given spectral class are the white dwarfs, wd; they are recognized by the extremely great width of their absorption lines.

17. Spectroscopic Distances of the Stars

THE GREAT importance of determining the luminosity class of a star as well as its spectral class is that we can then estimate its distance from us. Suppose, for example, that a star of the tenth magnitude has spectral class G2V. From the HR diagram of Fig. 13.15:2 we find that a G2 main-sequence star has an absolute visual magnitude close to 5. Knowing that $M_v = 5$ and $m_v = 10$, we can find the distance by substitution in the formula

$$M_v = m_v + 5 - 5 \log D.$$

For this star we therefore have

$$5 \log D = 10 + 5 - 5 = 10.$$

Hence the distance is 100 parsecs. This procedure for estimating how far away a star lies is called the method of *spectroscopic distance* or *spectroscopic parallax*. Although not precise, it is an important way of deducing stellar distances far beyond the range where annual parallaxes can be measured. The only observational data required are the apparent magnitude, spectral class, and luminosity class. Although this method surpasses that of annual parallax for stars farther away than some 30 parsecs, it is well to recall that the method depends on a knowledge of the annual parallaxes of many nearby stars, for it was only with this knowledge that their absolute magnitudes could be computed and the HR diagram constructed in the first place.

PROBLEMS

1. Referring to Table 4.17:1 and the star maps, write the lower-case Greek letter and Latin genitive for each of the following stars: Mu in the constellation of Pictor, Rigel, Zeta in the Wolf, Chi Dra.

2. The parallax of a star is $p = 0.040'' \pm 0.005''$. (a) What is its most probable distance in parsecs, and within what limits of distance does it probably lie? (b) Express the most probable distance also in light-years, astronomical units, miles, and centimeters.

3. Of the total of some 6500 stars whose annual parallaxes have been measured, 165 have parallaxes of $0.100''$ or more, and 2230 have parallaxes of $0.025''$ or more. If our discovery of the 165 stars in the smaller sphere is reasonably complete, (a) how many stars should there be in the larger sphere, and (b) about how many remain to be discovered?

4. How long will it take 61 Cygni to move across the stellar background through an angle equal to the moon's diameter of about $30'$?

5. Calculate the space velocity of a star with radial velocity -20 mi/sec, proper motion $0.30''$/yr, and parallax $0.032''$.

6. How many times as strong is the gravitational acceleration of the sun by the combined pull of the stars in the central parts of the galaxy as the acceleration of the sun by a single nearby star of one solar mass and one parsec away? For the central nuclear part of the galaxy use 3×10^{10} solar masses and a distance of 10^4 parsecs.

7. If you are given the right ascension, declination, and radial velocity of each of the 300 brightest stars, explain how you can use these data to deduce the direction and speed of the solar motion.

8. Use Tables 13.3:1 and 13.10:2 to estimate the intensity ratios of the sun to Sirius, Sirius to Castor, and Sirius A to Sirius B.

9. A 1-inch telescope is directed at Sirius A. Another telescope aimed at Sirius B delivers the same amount of energy per second to the focal plane. How big is the second telescope?

10. The following stars in a certain constellation have the magnitudes designated: Gamma has $m_p = 3.2$, $m_v = 2.5$; Iota has $m_p = 4.1$, $m_v = 4.3$; Psi has $m_p = 7.3$, $m_v = 5.7$. (a) What is the color index of each one? (b) Which is bluest? (c) Which is reddest? (d) Estimate the spectral class of each.

11. A star at 10 parsecs has $m_v = 9$. (a) What is its absolute visual magnitude? (b) Compare its luminosity with that of the sun, using $M_v = 5$ for the sun. A second star at 100 parsecs has $m_v = 12$. (c) Find its absolute visual magnitude and compare its luminosity with that of the sun. (d) At what distance would the second star have to be in order to appear as bright as the first one?

12. Describe the prominent spectral features in stars of the major spectral classes.

13. (a) Explain why the Balmer lines are not nearly so prominent in very hot stars or in cool stars as they are in stars at the intermediate temperature of 10,000°K. (b) Why are Ca I lines conspicuous in M stars and Ca II lines conspicuous in G stars?

14. List the names and numbers of the different luminosity classes of stars.

15. Use the HR diagram to estimate the distance of an F0V star whose apparent magnitude is 12.5.

14

MULTIPLE STARS

Hₐᵥᵢₙ𝓰 seen how to establish such intrinsic stellar characteristics as luminosity and surface temperature, we next look for ways of finding other fundamental characteristics such as mass and radius. We therefore turn to the study of multiple stars—pairs, triplets, or quadruplets of stars that are close enough together in space to exert relatively strong gravitational forces on one another. Most of these nonsingle stars are pairs, or *binaries*, although Alpha Centauri is a trio and Castor a sextet. Larger groups, the *star clusters*, form the subject matter of Chapter 17.

Not many decades after the invention of the telescope it was seen that some stars, like Mizar at the bend of the Big Dipper's handle, appear double when viewed through a telescope. A century and a half later, in 1803, William Herschel discovered that the two then-known stars of Castor were moving very slowly around one another in elliptical paths. Now as we have seen, elliptical motion is a consequence of Newton's laws of motion and gravitation, and therefore Herschel's discovery extended the known realm of validity of those laws far beyond the solar system. When the first stellar distances were established a few decades later, the Newtonian rules were seen to work not only locally, but also millions of astronomical units away. And when this fact was recognized, it became possible to use Kepler's generalized third law to establish the *masses* of binary stars, just as we have already deduced the masses of the sun and of planets accompanied by satellites.

In addition to determining stellar masses, we can sometimes find the sizes of multiple stars, even though no star other than the sun can be seen as a disk through a telescope. Because some binaries move in orbits with planes that are nearly edge-on to the solar system, the two stars periodically cross in front of one another, eclipsing each other. Study of these effects enables us to infer the *radii* of the two stars. Multiple stars thus add very importantly to our knowledge of fundamental stellar characteristics. Another strong reason for paying respect to binaries is that they are surprisingly frequent. Reference to Table 13.3:1 shows that of the 37 stars known within 4.0 parsecs, 13 are single, 18 are in 9 pairs, and 6 are in 2 trios. Hence in the best sample of stars we have there are 24 locations where stars are found, of which 13 are occupied by single stars and 11 by multiple systems. Of the 37 stars themselves, 13 (about 35 percent) are single and 24 (about 65 percent) are members of multiple systems. Isolation may be the exception rather than the rule.

Some binary pairs move around one another almost in contact, whereas others are separated from one another by many thousands of astronomical units and take millions of years to complete their orbits. Pairs with different orbital characteristics are discovered by quite different techniques, and astronomers classify them according to the methods of detection. *Visual binaries* are those that can be resolved as double by the eye or at the telescope. *Spectroscopic binaries* are discovered from the periodic variations in Doppler shift as the stars circuit around one another. *Eclipsing binaries* have orbital planes nearly in the line of sight and each star partially or totally blocks off the light of its partner once every orbital period. We should remember that these distinctions are not intrinsic to the stars concerned, but depend on our methods of observation. In fact, many binaries have been observed by more than one of these three techniques.

VISUAL BINARIES

1. Chance Pairs and Physical Pairs

WHEN ALL of the brighter stars are examined with the telescope, about 10 percent are found to be close pairs. The two components are sometimes of the same brightness, but radical differences in magnitude are not unusual. Sirius A, for example, is the brightest star in the sky, but its companion, Sirius B, is ten magnitudes fainter. Among the 6000 stars visible to the unaided eye, about 150 have been found to be pairs whose members are within 1″ of each other. The first question to be settled is whether these stars are true *physical pairs* close together in space or whether they simply line up by accident (see Fig. 14.1:1). The latter are *chance pairs* or *optical doubles*.

Let us assume for the moment that all stars are single and are arranged at random over the celestial sphere. Now think of some bright star and imagine another star placed aimlessly somewhere on the sky. The chance that it lies within 1″ of the bright star is less than 1 in 100 billion. Even when we account for all possible pairings of the 6000

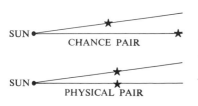

Fig. 14.1:1. The stars at the top are not physically associated; those at the bottom are close together in space.

naked-eye stars with the several million faint stars that could be seen in the glare of the brighter, the odds are very much against there being even *one* such close pair in the whole sky. The observed number is 150. The predictions of the laws of chance are therefore drastically at odds with the observed facts, and we are entitled to deduce that the vast majority of close doubles must be actual physical pairs rather than chance pairs. It is important to remember, however, that statistical reasoning of this sort can never tell us whether any *specific* pair is physical or chance; observations of that specific pair must be the basis for decision. Analogously, in 100 tosses of a coin we may expect heads approximately 50 times, but we cannot know whether the 82nd toss will be heads or tails until we make the toss and observe the result.

ABOUT 20,000 close pairs are known and catalogued, and nearly all of them are physical pairs. Only about 2000, however, have been observed often or long enough to show evidence of mutual orbital

2. Measuring and Analyzing Visual Binaries

1908   1915   1920

Fig. 14.2:1. Orbital motion of Kruger 60A and B. (*Yerkes Observatory photographs*)

motion. And only about 250 pairs have completed enough of a revolution so that their orbital characteristics are known. To determine the orbit of such a pair, the astronomer every so often measures the position of the fainter star relative to the brighter star. Each observation gives the angular separation or distance and the position angle, reckoned from north through east, as shown in Fig. 14.2:2. After many years, or perhaps decades, when the fainter star has revolved most of the way around the brighter, all the positions and times are plotted on graph paper, and a smooth curve is passed through the points.

We know from Kepler's laws that the relative orbit of the faint star must be some ellipse in space, with the brighter star at one focus, and that the fainter star moves according to the law of areas. From the earth we see the *apparent orbit*, which is the *true orbit* projected against the plane of the sky. The *inclination* of the orbit, *i*, is the angle between the perpendicular to the true orbital plane and *the line of sight*, as shown in Fig. 14.2:3. If $i = 0°$ for a certain binary, we see the true orbit, but if $i = 90°$ for another binary, we see the faint star move back and forth in a straight line. In general, however, any inclined ellipse is some other ellipse, and therefore we are guided, in drawing our smooth curve through the observed points, by the fact that the curve must be elliptical in shape. Also, the adopted apparent orbit must be an ellipse that is drawn so that the law of areas is obeyed by the motion of the fainter star. These guides are essential because the

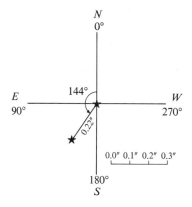

Fig. 14.2:2. The angular distance between the two components at the time of observation is 0.22″ and the position angle of the fainter star is 144°.

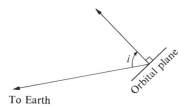

Fig. 14.2:3. The inclination of the orbital plane of a binary.

MULTIPLE STARS

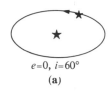

$e=0, i=60°$

(a)

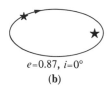

$e=0.87, i=0°$

(b)

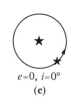

$e=0, i=0°$

(c)

$e=0.87, i=60°$

(d)

Fig. 14.2:4. Similar apparent orbits may represent very different true orbits. The location of the brighter star gives a clue to the nature of the true orbit.

Fig. 14.2:5. Data on the path of 70 Ophiuchi B around A, with the best-fitting ellipse shown. Orbit by K. Aa. Strand. Legend: ○ yearly mean of visual observations 1830–1873; ● yearly mean of visual observations 1873–1934; ⊗ photographic normal place. (*Yerkes Observatory*)

angles being measured are very small and there is a large scatter in the plotted points. It may at first seem that we should require the brighter star to be at one focus of the apparent ellipse, but a glance at Fig. 14.2:4 shows this to be incorrect. In (a) the bright star is at the center of the apparent ellipse, showing that the true orbit is a circle with inclination 60°. In (b) the inclination is 0° and we thus see the orbit face-on; it is an ellipse with $b/a = \frac{1}{2}$, or eccentricity 0.87. In (c) the inclination is 0° and the orbit is a circle, whereas in (d), which is the same shape, the true orbit is an ellipse with $e = 0.87$ rotated around its minor axis by 60°. Quite generally, the brighter star may be placed anywhere inside the apparent ellipse.

When the apparent orbit is carefully analyzed, most of the characteristics of the true orbit can be found. The period, P, is readily found from the time taken for one full sweep; among other derivable data are α, the semimajor axis in seconds of arc; e, the eccentricity; and i, the inclination. The inclination is ambiguous, for although analysis of the orbit may indicate an inclination of 29°, it cannot tell which end of the orbit is tipped toward the observer. This difficulty can be overcome by observing the radial velocities of the two stars at an appropriate time. The linear value of the semimajor axis, a, can be found only if the distance to the pair is known. We saw in the previous chapter that at a distance of 1 parsec the astronomical unit subtends an angle of 1″. Similarly, a visual binary at 1 parsec with an angular semimajor axis of 1″ has a linear semimajor axis of 1 a.u.; another at 1 parsec with angular semimajor axis of α'' has a linear semimajor axis of α a.u. In general, if a binary has an angular semimajor axis α in seconds of arc and a distance of D parsecs, the linear semimajor axis, a, in astronomical units, is

$$a = \alpha \times D.$$

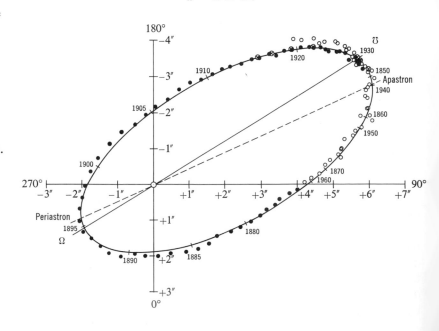

The pair 70 Ophiuchi, for example, has a parallax of 0.199″ and thus a distance of 5.0 parsecs; also $\alpha = 4.6″$. Therefore $a = 4.6 \times 5.0 = 23$ a.u., somewhat larger than the orbit of Uranus. The orbital period of the pair is 88 years, also a bit longer than that of Uranus.

3. The Masses of Visual Binaries

WE LEARNED in Chapter 7, Section 8 that Newton's generalized formula of Kepler's third law is

$$P^2 = \frac{4\pi^2 a^3}{G(M_1 + M_2)}.$$

If we express the orbital period in years, the semimajor axis in astronomical units, and the sum of the masses in solar masses, the formula is simplified to

$$P^2 = \frac{a^3}{M_1 + M_2}.$$

It is therefore possible to find the sum of the masses of the two stars in a visual binary if we can measure its orbital period, its angular semimajor axis, and its distance. For the pair 70 Ophiuchi we know that $a = 23$ a.u. and $P = 88$ years. Hence

$$M_1 + M_2 = \frac{a^3}{P^2} = \frac{(23)^3}{(88)^2} \simeq \frac{12,000}{7,700} = 1.5 \text{ solar masses.}$$

The combined mass of both stars is thus 50 percent greater than that of the sun, and presumably the mass of each star is somewhat less than one solar mass.

4. Individual Masses

IN ORDER to determine the individual masses of the two components of a binary, we must do more than plot the relative orbit of the fainter star around the brighter. We also need to examine the motion of each star around the center of mass of the pair. In the last chapter we found that a single star moves at constant speed in a straight line. For a double star it is the center of mass that moves in this way. When we plot the motion of the two stars against the background of faint distant stars, we find that each one follows a wavy line, as illustrated in Fig. 14.4:1. The center of mass always lies on the line joining the two stars and divides this line so that

$$M_1 D_1 = M_2 D_2.$$

We encountered this formula in Chapter 6 when we explored the mass ratio of the moon and earth. Here again the ratio of the distance of star 2 from the center of mass to that of star 1 from the center of mass, D_2/D_1, must equal the fixed quantity M_1/M_2. Given this requirement and the fact that the proper motion of the center of mass is a straight line, we can find the path of the center of mass and estimate D_2/D_1. Figure 14.4:1 shows the simple case of circular orbits of inclination 0°, and in this particular example $D_2/D_1 = 2.2$, and therefore the heavier

MULTIPLE STARS

star is 2.2 times as massive as its companion. Similarly, it has been possible to find the mass ratios of a number of visual binaries by plotting the motions of both partners against the celestial background.

The nearest known stars are the trio of Alpha Centauri. The two brighter stars, A and B, revolve around one another in 80.1 years with angular semimajor axis 17.7″ and linear semimajor axis 23.5 a.u. The combined mass is 2.0 times that of the sun and the individual

Fig. 14.4:1. On the left are positions of each star relative to the center of mass at eight different times. At the right top is the motion of the center of mass against the background stars during one orbital period. At the lower right are the actual observed tracks of the two stars.

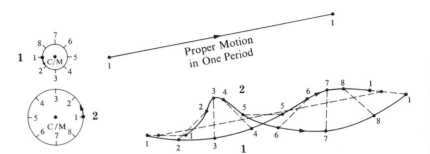

masses are 1.1 and 0.9 solar masses for the brighter and fainter respectively. The orbit is inclined by 79° and has eccentricity 0.52. Proxima, the third member of the group, lies 2.2° away from the bright pair, and no orbital motion for it has been observed. But it is certainly physically associated with A and B because it has about the same parallax and proper motion. It is at least 10,000 a.u. from the bright duo and its orbital period is 250,000 years at the very least. The visual binary Delta Cygni consists of a third-magnitude star of spectral class A0 and a much fainter eighth-magnitude star, with $P = 320$ years, $a = 62$ a.u., and $M_A + M_B = 2.4$ solar masses. The partners of 42 Comae Berenices are both fifth-magnitude F5 stars 17 parsecs away, completing an orbit every 26 years, and the mass of each star is about equal to that of the sun. The orbital plane is inclined almost exactly 90° and the stars move back and forth in straight lines; no eclipse has been seen, however. The lightest known stars are visual binaries and are included in the list of nearest stars in Table 13.3:1. Ross 614 B has a mass 0.08 times that of the sun, whereas each of the components of Luyten 726–8 is only 0.04 times as massive as the sun. Note that these stars are red dwarfs and among the least luminous stars of our local sample.

5. Unseen Companions

A NUMBER of binaries have been discovered by analyses of gravitational effects rather than by resolution at the telescope. Bessel found that the proper motions of both Sirius and Procyon were not straight lines but wavy, and in 1844 he suggested that both stars were binaries, each with a faint companion. For such a pair the track of the brighter star resembles that of star 1 in Fig. 14.4:1, and the track of star 2 is invisible. Sirius B was finally seen visually at the telescope in

1862 and Procyon B in 1896. Ross 614 was found to have variable proper motion in 1940 and later, in 1955, Ross 614 B was found photographically with the 200-inch telescope. Of the stars listed in Table 13.3:1, three have not been detected to date; the unseen companions of Barnard's Star, Lalande 21185, and 61 Cygni are known only by their gravitational effects on their partners.

6. Other Planetary Systems

THE THIRD and unresolved member in the trio of 61 Cygni moves in a relatively small path around one of the brighter stars and disturbs its motion slightly and periodically. The mass of the third component can be estimated from this effect and is probably near 0.01 solar mass. Since the mass of our largest planet, Jupiter, is 0.001 solar mass and the mass of the lightest star seen is 0.04 solar mass, it appears that the line of separation of stars and planets is somewhere near 1 percent of the mass of the sun. The actual nature of 61 Cygni C remains in doubt, however. The unseen companion of Barnard's Star was found by Peter van de Kamp in 1963 to have an even smaller mass, 1.5 times that of Jupiter. Barnard B appears to be the first planetary body to be discovered outside the solar system.

No other planets or planetary systems have yet been detected, and we can predict their detection to be a difficult and delicate business. One possible method would be to look for faint objects in the vicinity of nearby stars. But as we saw in Chapter 10, Jupiter would be near the limit of detection with existing telescopes if it were placed at the distance of Alpha Centauri. Barnard B is probably a thousand times too faint to be photographed with present instruments. Greater promise of progress by this technique awaits the establishment of space telescopes above the earth's atmosphere. A second possible method is suggested by the discussion in the preceding section. Can we use gravitational disturbance as a means of finding other planetary systems? Again, let us survey the solar system from Alpha Centauri. The proper motion of the sun as seen from there is a slightly wavy line with period 12 years, the wave arising from the motion of the sun around the center of mass of the sun and Jupiter. The other planets contribute smaller effects and are here ignored. Now, Jupiter is 5 a.u. from the sun and only $\frac{1}{1000}$ as massive, and therefore the center of mass of the pair is 0.005 a.u., or about one solar radius from the center of the sun. Existing telescopes do not show any star as a disk, and therefore only extended study can possibly reveal the waviness in the motion of a star that deviates by only one solar radius from a straight line. Barnard B is an exceptionally favorable example. At 1.8 parsecs, the system is the second closest known. Moreover, since Barnard A is itself a rather light star, only about 15 percent as massive as the sun, it lies nearly 10 solar radii from the center of mass of the pair. Even so, the discovery demanded concentrated effort for a long time. A third possible method for discovering other planetary systems is by an eclipse effect. If a transit of Jupiter were seen from afar, about $\frac{1}{100}$ of the sun's light would be blocked. This amounts to about 0.01

magnitude, on the verge of reliable detection with a photoelectric device. However, Jupiter can be in transit for at most only 30 hours every 12 years. Moreover, if an observer were placed at a random distant point, there would be only one chance in 1000 that he would be close enough to the extended orbital plane of Jupiter to be able to witness a transit at all. Trying to find planetary companions in this way is therefore an extremely long shot. Although it seems likely that planetary systems abound in our galaxy, their discovery by space telescopes or by analyses of minute gravitational effects belongs largely to the future.

SPECTROSCOPIC BINARIES

7. Discovery

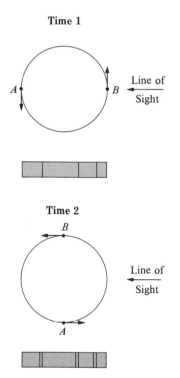

Time 1

Line of Sight

Time 2

Line of Sight

Fig. 14.7:1. Some spectroscopic binaries are discovered because their spectral lines periodically appear double.

THE BRIGHT star Mizar has a well-known fainter companion Alcor, readily visible to the unaided eye 11′ away. Mizar itself was the first visual binary discovered; in 1650 the Italian astronomer Giovanni Riccioli resolved it into 2 stars 14″ apart. In 1889 E. C. Pickering at the Harvard Observatory examined the spectrum of the brighter star and found that on occasion its spectral lines were double. He interpreted this effect as a periodic variation in radial velocity arising from the orbital motion of two relatively close and unresolvable stars around their common center of mass. Mizar thus has the added distinction of being the first discovered spectroscopic binary.

Suppose two unresolvable stars of the same mass and luminosity are revolving around their common center of mass, diagrammed as in Fig. 14.7:1. At time 1 the orbital motion of the stars is transverse to the line of sight and their radial velocities are thus the same. The slit of the spectrograph sees the joint light of both stars and both sets of absorption lines coalesce. At time 2, a quarter of a period later, star A is approaching relative to the center of mass and star B is receding. Now the lines of A are all Doppler-shifted to the violet and those of B are all shifted to the red. The lines are thus split, and the measured difference in wavelength establishes the differences in radial velocity of the two stars. Later they merge again, then split again, and after a complete orbit the lines are single once more. Such a pair is called a *double-lined spectroscopic binary* because the spectral lines of both stars are detectable. More frequently the stars of a close pair differ in brightness by more than one magnitude, and then the dark lines of the fainter star are filled in and obliterated by the overpoweringly bright continuous spectrum of the brighter star whenever the individual radial velocities differ. Such a double is called a *single-lined spectroscopic binary* and reveals itself by a periodic variation of the measured radial velocity of the brighter star. Among the 100 brightest stars more than 40 show variable radial velocity and about 20 are listed as spectroscopic binaries. Of the 30 brightest stars listed in Table 13.10:2, 6 systems are spectroscopic binaries: Capella, Rigel, Alpha

Crucis, Spica, Castor, and Lambda Scorpii. Altogether about 1500 spectroscopic binaries are known.

Fig. 14.7:2. Two spectra of Mizar, flanked by comparison lines of titanium. Lines are double in the upper spectrum and single in the lower. (*Yerkes Observatory photographs*)

8. The Velocity Curve

THE OBSERVATIONS that are collected in order to establish the orbital characteristics of a given spectroscopic binary are radial velocities at various known times. When points are plotted on a graph of radial velocity against time and a smooth curve drawn through them, the analyst is ready to go to work. When confronted with the symmetrical curves of the double-lined binary in Fig. 14.8:1, for example, he can tell that the radial velocity of the center of mass is $+12$ mi/sec and that the orbits are circular with period 22.8 days. Furthermore, because the radial velocities of the two components are always equal and opposite when reckoned from that of the center of mass, he knows that the individual masses are equal. Now, if the orbital inclination is 90°, he can determine from the graph that the velocity of each star around the center of mass is 37 mi/sec. Knowing that it takes 22.8 days to describe a circle at a speed of 37 mi/sec, he computes the circumference and then the radius of the orbit and finds that $a = 0.25$ a.u. He can then calculate that the mass of each star is 2.0 solar masses.

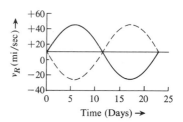

Fig. 14.8:1. An example of the velocity curve of a double-lined spectroscopic binary. Radial velocity is plotted against time.

These computations would be most informative if the inclination were known. The tilt of the orbit cannot, however, be deduced from the velocity curve. Suppose for example that the true inclination is only 30°. The speed of each star around the center of mass would then be 74 mi/sec, but because of the orbital tilt the radial velocity measures would reveal only half of the orbital velocity at any given instant. Since in this orbit the stars would complete their path in 22.8 days at the high speed of 74 mi/sec, the semimajor axis would have to be twice as big, or 0.50 a.u., and thus the individual masses 8 times as big. And yet the velocity curves of the two pairs would be identical. Quite generally, we cannot tell orbit size and inclination separately from a radial velocity curve. Our two specific examples give precisely the same plot. The best one can do is find a lower limit to the semimajor axis and the masses of any given pair. In addition to this difficulty, the mass ratio of the two stars can be found only if the pair is a double-lined

MULTIPLE STARS

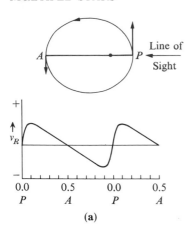

(a)

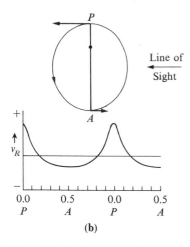

(b)

Fig. 14.8:2. The two orbits are similar in all respects except that the line of sight coincides with the major axis in **(a)** and with the minor axis in **(b)**. The observed velocity curves are very different.

9. Gas Streams

spectroscopic binary. In the extreme case of an orbit with inclination 0°, all the motion is transverse and the radial velocity does not vary. We cannot discover such systems by Doppler effects in their spectra.

In the more general case where the orbit is eccentric, the velocity curve may be highly unsymmetrical. Figure 14.8:2 shows two edge-on orbits, both with eccentricity 0.5 but with two different orientations. The major axis of the first one, (a), points toward the earth; that of the second, (b), is at right angles to the line of sight. The relative velocities are plotted against the fraction of the period, counted from *periastron* passage, the time when the stars are closest together. Both pairs are single-lined spectroscopic binaries, and the orbits and velocity curves are shown for only the more luminous star. The central horizontal line of each curve is the radial velocity of the center of mass. Notice that for pair (a) the radial velocities are zero at both *apastron*, or maximum separation, and at periastron. The peak radial velocities occur shortly before and after periastron because the star is moving fast in this part of its orbit. For pair (b) maximum recessional velocity coincides with periastron and maximum approach velocity with apastron. At the two moments halfway between periastron and apastron the star is approaching us, as can be understood from the law of areas.

Polaris, the North Star, provides a striking example of a complex triple system of stars. A ninth-magnitude companion lies 30″ away, thus qualifying Polaris as a visual binary with an orbital period of thousands of years. In addition, Polaris itself is a single-lined spectroscopic binary. The orbital period of the close pair is 30 years and the orbital eccentricity 0.64; the pair most recently passed periastron in 1959. The total variation in the radial velocity of the brighter component is 5.1 mi/sec; that of the fainter is of course not known. Because the orbital inclination cannot be found, we know only that the semimajor axis of the orbit is greater than 3.2 a.u. Polaris shows an additional oscillation in radial velocity of up to 4 mi/sec every 4 days, and this oscillation is matched by a variation in apparent magnitude every 4 days. This short-period effect cannot be interpreted as arising from a spectroscopic binary; as we shall see in Chapter 16, rhythmic swelling and shrinking of a single star is responsible for such variations of both luminosity and Doppler shift.

BINARIES most likely to be discovered spectroscopically are those with high orbital velocities, because the Doppler shifts are then large. Other things being equal, pairs with large velocities are those that have large masses and small separations. Indeed, a number of spectroscopic pairs are known that move around one another nearly in contact. Because of their proximity the two stars in such a system raise large tides on one another, and we may picture them as two eggs laid end to end. We saw in Chapter 12 that the sun, as it exhausts its hydrogen, is destined to swell slowly in size during a part of its future evolution. Now if one member of a close binary swells beyond a certain size during the course of its evolution, its partner will continually tear off the gaseous surface layers of the expanding component and the pair will become immersed in a common rotating and expanding cloud of rarefied gas. Such tenuous envelopes around binaries have revealed their presence by imprinting their own emission and absorption lines on the blended spectrum of the two stars. These complicating effects serve as a warning that a close spectroscopic binary must not be treated as though it were simply two point masses each adhering strictly to Kepler's laws. Recent studies of these gaseous streams, particularly those by the late Otto Struve and his colleagues at the Yerkes Observatory and later at the University of California, have formed a new chapter in the book of spectroscopic binaries and stellar evolution.

ECLIPSING BINARIES

10. Discovery

WE NOW KNOW about 3000 binary stars that vary in light for a fraction of the time. Usually they are of constant apparent magnitude, but periodically they dim for a while. The most celebrated of these stars is Algol, or Beta Persei, sometimes called the Winking Demon Star. Usually about magnitude 2.2, every 69 hours Algol decreases in brightness for a few hours, attaining a faintest magnitude of 3.4. Nearly two centuries ago the suggestion was made that Algol comprises two stars in orbital revolution around one another, with one eclipsing the other. The correctness of this view was established in 1889 when Algol was first identified as a spectroscopic binary and its velocity curve was found to have the same period as its light variation.

Any pair whose orbital inclination is nearly enough edge-on to the line of sight is an eclipsing binary. Figure 14.10:1 shows three pairs of stars moving in circular orbits of different inclination. The members of the first pair do not eclipse one another at all, as seen from our location in space. The members of the second pair partly hide one another twice each revolution; the eclipses are thus *partial*. If the inclination is close enough to 90°, as for the third pair, the eclipses are alternately *total*, when the larger star is in front, and *annular*, when the smaller star is in front. Virtually all eclipsing binaries are close to one another for a very good reason, which can be appreciated from Fig. 14.10:2. When doubles are very widely separated, there is only a tiny chance that their orbits are so inclined that we can witness their eclipses; we would have to be located in the disk-shaped volume of shaded space surrounding the wide pair (a) in order to experience an eclipse. When doubles are close, as in (b), eclipses are seen from a larger percentage of space; only from a point in one of the two non-shaded conical volumes are no eclipses detectable. If the radii of the two stars in a binary system are R_1 and R_2 and the stars move around one another in a circular orbit separated by a distance a, then the chance that we see them as some kind of eclipsing binary is $(R_1 + R_2)/a$, whereas the chance that we see them as a totally eclipsing binary is $(R_1 - R_2)/a$. If a is large, as it is for a visual binary, we stand little

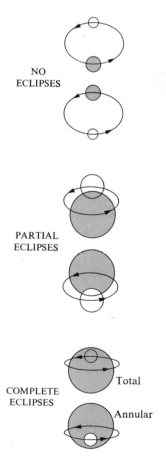

NO
ECLIPSES

PARTIAL
ECLIPSES

COMPLETE
ECLIPSES

Total

Annular

Fig. 14.10:1. Different kinds of stellar eclipses.

chance of seeing the pair as an eclipsing binary. Indeed, out of tens of thousands of known visual pairs, not one has been detected as an eclipsing system. On the other hand, if the two are in contact, then $R_1 + R_2 = a$, and $(R_1 + R_2)/a = 1$. Now a chance of 1 is certainty;

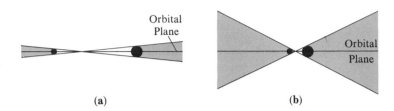

Fig. 14.10:2. The greater the separation of two stars the less likely we are to witness them as an eclipsing pair.

(a) (b)

thus such a pair can be seen as a partially eclipsing system from all points of space. It is clear from these various considerations that a hypothetical observer 100 parsecs from the earth would see a rather different group of eclipsing stars than those found in our catalogues.

11. Light Curves

THE DATA needed for analyzing the orbit of an eclipsing binary are apparent magnitudes at different times. Since no eclipsing pair is resolvable as two distinct stars, any one magnitude measurement tells the combined light received from the pair at that instant. The most precise method of obtaining an accurate plot of magnitude against time is to measure the binary frequently with a photoelectric cell at the telescope, with occasional measurements of one or more standard stars of constant magnitude in the same part of the sky. Once the orbital period of the binary is known, records obtained on different nights can be pieced together to give a host of observed points. The best smooth curve through these points is the light curve, and that for Algol is shown in Fig. 14.14:1. Time is reckoned from the moment of minimum light, or *primary minimum*; the shallow dip is called the *secondary minimum* and occurs halfway between successive primary minima if the orbit, like Algol's, is circular.

Study of the light curve of an eclipsing binary reveals not only the orbital period, but also the inclination and eccentricity of the orbit. If the orbit is eccentric, the secondary minimum does not generally occur halfway between primary minima and the duration of primary eclipse differs from that of secondary eclipse. Most eclipsing binaries, however, are found to have circular or nearly circular orbits. It is also possible to find from the light curve the radius of each star in terms of the semimajor axis of the orbit. Thus if $R_1/a = 0.30$ and $R_2/a = 0.15$, the larger star has a radius 30 percent of the mean separation of the pair and the smaller has only half this radius. In addition, the light curve reveals the luminosity of each star in terms of the combined light of the pair. Let us examine the light curves of several eclipsing stars in circular orbits edge-on to the line of sight in order to see how these physical characteristics reveal themselves. In Fig.

14.11:1 are diagrammed two stars of the same size observed from a great distance to the right. The duration of each eclipse is the same, and the pointed minima arise from the fact that each eclipse can be total only for an instant; immediately before and after totality a crescent slice of light from the rear star reaches the observer. If the two stars have identical luminosities, so that $L_A = L_B$, the shape and depth of both minima are the same, as shown in the first light curve. At minimum, we receive just one-half as much light as when the stars are not in eclipse, and this amounts to a dimming of 0.75 magnitude. The second light curve in Fig. 14.11:1 is that produced by two stars of the

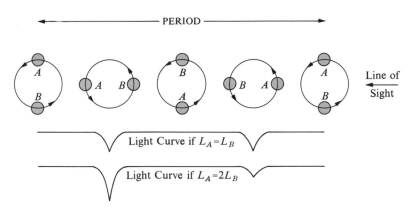

Fig. **14.11:1.** Stars A and B are the same size. The upper light curve results if A and B are equally luminous, and the lower if A is twice as luminous as B.

same size but with one twice as luminous as the other. Primary minimum now occurs when B is in front, blocking off the greater light of A. If $L_A = 2L_B$, we receive only one-third as much light at this time as outside of eclipse. Secondary minimum is shallower because even at mideclipse we still receive two-thirds of the combined light.

In Fig. 14.11:2 star A has twice the radius of star B and, as before, the orbits are circular and viewed edge-on. Under these circumstances the duration of each eclipse is the same. Unlike the previous example, however, the minima are flat-bottomed rather than pointed because the annular and total parts of the eclipses last a finite length of time.

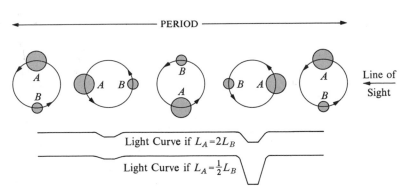

Fig. **14.11:2.** The radius of star A is here twice that of star B. The upper light curve results if A is twice as luminous as B, the lower if A is half as luminous as B.

The first light curve results if star *A* is not only twice the radius but also twice the luminosity of star *B*. During secondary minimum *B* crosses in front, and while the annular phase proceeds it blocks off one-fourth of the light of *A* because its area is one-fourth that of *A*. Half a period later, at primary minimum, star *A* during the total phase blocks off *all* of the light of *B*, which amounts to half that of *A*. Thus primary minimum does not necessarily occur when the brighter star or the larger star is in front; it occurs when the star of greater *surface brightness* is eclipsed. In this example star *B* is only half as luminous as *A*, but this radiation comes from only one-fourth the area, and thus its surface brightness is twice that of *A*. The second light curve exemplifies a frequent type of eclipsing binary, where a big dim star revolves round a small bright one. Here *A* is only half as luminous as *B*, and when *B* is in front it obliterates only one-fourth the light of the feeble star; the dimming is only slight. At primary minimum the big dim partner occults the strong light of *B* and the minimum is very deep. The system of Algol is rather similar to this latter example.

12. Spectroscopic Evidence

RECALL THAT the radial velocity curve of a spectroscopic binary will not reveal the orbital inclination and semimajor axis, *a*, separately. From the light curve of an eclipsing binary, however, the inclination *can* be deduced, although we cannot find the semimajor axis. Therefore if we can bring both observational methods to bear on any eclipsing binary, we can learn much about the orbits and the physical characteristics of the two stars. It is a happy consequence of the laws of chance and Newton's laws that eclipsing binaries are generally the most precisely measurable kind of spectroscopic binary. We have already seen that eclipsing pairs, statistically speaking, are relatively close to one another, and the more widely separated ones must have an orbital inclination near 90° in order to show eclipses. Now, the close pairs exert a strong gravitational pull on one another and their orbital speeds are great, whereas the more widely separated ones are somewhat slower but are inclined most favorably to observe maximum Doppler shifts. Both effects conspire to make eclipsing binaries excellent subjects for radial velocity studies.

To illustrate what can be learned, let us avoid the complexities actually found by astronomers and concentrate on one simplified example. We return to the first example of Fig. 14.11:1, where the stars are of the same luminosity and radius in circular orbits seen edge-on. Let us assume the stars also have the same mass, so that they circle at equal distances from their center of mass. Figure 14.12:1 shows an expanded view of the system. The velocity curves of the pair indicate at time 1 a maximum velocity difference of 176 mi/sec, with the spectral lines of *A* shifted to the red and those of *B* to the violet; each star is therefore moving around the center of mass at one-half this speed, or $v = 88$ mi/sec. From either the velocity curve or the light curve the orbital period is found to be 2.67 days. The separation of the stars is *a*, and since they are equally massive, each star lies at a

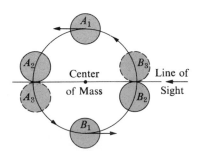

Fig. 14.12:1. Example of an eclipsing binary also observed spectroscopically. The observer is thousands of miles to the right on the scale of the figure and sees the pair as a single point of light.

distance $a/2$ from the center of mass and travels a distance $2\pi a/2 = \pi a$ around the center of mass in one orbital period. Since distance traveled is the product of speed times the time taken, we find that

$$a = \frac{vP}{\pi}.$$

Numerically,

$$a = \frac{vP}{\pi} = \frac{1}{3.14} \times \frac{88 \text{ mi}}{\text{sec}} \times 2.67 \text{ day} \times \frac{8.64 \times 10^4 \text{ sec}}{\text{day}}$$
$$= 6.47 \times 10^6 \text{ mi}.$$

Thus the distance from the center of A to that of B is 6.47 million miles, or 0.0695 a.u. Next we can find the masses of the stars from Kepler's third law, from the known values of a and P. Converting the period of 2.67 days into years, we find $P = 0.00731$ yr. Therefore

$$M_A + M_B = \frac{a^3}{P^2} = \frac{(6.95 \times 10^{-2})^3}{(7.31 \times 10^{-3})^2} = \frac{336}{53.4} = 6.28 \text{ solar masses.}$$

Since the masses are the same, each has a mass 3.1 times that of the sun.

Next, one of the two equal eclipses begins at time 2 in Fig. 14.12:1, when star B begins to cover up A; this minimum is over at time 3 when A moves clear of B. The light curve allows us to estimate that the total duration of the eclipse is 6.1 hours. We note that in this interval star B moves around the center of mass a distance very nearly equal to its own diameter. Its speed around the center of mass is 88 mi/sec, and the diameter of the star is the product of this speed times the duration of the eclipse. Its radius is one-half of this quantity, or

$$R_B = \frac{1}{2} \times \frac{88 \text{ mi}}{\text{sec}} \times 6.1 \text{ hr} \times \frac{3.6 \times 10^3 \text{ sec}}{\text{hr}} = 9.7 \times 10^5 \text{ mi.}$$

In this example the radii are the same, and therefore each star has a radius of 970,000 miles, or 2.2 solar radii. Since the masses and radii have been deduced, we can go on to find the average density of matter in these twin stars. It is $3.1/(2.2)^3$, or 0.30 times the density of the sun. Although we have dealt with a simplified case, the same techniques can be applied to any eclipsing binary that is also observed spectroscopically. Notice, however, that our pair have revealed only two of their fundamental characteristics, mass and radius. To find the third, luminosity, we need the distance to the system, and we have not needed the distance thus far. If the spectroscopic observer can tell us that we are dealing with two main-sequence A0 stars, then from the HR diagram we can estimate each to be about 100 times as luminous as the sun. Their distance from us can then be estimated, if we wish, since we now know the absolute magnitude of each from the spectral class and the apparent magnitude of each from the light curve.

13. Other Effects

In Fig. 14.11:2 the secondary minimum of each light curve, when B crosses in front of A, is plotted as flat. Actual observations show that when the smaller star transits the larger one the minimum is *round-bottomed.* The origin of this effect is the dimming toward the limb of the larger star. When the annular phase starts or ends, the smaller star blots out a circle of low surface brightness near the edge of the disk of the bigger star. At the middle of the annular phase more light is screened off. Limb-darkening thus can be studied on these stars as well as on the sun.

The light curve of Algol reveals another special feature, as shown in Fig. 14.14:1. The combined light of the pair is greater just before and just after the shallow secondary minimum. Here the more luminous and smaller star sends roughly as many photons onto the facing hemisphere of the feebler companion as the latter itself emits. We have thus a reflection effect; near secondary minimum the intensity of the farther star is nearly twice its value near primary minimum when the reflecting hemisphere is turned away from us.

Sometimes the magnitude of a pair is not constant outside of eclipse. Instead, the light curve is bowed slightly up so that the peak light is received about halfway between minima, as at time 1 in Fig. 14.12:1. Because of their proximity the two stars elongate each other tidally, as described in Section 9. Maximum light occurs when the stars expose their greatest joint surface area to the observer, at time 1 between the minima. Such pairs usually rotate with the same period as their orbital revolution; they are tidally coupled.

In a few eclipsing binaries that have moderately eccentric orbits, the secondary minimum at one time occurs halfway between primary minima, although some years later it does not. This slow back-and-forth migration of the secondary minimum means that the major axis of the orbit rotates slowly in space. We have seen that the oblateness of the earth produces this effect in the motion of close earth satellites and that the Martian oblateness gives rise to a similar rotation of the major axis of the orbit of Phobos. The effect in close eclipsing binaries originates in the tidal elongation of the stars, and the rate of rotation of the orbital axis allows us to discover something about the run of *internal density* inside the stars. The periods of rotation of the major axes of the best-known pairs range from 25 years to several centuries, and the data indicate that the stars involved are not of constant density throughout their interior, but are highly concentrated toward their centers. A typical deduced value is that the central density is about 100 times the mean density of these stars. All these special effects—limb-darkening, reflection, elongation, and rotation of orbital axis—give us important information about distant stars that can be learned in no other way.

14. Algol

ONE OF THE best-observed stars in the sky, Algol, the Winking Demon Star, has an orbital period of 2.8673 days and the primary minimum lasts for 14 percent of the period, or 9.7 hours. The light curve is shown in Fig. 14.14:1, and analysis shows that the orbit is practically circular and inclined 82°. The eclipses are partial, and the middle of primary minimum occurs when the larger star blots out some 70 percent of the disk of the smaller but brighter partner. The stars are separated by 6.5 million miles. The brighter component has mass 4.7, radius 3.1, and average density 0.16, and the fainter has mass 0.95, radius 3.7, and density 0.02, all of these quantities being expressed in terms of the sun.

In Fig. 14.14:2 the stars and their orbits around the center of mass are plotted to scale. The system is viewed from the direction of the sun and at a time between eclipses. The separation of the stars is only a bit more than twice the sum of their radii, so that they are slightly elongated by tidal forces. In the light curve, however, the reflection effect is much more promine..t than other special effects. When we see its brighter hemisphere near secondary minimum, the larger and fainter star is nearly 20 times as luminous as the sun, but only 10 times as luminous when the fainter hemisphere presents itself to us near primary minimum. The brighter and more massive component is about 150 times as luminous as the sun. As with certain other systems we have studied, Algol has an undetected third member. Superposed on the radial velocity curve of the two close stars is a slower velocity variation which shows that an unseen companion is revolving around the close pair every 1.9 years at a mean distance of about 3 a.u.

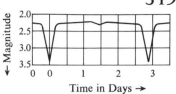

Fig. 14.14:1. The light curve of Algol.

Fig. 14.14:2. The Algol system outside of eclipse. The circular orbit of each star around the center of mass is shown projected against the celestial sphere. The brighter and smaller star is centered at point A; the other at point B.

15. Binaries in General

BRINGING together the evidence from all three kinds of binary stars—visual, spectroscopic, and eclipsing—we notice first that pairing is a very frequent phenomenon among the stars. All types of pairing occur, from close stars with orbital periods of only a few hours to distant duos with periods of millions of years. The median period of eclipsing binaries is only two or three days and the orbits are nearly circular. The stars themselves are most frequently of spectral class B or A and several times as massive as the sun. The median orbital period of spectroscopic binaries is about 9 days and the median eccentricity less than 0.1; about 70 percent of the brighter components are also spectral class B or A. The median period of visual binaries with accurately known orbits is thousands of times as long, about 70 years, and the median eccentricity is 0.5. About half of the member stars of visual pairs are in the range of spectral class from F5 to G0. These various figures are typical only; it should be stressed that all eccentricities up to 0.9 and all spectral classes from O to M are found among double stars.

The great differences in average characteristics of the three types of binary reflect the very different methods of discovery. The visual binaries must be either well separated or close to the sun to be seen as doubles at the telescope. Our sampling is thus biased: we tend to discover both long-period systems and pairs near the solar system. Other things being equal, a visual binary with high eccentricity is more likely to be discovered than one in a circular orbit, because the law of areas dictates that the stars of the eccentric pair spend the majority of their time near apastron, close to maximum separation. The spectroscopic binaries are more likely to be discovered if the stars have velocities great enough to give perceptible Doppler changes. We thus play favorites with stars of high mass or small orbits or both. A similar bias operates for eclipsing binaries: the overwhelming majority of eclipsing pairs are no more than a few radii apart, and we thus tend to discover short-period systems and large stars. This host of *selection effects*, along with many others, makes it extremely difficult to decide statistically whether the observed correlations among binary stars, such as period with eccentricity, are real or false. The same sort of problem comes up often in astronomy and in other fields. It would be unwise, for example, to predict that a given candidate will win the next election on the basis of polling people in just one economic area of a city. Similarly, it would be foolhardy to assert that women eat more than men because we have noticed that women do more of the food-buying at the supermarket.

Statistical difficulties aside, we know that close pairs affect each other tidally and often tear gases from one another. The more widely separated binaries, on the other hand, pursue their evolutionary courses without mutual interference. It is virtually certain that the stars in any given multiple system were born together and are now of the same age; yet we witness such strikingly different stars as Sirius A and Sirius B in the same system and the components of Algol in another system. These clues, as we shall see, are important evidence in studies of how the stars evolve with time.

PROBLEMS

1. Explain what kinds of observations are collected in order to learn about the orbital characteristics of each of the three kinds of binary stars.

2. What conditions would have to be fulfilled if certain pairs of stars were to be included (a) in our catalogue of known visual binaries, (b) in our catalogue of known spectroscopic binaries, and (c) in our catalogue of known eclipsing binaries? Give reasonable sets of numerical characteristics of such pairs.

3. How is it possible from statistical reasoning alone to prove that most close star pairs are physical doubles rather than chance doubles?

4. Close pairs are often classified as actual binaries because the two stars have the same proper motion vector, even though no orbital motion has been detected. Why is common proper motion a valid criterion for deciding that a given pair is a physical pair?

5. The visual binary Gamma Centauri has angular semimajor axis 0.917″ and parallax 0.032″. Find the distance, the linear semimajor axis, and the mass of the system.

6. Describe some of the difficulties in trying to discover other planetary systems.

7. Explain why some spectroscopic binaries are single-lined and others double-lined.

8. A double-lined spectroscopic binary has a highly eccentric orbit with inclination 90°. The line of sight is parallel to the minor axis of the orbit. Assuming the masses of the two stars are equal, make a qualitative sketch of the velocity curve.

9. Two stars, each of one solar mass, are in a circular orbit separated by 1 a.u. What is the maximum velocity difference of the pair as observed from the earth (a) if the inclination is 0°, (b) if it is 90°, and (c) if it is 45°?

10. The stars of a close pair are of about the same apparent magnitude but of different spectral classes. The orbital inclination is 0°. Suggest a way of discovering that the star is a binary.

11. Two stars are revolving around one another in circular orbits. The distance from center to center is four solar radii. One star has the same radius as the sun and the other has twice the radius of the sun. (a) From what fraction of space can some kind of eclipse be seen, and from what fraction of space is the eclipse total? (b) For a similar pair of stars separated by 50 solar radii, answer the same questions.

12. Is it possible for the light curve of an eclipsing binary to have only one minimum instead of two during a complete orbital period? Explain.

13. Explain why primary minimum occurs in the light curve of an eclipsing binary when the star of greater surface brightness is eclipsed.

14. The light curve of an eclipsing binary is likely to have one flat-bottomed minimum and one round-bottomed minimum. Why?

15. Discuss some of the things that can be learned about an eclipsing-spectroscopic binary in addition to its orbital characteristics.

15

THE STARS:

INTRINSIC PROPERTIES

Studies of the sun, of other stars, and especially of binary stars have helped us to deduce in one way or another something about the several inherent characteristics of stars. In this chapter let us examine what is known of these characteristics and of the correlations between them. The material here covers a large part of the territory of *astrophysics*, a science concerned with the physical nature of the stars.

1. Surface Temperature

We saw in Chapter 13, Sections 11 and 14 that the color index or spectral class of a star indicates one of its intrinsic physical characteristics, the surface temperature. This characteristic is the most widely known of all, because the spectra of hundreds of thousands of stars have been classified. Temperatures range from 50,000°K or more for the bluest stars of class O down to 3000°K or less for the reddest stars of late spectral class. Red dwarfs are the most abundant stellar type, and thus relatively cool stars are the most common in space.

2. Luminosity

The astronomer's measure of the luminosity of a star is, as we learned in Chapter 13, Section 13, its absolute magnitude. This quantity can be established for any star whose distance and apparent magnitude are known or for any star whose luminosity classification can be estimated from the spectrum. The absolute magnitudes of stars range from about

$M_v = -9$ to $M_v = 19$, and thus the most luminous known stars pour energy into space at a rate many billion times that for the least luminous stars. Counteracting the individual brilliance of the luminous stars is their great rarity in space. Only one star in 10 million is more luminous than $M_v = -5$, and only about one in every 3000 is more luminous than $M_v = 0$. Perhaps one star in every 30 is more luminous than the sun at $M_v = 5$.

3. Correlations: HR Diagrams and Stellar Populations

THE LUMINOSITY of a star is not independent of its surface temperature, as we noted in Figs. 13.15:1 and 13.15:2. The majority of the stars in our part of the galaxy lie somewhere on the main sequence, minority groups are the white dwarfs and red giants, and a sprinkling of supergiants appears at the top of the HR diagram. The HR diagrams we have studied thus far, however, include only stars whose parallaxes can be measured and which are thus relatively nearby. They therefore represent the kinds of stars we find *in our own neighborhood*. Let us next inquire: do stars elsewhere always show the same kind of correlation as those near the sun? The major difficulty in answering this question is that stars halfway across the galaxy are too distant to have measurable parallaxes. Hence we cannot compute their absolute magnitudes and assign them a place on the HR diagram. Escape from this dilemma seems impossible at first, but there is an excellent way out: the study of star clusters. Because every star in a distant cluster is at virtually the same distance, the apparent magnitude of each star is greater than its absolute magnitude by a fixed amount. Let us imagine a spherical cluster of stars 10,000 parsecs away and 50 parsecs in radius. Each member is very close to 10,000 parsecs from us, and thus the absolute magnitude of each is

$$M = m + 5 - 5 \log 10,000 = m - 15,$$

or 15 magnitudes less than the apparent magnitude. The fact that some stars are on the near side of the cluster center and some on the far side makes an error of only about two-hundredths of a magnitude. We can therefore plot a *relative* HR diagram by finding the *apparent* magnitude and the color index or spectral type of many stars in the cluster and plotting the points.

Many star clusters have been studied in this way, and a number are found to have HR diagrams rather similar to those of the stars in our own neighborhood. But there are notorious exceptions, as first discovered by Harlow Shapley in his investigations of the *globular clusters* (Chapter 17). Figure 15.3:1 shows the HR diagram of a typical globular cluster. Although we shall defer until later an examination of the detailed differences between this diagram and those of Chapter 13, let us note the major points of comparison, the significance of which was described by Walter Baade of Mount Wilson in 1944. (1) Moderately luminous main-sequence stars like the sun are also found in the globular clusters. (2) Main-sequence stars brighter than $M_v = 3$ or 4 are either absent from or very scarce in these systems. (3) There are no super-giants in globular clusters; the most luminous stars to be found are red giants of absolute magnitude -2 or -3. The mixture of stellar types found in the globular clusters was designated by Baade as Population

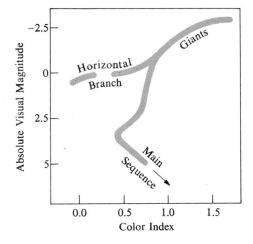

Fig. 15.3:1. The HR diagram for the stars in a globular cluster. The shaded regions are those in which most stars are located.

II and the kinds of stars found in the solar neighborhood Population I. But whatever kind of stellar population may be examined, we find in the HR diagram a strong correlation between stellar luminosity and surface temperature.

4. Radius

WE KNOW the radius of the sun because we can measure its angular radius and its distance. The radii of eclipsing binaries reveal themselves if the stars are also observed spectroscopically to determine the velocity curve. For single stars two techniques have been used. With a specially designed interferometer attached to the 100-inch telescope at Mount Wilson, the angular diameters of a few stars have been measured. Another technique is to use the moon, which moves eastward through the stars at a rate of about 0.55" per second and takes a finite time to cover up a star. The light of the star can be tracked photoelectrically and the time for occultation estimated. But the stars of greatest known angular diameter take only 0.1 second to disappear. To date, these methods have been limited to a handful of stars of large angular diameter, such as Betelgeuse and Antares.

Of far greater generality is an indirect determination from other known quantities. From the spectral type or color index of a given star we find its temperature. Knowing the temperature, we compute from Stefan's law the quantity Q, which was described in Chapter 11 and is the total amount of energy emitted per second by *unit area* of the surface of an ideal radiator. If we know the absolute magnitude of the star as well, we can compute L, the luminosity or total amount of energy emitted per second by the *entire surface*, and this quantity must be the product of Q and the surface area of the star. The surface area of a sphere with radius R is $4\pi R^2$, and therefore the fundamental relation is

$$L = 4\pi R^2 Q.$$

In practice it is helpful to use the sun as a standard reference body. If we apply this formula first to any star and then to the sun and divide the two, we find

$$\frac{L}{L_{sun}} = \frac{4\pi R^2 Q}{4\pi R^2_{sun} Q_{sun}} = \frac{R^2 T^4}{R^2_{sun} T^4_{sun}}.$$

The symbols T and T_{sun} refer to the surface temperatures of the star and the sun, and it will be remembered that Stefan's law states that Q is proportional to T^4. If the formula is solved for radius, we have the important relation

$$\frac{R}{R_{sun}} = \frac{\sqrt{L/L_{sun}}}{T^2/T^2_{sun}}.$$

Sirius for example has an absolute magnitude of 1.5, or is between 3 and 4 magnitudes brighter than the sun. From the definition of the magnitude scale this means that the luminosity of Sirius is about $25L_{sun}$. The surface temperature of an A1 star like Sirius is near 10,000°K, whereas that of the sun is not far from 6000°K, Thus

$$\frac{R_{Sirius}}{R_{sun}} = \frac{\sqrt{25}}{(10,000/6,000)^2} = \frac{5 \times 6^2}{10^2} = \frac{180}{100} = 1.8.$$

We have now learned that the radius of Sirius is about two solar radii. Proxima Centauri's absolute magnitude is between 10 and 11 magnitudes fainter than the sun's, so that its luminosity is only about 1/1600 that of the sun. At spectral class M5 its surface temperature is near 3000°K; therefore

$$\frac{R_{Proxima}}{R_{sun}} = \frac{\sqrt{1/1600}}{(3000/6000)^2} = \frac{1}{40} \times \frac{6^2}{3^2} = \frac{1}{10},$$

and Proxima has roughly one-tenth the solar radius, or about the same size as Jupiter.

In the Population I HR diagram (Fig. 13.15:2) we find a steady decrease in stellar size as we move down the main sequence, from about 10 solar radii at spectral class B0 to 2 solar radii near A2, one solar radius at G2, 0.5 at M1, and 0.1 for small red dwarfs. The largest stars are the red supergiants in the upper right part of the diagram. Although cool and emitting little energy per unit area, these stars have great total luminosities. This can only mean that they have enormous sizes. Indeed the radius of Antares is about 2 a.u. and that of Betelgeuse is slightly larger (and variable). If these voluminous stars were placed at the center of the solar system, the earth would find itself well inside them. The partially eclipsing binary Epsilon Aurigae consists of an F5 supergiant with radius 1.5 a.u. moving around an invisible infrared star with radius 15 a.u. The orbital period is 27 years, the longest on record for eclipsing binaries; the orbital period for this enormous pair has to be large if the two stars are not to be inside one another. If it were centered at the sun, the infrared partner would fill the solar system well beyond the orbit of Saturn. The smallest stars are the white dwarfs in the lower left portion of the HR diagram. They are relatively hot and thus emit considerable energy per unit area. But since their total energy output is very feeble, only about 1/10,000 that of a main-sequence star of the same surface temperature, these stars are very small. The radius of a typical white dwarf is only about two-hundredths that of the sun, or twice that of the earth; the smallest one known is tinier even than Mercury.

We have seen that an HR diagram correlates luminosity with surface temperature and that the radius of a star depends on both of these quantities and therefore can be read approximately from the position of a star in the diagram. Lines of constant radius in the diagram slope downward from left to right, sloping more gently than the main sequence. The higher and further to the right a star is located the greater its size. The largest known star has about a million times the radius of the smallest and occupies a volume approximately 10^{18} as great. The number of small white dwarfs that could fit into the infrared member of Epsilon Aurigae is roughly equal to the number of grains of salt that could be accommodated in a thousand mile-long freight trains.

5. Mass

THE MASS OF a star can be found only by assessing the gravitational effect the star has on the motion of a nearby body. Our information on individual stellar masses is thus restricted to the sun, visual binaries in which the center of mass can be located, and eclipsing binaries that are also observed spectroscopically. We have studied all these methods in earlier chapters. Actual observational results indicate that main-sequence stars range from about 30 solar masses or more for luminous O5 stars down to 10 solar masses at class B2, 3 at A0, 1 at G2, 0.5 at M0, and 0.1 to 0.2 for late M dwarfs. Giant stars like Capella and Arcturus stand at around 3 solar masses, and red supergiants like Antares lie near 10. The white dwarfs occupy the range from about 0.5 to 1.0 solar mass. The least massive stars known are the two red dwarf components of the visual binary Luyten 726–8, at 0.04 solar mass. The heaviest stars known are the class O components of Plaskett's star, a double-lined spectroscopic binary with an orbital period of two weeks. Each star is at least 75 times as massive as the sun and each is vigorously lifting gases from the other. Such heavyweights are extremely rare in space, however, and the overwhelming majority of stars have masses between about 5 and 0.1 times that of the sun.

IF BOTH THE mass and absolute visual magnitude of a star are known, we can represent the star as a point in a mass-luminosity diagram of the kind shown in Fig. 15.6:1. When all such stars are plotted, we find that most lie in a relatively narrow band. Thus the

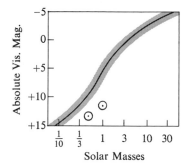

Fig. 15.6:1. The mass-luminosity relationship. Except for white dwarfs (circled points), the luminosities of stars are strongly correlated with their masses. Most stars occupy points in the shaded band.

6. Correlations: Mass-Luminosity Diagrams

more massive a star the greater the radiant energy it pours into space. Roughly, the visual luminosity of a main-sequence star is proportional to the cube or even the fourth power of its mass. In an HR diagram lines of constant mass are horizontal for the main-sequence stars, like lines of constant luminosity. Stars above the sun on the main sequence are more luminous and therefore heavier than the sun; stars below it are less luminous and lighter. Off the main sequence the giants and supergiants generally follow the mass-luminosity relationship, falling in the upper part of the band. The only nonconformists are the white dwarf stars, as represented by the two circled points in Fig. 15.6:1. These stars are very subluminous as compared with main-sequence stars of the same mass.

7. Dynamical Distances of Stars

UNLIKE LUMINOSITIES and radii, the masses of stars do not vary over a large factor. This fact permits us to estimate the distance, or parallax, of a visual binary by the method of *dynamical parallaxes*, reversing our usual usage of Kepler's generalized third law. Of the quantities in the formulas of Chapter 14, Sections 2 and 3, we are now interested in estimating the distance, D. Measurement of the orbit gives the period, P, and the angular semimajor axis, α. The only remaining quantity is $M_1 + M_2$, which we may *guess* to be two solar masses. Inserting this value, we can solve for the linear semimajor axis, a, and then for the distance. Now, suppose our guess is wrong and that $M_1 + M_2$ is really twice as great as our first guess. The true distance is only $\sqrt[3]{2} = 1.26$ as large as our estimate, for an excess of 26 percent. In practice the procedure can be sharpened if spectra are available; then the HR diagram and mass-luminosity diagram may provide a better estimate of $M_1 + M_2$ and hence a more accurate dynamical distance.

8. Density

THE AVERAGE density of a star can be computed if we know its mass and volume. We have already seen that the mean density of the sun is 1.4 gm/cm³, or 1.4 times the density of water. Although stellar masses do not vary by a great factor, we are entitled to expect great differences of density from one star to the next because of the vastly differing sizes. On the main sequence the mean densities increase steadily from about 0.1 gm/cm³ at spectral class B5 to 1 gm/cm³ at G0 and up to 10 gm/cm³ near M3. The decreasing masses as we move down the sequence are more than offset by the shrinkage in volume. The average density of the red giants is low; a G5 giant star averages about 0.001 gm/cm³, which is the density of air at sea-level. The red supergiants are the most tenuous of all, a star like Antares averaging only 1 percent or less of the density of air. The white dwarfs, on the other hand, have respectable masses but tiny sizes, and therefore high densities. The average density of matter in a white dwarf is 100,000 to 1,000,000 gm/cm³ and thus at least 1000 times that of solid lead. A typical volume the size of a small matchbox contains a ton or so of material.

Although the tenuity of a red supergiant may not be hard to imagine, doubts are likely to be raised about the enormous densities of white dwarfs, even though these high values have been estabished by observation. The point to be understood here is that the interior of a white dwarf star is at extremely high temperature and therefore the atomic nuclei are stripped of most or all of their electrons. Each particle therefore occupies an ultrasmall fraction of the space needed by a neutral atom. The radius of an atomic nucleus is about 10^{-12} cm as compared with the radius of 10^{-8} cm for a neutral atom, and the relative volumes occupied bear the same relationship as the volume of a marble to that of a large skyscraper. Thus, because even at the enormous densities of white dwarfs there is plenty of room between the particles, the material is gaseous.

9. Chemical Composition

THE CHIEF building block of most stars is hydrogen, which accounts for about 90 percent of all the atoms. Nearly all of the rest is helium. The *relative* abundance of the heavier atoms is roughly the same as in the earth's crust and in meteorites; carbon, oxygen, and iron, for example, are much more abundant than silver, gold, and uranium. In the stars, however, all the heavy atoms together account for only a very small fraction of the total. A typical composition is 90 percent hydrogen, nearly 10 percent helium, and a whiff of all the rest together.

Although generally similar to one another, stars exhibit definite differences in composition. Most stars in the sun's neighborhood, for example, have about one atom in every thousand that is heavier than hydrogen or helium. In Population II stars, however, the scarcity of heavy elements is even more extreme; only about one atom in every 10 thousand is not hydrogen or helium. A second difference occurs in the cool red stars; as we saw in Chapter 13, stars of spectral classes R and N contain an excess of carbon compounds, whereas the S stars have an excess of zirconium oxide. A third difference is the relative abundance of the two major constituents, hydrogen and helium. Any star that is operating on the proton–proton or carbon cycle is converting hydrogen to helium in its core; the deep interior is therefore slowly but steadily gaining in helium at the expense of hydrogen. These changes may not reveal themselves in the spectra of the stellar surfaces because the material in one layer of a star is not necessarily well mixed with that in another layer. The spectra of a very few white dwarfs show no lines of hydrogen but only those of helium; such stars are apparently devoid of hydrogen even at their surfaces. These several examples show that there is not strict uniformity of composition everywhere; nevertheless, from a microscopic point of view our galaxy consists chiefly of the two lightest atoms in nature, and in particular of the lightest atom of all.

10. Rotation

THE SUN SPINS on its axis about once a month, as inferred from the parade of sunspots across the disk or from Doppler measurements at

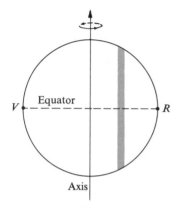

V — Equator — R

Axis

Fig. 15.10:1. Illustration of
how the rotation of a star
broadens each of its spectral
lines. All photons leaving the
thin strip are Doppler-shifted
by the same amount; those in
any other parallel strip are all
shifted by some other fixed
amount.

various points on its surface. Neither kind of measure is possible for
other stars, however, because a star is an unresolved point of light. The
first indication of stellar rotation was found in the velocity curves
of eclipsing binaries. Refer to Fig. 14.12:1 and imagine that the
rearward star is spinning counterclockwise, in the same direction as
its orbital motion. Between the beginning of the eclipse and mideclipse a part of the approaching hemisphere is blocked by the front
star, so that a predominance of red-shifted photons reaches the spectrograph from the rearward star. From mideclipse to the end of the eclipse
the situation is reversed. Rotation is thus revealed by a peak red shift
in the velocity curve just before mideclipse and a peak violet shift
just after mideclipse. All binary stars studied in this way have been
found to spin in the same direction as their orbital motion.

Single stars may reveal rotation by broadened lines in their spectra.
Imagine, for simplicity, a star that is spinning rather rapidly around an
axis that is perpendicular to the line of sight, as indicated in Fig.
15.10:1. Let us also agree that it rotates as a solid body, although we
have learned that the rotational period of the solar surface increases
somewhat with latitude. Photons emitted from point V are shifted to
the violet more than any others coming from the star, whereas those
from point R have a maximum red shift. All of those coming from any
thin strip parallel to the axis of rotation have the same Doppler shift.
Although the slit of our spectrograph sees all of this mixed light, the
prism breaks the light into its component colors. Each dark line is the
joint contribution of absorbing atoms all over the stellar hemisphere
and is broadened by the rotation, the width being proportional to the
equatorial velocity of rotation.

Another star whose axis of rotation points at the solar system will
not reveal its rotation, because all of its emitting atoms are moving
at right angles to the line of sight and therefore the photons are not
Doppler-shifted. All the absorption lines are sharp and narrow.
Here we encounter the same restriction as with spectroscopic binaries:
pairs with orbital planes perpendicular to the line of sight cannot be
detected by Doppler effects. In general, the axis of rotation of a star
makes some intermediate angle to the line of the sight. All we can tell
for any particular star is that the equatorial velocity of rotation is at
least as great as that deduced from measurement of the width of its
spectral lines.

If it is assumed that the individual axes of rotation point in random
directions, statistical studies of many stars can yield the average
turning speed. Such investigations indicate a strong correlation of
rotational speed and location in the HR diagram. The cool stars of the
main sequence, from spectral type F5 on through M, rotate slowly;
an example is the sun with its equatorial velocity of 1 mi/sec. The
hotter stars of the upper main sequence rotate faster. Among the B
stars the median equatorial velocity is about 50 mi/sec and the fastest
about 300 mi/sec. The most rapid of these spinners may not only be
highly flattened but may even lose gaseous material into space from

their equatorial regions. The spectra of such stars often show emission lines of hydrogen along with the absorption lines, implying that the spectrograph is recording the combined light of the star and a rarefied surrounding shell or ring that has been lost to the star. The giants have slower rotational velocities than the luminous stars of the upper main sequence. As we shall see in our study of stellar evolution, the red giants are stars that are relatively old in the sense that they have used

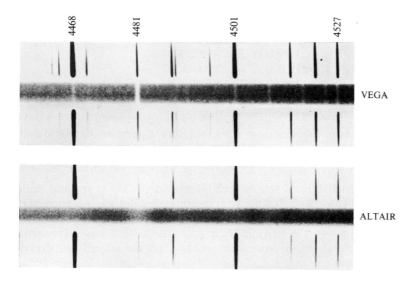

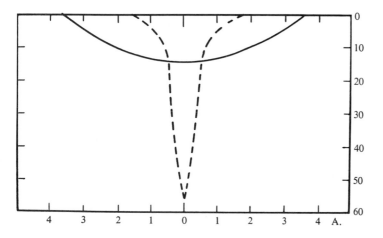

Fig. 15.10:2. Spectra of Vega and Altair, showing the magnesium line at 4481 A broad in one star and narrow in the other. Line contours are shown below. (*Yerkes Observatory*)

up most of their hydrogen resources, evolved away from the main sequence, and swollen in size. The law of conservation of angular momentum demands that the rotational speed of a swelling sphere decrease. Therefore the slow rotation of the red giants is consistent with current ideas of stellar evolution.

PROBLEMS

1. Survey the data of Table 13.3:1 to find the range of surface temperatures and luminosities covered by the nearby stars.

2. Compare the HR diagrams of Figs. 13.15:1, 13.15:2, and 15.3:1, and describe the differences between Population I and Population II.

3. Compute the radius of each of the following stars and tell in what part of the HR diagram each is located:
   (a) $L/L_{sun} = 1/10,000$, $T = 2,500°K$.
   (b) $L/L_{sun} = 10,000$, $T = 22,000°K$.
   (c) $L/L_{sun} = 1/10,000$, $T = 10,000°K$.
   (d) $L/L_{sun} = 30,000$, $T = 3,000°K$.
   (e) $L/L_{sun} = 100$, $T = 4,000°K$.

4. Compare the masses of stars in different parts of the HR diagram.

5. Use the mass-luminosity relationship to estimate the mass of (a) a main-sequence star with $M_v = -3$, and (b) one with $M_v = +10$.

6. A visual binary has an orbital period of 200 years and angular semimajor axis $0.40''$. The apparent magnitude of each star is about 8.5 and the spectral class close to F0. Estimate the dynamical distance to the pair. Is there any chance that you have wrongly estimated the distance because the stars are actually supergiants? Explain.

7. Review the range of values of average density for stars in different parts of the HR diagram.

8. How is it possible that the matter in a typical part of a white dwarf star can be thousands of times as dense as solid lead and yet be in the gaseous state?

9. Compare the chemical composition of a typical star that belongs to Population II with that of a typical member of Population I.

10. Sketch a qualitative velocity curve for an edge-on eclipsing-spectroscopic binary in which the stars are tidally coupled. Assume the system is a single-lined binary.

11. The $H\alpha$ line of a luminous main-sequence star is measured and found to have an extreme width of 2.1 A. What can be said about the rotation of this star?

16

THE VARIABLE STARS

T HE STARS we have encountered so far are constant objects, their masses, sizes, and luminosities remaining much the same for thousands and even millions of years on end. A small percentage of stars, however, are variable in light or in spectral characteristics or in other observable ways. Because most of these *variable stars* are considerably more luminous than the sun, they command our attention even though they are rare in space. More than 10 thousand of them have been discovered and catalogued. This number excludes the eclipsing binaries which we studied in Chapter 14; the light variations of eclipsing stars are caused by the periodic blocking of light from the rear partner by the front partner. Now we are concerned with the *intrinsic* variable stars, objects that change all by themselves.

The intrinsic variables divide into two broad groups, the *pulsating stars* and the *explosive stars*. A member of the first group swells and shrinks more or less rhythmically, whereas an explosive star periodically ejects gusts of gas into space. A third and rather ill-defined group may be called the *erratic stars*. The distinction between pulsating stars, explosive stars, and erratic stars is convenient, but it should not be considered complete. All three groups are important to astronomers for several reasons. (1) The light changes and the many subtle spectral variations of a variable star challenge the specialist in spectroscopy or in stellar structure to interpret correctly the physical nature of his chosen object. (2) It is possible to determine the distances of many variables, even if they are exceedingly remote; in this chapter we shall add two new methods of distance determination to our growing list. (3) Another kind of study, still in its formative stages, seeks to learn how different types of variable stars fit into the scheme of stellar evolution.

PULSATING STARS

1. Discovery and Designation

THE FIRST of the pulsating stars was discovered by D. Fabricius in 1596, only a short time before the beginning of telescopic astronomy. He noticed a third-magnitude star in Cetus that did not appear on contemporary charts of the sky. The star faded from visibility after several weeks, but it was not recognized as periodically variable until 40 years later, when it was found to return to peak brightness every 11 months. The star was caught by Bayer and designated as Omicron Ceti; it has also long been known as Mira the Wonderful. Apart from Algol, which is an eclipsing binary, no other variable star was known until the discovery of Delta Cephei in 1784. Since that time variables have been found at an increasing rate. Photography has permitted easy comparison of stellar brightness on exposures of the same area of the sky made at different times. Also, photoelectric methods have made it a simple matter to detect small differences of magnitude and thus have encouraged the discovery of stars that are only slightly variable in luminosity.

Variable stars that have not already been assigned a Greek letter in the Bayer system are designated by one or two Roman letters. The first one discovered in a given constellation is assigned the letter R, such as R Andromedae. The sequence is R, S, T, U, . . ., Z, followed by RR, RS, . . ., RZ, SS, ST, . . ., SZ, and so on to ZZ. When these 54 combinations are exhausted in any one constellation, the assignments continue as AA, AB, . . ., AZ, BB, BC, . . ., BZ, and so on to QZ, with the letter J always omitted. All in all, the letter designations accommodate 334 stars. In some constellations where variables abound, such as Sagittarius and Cygnus, the letter system has been used up. The assignments then continue with simple Arabic numerals. Thus V335 Cygni follows QZ Cygni. Most variable stars can be confidently assigned to one of a number of groups of stars, the members of any one group all having rather similar physical characteristics. These groups are usually named after the first-discovered member or the brightest member. We shall, for example, soon study the RR Lyrae stars and the W Virginis stars.

2. Data of Observation

THE MOST DIRECT information the astronomer can collect is the apparent magnitude of a variable star at different times. The plot of magnitude against time is the light curve. Observations can be made visually or photographically from time to time, or continuous records may be obtained photoelectrically during the nighttime hours. If observations are made at different wavelengths, a record of changes in color index with time can also be accumulated. A wealth of additional information is contained in spectrograms made at various times of the night or on different nights; from them variations of spectral type can be estimated and radial velocities measured. When a star under study varies regularly with a well-defined period, data collected weeks or years apart can be put together, thereby increasing the precision of the plots. If a regular variable has been well observed, the astronomer knows not only the *period* of its variation, but also at each time in its cycle the *relative luminosity*, the *surface temperature*, and the *radial velocity*.

3. Varieties

MOST PULSATING stars are members of a specific group, just as a dog may be a pointer, a beagle, or a collie. As with dogs, however, there are mongrels which defy easy classification. The major groups presently recognized are given in Table 16.3:1, along with typical

TABLE 16.3:1.   Groups of Pulsating Stars

	Typical Period	Typical Range	Typical M_v	Typical Sp
Population I				
Dwarf Cepheids	3 hours	1 mag	+2	A, F
Beta Cephei stars (Beta Canis Majoris stars)	5 hours	0.1 mag	−3	Early B
Cepheids	1 week	1 mag	−3	F, G
Very-long-period variables	1 year	6 mag	0	Late M
Population II				
RR Lyrae stars	12 hours	1 mag	0	A, F
W Virginis stars (Type II Cepheids)	2 weeks	1 mag	−2	F, G
RV Tauri stars (Type II Cepheids)	2 months	1 mag	−4	F, G, K
Long-period variables	6 months	4 mag	−2	Early M
Mixed population				
Red semiregular and irregular variables	3 months	1 mag	−1	M

characteristics of behavior, place in the HR diagram, and population membership. Recall from the last chapter that Population I stars are found in our own part of the galaxy and Population II stars in the globular clusters. The distinction between the two populations is more fundamental, however. When our entire Milky Way galaxy is

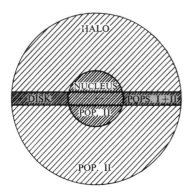

Fig. 16.3:1. A schematic representation of our galaxy. Population II objects are found everywhere but are concentrated toward the nucleus. Population I objects are confined to the galactic disk.

surveyed, it is found that the Population I stars move throughout the entire coin-shaped galactic disk of which the solar neighborhood is just a small part. Similarly, the Population II stars are not confined to the globular clusters; they also roam as individuals either in the relatively crowded regions of the central nucleus of the galaxy or farther out in the thinly populated spherical halo. The nucleus and halo of the galaxy are also the places where globular clusters themselves are found. Thus, as can be seen from Fig. 16.3:1, Population II objects are found more or less spherically distributed in our galaxy, and Population I objects are strongly concentrated toward the central disk. Because of this correlation of type of star with place of residence, it becomes possible to assign objects to one or the other population type on the basis of location in the galaxy in addition to our earlier criterion of place in the HR diagram. The groups of variable stars are assigned to population type in Table 16.3:1 on the basis of their distribution in the galaxy.

Of the Population I variables, those of the shortest period are the so-called dwarf Cepheids. SX Phoenicis varies in light every 79 minutes, the quickest of all known pulsating stars. White and of spectral type A, this star and a few others of this small group are subluminous, lying below the main sequence on the HR diagram. The difference between brightest and faintest light is called the *range*, and is about one magnitude for the dwarf Cepheids. The Beta Cephei stars, of which only a few are known, also have short periods, between 4 and 6 hours. Their range, however, is very small. They are of spectral type B1 or B2 and are so luminous that they lie above the main sequence. The Cepheids and very-long-period variables will be described later.

Of the Population II pulsating stars, those of the shortest period vary every few hours and are members of the RR Lyrae group. The W Virginis and RV Tauri stars, on the other hand, spend weeks or months completing one light cycle; these two groups comprise a single sequence of similar stars and are often called Type II Cepheids. We shall return later to these three groups and the six-month variables.

The red semiregular and irregular variables form a mixed group. Their distribution in space indicates that these stars are not clearly members of either population. The light curves of the irregular variables show changes, but the fluctuations are so haphazard that no definite periods can be recognized. The semiregular stars vary somewhat rhythmically, but irregularities occur too. They fluctuate with periods of three months or so, with ranges of about one magnitude; they are giants in luminosity and reddish in color. Although their absolute magnitudes often are near −1, the much larger and more luminous Betelgeuse and Antares are also members of this group. Indeed it appears likely that all luminous red stars are at least somewhat variable in light.

4. Cepheids

PERHAPS THE most important group of pulsating variables are the Cepheids, named in honor of the first-known member, the fourth-magnitude star Delta Cephei. More than 500 of these stars have been discovered in our galaxy, and they are confined rather closely to the galactic disk in which our solar system moves. In our part of the Milky Way only one star out of every one or two million is a Cepheid, and the average distance between nearest neighbors in this group is about 100 parsecs. Although few and far between, these stars are very luminous supergiants. Thus even those Cepheids that are extremely distant send enough radiation to us so that they can be studied profitably. The absolute visual magnitudes of these several hundred variables lie in the range from -2 to about -5, and their luminosities are therefore one to ten thousand times as great as the sun's. They are yellow stars and belong to spectral classes F and G; generally speaking, the greater the average luminosity of a Cepheid the larger its color index and the later its spectral type.

Some of these stars vary in light with periods of slightly more than a day; others complete a cycle only once every 50 days. The most common period among the Cepheids in the galactic disk is one week. But whatever the period, it is repeated faithfully from one cycle to the next. The light curve of a typical Cepheid is shown in Fig. 16.4:1. Times are

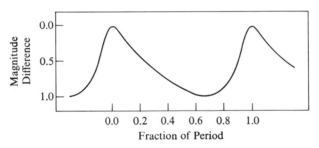

Fig. 16.4:1. The light curve of a typical Cepheid variable.

counted in fractions of the period, reckoned from zero at the moment of maximum light. Magnitudes are counted from the magnitude of maximum light. Note first that the typical range of a Cepheid is one magnitude; when brightest it therefore emits 2.5 times as much radiant energy into space as when faintest. The illustrations also show that these stars spend only about 30 percent of their time brightening. The light curve is therefore asymmetrical, with the rising branch steeper than the declining branch. It should be stressed that this curve is only an average one; there are many differences in detail. Polaris, the brightest Cepheid in the sky, serves as an example. Its period is 4.0 days, which is normal enough, but its range is only 0.1 magnitude. Generally, the short-period Cepheid variables have the smallest ranges, about 0.8 magnitude, whereas the Cepheids with periods of more than a month have about twice this range. Those of moderate period, seven or eight days, show an extra feature: a few days after maximum light the decline stops temporarily and some stars even brighten slightly for a day or so before the decline continues.

5. Spectra and Pulsations of Cepheids

WHEN SPECTROGRAMS are obtained at different times in the cycle of light variation, it is found that the spectral type of a Cepheid changes in the same period as the apparent magnitude. As a given star decreases in luminosity its spectral type becomes later. A typical Cepheid of spectral class F5 at maximum light will be about class G5 when at minimum light. The surface of the star is therefore hottest when the luminosity is greatest; at minimum light the surface is about 1500°K cooler. We learned in Chapter 15, Section 4 that the luminosity of a star depends both on its radius and on its temperature, and since both the luminosity and temperature of a Cepheid are observed to change periodically, we are entitled to guess that the size of such a star may also change periodically.

Measurement of the spectrograms of a Cepheid indeed shows that the wavelengths of the spectral lines vary cyclically in the same period as the light and temperature variation. These oscillations are interpreted as an actual pulsation: when the star is swelling, the hemisphere facing us is approaching and the spectral lines are shifted to the violet; later, during contraction, they are shifted to the red. At maximum and minimum size there is no effect and the shift at these times is simply the radial velocity of the star as a whole as it moves through space. The velocity curve of a Cepheid resembles the light curve turned upside down, as shown schematically in Fig. 16.5:1 with maximum expansion velocity occurring near the time of maximum light and maximum contraction velocity near minimum light. At time A the radial velocity is zero, apart from whatever space motion the star may have. A short time later it is negative and thus the surface gases are approaching. At time A the star is therefore of minimum size. At time B it is expanding fastest and is of intermediate size. Swelling continues through the entire interval from A to C, at which time the star is of maximum size. Shrinking then begins, with maximum con-

Fig. 16.5:1. *Above*: the light curve of a Cepheid. *Below*: the radial velocity curve of the same star.

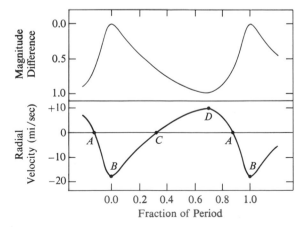

traction speed at time D and minimum size again at time A. When the velocities at various times are added together, the difference in miles between maximum and minimum radius can be determined. For a typical Cepheid this difference is about 10 percent of the average radius of the star.

As we saw in studying the sun, the slow gravitational contraction of a star releases energy. Part of this energy is radiated into space; the rest becomes added kinetic energy of the atoms in the star. Therefore, if all layers of a variable star were to contract simultaneously, we should expect maximum luminosity to occur at minimum size, the increased temperature and radiation more than making up for the decreased surface area. A look at Fig. 16.5:1 shows, however, that a typical Cepheid does not behave in this fashion. Instead, greatest luminosity occurs after minimum size at about the time when the star is expanding fastest, and the star is feeblest after maximum size when the rate of shrinkage is greatest. It appears that the inner layers of the star may throb simultaneously, with the maximum luminosity of any shell occuring when it is of smallest size. In the outer parts, however, there is a time lag, as when one topples a row of dominoes, and the peak surface luminosity and temperature do not occur until about a quarter of a period after minimum size.

It is not known what starts a star pulsating, but it is certain there are places in the HR diagram that are regions of instability. The modern view is that a pulsating star does not pulsate all of its life, but only during certain parts of its evolutionary history. As a given star evolves, its luminosity and surface temperature undergo slow changes and it therefore follows a certain track in the HR diagram. When this track passes through a region of instability, the star begins to pulsate. Much later, perhaps millions of years later, the star emerges from the area of instability, the vibrations die away, and the body is of constant radius once again.

The process of pulsation resembles the swing of a pendulum. To begin with, we pull the pendulum to one side; in the star we increase the temperature and thus the pressure of the gas. Now we let go. The pendulum begins its downswing under the force of gravity, moving faster and faster; the star begins to expand because the outward pressure force exceeds the inward gravitational force. At the bottom of its swing there is no net force causing the pendulum to swing further, but its speed is then a maximum and it swings past the vertical position. Similarly, when pressure and gravitational force cancel each other, there is no net force, but because the star is expanding it moves past the equilibrium position. Later the star is distended and the gravitational downpull exceeds the upward pressure force, decelerating and finally stopping the expansion. Meanwhile the pendulum is at the top of its swing on the side opposite its release point. The other half of the oscillations proceed in the reverse order and one period is completed. Unlike the pendulum, which finally stops swinging because of frictional forces, a pulsating star continues its cycles of variability for exceedingly long periods of time.

6. Correlations: Period-Luminosity Diagrams

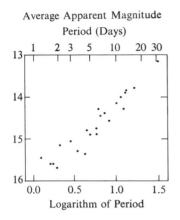

Average Apparent Magnitude

Period (Days)

Fig. 16.6:1. Correlation of magnitudes and periods of light variation for Cepheids in the Small Cloud of Magellan.

IN THE EARLY years of this century Miss Henrietta Leavitt of the Harvard College Observatory studied many photographs of the Small Cloud of Magellan. This patch of light and its companion, the Large Magellanic Cloud, are in the far southern sky and were reported by the survivors of Magellan's expedition around the world. We know now that the two Clouds are galaxies, smaller than our own galaxy and satellites of it. Miss Leavitt identified a number of Cepheids in the Small Cloud and determined the period and average apparent magnitude of many of them. When the magnitude of each star was plotted against its period of light variation, it was discovered that there was a strong correlation between the two properties. Figure 16.6:1 is a plot of Miss Leavitt's 1912 data and shows generally that the longer the period the brighter the star. What is the significance of this discovery? Recall that the apparent magnitude of a star depends both on its distance and on its absolute magnitude. But in the Small Cloud the distance of every star from the earth is the same to within a small percentage. Therefore, even though the distance of the Cloud may be *unknown*, the absolute magnitude of each star differs from its apparent magnitude by a fixed amount. Thus the *absolute* magnitude of the Small Cloud Cepheids must correlate with their periods; the longer the period the greater the average luminosity.

Not only is this relationship important for the student of stellar structure, but it is crucially important for determining distances. Why? (1) If we assume that a Cepheid is a Cepheid whether it is in the Small Cloud, the Large Cloud, our own galaxy, or elsewhere, we can say that the period-luminosity relationship is valid everywhere. (2) If we can find the distance of any *one* Cepheid, we can compute its average *absolute* magnitude and thereby assign the proper scale of absolute magnitude to Fig. 16.6:1. (3) We can then determine observationally the average apparent magnitude and period of any other Cepheid. When we know the period, the period-luminosity diagram tells us the average absolute magnitude. The distance is then deduced from the formula we have already encountered,

$$M = m + 5 - 5 \log D.$$

Finding the distance and then the absolute magnitude of any one Cepheid has challenged the ingenuity of astronomers for several decades, and only recently have the various bits of evidence become consistent with one another. Cepheids are so remote that their annual parallaxes are very uncertain; statistical distances based on solar motion are likewise uncertain. Present evidence suggests that Cepheids are twice as far away as was thought before 1950; their absolute magnitudes are thus 1.5 magnitudes brighter. Because the original method of finding the distances of external galaxies was to identify and measure Cepheids within them, astronomers have also been forced to double the size of the universe.

The revised period-luminosity relationship for normal Cepheids of Population I is shown in Fig. 16.6:2, along with curves for two other groups that we shall consider later. As an example of finding how far away a remote Cepheid is, suppose that such a star is found to have apparent visual magnitude $+10.4$ at maximum light and $+11.6$ at minimum light and that its period is found to be 10 days. From Fig. 16.6:2 the average absolute visual magnitude is about -4.0. From the apparent magnitudes the average is $+11.0$. Applying the formula, we have

$$5 \log D = m_v - M_v + 5 = 11.0 - (-4.0) + 5 = 20.0.$$

Therefore $\log D = 4$, and the estimated distance is 10,000 parsecs. Although this calculation summarizes an extremely important way of determining very large distances, the result should be looked at with a wary eye. For one thing, the period-luminosity diagram is a band rather than a line; a 10-day Cepheid may actually be slightly more or less luminous than $M_v = -4.0$. For another thing, dust lies between the stars, especially in the galactic disk where the Cepheids roam. If the light of such a star is obscured by dust, its measured apparent magnitude will be too large and thus its distance overestimated.

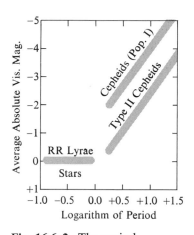

Fig. 16.6:2. The period-luminosity relationship for normal Cepheids, for Type II Cepheids, and for RR Lyrae stars.

7. RR Lyrae Stars

SOME 3000 variable stars are known that have periods of less than a day, and the overwhelming majority of them belong to Population II. They are the RR Lyrae stars and are named after the brightest member of the group, a variable of the seventh magnitude. White giants, these stars are about 100 times as luminous as the sun. They occupy a horizontal strip of the HR diagram somewhat above the main sequence and are of spectral class A or F. Like the longer-period Cepheids, the RR Lyrae variables oscillate periodically in spectral type and radial velocity as well as in apparent magnitude. The range is about one magnitude, and a star of spectral class A2 at maximum light has cooled to about F0 at minimum light. The *average* light curve of the RR Lyrae variables resembles that of the Cepheids, but there are distinct differences with period. The stars of shorter period, about 8 hours, tend to show regular oscillations and small range. Those of longer period, such as 16 hours, usually have larger ranges, spend about half their time at or near minimum light, and rise very abruptly to maximum light in about two hours. The velocity curves show that these stars pulsate, but careful spectral studies of RR Lyrae itself reveal that at maximum red shift the lines fade away while simultaneously a new set of lines appears, shifted to the violet. This phenomenon is not interpreted as a rise and fall of the entire stellar surface, but rather as successive oscillations of layers. As the old layer sinks down, it is replaced by another shell which rises and then falls; this shell is in turn replaced by a new rising layer one period later.

The RR Lyrae stars belong to Population II. Roughly half of the known members of the group are single stars and are located throughout the galaxy. Many inhabit the nuclear regions, while others move in the nearly spherical galactic halo. At any one time a few are also found in the Population I disk, but these stars, like RR Lyrae itself, are only transients; they spend the great majority of their lives far above or below the disk. More than a thousand other RR Lyrae stars belong to the globular clusters, which themselves are Population II systems and are found in the galactic nucleus and halo.

Fig. 16.7:1. The globular cluster Messier 3, containing many RR Lyrae variable stars, photographed with the 200-inch telescope. (*Mount Wilson and Palomar Observatories photograph*)

Although not so luminous as Cepheids, the RR Lyrae stars are also useful as distance indicators. They all have absolute visual magnitudes close to zero, as can be seen from Fig. 16.6:2. In this respect they differ from Cepheids; their average luminosities are the same whether the period is only a few hours or as long as a day. To find the distance of an RR Lyrae star or of a globular cluster that contains such variables, we need only to determine the average apparent magnitude from the light curve. For example, if $m_v = 15$ for several RR Lyrae stars in a globular cluster, we can compute the distance of the cluster to be about 10,000 parsecs because we may assume $M_v = 0$. More accurately, the mean absolute visual magnitude of RR Lyrae stars is close to $+0.3$. As with Cepheids, the computed distances may be erroneous if we forget to account for such effects as interstellar dust.

8. Type II Cepheids

THE CEPHEIDS we have already studied are often called *classical Cepheids* to distinguish them from the short-period dwarf Cepheids and from the stars we shall examine now. The Type II Cepheids have periods comparable to those of the classical Cepheids, but they are

Population II stars. We may pool the W Virginis stars and the RV Tauri stars together in this single group, as they probably constitute a single sequence of stars. The known number of these variables is only a small percentage of the number of known RR Lyrae stars. But those that we do know are either in globular clusters or are single stars in the halo. The W Virginis stars have periods ranging from 10 to 30 days, with the most typical period around 16 days. They can be distinguished from classical Cepheids of the same period because the light curves are shaped differently and because the absorption lines of the W Virginis stars are double for a part of each period. This behavior resembles that of the shorter-period RR Lyrae stars. The RV Tauri stars have periods from 30 to 150 days and are yellow supergiants. They pulsate less regularly than do the variables of shorter period, but at least some of them show occasional doubling of the spectral lines.

As can be seen from Fig. 16.6:2, which includes only periods shorter than a month, the Type II Cepheids reveal a period-luminosity relationship that is similar to that of the classical Cepheids but below it. For any given period of pulsation a Population II star is about 1.5 magnitudes fainter than its Population I counterpart. The distance of such a star can be estimated in the same way as that of a Cepheid.

9. Red Variables of Long Period

SEVERAL THOUSAND stars are known that vary in light with periods between 100 and 1000 days, and are the *long-period*, or *Mira-type*, variables. They are red in color, of spectral types M, R, N, or S, and are giants in size and luminosity. A typical period is around 300 days, and a common range is 5 magnitudes, substantially greater than for variables of other groups. Mira itself varies with an average period of 331 days, although single oscillations have differed from this average by as much as 25 days. At brightest light it reaches second magnitude on some occasions but only fifth magnitude on others. The individual minima also differ, Mira sometimes declining only to the eighth magnitude and on other occasions to the tenth.

The large range in visual magnitude is not matched by a large variation in total luminosity; the bolometric magnitude changes by only about one magnitude. If a long-period variable is at 2500°K when brightest, a small share of its radiation is in the visual part of the spectrum; if when faintest the surface temperature has cooled to 2000°K, then practically none of the radiation is visible to the eye. The variation looks more extreme than it actually is. The effect is exaggerated because at the cooler temperatures more molecular bands occur, absorbing more of the continuous spectrum. It has also been suggested that near minimum light molecules in the outer atmospheric layers may combine to form sootlike particles. Temporary clouds of these particles may partly screen the stellar surface and produce the observed irregularities in the light curve. The red variables display a puzzling feature during much of the light cycle. Except near minimum light their spectra have emission lines, especially of hydrogen, along with the usual dark lines and bands. Radial velocity variations are rather small and therefore difficult to measure, but apparently these stars pulsate like the others we have studied. Velocities derived from the emission lines are systematically faster toward the observer than are those derived at the same time from the absorption lines. These differences are perhaps caused by hot shells moving outward relative to the surrounding atmosphere. Much remains to be learned about the physical nature of these stars.

The red variables belong to both stellar populations. The stars with the shorter periods, about six months, show fairly strong allegiance to Population II. A few are resident in globular clusters; the others on the average lie rather far from the galactic disk. The very-long-period stars, with cycles of about 12 months, are not found in globular clusters; they are less distant from the main plane of the galaxy and are thus more characteristic of Population I. There is no abrupt change of affiliation, however, as we study stars of longer and longer periods; rather the transition is smooth. Other characteristics are correlated with the periods of the red variables, as suggested in Table 16.3:1. The very-long-period stars tend to have a greater visual range, a lower visual luminosity, and a later spectral type than do the six-month stars. But the correlations and population membership are not nearly as sharp and clear-cut as for Cepheids, RR Lyrae stars, and Type II Cepheids. The red variables therefore have not been used extensively to estimate great distances.

EXPLOSIVE STARS

10. Novae

IN THE YEAR 1054 a star suddenly shone forth in Taurus, brighter than Venus and nearly matching the combined light of all the stars. As the months passed, this so-called Guest Star dimmed and finally faded from view. The event was recorded by the Chinese and Japanese, although no mention of it is found in European annals of the time. In 1572 Tycho's Star appeared in Cassiopeia, rivaling Venus and visible even in daylight. After more than a year it too disappeared, but it left its impact on the thinking of that vigorous era; no longer could the starry sphere be regarded as eternally unchanging. In 1604 Kepler's Star, as bright as Jupiter, came into view in Ophiuchus and later sank from sight. The first half of the twentieth century witnessed five stars that increased to first magnitude or brighter. Such stars have long been called *novae*, from the Latin for "new," although it is now known that these outbursts are performed by relatively feeble stars that were already in existence and are still in existence. A given nova is known either by its constellation and year of discovery or by its regular variable star designation. Nova Persei 1901, for example, is also GK Persei.

About 150 novae have been discovered in our galaxy. Records have survived for only a few of the very brightest of pretelescopic novae, and the great majority have been discovered photographically in the present century. Even today we are aware of only a small percentage of the nova explosions in the Milky Way; most are too distant and too much obscured by interstellar dust clouds to be noticed. Studies of

Fig. 16.10:1. Nova Herculis 1934, showing a large decrease in brightness over an interval of two months. (*Lick Observatory photographs*)

the Andromeda spiral galaxy, the nearest galaxy similar to our own, suggest by analogy that about 25 novae per year occur in our own stellar system.

THE LIGHT curves of novae are generally similar to one another, although they differ in detail. The rise in luminosity is extremely fast, taking only a day or two, with a brief pause about two magnitudes below peak light. The maximum occurs shortly thereafter and is followed by a decline that is initially steep but steadily levels out. When a typical nova has dimmed 3 or 4 magnitudes below maximum, it begins to oscillate in light for a time. These changes later die out and the slow general fading continues, with some variability, until the star ultimately returns to its original prenova brightness. Figure 16.11:1 shows the general characteristics of the early part of the light curve of a fast nova. Such a star rises by 12 or 13 magnitudes, or about 100,000 times in luminosity, to absolute magnitude −8 in a day or two. It then declines by 3 magnitudes in a week or 10 days, followed by a slower dimming. The original magnitude is not recovered, however, for a few years. Slower novae are not quite so luminous at peak light, but their decline is more leisurely. A nova with peak absolute magnitude −6, for example, takes about 3 months to dim by 3 magnitudes and perhaps a century to recover completely from its eruption.

On the few occasions when the spectra of brightening novae have been obtained, they reveal essentially an absorption spectrum of class A but with the dark lines broadened and shifted well to the violet. Just after maximum light an abrupt change occurs in the spectrum: a new set of absorption lines appears, each line shifted even farther to the violet. These fresh dark lines lie at the violet edges of broad emission lines of hydrogen and ionized metals. Doppler measurements of the

11. Changes of Light and Spectrum in Novae

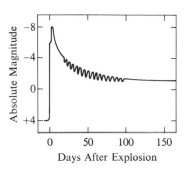

Fig. 16.11:1. A typical light curve for a fast nova.

dark lines show approach speeds of several hundred or a thousand miles per second. As the over-all brightness of the star continues to fade, the emission lines strengthen. Later other sets of absorption lines appear for a time, displaced even more to the violet and giving approach velocities up to 2000 mi/sec. In the later stages the absorption

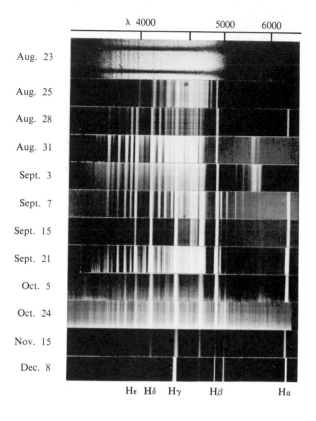

Fig. 16.11:2. Twelve objective prism spectra of Nova Cygni 1920. (*Yerkes Observatory photographs*)

lines disappear, and a pure emission spectrum survives, the brightest lines usually arising from doubly ionized oxygen. At long last, decades or centuries after the outburst, even the emission lines fade away and only the continuous spectrum of a class O star remains, perhaps crossed by absorption lines of hydrogen and helium.

The rather complex changes in light and spectrum are fairly well explained if the nova phenomenon is viewed as a stellar explosion, although why the explosion occurs at all is not certain. The prenova star is a subluminous blue star of absolute magnitude near +4. If there is a sudden release of energy beneath the stellar surface, the increased pressure pushes the upper layers rapidly outward. Because the cooling does not keep pace with the rapidly growing surface area, the luminosity of the star increases swiftly. At maximum light a spectrograph sees the approaching hemisphere of a swelling white photosphere, the absorption lines being Doppler-shifted to the violet. Shortly after maximum light an even faster shell, perhaps one-ten-thousandth as massive as the parent star, penetrates the surface and speeds outward at about 1000 mi/sec. As this shell expands in all directions about the star, we begin to see a composite spectrum: a Balmer line of hydrogen, for example, is now a broad emission line with a thinner absorption line at its violet edge. Figure 16.11:3 shows how such a line is formed. Atoms in that part of the shell behind the star cannot send any light to us. Those in front of the star absorb photons coming up from the star and reradiate the energy in random directions. Atoms in all other parts of the tenuous shell catch outbound photons and reradiate some energy in our direction. Because the absorption lines are produced in that part of the shell that is approaching us fastest and because the emission lines are produced in parts that are both approaching and receding, the spectrogram reveals very broad emission lines with absorption lines at their violet borders.

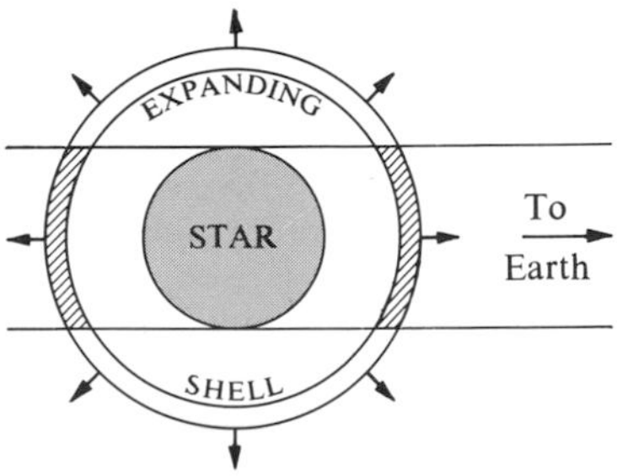

Later other shells are released, generally at even higher speeds, accounting for the successive appearance of new sets of absorption lines with even larger Doppler shifts toward the violet. As the several shells expand into space, they cover a smaller and smaller fraction of the stellar disk, and therefore the absorption lines become thinner and thinner and finally disappear, leaving only the broad emission lines from the rarefied expanding gases. As the years pass, the expanding material becomes more and more tenuous and the pattern of visible emission lines changes in response to the changing physical conditions. Ultimately, the material is completely dispersed, the emission lines fade out, and only the continuous spectrum of the postnova star remains, revealing a hot blue subluminous star once again.

Fig. 16.11:3. The rarefied expanding gases that are not in front of the parent star produce an emission spectrum, while those that are in front approach us the most rapidly and produce an absorption spectrum that is Doppler-shifted to the violet.

12. Nova Shells and Distances

THE RAPID expansion of a nova envelope suggests that ultimately the size will become great enough so that large telescopes can resolve the cloud as a disk. Shells around a few of the brighter and therefore nearer novae have indeed been discovered. The brightest outburst of this century was Nova Aquilae 1918, which attained the brilliance of Sirius. Its expanding cloud was found a few months after maximum light. Nova Persei 1901, the second brightest recent nova, with peak

Fig. 16.12:1. The expanding gaseous shell around Nova Persei 1901, photographed with the 200-inch telescope. (*Mount Wilson and Palomar Observatories photograph*)

THE VARIABLE STARS

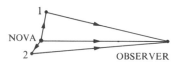

Fig. 16.12:2. Illustration of how a delayed light echo may be received from interstellar dust particles in the vicinity of a nova.

Fig. 16.12:3. The light echo around Nova Persei 1901, photographed on September 20 and again on November 13 of that year. (*Yerkes Observatory photographs*)

13. Spatial Distribution of Novae

magnitude 0.0, revealed its shell 16 years after the explosion. A 1949 photograph of Nova Persei is shown in Fig. 16.12:1. Successive measurements of this incomplete shell show that its average angular rate of expansion is about 0.5″/yr. Spectrograms of that part of the cloud near the parent star show doubled bright lines, indicating that the near surface of the shell is approaching at 700 mi/sec and the far surface is receding at 700 mi/sec. To maintain a roughly spherical shape, the transverse velocity of the shell must also be about 700 mi/sec outward from the parent star. In Chapter 13 we found that the transverse velocity is given by

$$v_T = 3D\mu.$$

For Nova Persei we know that $v_T = 700$ mi/sec and that the proper motion, or angular rate of expansion, is $\mu = 0.5″/yr$. The only unknown is the distance. Therefore for the shell and hence its interior star we have

$$D = \frac{v_T}{3\mu} = \frac{700}{3 \times 0.5} \simeq 500 \text{ parsecs.}$$

Here is a new method of determining large distances that is entirely independent of annual parallax or of methods that may be imperiled by interstellar dust. Although not precise, it is the best of several ways of estimating the distances of novae. In 1961 the shell around Nova Persei was 60 years old and its radius exceeded 10^4 a.u. Ultimately, like the shells of other novae, it will disappear as the gases become more and more rarefied and merge with the general gas and dust of interstellar space.

A unique feature enveloped Nova Persei for a few years after the outburst, long before the gaseous shell was found. A patchy luminous cloud appeared and expanded at a rate of a few seconds of arc per *day*. Such a larger proper motion implies an enormous linear velocity, and this phenomenon has been interpreted as a *light echo* produced by reflection of the nova outburst from interstellar dust particles not many parsecs away from the erupting star. Light from the nova itself took perhaps 1500 years to reach the earth. Light scattered by particles 1 and 2 in Fig. 16.12:2 took a few months more to get here because the interstellar particles reflecting the outburst were in a long ellipsoidal shell with nova and observer at the two foci. At a later date other particles in a larger shell were briefly visible. The over-all effect from the earth was an expanding and weakening cloud that finally disappeared.

As a group the novae appear to belong to a population that is intermediate between I and II. About one-third of the known novae lie within 10° of the direction of the galactic center in Sagittarius, a patch of sky that is less than 1 percent of the area of the whole celestial sphere. In three dimensions, therefore, the novae prefer to dwell in or near the galactic nucleus. The outlying novae are neither distributed throughout the spherical halo like the RR Lyrae variables nor confined closely to the disk like the Population I Cepheids; they appear to occupy an intermediate oblate-spheroidal volume of space. Here we have encountered a group of objects which, like the red variables, are not extremists. It is clear that there are not just two distinct populations, but a continuous gradation. We shall interpret this gradation later.

14. Explosive Stars That Repeat

ABOUT SIX stars are known that are called *recurrent novae*. They are characterized by a fast rise in luminosity and a slower decline, but the total rise is only about 8 magnitudes as compared with some 12 magnitudes for the ordinary novae. These lesser outbursts occur every few decades, the median cycle being 30 years. More than a hundred other novalike objects are known and are called the *U Geminorum stars*. They rise swiftly by 3 or 4 magnitudes and then decline fairly rapidly to a constant minimum until the next eruption weeks or months later. The prototype star itself averages 97 days between light peaks, although individual cycles have been as short as 2 months and as long as 9. Among these novalike stars generally there is a correlation of rise in magnitude with cycle: the longer the interval between outbursts the greater the violence of each burst. It appears that the longer a U Geminorum star waits to release its excess radiation the greater the amount of radiation it must release. This correlation extends to the recurrent novae, which rise a thousand-fold in luminosity every few decades. If it extends even to the novae themselves, we are entitled to guess that their 12-magnitude rises may recur every few thousand years.

Between eruptions all of these explosive stars seem to be hot blue objects that lie below and to the left of the main sequence in the HR diagram. They occupy a fairly empty part of the diagram intermediate between the main sequence and the realm of the white dwarfs. All of them are ejecting mass into space, whether frequently like a machine gun or more rarely but more energetically like a large cannon. It has often been suggested that these stars will slowly but steadily decline in energy output as they lose mass into space and that they will finally become white dwarfs.

15. Supernovae

THE MOST VIOLENT known explosions in nature are those of the *supernovae*, which rise to peak luminosities about 100 million times that of the sun and later fade away. Although ultraenergetic, supernova outbursts occur extremely rarely. Only three are known in our Milky Way galaxy: the Guest Star of 1054, Tycho's Nova of 1572, and Kepler's Nova of 1604. The rest of more than 50 known supernovae have been detected in other galaxies beyond our own. If caught near maximum light, an extragalactic supernova may match or even exceed the total combined luminosity of all the other billions of stars resident in the same galaxy. All supernovae rise rapidly to maximum light and fade much more slowly. The majority rise to an absolute magnitude near -14, with light curves that differ from one another in detail. These stars, like novae, show widened emission lines after maximum light. Studies of other galaxies suggest that they are Population I objects. The minority of supernovae rise to absolute magnitude -16 and are therefore more spectacular. Their broadened bright lines become prominent before maximum. The decline in light of these

Fig. 16.15:1. Two views of the galaxy Messier 101, without and with supernova. Except for the supernova, all stellar images on these pictures are stars within our own galaxy, past which we look to see Messier 101. (*Mount Wilson and Palomar Observatories photographs*)

ultrasupernovae is smooth, with a drop of three magnitudes in the first month or so and then a slower sinking afterwards. These objects seem to belong to Population II. On the average there is perhaps one ultrasupernova to every five of the less luminous supernovae. If both groups are considered together, there is about one outburst per century in a galaxy like our own. When we compare this rather uncertain figure with that for ordinary novae, only one supernova erupts for every few thousand regular novae. On the other hand, the peak luminosity of a supernova is greater by a thousand-fold. It appears that a supernova outburst removes a good fraction of the star's mass and that, unlike ordinary novae, the star undergoes a major alteration in a very short time. What kind of alteration, however, is not known from observation, because postsupernovae are too faint for detection in other galaxies or for certain identification in our own.

Like ordinary novae, supernovae should be surrounded by rapidly expanding nebulae, or clouds. Search of the regions where Tycho's Nova and Kepler's Nova exploded four centuries ago has shown nearby nebulosity which may be associated with the supernovae. The gases ejected by the Guest Star of 1054 are well known and constitute the celebrated Crab Nebula, which was discovered more than two centuries ago and is shown in Fig. 16.15:2. The angular rate of expansion of the nebula is about 0.20″/yr and the doubled emission lines indicate that the radius is increasing at about 800 mi/sec. The distance, computed as in Section 12, is about 1300 parsecs. From its present average angular radius of 6′ we can deduce two things. (1) Its outer radius is now more than 2 parsecs. (2) At a rate of 0.20″/yr it has taken 900 years to grow to the present radius. Coupling both the position in Taurus and the estimated age of the Crab Nebula, it appears certain that this filamentary gaseous structure is the remnant of the supernova of 1054.

Fig. 16.15:2. The Crab Nebula in Taurus, remains of a supernova explosion, photographed in red light with the 200-inch Hale telescope. (*Mount Wilson and Palomar Observatories photograph*)

Spectral studies of the Crab Nebula indicate that the fine-scale network of threadlike features has an emission spectrum that is rather similar to the later stages of an expanding ordinary nova. The less well-defined component of the nebular light has a continuous spectrum. In addition, the Crab Nebula is one of the strongest sources of radio emission in the sky and was the first radio source to be identified with a known optical object, in 1950. The radio emission and the continuous spectrum at visual wavelengths are emitted by ultraenergetic free electrons that are spiraling in the tangled magnetic fields of the nebula. This type of emission is called *synchrotron radiation* because it was first observed coming from fast electrons circling in the magnetic field of a synchrotron. The latter is used in the physics laboratory to accelerate particles to extreme energies. In the Crab Nebula the more energetic electrons emit visible light, whereas the more abundant but less energetic ones emit radio radiation. Thus the supernova remnant can be detected through both windows of the electromagnetic spectrum.

The strongest radio source in the sky, known as Cassiopeia A, has been identified with turbulent high-speed shreds of nebulous material. Several other radio sources have been similarly identified, and it is likely that they too are the remnants of supernovae that were not recorded at the time of their explosions. Some of them perhaps erupted many thousands of years ago; others may have burst forth more recently behind obscuring clouds of interstellar dust and gone unnoticed. In such nebulae not only do the electrons acquire high energies; so also may protons, helium nuclei, and heavier atomic nuclei. It is tempting to identify these nuclei with the *cosmic ray particles*. Discovered in 1900 and studied extensively by physicists since that time, the cosmic radiation is known to consist chiefly of high-energy protons, with helium nuclei present, and heavy nuclei in lower abundances. They bombard the earth's upper atmosphere from all directions at the rate of about one per square centimeter per second. Perhaps supernovae are the source of some or even most of the cosmic radiation.

ERRATIC STARS

16. Shell Stars

NOVAE AND supernovae are not the only objects surrounded by gaseous shells. Several dozen *P Cygni stars* are known. Their prototype is a fifth-magnitude object of spectral type B1*e*, with the Balmer lines of hydrogen appearing as rather broad emission lines, each with absorption lines at its violet edge. The lines are generally similar in appearance to those of novae after maximum light, and they are produced by an expanding shell, as in Fig. 16.11:3. Unlike novae, however, the P Cygni stars eject gas continually for long periods of time at modest velocities; Doppler measurements reveal typical expansion speeds of about 100 mi/sec. The parent stars are hot and very luminous, with absolute magnitudes near −4.

Less mild-mannered are the Wolf-Rayet stars. About 200 are known and constitute spectral class W. They are the hottest stars known, with typical temperatures of 50,000°K to 100,000°K, and with absolute magnitudes not far from −5. Superposed on the background continuous spectrum are very broad emission lines, and in some Wolf-Rayet stars the lines are bordered with absorption lines at the violet sides. Here again we may be seeing the spectral effects of an expanding cloud of gas that is continually fed by atoms ejected from the stellar surface. Measured widths of the lines indicate outward velocities up to 2000 mi/sec. The W stars divide into two groups with respect to chemical composition. One has prominent emission lines of ionized helium and also lines produced by highly ionized carbon and oxygen; the other group also has prominent lines of ionized helium, but most of the other lines arise from highly ionized nitrogen. The carbon-oxygen stars, called WC, have no nitrogen lines, whereas the nitrogen stars, WN, show no oxygen and little carbon. As with luminous blue stars in

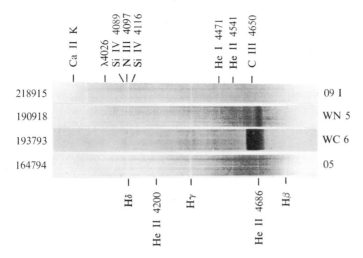

Negative prints of the spectra of two O stars and two Wolf-Rayet stars. The spectral types of the two Wolf-Rayet stars were determined by Sanford and Wilson. HD 218915, a supergiant of class O9, has a spectrum similar to HD 190918, except for the emission lines. HD 164794 has a pure absorption spectrum which is very early in type. (*From* An Atlas of Stellar Spectra, *by Morgan, Keenan, and Kellman, University of Chicago Press, 1943*; *Yerkes Observatory photographs*)

general, the frequency of close binaries is high among the Wolf-Rayet stars. It has been suggested that all W stars may be members of pairs, and that the continual ejection of gases may be connected with the proximity of the partners.

17. Planetary Nebulae

THE SHELLS OF P Cygni stars and Wolf-Rayet stars are too small to be resolved at the telescope, but other stars are known that are surrounded by enormous and slowly expanding envelopes. Many of these envelopes are easily seen telescopically as disks or rings, greenish in hue. They look something like Uranus and Neptune; hence their

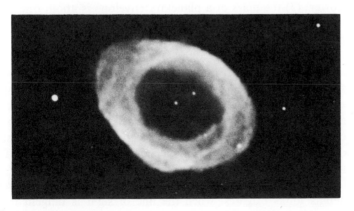

Fig. 16.17:1. The Ring Nebula in Lyra, Messier 57, photographed with the 200-inch telescope. (*Mount Wilson and Palomar Observatories photograph*)

pretty but misleading name. About 500 of these *planetary nebulae* are now known. A typical one is a thick shell of rarefied gas surrounding its parent star. The outer radius of most is about 10,000 a.u., but others are 10 or more times as large. Typical expansion velocities are 10 mi/sec and the fastest known is 35 mi/sec. A cubic centimeter of the gaseous shell contains about 10^4 atoms. This number density is of course extremely low; it is about equal to what we would experience if the earth's atmosphere were removed and the air in one modest-sized house were allowed to spread over the whole earth and to a height of one mile. The kinetic temperature of the rarefied nebular gas is close to 10,000°K.

The spectrum of a planetary nebula is a series of emission lines. The Balmer lines are prominent, but so too are other lines. Originally it was thought that these other lines were produced by a new chemical element, and the element was called *nebulium*. It is now known, however, that these lines are caused by photons produced by downward transitions of electrons that belong to highly ionized atoms of well-known elements. The characteristic tint of planetary nebulae observed visually at the telescope is due to the fact that the strongest emission lines are the pair at 4959 A and 5007 A in the green part of the spectrum. These photons are emitted by doubly ionized oxygen, O III. The O II line at 3727 A is also relatively strong. Lines of other atoms are observed, among them helium, carbon, nitrogen, and neon.

The entire light of a planetary nebula comes ultimately from the radiation of the central star, and studies of these stars indicate they are small, blue, and ultrahot. A typical central star is of absolute magnitude +2 and temperature 50,000°K, although there are variations from one to the next. Some have Wolf-Rayet spectra; others are stars of class O. There are likenesses between planetaries and ordinary novae: (1) their distributions in the galaxy are similar; (2) both kinds of stars are small and blue; and (3) the surrounding gases are expanding. But there are major differences too: (1) before and after outburst the central stars of planetary nebulae seem to be somewhat more luminous than novae; (2) the expansion speeds of planetary shells are much slower; (3) the mass of a planetary envelope is about one-tenth of the sun's mass, whereas the mass of a nova shell is probably less than 1 percent that of a planetary shell.

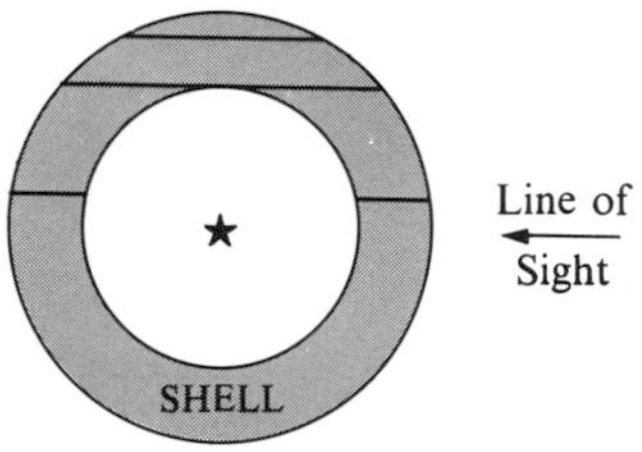

Two apparent puzzles about planetary nebulae demand an accounting. First, why do astronomers think the surrounding gases occupy a spherical shell instead of a ring? If the nebulae are ring-shaped, those seen nearly edge-on, like the system of Saturn, would appear as very elongated ellipses. The fact that planetaries seen in projection are nearly circular means that as a family they are roughly spherical shells. The darker central regions of many planetaries are accounted for by the smaller number of emitting atoms along the line of sight when one looks through the shell. Figure 16.17:2 shows that a uniform planetary nebula looks brightest when the line of sight is tangent to the inner edge of the shell.

The second puzzle is that the tenuous expanding gas of a typical planetary sends us about 10 or 20 times as much light as does the central star itself. How can this be if the radiation of the star is entirely responsible for the radiation of the nebula? The essential point is that the central star is extremely hot and most of its emitted photons are in the ultra-violet. At 50,000°K a star radiates only 1 percent of its energy

Line of
Sight

SHELL

Fig. 16.17:2. In many planetary nebulae the brightness is a maximum well away from the center, causing the ringed appearance.

in the visual part of the spectrum between 4000 A and 7000 A. More than half of the energy emitted by such a body is in the form of extreme ultraviolet photons energetic enough to ionize hydrogen. In the tenuous shell a neutral hydrogen atom will sooner or later absorb a high-energy photon from the central star and its electron will be released and fly away. Later the proton will recapture some other passing electron. What may happen then? The electron may land directly in the innermost orbit, with the emission of a photon in the Lyman continuum.

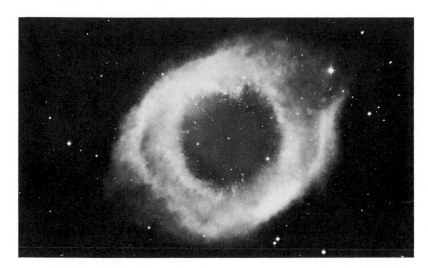

Fig. 16.17:3. NGC 7293, a planetary nebula in Aquarius, photographed in red light with the 200-inch reflector. Note the jets inside the ring that are directed radially away from the central star. (*Mount Wilson and Palomar Observatories photograph*)

This photon will buzz away and ionize some other hydrogen atom. Alternatively, the captured electron may jump down by some other route. If it lands in the fourth orbit, then the second, and finally in the first, out go a photon in the Brackett continuum, then one of Hβ, and finally one of Lα. The Hβ photon speeds through the tenuous shell without any appreciable chance of finding an already excited hydrogen atom that can accept it. It escapes from the nebula and may reach our spectrograph. We are here seeing *fluorescent radiation*, which is light emitted by atoms that have previously absorbed light. Generally speaking, then, when we observe the bright Balmer lines of a planetary nebula, we are seeing the quanta sent in our direction by atoms that are recombining with electrons. In particular, each electron that emits a Balmer photon must stop briefly in the second orbit on its way to the innermost orbit.

18. Ring Stars

THE P CYGNI stars, the Wolf-Rayet stars, and the central stars of planetary nebulae are surrounded by minor or major gaseous shells that are expanding outward. We now turn to a large group of objects called the *B emission stars*. They are luminous and blue and seem to be surrounded by gaseous rings or shells that are not expanding. In these stars we do not see emission lines with the violet absorption

THE VARIABLE STARS

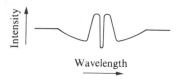

Fig. 16.18:1. The profile of a single line in the spectrum of a ring star.

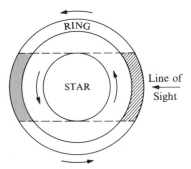

Fig. 16.18:2. Schematic diagram of a ring star seen from above its pole of rotation.

edges that characterize a swelling nebula. Instead, a typical Balmer line is a very wide absorption line, and sitting atop the absorption line is a narrower emission line. In addition, often cutting into the emission line is a central narrow absorption line. Figure 16.18:1 is a schematic plot of intensity against wavelength over about 10 A centered on such a line. The broad but shallow absorption is caused by the rapid rotation of a B star whose rotational axis makes an angle of about 90° with the line of sight. The broadening of spectral lines arising from stellar spin was described in Chapter 15, Section 10. We may imagine around the star a ring of gas revolving in the equatorial plane, as shown in Fig. 16.18:2. Part of the ring is occulted by the star. Other portions are clear of the star and are emitting fluorescent radiation, some of which is moving toward us and some away. The rest is in front of the stellar disk and absorbing light; its motion is chiefly transverse and so the central absorption feature is very little broadened by the Doppler effect.

A popular interpretation of the existence of such rings or partial shells is that of a rapidly rotating star with material seeping off the equatorial latitudes of its surface. Suppose, for example, a B0 star contracts. To conserve angular momentum it must spin faster. Ultimately, the time may come when the velocity of an atom at the equator exceeds the circular velocity; it may then go into free orbit around the star. The circular velocity at the earth's surface is 5 mi/sec; at the surface of a B0 star it is several hundred miles per second. But great as this speed is, it does not much exceed the observed equatorial rotational velocities of these rapidly spinning stars. The gases released will adhere to the law of areas, and the farther out the matter moves the slower its orbital speed. Therefore the prediction that the shell must rotate more slowly than the star agrees with the observed fact that the width of an emission line is less than that of the broad underlying absorption line due to the star itself.

The ring stars show spectral variations and their lives are not very placid. Pleione, a member of the Pleiades star cluster, had lines of the sort we have been discussing from 1888 to 1906 and then the emission features disappeared. They reappeared again in 1938 and lasted until 1952. Another well-known B emission star that has shown rather drastic variations several times in this century is Gamma Cassiopeiae, at the center of its W-shaped constellation. Apparently, the rings of such stars are blown away from time to time and are replaced later by new ones from below. Thus these stars contrast with the objects which we studied earlier and which have continuously expanding shells.

19. Flare Stars

A FEW RED dwarf stars have been caught in the act of flaring. Examples among the nearby stars of Table 13.3:1 are Proxima Centauri, Luyten 726–8 B, Ross 154, and Kruger 60 B. On occasion they suddenly brighten by 1 or 2 magnitudes and then decline more slowly, the entire flare-up lasting only a few minutes. These stars are of spectral class M5

Fig. 16.20:1. The Great Nebula in Orion, a breeding ground of T Tauri stars, photographed with the 36-inch Crossley reflector. (*Lick Observatory photograph*)

or M6 and many of them show emission lines. The phenomenon may resemble a solar flare, but it is on a grander scale. Although it is hard to imagine a star increasing its radiation by five or even ten times in only a minute or so, we should remember that a cool M6 star radiates only 1 percent of its energy in the visual part of the spectrum. Thus when a sudden hot patch develops on the stellar surface, it can emit more radiation in the visual than can the feeble star itself.

20. The T Tauri Stars

THE FINAL group of erratic stars is a most unusual one. The other groups are all composed of either extremely hot blue stars or extremely cool red dwarfs. Most stars of intermediate temperature and luminosity behave themselves; not so the *T Tauri stars*. They are of spectral type F, G, K, or early M and also have emission lines of Hα and ionized calcium. Their light varies in an irregular and unpredictable fashion, with fluctuations of 2 or 3 magnitudes. These stars are always found in enormous nebulae, which are chaotic clouds of tenuous gas and dust particles with dimensions of many parsecs. Over 200 T Tauri stars have been identified in the great Orion Nebula alone.

A clue to their nature is that the redder T Tauri variables are more luminous than normal main-sequence stars of the same spectral type. It appears likely that they are relatively young stars that are still in the process of gravitational contraction. As the millions of years pass, each one will migrate slowly to the left on the HR diagram and ultimately reach the main sequence and begin to operate by converting hydrogen into helium. Right now, however, they appear to be undergoing the vacillating process of gravitational contraction. Later we shall cite strong evidence that the great gaseous and dusty nebulae where T Tauri stars are found are indeed the breeding grounds of stars and that stars are being born even in our times.

PROBLEMS

1. We have encountered a number of techniques that have been used to estimate the distances of objects beyond the solar system. Mention at least five of them.

2. What kind of data must be collected if we are to study a given variable star as completely as possible?

3. (a) Sketch a Population I HR diagram and include in it the groups of Population I variables that are given in Table 16.3:1. (b) Do the same for Population II.

4. Sketch the light curve and under it the velocity curve of a Cepheid. Interpret the motion of the star at different times during the light cycle.

5. Use the method given on pages 355–356 to find the average radius of a Cepheid if $L/L_{\text{sun}} = 3000$ and $T = 6000°K$ at mean brightness. Estimate the maximum and minimum radii.

6. Estimate the average apparent magnitude of a classical Cepheid with period 4 days and distance 1000 parsecs, assuming there is no intervening interstellar dust.

7. The average apparent magnitude of an RR Lyrae star is 12.8. (a) What is its distance, assuming there is no interstellar dust between the earth and the star? (b) What is its true distance if the light from the star is actually dimmed by 2.5 magnitudes on its trip to the earth?

8. Account for the fact that the range of the long-period red variables is very great even though the total luminosity of these stars does not vary by a large factor.

9. (a) How many novae would you expect to erupt within 1000 parsecs of the earth in one century, assuming that 25 erupt each year in the whole galaxy? Assume for simplicity that the whole galaxy is a sphere of radius 10,000 parsecs that completely includes the local neighborhood of interest. (b) How bright would such a neighborly nova be at maximum?

10. Explain what the spectral lines of a nova should look like a week after maximum light and a year after maximum light, given that a thin spherical shell travels outward at constant speed.

11. The radius of a circular nova shell is now $110''$ and is increasing by $0.40''$ per year. The emission lines near the center of the disk are double and separated by the Doppler shift by 1800 mi/sec. Estimate the distance of the nova and the age of the shell.

12. Discuss the general characteristics of supernovae and their frequency of occurrence.

13. Describe the general structure and motions of planetary nebulae. Give similarities to and differences from ordinary novae.

14. Explain why we receive many times more light in visual wavelengths from the envelope of a planetary nebula than from its central star.

15. Account for the peculiar nature of the spectral lines of a ring star whose rotational axis is inclined $90°$ from the line of sight.

17

STAR CLUSTERS
AND ASSOCIATIONS

Mᴀɴʏ stars are single, and many more are members of multiple systems. Perhaps one star in every thousand belongs to a larger aggregation. These aggregations are the *star clusters* and the *stellar associations*. We learned in Chapter 14 that nearly all close double stars in the sky are physically associated and not merely chance pairings. Similarly, no larger stellar group can be an accidental clumping on the celestial sphere. Each cluster or association is a physical entity, bound together more or less strongly by the gravitational forces between all pairs of member stars.

The *galactic clusters* are so called because they are found near the equatorial plane of the galaxy, and from our station near this plane we see most of them very near the center line of the Milky Way. These groups are sometimes called *open clusters* because the angular separations of the stars are large enough so that the telescope can resolve the individual members. *Stellar associations* are loose groups of stars of the same physical type. The number density of stars in an association may be much less than that of *all* stars in its neighborhood, but it is much greater inside the association than it is outside for stars of the same type. Analogously, the number density of babies less than three days old in a given hospital is much greater than that for similar infants in the whole community but is much less than that for all people in the hospital. Stellar associations are found in the same region of the galaxy as are galactic clusters.

Richer groups are the *globular clusters*. They are all very far away and not all of their individual stars are resolvable. The name originates in their beautiful spherical or near-spherical symmetry. Unlike the galactic clusters and stellar associations, the globular clusters move in a vast spherical space whose center coincides with the nucleus of our galaxy.

Some clusters have proper names, but most go by their catalogue numbers. An early and celebrated catalogue of about 100 nonstellar objects was compiled in 1781 by the French astronomer Charles Messier, who was interested in comets. He found these fuzzy objects of constant position a nuisance because they can be mistaken for comets in a small telescope. The Messier objects include gaseous nebulae and external galaxies as well as star clusters. Messier 1 or M1, for example, is the Crab Nebula, M13 the globular cluster in Hercules, and M31 the great spiral galaxy in Andromeda. The great catalogues of William Herschel and his son John were put together over a period of 80 years and were added to by J. L. E. Dreyer. Dreyer catalogued more than 13,000 objects in his *New General Catalogue* of 1888 and in two supplementary *Index Catalogues* published later. Thus the Crab Nebula is M1 and also NGC 1952, and one of the external galaxies nearest to our own is IC 1613.

GALACTIC CLUSTERS

1. Bright Clusters

INDIVIDUAL stars can be seen by the unaided eye in several galactic clusters. The most celebrated and revered group is the Pleiades in Taurus, mentioned by the Chinese in the twenty-fourth century B.C., by Homer in both the *Iliad* and the *Odyssey*, and alluded to in the Book

Fig. 17.1:1. Praesepe, the Beehive Cluster. (*Yerkes Observatory photograph*)

of Job. Mythologically, the Pleiades were the seven daughters of Atlas and Pleione. Orion pursued them and so Jupiter changed the sisters into a flock of doves and elevated them to the sky. Also in Taurus several stars of the Hyades cluster are easily visible without aid. The faint constellation of Coma Berenices near the north galactic pole is chiefly composed of stars that belong to a cluster. Praesepe, the Bee-hive Cluster in Cancer, is seen as a faint patch of light. The individual stars of Praesepe are too faint to be seen, but their joint light is enough to impress the eye. Galileo was the first to see the stars themselves. The Double Cluster is in Perseus near the Cassiopeia boundary; it appears as a pair of faint patches separated by about 0.4°.

2. Moving Clusters

A FEW CLUSTERS are near enough to us so that the proper motions of their individual stars are reasonably large and have been measured precisely. Moreover, the stars are bright enough subjects for slit spectrograms and therefore their radial velocities have been deduced accurately. These groups are called *moving clusters*, the outstanding example of which is the Hyades. More than 150 member stars are known and perhaps as many more are too faint to have yet been found. Although the brightest members lie in a small central region, the fainter stars occupy a circle more than 20° in diameter. When the positions and proper motions are plotted, as shown in Fig. 17.2:1 for a few of the brighter stars, we can immediately segregate the cluster stars from the noncluster stars. To *remain* a cluster for millions or billions of years on end, the individual stars must move on parallel tracks at the same speed. A parade dissolves and becomes unrecognizable if the marchers fail to maintain the same velocity vector and wander away at random. From the illustration it is clear that first-magnitude Aldebaran is not a member. In 30,000 years the stars will lie at the arrowheads. Recall from Chapter 9 that meteors of a shower appear to radiate from a given point among the stars because the individual particles are following parallel paths in three-dimensional space. Similarly, the proper motions of the stars of a nearby cluster appear to radiate from a given point on the celestial sphere and converge to the opposite point. The Hyades stars are converging toward a point about 5° east of Betelgeuse, and some tens of millions of years from now the cluster will be seen as a relatively compact group in that general direction.

Let us return to the cluster as it is today and measure the radial velocity of one member star as accurately as possible. Suppose we determine it for the star closest to the sun in Fig. 17.2:2. Now the space velocity, v, of the star must be directed toward the convergent while its radial velocity, v_R, is directed away from the sun. Note from the diagram that the angle between the two equals the angle between the star and the convergent point, which is known. Therefore we can solve the velocity triangle graphically or trigonometrically and find the space velocity of the star. Next, the space velocity of any other cluster star must be the same or the cluster would not remain together. We can make use of this fact along with the angular distance from

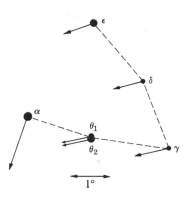

Fig. 17.2:1. Bright stars of the Hyades cluster. The proper-motion arrows show that all stars except first-magnitude Aldebaran (α Tauri) belong to the group.

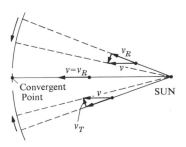

Fig. 17.2:2. The convergent point of a moving cluster is infinitely far away at a fixed point on the celestial sphere. Each member star is moving at the same speed toward this point.

the convergent to find the transverse velocity of every member star. Since the proper motions are known, we can compute the distance of each star from the formula $v_T = 3D\mu$ and construct a three-dimensional model of the cluster. In actual practice the astronomer is not content to put all his faith in a radial velocity measurement of just one star of a moving cluster. He will obtain as many as he can. Not only is there sometimes safety in numbers, but one must remember that stars are more closely spaced in clusters than in the general field and they therefore affect one another gravitationally. Any given star is moving in a complex path relative to the center of mass of the cluster. In typical open clusters, however, the internal motions are very slow—only a small fraction of a mile per second. Therefore the parade as witnessed from the sun is nearly perfect, although not completely so.

With the help of these various techniques it has been found that the center of the Hyades is 40 parsecs from the sun and about half of the stars are contained in a sphere of radius 6 parsecs. The cluster as a whole has a space motion of 27 mi/sec relative to the sun. The estimated number density of stars near the center of the Hyades is about 0.5 per cubic parsec, or several times that in the general neighborhood of the sun. Another well-known moving cluster is the Ursa Major group, whose nucleus is composed of 14 known stars in a volume of radius about 6 parsecs. The brightest members are the 5 central stars of the Big Dipper. The center of the group lies at 23 parsecs from the sun and the space motion is about 11 mi/sec, diverging from a point not far from Castor and Pollux. A much larger number of outlying stars, nearly 150 altogether, have about the same space velocities as the nuclear members of the Ursa Major group; among them are Sirius, Beta Aurigae, and Alpha Corona Borealis. The solar system itself happens to be inside the large spatial volume occupied by the extended Ursa Major group.

3. More Distant Clusters

ONLY A HANDFUL of the 800 known galactic clusters are close enough and therefore of sufficiently large angular diameter to reveal their convergent points by proper-motion studies. The distances of the vast majority must be estimated by other methods. One technique requires the measurement of apparent magnitudes and color indexes of the member of a cluster, as described in Chapter 15, Section 3. A plot of the data then gives a relative HR diagram, or *color-magnitude diagram*. Because all stars of a cluster lie at essentially the same distance from the sun, the apparent magnitude of each star is fainter than its absolute magnitude by a constant amount. As an example, Fig. 17.3:1 shows the magnitudes and colors of 20 stars of the Pleiades brighter then twelfth magnitude. They were picked at random from the more than 250 known members. Notice that the stars of middling brightness define the run of the main sequence very nicely, apart from the few stars that are a trifle too bright and therefore may be unresolved binaries. When the Pleiades main sequence is matched to the absolute HR diagram described in Chapter 13, Section 15, it is found that the

Pleiades are about 5 magnitudes dimmer than they would be at 10 parsecs. Therefore the distance of the cluster is about 100 parsecs. More precisely, the difference is 5.6 magnitudes and the estimated distance 130 parsecs.

Similar pioneering studies of many clusters were made by Robert J. Trumpler at the Lick Observatory around 1930 and the deduced distances were tabulated. As a check on this technique Trumpler estimated the angular diameter of each cluster, assuming a linear diameter of a few parsecs. The latter figures were known from studies of nearby clusters like the Hyades and Coma Berenices. These data were then combined to give an independent value for the distance of each cluster. An astonishing result was found when the two distance estimates were compared: the farther away a cluster the more discordant the two estimates. Furthermore, matching of HR diagrams generally gave much bigger distances than did the method of angular diameter. What was wrong? If the geometrical method were incorrect and the clusters were really farther away, we should have to agree that the linear size of clusters increases with distance from the solar system. Such a situation if of course exceedingly implausible. If the HR method were incorrect and the clusters were really closer to us, we should have to agree that something in space dims the light of stars and the farther away the more the dimming. Trumpler was well aware of the dark obscuring clouds of the Milky Way; many of them are visible to the unaided eye. He was the first, however, to recognize from his comparative studies that there is a more rarefied but all-pervasive medium of obscuring interstellar matter in and near the equatorial plane of the galaxy.

More recently it has become possible to overcome these hazards by precise photoelectric measurements of starlight at three wavelengths instead of two. If space were transparent, then a single color index would be sufficient to indicate the Planck curve and thus the surface temperature of the star being measured. But the interstellar smoke extinguishes blue light more than yellow light. Thus a third measurement, preferably in the ultraviolet, is required to tell whether a certain star is, let us say, either an intrinsically cool red star or a yellow star that *looks* red because intervening interstellar dust has depleted the blue radiation from the star.

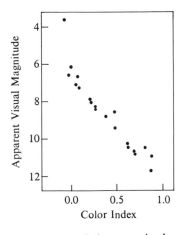

Fig. 17.3:1. Color-magnitude diagram of the Pleiades as defined by 20 stars selected at random.

4. Dimensions and Contents

THE KNOWN galactic clusters are as a group rather ragged in appearance, but they may be thought of as approximately spherical in shape. Their linear radii range from less than 1 parsec up to about 10 parsecs. The majority have radii of less than 3 parsecs and the most frequent radius is between 1.0 and 1.5 parsecs. The number of stars per cluster runs from about a dozen for the sparsest to over a thousand for the most populous, and the membership of a typical cluster is between 50 and 100.

The kinds of stars in a galactic cluster can of course be read from the color-magnitude diagram of the cluster. The recent impetus to establish such diagrams is rooted only partly in the desire to find distances;

the strongest reason is to identify the types of stars present, because it is likely that each member of a given cluster was born at about the same time in the past. In a cluster we can therefore study the effects of evolution on a group of stars of different mass but of the same age. In Chapter 19, when we have accumulated the evidence, we shall interpret carefully the differences between the HR diagrams of various clusters. For the moment let us look at just a few general results. In the Pleiades the most luminous and bluest star is Alcyone, of spectral

Fig. 17.4:1. The Jewel Box, a galactic cluster near the Southern Cross, photographed with the 74-inch reflector. (*Mount Stromlo Observatory, Australia*)

class B6; no O or early B stars exist nor are there any red giants. In both the Hyades and Praesepe the bluest stars are of spectral class A1; each contains four giant stars of spectral class K but no O or B stars whatever. The rich cluster M67, with perhaps a thousand stars, counts red giants in its membership, but no main-sequence stars of classes O, B, A, or early F. These profound differences are not accidental; they are a result of growing old. When a cluster of stars is born out of an enormous concentration of interstellar matter, it is likely that main-sequence stars of all luminosities and spectral classes are present. The more massive stars are spendthrift, pouring radiation into space at a great rate. For example, a main-sequence star of absolute magnitude −2.5 is one thousand times as luminous as the sun and is therefore consuming its hydrogen at one thousand times the rate of the sun. But with only about ten times as much mass to feed on as the sun, this luminous star uses up its hydrogen in a relatively short time. In response to its changed central composition it evolves away from the main sequence. As time goes by the stars of lower and lower luminosity successively peel off the main sequence. Thus the Pleiades are relatively young; stars more luminous than B6 have migrated away from the main sequence, but no others have yet left it. The Hyades and Praesepe are several times older; all stars more luminous than A1 have departed from their main sequences. In each of these two clusters we catch four red giants that relatively recently left the main sequence at A0 and are now evolving rather rapidly through a later stage of their history. Messier 67 is many billions of years old; only main-sequence stars redder and less luminous than F5 are still to be seen, along with some red giants that left the main sequence recently.

In addition to containing a segment of main-sequence stars and in some cases red giants, galactic clusters may have other sorts of objects within their boundaries. The Hyades has a number of binary stars

Fig. 17.4:2. The Double Cluster in Perseus, photographed with the 20-inch astrograph. (*Lick Observatory photograph*)

and a few white dwarfs. Young clusters contain T Tauri stars, the erratically variable objects we studied in the last chapter. The Double Cluster in Perseus is extremely young, with ultraluminous stars of $M_v = -7$, and surrounding the cluster are several red supergiant stars.

5. Stellar Associations

HERE AND THERE in the galactic disk are extended clumpings of stars of the same spectral type. The Russian astronomer V. A. Ambartsumian has called these concentrations stellar associations. In particular, nearly all O and early B stars are located in such regions; very few are found in the intervening spaces. Such groupings are the O associations. A second class are the T associations, containing T Tauri stars. In some associations T Tauri stars are found with superluminous O and B stars; in others they are not. But, as we have seen, the T Tauri variables are always found together with interstellar dust.

It has already been argued that O stars and T Tauri stars are relatively young objects, and therefore the concentration of young stars into clusterings suggests that all or most stars are born in clusters rather than in the general field. When each young star is born, it has its own small velocity relative to the center of mass of the group, and the group flies apart unless, as with a galactic cluster, the bonds of gravitation are strong enough to hold it together. The proper motions and radial velocities of several O associations have been analyzed with the striking result that the stars are expanding outward from a common center. In particular, about a dozen stars constituting the Zeta Persei association are moving outward at such a rate that they were close together some 1.3 million years ago. As in estimating the age of the Crab Nebula, the astronomer divides the present angular distance of a star from the center by the annual outward proper motion to find the starting time, and therefore presumably the birthdate of the group. The linear rate of expansion of the fastest stars in the Zeta Persei association is about 8 mi/sec, and they are now nearly 20 parsecs from the center of the group. As the millions of years go by, these young superluminous stars move farther and farther from one another in space, and at the same time each star evolves away from the main sequence and eventually ceases to be an O star or a B star. Thus it is that these unbound groups can be recognized only while they are youthful and therefore still close together and still very luminous.

6. Disintegration

WHEN A SMALL group of stars is born in a region of space with over-all dimension greater than 0.1 parsec, the escape velocity is only about 1 mi/sec. Thus if each star to begin with has even a small velocity relative to the center of mass, it will move away from the scene. The gravitational backpull of the other stars is not strong enough to decelerate it and keep it in the family. The same is true for the other stars, as shown schematically in Fig. 17.6:1(a). Each will move essentially in a straight line away from the others. At birth the positions and velocities look very random. But much later, perhaps in a few million years when each star has traveled 100 arrow lengths, the astronomer will note that the proper motions radiate from a small area of the sky, as in Fig. 17.6:1(b). He will have found an expanding stellar association, a loose-knit group that is on its way to dissolution.

When a larger group of stars is born in a limited volume of space, the escape velocity from the cluster is greater and only some of the stars have enough original velocity to escape. The rest are bound together gravitationally. Such groups are the galactic clusters, with average memberships of 100. Each individual star wanders around in the cluster under the combined gravitational pull of all the others. And every so often the star's orbit is changed as it passes its fellows more closely than usual. After 10 to 100 million years the general effect of all these wanderings and relatively close approaches is to make the clusters of stars something like a gas of atoms. When each star has had this long interval to interact gravitationally with the other ones, it is found that some stars are moving faster and some slower. But as with a gas, the stars of a cluster have a definite average velocity. More than that, the long mixing process leads to the equipartition of energy, which was defined in Chapter 11. Thus the lighter stars move faster on the average than do the heavy ones. With their greater speeds they are able to wander farther from the cluster center before being drawn back. The principle of equipartition explains why the more massive and therefore more luminous stars of the Pleiades and the Hyades are grouped compactly, whereas the fainter and less massive members are found in a much larger volume of space. Unlike the atoms of a gas, which affect each other's motions by actual collisions, the stars influence each other's motions gravitationally, even though the

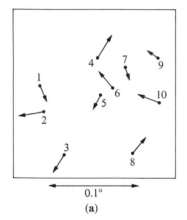

0.1°

(a)

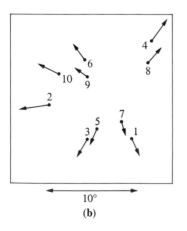

10°

(b)

Fig. 17.6:1. Schematic plot of a stellar association. **(a)** The stars are in a limited area at the time of their birth. **(b)** The same stars millions of years later.

distances between them are large. Actual direct collisions of stars must be exceedingly rare, and none has ever been witnessed.

Can galactic clusters last indefinitely or will they ultimately disband? Like stellar associations, they will disband, although more slowly and for different reasons. One disrupting effect is tidal forces. Just as the moon exerts tidal forces on different parts of the earth, so do external masses influence a cluster. One kind of tide arises from the combined gravitational pull of the stars in the nucleus of the galaxy. Galactic tides will pull stars away from any cluster of low density. To survive them a cluster in our part of space must have a number density greater than about 0.1 star per cubic parsec, and observation shows that the known galactic clusters are indeed denser than this value. A minor but interesting effect is produced by the gravitational force of field stars which pass through a cluster. For example, at any given time there are several dozen intruders moving through the central part of the Hyades, and the net result is a slight loosening of the cluster. Such stars come in on hyperbolic orbits, do their work, and then wander off again; they are not captured and brought into the fold. Another important kind of tidal disruption is caused by massive clouds of interstellar gas that occasionally pass by a cluster. In the long run they cause the cluster stars to increase their velocities and thus the cluster slowly expands. Ultimately, the speeds are high enough so that the stars escape from one another. The Hyades can survive the effect of passing clouds for perhaps 10^8 years; the denser Pleiades for about 10^9 years.

A different and internal effect limits the lifetime of a small and dense cluster. In such a compact group the stars interact more strongly and frequently with one another. At any time a small number of the stars is moving substantially faster than the average speed, and may therefore be able to escape the cluster. The situation brings to mind the escape of atoms from the upper atmosphere of a planet or satellite. As a fast-moving star leaves the cluster for good, it carries a good deal of kinetic energy with it, with the result that the energy of the cluster is reduced. The cluster then adjusts by shrinking a bit. Recall that a young star contracts gravitationally as it radiates energy into space. Remember also that the jump of an electron from an outer orbit inward is accompanied by the emission of a quantum of energy outward from the atom. In a similar way, every time a star escapes from a galactic cluster, the remainder of the system contracts. And the more the contraction the more frequently other stars escape. Finally, there is nothing left of the cluster except perhaps a multiple star.

Thus a galactic cluster disintegrates in the long run. If to begin with it is less than 1 or 2 parsecs in radius, its members occasionally acquire escape velocity and evaporate away; ultimately the cluster shrinks away to nothing. If another cluster begins its life with a radius greater than 1 or 2 parsecs, it is at the mercy of external tidal forces, especially those exerted by passing interstellar gas clouds. The cluster is stretched and grows in size, and the stars are pulled away from one another. An average galactic cluster cannot survive for more than about 10^9 years; many small and big ones disperse in much shorter intervals. It thus seems likely that the great majority of galactic clusters we see today have been born since the birth of the galaxy itself 5 or more billion years ago. This conclusion will be reinforced when we re-examine the HR diagrams of galactic clusters in Chapter 19.

7. Distribution in Space

THE VAST MAJORITY of galactic clusters and stellar associations lie near the center line of the Milky Way. Fully half of them are concentrated in a narrow belt only about 7° wide and centered on the galactic equator. A notable exception is the Coma Berenices cluster, which lies nearly at the north galactic pole. But it is only 80 parsecs away, so that its linear distance above the equatorial plane of the galaxy is not large. In three-dimensional space the system of known galactic clusters and associations occupies a coin-shaped space centered on the sun and with its face parallel to the main plane of the galaxy. Our view in the main plane is confined to distances less than about 5000 parsecs. Beyond that limit groups of stars either are hidden by interstellar dust or they blend with the general foreground and background of Milky Way stars and remain undetected. Doubtless the great majority of galactic clusters and stellar associations remain undiscovered; it is estimated that there are 10,000 or more in the whole galaxy. Our view at right angles is not limited by obscuring dust or bright starlight, and the thinning out of these objects as we move above or below the galactic plane is a genuine effect. Nearest neighbors average about 75 parsecs apart in the plane, but at 500 parsecs the number density of these objects has decreased to only 1 percent of its value in our neighborhood. In the galaxy at large the majority of galactic clusters and associations lie in an extremely flat disk. The ratio of thickness to diameter of this volume is more extreme than that for a 12-inch phonograph record.

GLOBULAR CLUSTERS

8. Census and Appearance

ABOUT 120 globular clusters have been discovered in our galaxy and a number of others probably remain hidden from our view by the dust clouds in the galactic disk. The two brightest have long been known; they are Omega Centauri and 47 Tucanae in the southern hemisphere. Each is a fourth-magnitude object with angular diameter about 1°. The brightest globular cluster in the northern hemisphere is Messier 13 in Hercules; it is barely detectable to the unaided eye as a dim and fuzzy patch. Figure 17.8:1 records its striking appearance when photographed. Hosts of individual stars are sprinkled symmetrically outside a central unresolved glow that comes from the combined light of hundreds of thousands of additional stars. Even the largest telescope is unable to distinguish all of the individual stars of a globular cluster that are within the light-gathering capacity of the instrument. In the central regions of Messier 13, for example, the stars are so crowded that nearest neighbors are much less than 1″ apart. It is of some interest to contrast this apparent thronging with the fact that the actual disks of the central stars occupy less than one-

Fig. 17.8:1. The globular cluster Messier 13 in Hercules, photographed with the 200-inch telescope. (*Mount Wilson and Palomar Observatories photograph*)

millionth of the area; all the rest is black sky. The crowding is simply a consequence of the great distances of the globular clusters and the finite size of star images on our photographs.

9. Distances, Dimensions, and Contents

MOST CLUSTERS have been examined for variable stars and many contain them. Of the 1500 known variables in globular clusters about 90 percent are RR Lyrae stars and many of the rest are Type II Cepheids. Both kinds of stars serve usefully as distance indicators. In particular, the distance of a globular cluster containing RR Lyrae stars may be found by the method described in Chapter 16, Section 7, providing the effect of interstellar dust is carefully determined. Once the distance is learned, we can then compute the linear radius from the measured angular radius and also we can calculate the integrated absolute magnitude from the observed apparent magnitude. When these data are in hand for a number of clusters, we can then go on and estimate crudely the distances of systems without RR Lyrae stars by assuming a typical value for the linear radius or for the integrated absolute magnitude. Even the nearest globular clusters are extremely remote when compared with objects we have studied thus far; they all dwell beyond the realm of the known galactic clusters. Messier 13 lies at 10,000 parsecs, and we therefore see it as it was more than 30,000 years ago. Omega Centauri and 47 Tucanae are somewhat closer, but the great majority of the 120 systems are much farther away. A few are known as far as 100,000 parsecs. The most celebrated of these ultradistant clusters is NGC 2419. Because of its great distance of 75,000 parsecs it is fondly called the intergalactic tramp, although there is no good reason to suspect that this object is truly intergalactic. It is almost certainly bound gravitationally to the galaxy, just as distant Pluto is bound to the solar system.

The deduced size of a globular cluster depends very much on how we define the size; the problem is similar to that of defining the height of the earth's atmosphere. We may define the extreme, or limiting, radius by the boundary that encloses nearly all of the cluster stars visible on a long-exposure photograph. The median limiting radius is about 25 parsecs, with a range from 10 parsecs for the smallest globular clusters to perhaps 75 parsecs for the largest. The peripheral parts are sparsely populated and contrast sharply with the high number density of stars near the center. If we define a core radius as the distance where the brightness of the image is half the central brightness, then the median core radius is only 1 or 2 parsecs.

The total number of stars in a globular cluster ranges from 10,000 to 1,000,000, with a typical figure of perhaps 300,000 stars in a bright and conspicuous cluster. Only a fraction of the individual stars can be resolved and counted: the outer stars can be tallied on long-exposure photographs and the more luminous central stars show up on short-exposure photographs. The total number of stars can be judged from the combined luminosity of the whole cluster. As an example, let us assume that the average star in a globular cluster is similar to the sun and therefore has a visual absolute magnitude of $+5$. Now the median visual absolute magnitude of globular clusters is near -8. From Chapter 13 we know that a difference of absolute magnitude of 13 corresponds to a luminosity ratio of 160,000. Therefore the joint light of 160,000 solar-type stars equals that of a typical globular cluster. A more precise estimate of total numbers requires that we know the luminosity function of the member stars so that we can judge the relative contributions of light from the few giants, the more abundant solar-type stars, and the very numerous red dwarfs.

If 300,000 stars are scattered throughout a sphere of radius 25 parsecs, the number density is 5 stars per cubic parsec, or about 50 times that of field stars in the solar neighborhood. An actual globular cluster of course displays strong central condensation, and the number density of stars in the core probably far exceeds 1000 times that in our part of space. Suppose for a moment that the figure is 1000 and that you are there. If 1000 times as many stars are packed into a given sphere, the average separation of nearest neighbors is reduced tenfold. Thus your nearest neighboring star is 10 times closer and its intensity 100 times greater. From the definition of apparent magnitude, it is brighter by 5 magnitudes. Your Alpha Centauri is now brighter than Venus; and so with all other stars around you. What is sixth magnitude here is seen as first magnitude there. Your sky is speckled with 1000 stars that are brighter than Sirius and with myriads of fainter ones—a spectacular view indeed.

10. The Stars in Globular Clusters

As WE SAW in Chapter 15, Section 3, the globular clusters are Population II objects. Their color-magnitude diagrams are generally similar to one another and fundamentally different from the local HR diagram and from those of such galactic clusters as the Pleiades and Hyades. In globular clusters fainter main-sequence stars are present, but luminous main-sequence stars are either missing or very scarce. The color-magnitude plot of Messier 3, shown in Fig. 17.10:1, reveals a *turn-off point* near magnitude 19. Stars less luminous than the turn-off point belong to the main sequence; the overwhelming majority of the brighter ones do not. Most of the luminous stars are red and constitute a conspicuous sequence, the *giant branch*, that extends upward and redward to a terminus near magnitude 13 and color index 1.5. A minority of the luminous stars belong to a *horizontal branch* that extends blueward from the giant branch. The conspicuous gap in the horizontal branch is not really devoid of stars; it is the region of the RR Lyrae variables. Of all globular clusters in the sky, Messier 3 is the richest in variables, containing 170 known RR Lyrae stars. They are all resident in the gap that is shunned by nonvariable stars.

If we assume the average apparent magnitude of the RR Lyrae stars in Messier 3 to be near zero, Fig. 17.10:1 reveals that the reddest and most luminous stars have absolute magnitude -3 and that the turn-off point occurs near absolute magnitude $+3$. We interpret the distinctive color-magnitude diagrams of globular clusters as indicating great age. Born along with its fellows 5 or more billion years ago, each star of a cluster evolves at a rate that depends on its mass. The massive and luminous blue supergiants are the first to run out of hydrogen and to evolve away from the main sequence. Later the white stars leave. Today only the fainter main-sequence stars remain; they continue to derive their radiant energy by converting hydrogen to helium. The stars now on the giant branch of the color-magnitude diagram have relatively recently evolved away from the main sequence just above the turn-off point. The stars now on the horizontal branch probably left the main sequence somewhat longer ago, spent some time as red giants, and now are slowly evolving in the horizontal direction. It appears conclusive that as one of these aging stars evolves it enters a region of instability where it is forced to swell and shrink. The RR Lyrae variables in any globular cluster are those stars that happen now to be spending a small part of their lives passing through a stage of pulsation.

Messier 3 contains a small number of main-sequence stars that are more luminous than the turn-off point; one is plotted in Fig. 17.10:1 at magnitude 18.3 and color index 0.2. The inference is that globular clusters may contain a small percentage of stars that have formed since the birth of the cluster itself; otherwise these bluish stars would long since have evolved away from the main sequence. Support for this view is provided by the appearance of star-building material in

Apparent Visual Magnitude

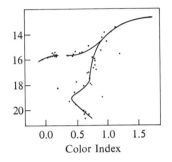

Fig. 17.10:1. Color-magnitude diagram of the globular cluster M3 as defined by about 50 stars selected at random.

some globular clusters. Here and there are patches of obscuring dust superposed on the light of the cluster stars; several can be seen in the photograph of Messier 13 (Fig. 17.8:1). Globular clusters are almost pure Population II systems and are certainly as elderly as anything we know in the galaxy. But it seems likely that even in these mature systems it is possible for stars to be born once in a while.

11. Differences Between Globular Clusters

DESPITE THE apparent resemblance of globular clusters to one another, a number of differences between them have come to light in recent years. Since the absolute magnitudes range from -5 to -10, the luminous globular clusters outshine the feeble ones a hundredfold. The masses, which are chiefly deduced from the luminosities, must also

Fig. 17.11:1. A very loose globular cluster, Abell 5, photographed with the 120-inch reflector. (*Lick Observatory photograph*)

cover a large range. The mass of Messier 3 is around 200,000 solar masses; estimates for other clusters run from less than one-tenth of this figure to more than ten times as great. The spectrum produced by the integrated light of a globular cluster generally resembles that of a star of class F or G. The whitest clusters are of late A or early F type and the spectral lines due to their metallic elements are very weak; these clusters lie far from the galactic circle. Another group of redder clusters is located in the galactic disk and particularly in the galactic nucleus. These systems have spectra of class G and their metallic lines are strong. It appears likely that the stars in globular clusters far out in the halo of the galaxy contain substantially smaller amounts of heavy elements than do those in the nuclear globular clusters. Another striking difference from one system to the next is the variable star population. Messier 3 has 170 known RR Lyrae stars, but fully half of the globular clusters that have been examined for variables contain no RR Lyrae stars at all. Presumably, they are in a different evolutionary stage from that of the systems where pulsating stars abound. Thus the globular clusters, similar at first sight, come in a variety of masses and sizes, and the chemical composition of the material from which they formed depends on where and when they were born. Although they are all very old, the ages of the globular clusters may differ significantly from one another.

12. Internal Motions

EACH STAR in a globular cluster meanders in response to the ever-changing net gravitational force exerted on it by its fellows. We have noted that a typical speed in a galactic cluster is a fraction of a mile per second. Because of the larger and more concentrated mass in a globular cluster, the average milling speed there is greater, perhaps 3 mi/sec. In 5 billion years a star moving at this average speed covers a distance of 25,000 parsecs as it wanders through and around the cluster hundreds of times. It has visited most parts of the system, and a fair percentage of its fellows have at one time or another been its nearest neighbor. It is possible that a star may be accelerated by others up to the escape velocity and leave the cluster. But this process of escape is of minor importance compared with its effect on small galactic clusters. Thus a typical globular cluster is a stable community: very few new citizens have been born, and those that have died upon running out of nuclear resources are still present in some form or other. No new citizens have moved into the community; they have simply passed through. Only a few have moved out.

In addition to their random motions, the stars in some globular clusters appear to participate in a general slow rotation. The evidence for the spin of globular clusters comes not from radial velocity measurements but from a slight flattening of the inner contours of constant brightness. We have seen before that oblateness and rotation go hand in hand; we encounter it again among the globular clusters. But the equatorial velocity of rotation cannot be many miles per second or the stars would escape en masse; the spin periods are millions of years or more.

The outer parts of some globular clusters are known to be distended; the outlying stars may be thought of as occupying a volume of space that is shaped like a football with its long axis pointing toward the galactic nucleus. This effect is caused by galactic tidal forces, just as the earth's oceans are distorted by lunar tidal forces. The dense central regions of the cluster are scarcely affected, but the outer peripheral regions are stretched. Stars that may have moved even farther from the cluster center have been removed by these tidal forces. There is thus a maximum size that a globular cluster can have. Ultradistant clusters like NGC 2419 are very large because the tidal forces exerted on them by the galactic nucleus are always small. Systems closer to the

STAR CLUSTERS AND
ASSOCIATIONS

heart of the galaxy are subjected to stronger tidal forces and their limiting radii are smaller.

The great globular clusters are subjected to the same disintegrative forces as are the smaller galactic clusters. But because of their much greater densities they are able to survive disruption for long intervals. They will last as dynamical units for times much longer than their present ages of several billions of years.

13. Distribution in Space

WHEN THE positions of the known globular clusters are plotted on a globe and the pattern is surveyed, it is strikingly clear that the points are very strongly concentrated in the constellations of Sagittarius, Scorpio, and Ophiuchus, where the Milky Way itself is brightest and broadest. The center of symmetry of the plotted points coincides with the direction of the galactic center as defined by the distribution of stars and of radio energy received at the earth. A few globular clusters lie at high galactic latitudes, and only 10 percent lie in the celestial hemisphere opposite the galactic center. Fully half of them are within 30° of the galactic center in an area that covers 7 percent of the sky; their distribution is shown in Fig. 17.13:1. The arrangement is

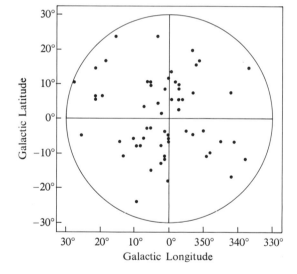

Fig. 17.13:1. Locations of the globular clusters that lie within 30° of the galactic center.

upset only by the absence of globular clusters in a thin strip 4° wide that coincides with the center line of the Milky Way. But this void is only apparent; the thin dust layer in the galactic disk obscures distant objects that are located near the equatorial plane of the galaxy. If the interstellar matter could be cleared away, we would very likely find a score or so of additional objects to add to our list of globular clusters in this area of the sky.

From the pioneering work of Herschel around 1800 until the time of World War I, studies of the distribution of stars indicated that the sun lies near the main plane of our flattened galaxy and not far from its center. In about 1917 Harlow Shapley, then at the Mount Wilson Observatory, noted that the direction of the center of the system of globular clusters was the same as that of the center of the stellar Milky Way. At the same time he estimated the distance of many individual clusters from the magnitudes of their RR Lyrae stars or by other techniques we have studied. Given the right ascension, declination, and distance of each cluster from the sun, he constructed a three-dimensional model of the whole system. Shapley's results showed that the sun is nowhere near the center of the system of globular clusters, but is instead far out toward the boundary. On the likely assumption that the center of mass of the assembly of globular clusters coincides with that of the entire galaxy, it was determined that we are located near the equatorial plane of the galaxy but far from the nucleus. Present studies suggest that the nucleus is around 9000 parsecs from the sun. Here was a major conceptual revolution: as Copernicus dethroned the earth from its centrality four centuries ago, so Shapley dethroned the sun and nearby stars from their central role. The long-standing and erroneous impression that the solar system is located near the center of our galaxy was a consequence of the interstellar dust. On a foggy day one feels at the center of the world wherever one walks; similarly, the galactic dust long lured us into believing the sun was central. Study of the globular clusters modified our view.

The globular clusters themselves are distributed quite differently from the bulk of the Milky Way stars and from the flat system of galactic clusters. They are located in an essentially spherical volume of space and their number density increases as the galactic nucleus is approached. Perhaps half of them lie within 6000 parsecs of the nucleus, and the great majority are closer to the nucleus than is the solar system. A few outlying members are found in the galactic halo as far as 100,000 parsecs from the center. Imagine plucking out at random all but 150 or 200 of the stars of a single globular cluster. What is left is a fair scale model of the system of globular clusters itself. But recall that the typical limiting radius of a single cluster of stars is only 25 parsecs, whereas that of the entire system of 150 or 200 clusters is about 100,000 parsecs.

Globular clusters are all so very far away that their proper motions are extremely small and have not been measured with precision. The radial velocities can be observed, however, and are found to be large as compared with speeds we have encountered before. For example, the clusters within 30° of the galactic center are about evenly divided between approaching systems and receding systems. If the distinction between approach and recession is ignored, the median radial velocity of these clusters is about 50 mi/sec. The slowest quarter of the group have radial motions of less than 10 mi/sec, but the radial speeds of the fastest quarter exceed 80 mi/sec. We shall defer interpreting these motions until we study the dynamics of the galaxy in Chapter 20. Remember for now that the galaxy is an enormous and massive assemblage and that all of its members exert gravitational forces on one another. It is therefore not surprising that stars and clusters move in great orbits around the galactic nucleus in response to these forces. Now, if stars like the sun are to stay near the main plane so that they are always found in a disk-shaped region, their orbits must lie in or near this plane. The situation resembles the planetary orbits in the solar system. On the other hand, if the globular clusters are to maintain a spherical distribution, their orbits must be inclined at all angles, like those of the spherical reservoir of comets in the solar system. When we observe the radial velocity of a globular cluster in one kind of orbit from a platform that is moving in another kind of galactic orbit, we are entitled to expect some rather large radial velocities. And what we anticipate is indeed found.

PROBLEMS

1. Distinguish between galactic clusters, stellar associations, and globular clusters as to spatial location in the galaxy as well as kinds and numbers of stars.

2. One star of a moving cluster lies 180° from the convergent point and has a radial velocity of −20 mi/sec. Another star of the same cluster lies 45° from the convergent point and has a proper motion of 0.15″/yr. What are the radial velocity and distance of this star?

3. Describe the studies made by Trumpler that led to an understanding that dust is distributed tenuously throughout interstellar space in our part of the galaxy.

4. (a) What is the size of a typical galactic cluster, and what is a typical total number of stars in such a system? (b) How does the number density of stars in a typical galactic cluster compare with that in the general solar neighborhood?

5. How can we tell from their color-magnitude diagrams that the Pleiades are younger than the Hyades?

6. What observational data are needed in order to show that a certain clump of O stars is an expanding association?

7. Give some of the reasons why galactic clusters ultimately disintegrate.

8. The nearest globular clusters are thousands of parsecs away. How is it possible to determine the distances of such remote objects?

9. Discuss the sizes of globular clusters.

10. Explain why the main sequence of a globular cluster is not fully populated.

11. Globular clusters closely resemble one another, but there are definite differences from one to the next. List some of them.

12. Describe the nature of the motions of stars inside a globular cluster.

13. Describe the studies made by Shapley that helped to unseat the sun from its apparent central position in the galaxy.

14. Summarize what we know about the motions of globular clusters in our galaxy.

18

MATTER

BETWEEN THE STARS

THE stars themselves occupy only a tiny fraction of galactic space: they take up only about one part in 10^{21} of the available room. What is found in the great expanses between them? We have already seen that there are planetary systems associated with at least some stars. We have learned too that some comets have been expelled from the solar system after passing too close to Jupiter; they must now be roaming through interstellar space. And surely the radiation of the sun and other stars blows small particles outward. The outbound solar wind of protons and electrons and the expanding shells around hot stars and novae add gases to the space between the stars. We are entitled to think, therefore, that interstellar space is not a complete and absolute vacuum. In this chapter we shall study the evidence for and the nature of the stuff between the stars. The subject divides rather naturally into two parts: (1) the nebulae are the more obvious concentrations of gas and dust, and many of them have been known for a long time; (2) the more tenuous and extended interstellar material has revealed itself in subtler ways and only in the present century.

THE NEBULAE

1. Names and Types

NEBULAE HAVE been discovered visually at the telescope or on photographs. Many of the prominent ones have proper names that suggest their shape or tell their locations. Among this group are the Rosette Nebula, the Dumbbell Nebula, the North America Nebula, the Coalsack, and the Orion Nebula. Because they have finite angular extent, many of these clouds of gas and dust are included in the Messier and Dreyer catalogues. Thus the Lagoon Nebula in Sagittarius is Messier 8 and NGC 6523 and the Horsehead Nebula in Orion is IC 434. Long ago the nebulae were classified according to appearance: the more regular and symmetrical structures are the *planetary nebulae*, whereas the more irregular and turbulent ones are the *diffuse nebulae*. We have already encountered the planetaries in Chapter 16 and discovered that they are gaseous shells expanding outward from hot blue stars. The diffuse nebulae are more chaotic in appearance and differ markedly from one to the next. The central parts of the Lagoon Nebula are bright and studded here and there with stars, and a

Fig. 18.1:1. Messier 8, the Lagoon Nebula in Sagittarius, photographed in red light with the 200-inch telescope. (*Mount Wilson and Palomar Observatories photograph*)

swath of blackness divides the cloud in two. The outer parts fade in surface brightness, but the nebula can be traced over an angular area larger than that of the full moon. The Veil Nebula in Cygnus consists of thin and tangled filaments and looks rather like the high cirrus clouds of the earth's atmosphere. The individual fibers are only a few seconds of arc wide but several minutes of arc long. Taken together, the intertwining fibers of the Veil seem to form an enormous shell 2' to 3' thick and nearly 2° in over-all diameter.

A more useful classification of the nebulae divides them according to the way they shine. If an extensive cloud of rarefied matter lies near a hot star, a majority of the light is emitted by the atoms in it. The spectrum of such a cloud is dominated by bright lines. These masses are the *emission nebulae*. The Orion Nebula, visible to the unaided eye as the central star of Orion's sword, is an outstanding example. All of the planetaries have emission spectra too. If another cloud of gas and dust lies near a relatively cool star, the majority of its illumination comes from starlight that has been reflected or scattered by the dust particles. The spectrum of the nebula is the same as that of the associated star

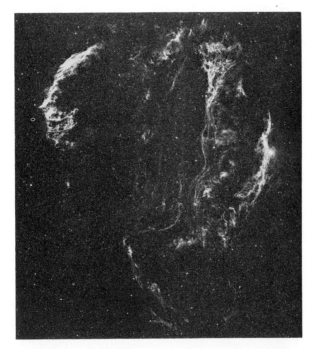

Fig. 18.1:2. The Veil Nebula in Cygnus, photographed in red light with the 48-inch Schmidt. (*Mount Wilson and Palomar Observatories photograph*)

and therefore crossed by dark lines. These clouds are the *reflection nebulae*, a celebrated member of which is the nebulosity surrounding the bright stars of the Pleiades. Finally, if another assemblage of gas and dust is not near any star, it is too feebly illuminated to be bright. Instead, the dust particles act as a very efficient filter and screen out some or most of the light from stars beyond. These structures are therefore seen as black patches and are known as the *dark nebulae.*

2. Emission Nebulae

IF ONE OR more luminous stars of spectral class O or B0 are embedded in a mass of interstellar gas and dust, the enormous number of energetic outbound photons will tend to drive the dust particles away and to ionize the atoms. Imagine, for simplicity, a star of class O with a surface temperature of 30,000°K and surrounded by a dust-free nebula of pure hydrogen. The Planck curve of the star peaks in the far ultraviolet, and approximately one-tenth of the photons emitted

MATTER BETWEEN THE
STARS

by the stellar surface have wavelengths less than 912 A and are therefore energetic enough to ionize a neutral hydrogen atom in the nebula.
Contrast this abundant supply of ultraviolet photons with the case
of the cooler sun. For every billion photons radiated by the quiet
solar surface only two or three have enough energy to ionize hydrogen.
Returning to the nebula around the O-type star, we find that much of
the hydrogen at any moment is ionized, so that the gas is a mixture of
free electrons, protons, and neutral hydrogen atoms. At any given
distance from the star we can ask the nebular gas to be in equilibrium
and have a fixed fraction of its atoms ionized and the rest neutral.
For such constancy to be maintained it is necessary that the number of
neutral atoms ionized each second in a small volume equal the number
of ion-electron pairs that recombine each second in that volume. If a
city is to have the same population from year to year, the annual number

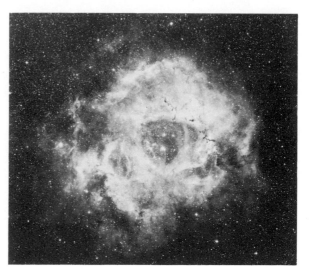

Fig. 18.2:1. The Rosette Nebula in Monoceros, photographed in red light with the 48-inch Schmidt. (*Mount Wilson and Palomar Observatories photograph*)

of births plus immigrations must equal the annual number of deaths
plus emigrations. And so it is in the nebula. Now, when a proton
captures an electron, the electron may land in the inner orbit with the
emission of a Lyman-continuum photon. But instead the electron
may cascade inward and emit a Balmer photon en route. The sum of
all such Balmer emissions toward our telescope constitutes the bright
Balmer lines we see in the spectrum of an emission nebula. The physical
processes here are the same as in nova shells and planetary nebulae;
ultraviolet radiation from the star is transformed by the surrounding
gas into radiation of longer wavelengths.

The composition of an actual emission nebula resembles that of
typical stars, and emission lines of helium and ionized nitrogen and
oxygen are seen in addition to the Balmer series. Among the most
prominent features are the so-called *forbidden lines* of O II at 3727 A
in the violet and of O III at 4959 A and 5007 A in the green. Electrons

in excited orbits usually jump downward after a pause of 10^{-8} second or so, emitting a photon as they go. But before emitting one of the green lines, a doubly ionized oxygen atom stays excited for a minute or two. And the electron of a singly ionized oxygen atom lingers in its excited orbit for a matter of hours before jumping down and producing a photon of wavelength 3727 A. These transitions are therefore not strictly forbidden by the rules of the quantum game; the average time spent in the excited state is simply much longer than usual. Such lines are not observed in the laboratory because the gas densities there are much greater and excited atoms get rid of their pent-up energies by ramming each other or the sides of their container. In an emission nebula, however, the number density is only one thousand to ten thousand per cubic centimeter, and an excited oxygen ion may move for minutes or even days before encountering anything. It is therefore likely to have time to radiate a "forbidden" photon.

Let us return for a moment to our hot and rarefied gas of pure hydrogen, part of it ionized and the rest neutral. In any volume of the gas in some short interval of time there will be some neutral atoms in which electrons jump from one orbit to another; these jumps are called *bound–bound transitions* because the electron belongs to its parent proton both before and after the jump. In addition, a certain number of neutral atoms will be ionized and lose their electrons; these ionizations are called *bound–free transitions* because the electron was attached but now is free. Similarly, there will be a number of recombinations, or *free–bound transitions*, in which the electron was free but now is circling its proton. To complete the sequence there are also *free–free transitions*. A free electron will occasionally come close to a proton and move around it in a hyperbolic orbit. During the encounter it may absorb a passing photon and fly away with increased energy or it may emit a photon and fly away with less energy. The energy differences of many of these transitions are extremely feeble, and the photons involved in them form a continuum in the radio part of the spectrum. Dozens of emission nebulae have been detected by radio telescopes operating at centimeter wavelengths, among them the Orion Nebula, the Rosette Nebula, and the Veil Nebula. They are recorded as bright patches on the radio sky; their emission is produced by free electrons passing near protons in a tenuous ionized gas.

3. Strömgren Spheres

In addition to the more obvious emission nebulae, a number of fainter clouds have been found surrounding hot stars. Because of their low surface brightness they are best detected on photographs made behind a red filter that screens out all but a narrow band of wavelengths centered on the Hα line at 6563 A. Thus the light of the strong nebular emission line is let through while most of the competing continuum light from other objects is blocked out. Many of these objects are approximately circular in outline, suggesting that the emission of light by the nebular gas is confined to a spherical zone centered on the hot blue star. Bengt Strömgren, now at the Institute for Advanced

Studies in Princeton, found in the 1930s that such an emission sphere is sharply bounded and that its radius depends chiefly on the temperature of the central star and the number density of the surrounding gas. A star of class O5 ionizes a sphere out to 1.5 parsecs if there are 10^3 hydrogen atoms per cubic centimeter. If there is only one atom per cubic centimeter, the radius of ionization is 150 parsecs. The corresponding figures for a B0 star are 0.3 parsec and 30 parsecs, and for a B5 star are 0.04 parsec and 4 parsecs.

Close to the star only a minute percentage of the atoms is neutral at any moment, but the percentage increases with distance from the star. Halfway out to the boundary of the Strömgren sphere, for example, some of the outbound Lyman-continuum photons have already been absorbed closer in. Thus the few neutral atoms at the halfway point are not ionized quite so frequently. The boundary of the sphere is a narrow transition region; the percentage of ionized atoms decreases abruptly from 90 percent to 10 percent in a distance that is only about 1 percent of the radius of the entire sphere. At the inner surface of this thin shell there are enough ultraviolet photons so that on the average a given proton manages to retain an electron partner only 10 percent of the time. At the outer surface the supply of energetic photons is much reduced because most have been absorbed while trying to cross the transition region. The smaller number of arrivals at the outer surface means that a typical proton there can hang on to an electron 90 percent of the time. A short distance beyond, virtually no photons have survived their trip from the star and the hydrogen is almost entirely neutral. To picture the process, imagine that your eyes are sensitive only to wavelengths shorter than 912 A. If you are close to the center of the sphere you see an extremely bright star. As you move away, its intensity decreases, both because of the inverse-square law and also because an increasing amount of its light has been absorbed by nebular atoms between you and the star. At the boundary it begins abruptly to get dimmer and dimmer, and just beyond the boundary it fades from view. It simply fails to reveal itself if you look for it from the solar system with this pair of eyes.

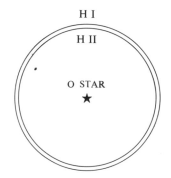

Fig. 18.3:1. The Strömgren sphere surrounding a hot star. Inside, the interstellar hydrogen is nearly all ionized; outside the thin transition region it is nearly all neutral.

4. Reflection Nebulae

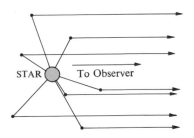

Fig. 18.4:1. Dust particles near a cool star scatter starlight in all directions. The observer sees a patch of reflected light surrounding the central star.

WHEN A STAR of spectral class B1 or later is situated in a complex of interstellar gas and dust, the stellar supply of ultraviolet photons is limited. At a black-body temperature of 20,000°K only about 1 percent of the emitted photons are capable of ionizing hydrogen, and cooler stars radiate an even smaller percentage. In such nebulae, therefore, the emission lines are either weak or entirely absent. The spectrum of the nebula is an absorption spectrum and duplicates that of the embedded star, just as the spectrum of the moon is that of sunlight. Also, the color index of the nebula is close to that of the associated star. The cloud is illuminated by reflection of starlight from the solid particles of the nebula, as illustrated in Fig. 18.4:1. Only light scattered toward the observer is indicated, but of course the starlight is scattered in all directions and the nebula is visible from any direction.

Fig. 18.4:2. The Pleiades cluster and surrounding reflection nebulosity. (*Lick Observatory photograph*)

5. Dark Nebulae

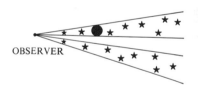

Fig. 18.5:1. The dusty region scatters light from distant stars that would otherwise reach the observer; the result is a dark nebula.

HERE AND THERE along the Milky Way are dark areas, some of them conspicuous to the unaided eye. Long ago it was thought that these black patches might actually be regions devoid of stars. But it is clearly inconceivable that a large number of long, narrow, empty cones should elect to point toward the sun. The dark regions are simply nebulae whose dust particles block or dim the light of stars beyond, as shown in Fig. 18.5:1. If the nebula is completely opaque, no stars beyond are visible, while in the adjacent area many are seen. In actuality, no dark nebula is completely opaque; the less dense ones scatter perhaps 50 percent of the light passing through, whereas the more compact ones may filter out all but about 1 percent. For a given opacity a relatively nearby dark nebula is more noticeable than a distant one because it obscures the light of all but a few of the nearer stars. Many stars lie in front of the more distant counterpart.

A good look at the summer Milky Way will reveal a number of dark areas. Most striking is the Great Rift which divides the Milky Way in two from Scorpio to Aquila and around to Cygnus. This great flattened complex of dust is upwards of 100 parsecs away and dims light passing through it by about one magnitude. At the other extreme are the tiny black wisps and globules. They are of such small angular diameter that they are seen only when highlighted against bright nebulosity behind them. The Lagoon Nebula is especially rich in these small dark features. The smallest globules have radii of about 5000 a.u. and are extremely opaque. It has been suggested that dark globules may be stars in the making. The radiation pressure of surrounding starlight squeezes such a dusty sphere together and the mutual gravitational pull of its parts on one another may complete the job of contracting the globe into a star.

6. Distances and Dimensions

THE DISTANCE to a bright nebula is the same as that of its associated star, and we can therefore employ methods we have studied before. The Pleiades nebulosity is thus at 130 parsecs, as deduced from the HR diagram of the cluster stars. The spectral types and estimated luminosities of the O and B stars in the Orion Nebula yield a distance of 400 or 500 parsecs. When the distances are known and the angular sizes are measured, we can then compute the linear radii of nebulae. The bright central part of the Orion emission nebula has a radius of about 3 parsecs, which is consistent with the Strömgren theory. The Pleiades reflection nebula also has an over-all radius of 2 to 3 parsecs, whereas the brighter individual knots surrounding the more luminous individual stars have typical radii of only about 0.3 parsec. In general, the fainter the illuminating star the smaller the resultant nebulosity. The mass of a nebula can be estimated roughly. For example, a sphere of radius 3 parsecs that contains 1000 hydrogen atoms per cubic centimeter has a mass of about 3000 suns. The extreme tenuity of the gas is more than made up by the vast volume occupied.

A new problem is posed when we try to find the distance of a dark nebula. To illustrate the method, let us imagine an oversimplified situation in which stars are distributed uniformly in space and are all of the same luminosity. Let us say that each star is like the sun, with absolute magnitude 5. On a photograph of the clear part of the sky shown in Fig. 18.5:1 we notice that stars of all apparent magnitudes are present in the clear comparison area. But in the direction of the dark nebula we find a conspicuous gap: we see stars of all apparent magnitudes brighter than 10 and fainter than 12. None lies in the magnitude range between 10 and 12. Our conclusions are twofold. (1) The fainter and thus more distant stars are dimmed by 2 magnitudes because of the nebula. Recall that 2 magnitudes is a factor of 6 in intensity, and so only about one photon in 6 is able to penetrate the cloud; all the rest are scattered when they hit a dust particle. (2) The most distant unobscured stars are of magnitude 10. With $M = 5$ and $m = 10$ we can calculate the distance of the dark nebula to be 100 parsecs.

In practice the procedure is by no means so clear-cut, and the chief difficulty is the enormous variation in stellar luminosities. Given a dark nebula at 100 parsecs with an obscuring power of 2 magnitudes, it is clear that some feeble stars in front of the nebula will be recorded in the magnitude range between 10 and 12. So too will some luminous stars beyond the nebula. The effect one is looking for is badly smeared out, and it is therefore extraordinarily hard to determine a reliable distance.

It is well to remember that a dark nebula, like a sunspot, is not completely black. Some of the radiation entering the cloud is scattered by dust particles one or more times, but it finally re-emerges in random directions. The greater the obscuring power of the nebula the more scattered starlight must come out. An isolated dark nebula that dims distant stars by 2 magnitudes is actually a feeble patch of light with a surface brightness comparable to that of the winter Milky Way or of our own gegenschein. What makes such a cloud conspicuous, however, is not its pale surface brightness but the missing background stars whose light cannot pass through the dust.

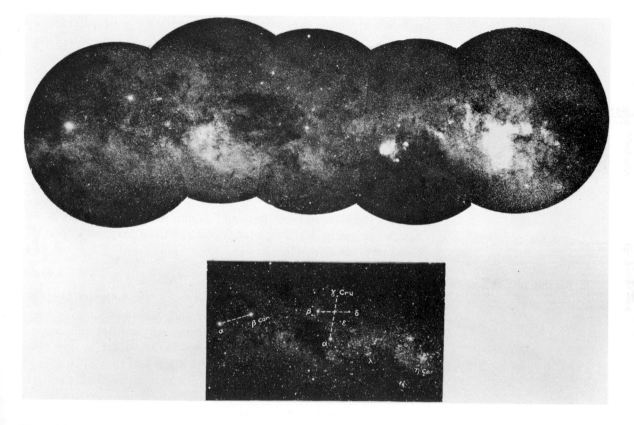

Fig. 18.6:1. The Coalsack in the Southern Cross, astride the Milky Way. The lower picture serves as a key to the upper mosaic of five photographs taken with an 8-inch Schmidt. Alpha and Beta Centauri are at the left, the nebula near Eta Carinae at the right, and the stars of the Cross near the center. (*Mount Stromlo Observatory, Australia*)

The dark nebulae whose distances have been estimated lie between 60 parsecs and 800 parsecs from the sun. More distant ones doubtless exist but are not prominent because of the overlying foreground stars. The sizes of these objects range from the smallest known globules with radii of a few thousand astronomical units to giant cloud complexes with dimensions exceeding 100 parsecs. The Coalsack, prominent in the Southern Cross, is estimated to be about 150 parsecs away and to have a radius of some 4 parsecs. It dims background light by about 1.5 magnitudes, and therefore one photon in every 4 passes through the Coalsack and 3 out of every 4 are scattered. Very crudely, therefore, we can estimate that three-fourths of the physical area of the nebula is blocked by solid particles. This estimate could be justified if the Coalsack contained bodies either the size of golf balls about 100 miles apart or the size of small smokelike particles with diameters of about 10^{-5} cm and with about 40 feet between nearest neighbors. If the former were true, the mass of the Coalsack would be several hundreds of thousands of times that of the sun. If smokelike particles are the case, the nebular mass is only a few times that of the sun. We shall see presently that the interstellar dust particles are indeed very small, with diameters of about 10^{-5} cm and perhaps even smaller.

7. Spatial Distribution

WHEN THE planetaries are excluded, the known nebulae are Population I objects and are strongly confined to the galactic plane. Half of the reflection nebulae are within 9° of the galactic circle, half of the dark nebulae within 6°, and half of the emission nebulae within 2°. Because the emission clouds are associated with hot young stars or star clusters, it is clear that youthful objects inhabit a broad, thin, disk-shaped region of the galaxy that coincides with its plane of symmetry. Because the solar system, although 5 billion years old, happens in our time to be nearly in the equatorial plane of the galaxy, we witness the chaos of youth fairly close at hand.

8. Kinship of Gas and Dust

THUS FAR WE have dealt separately with the different kinds of nebulae. Actually, however, the bright and dark nebulae may fairly be considered a single group because it is clear that gas and dust go together in most parts of interstellar space. There are several clues to this kinship. In dark nebulae the gas is not hot enough to emit at optical wavelengths, but its presence is known, as we shall soon see, by studies of neutral interstellar hydrogen with radio telescopes. In some bright nebulae where the central stars are of spectral type B0 or B1, both emission lines from the gas and the absorption spectrum of the dust can be seen. The close association of gas atoms and dust particles can also be inferred from less direct evidence. For one thing, a dust grain must consist of a combination of atoms, and the interstellar gas is an obvious source. The grain probably grows in size as gas atoms ram it and stick to it. Thus for a solid particle to grow there must be gas present in the same region. For another thing, if a large cloud of pure gas should collide with a large cloud of pure dust at a speed of several miles per second, each would be slowed down by the collisions of atoms with dust particles. The two would unite and move together from then on. Thus it is thought that the gas and dust are well mixed except in those parts of space near hot stars. If a small solid particle is placed in a Strömgren sphere, the strong radiation of the central star pushes it outward. Elsewhere the gas and dust coexist.

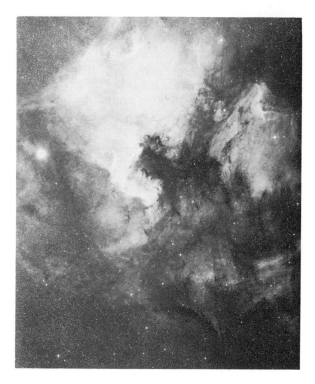

Fig. 18.8:1. The North America Nebula in Cygnus, photographed with the 48-inch Schmidt. (*Mount Wilson and Palomar Observatories photograph*; *Copyright National Geographic Society—Palomar Observatory Sky Survey*)

Present evidence suggests that only a minor percentage of interstellar atoms belong to a dust particle. The overwhelming majority wander singly as members of the tenuous gas. Each single solid particle is constructed of many atoms bonded together, possibly a billion of them.

Fig. 18.8:2. The Horsehead Nebula in Orion, photographed in red light with the 200-inch telescope. (*Mount Wilson and Palomar Observatories photograph*)

But these concentrations of atoms in single particles are far more than offset by the great distances between neighboring particles. Far from hot stars the kinetic temperature of the interstellar gas is only about 100°K and the average speed of the hydrogen atoms is 1 mi/sec. Since we know that kinetic energy is shared equally by the different types of members, it is clear that the more massive solid particles move much more slowly. Dust particles with masses a billion times that of a hydrogen atom move in random directions at an average speed of only 2 or 3 miles a day. They are the only astronomical objects that we can keep pace with.

THE TENUOUS INTERSTELLAR MATTER

9. Gas and Interstellar Lines

As WE HAVE seen, the nebulae are visible on photographs and their discovery is no serious problem. But the more rarefied material that pervades the central layer of our galaxy is not at all obvious. Both gas and dust have been found in these internebular regions, however, and we shall study the gaseous component first.

The earliest evidence for a general low-density interstellar gas was found in 1904 in the spectrum of Delta Orionis, the westernmost star of Orion's belt. This object is a single-line spectroscopic binary as well as an eclipsing binary, and the absorption lines oscillate with a period of 5.7 days. A striking exception is the dark line at 3934 A arising from ionized calcium. It is stationary and does not share the orbital motion. This line cannot, therefore, be produced in the atmosphere of the Delta Orionis pair, but rather must originate in an intervening interstellar medium. Now, imagine a distant single blue star. If the temperature is much above 10,000°K, the stellar atmosphere is too hot to have any appreciable number of neutral or singly ionized calcium atoms. Virtually all the calcium atoms are multi-ionized. And yet a look at the spectrum of this star reveals that it is crossed by a pair of dark lines at 3934 A and 3968 A due to ionized calcium. They have no business being there unless they too are produced in a cool and rarefied gas between the star and the spectrograph. The situation is shown in Fig. 18.9:1, enormously exaggerated, with a few singly ionized and unexcited calcium atoms in the long narrow cone between the star and the observer. Each absorbs a photon from the star and the outer electron jumps to an excited orbit. After 10^{-8} second the electron spontaneously jumps down again and a photon of the same wavelength is emitted in a random direction. Each ion then rests for a long time until another photon comes along and the process is repeated. The dark interstellar line on a spectrogram represents all the continuum light from the star that fails to reach us during our time exposure because of absorption by singly ionized calcium atoms in interstellar space.

Studies of spectroscopic binaries and more particularly of single hot stars have yielded considerable information on the nature and composition of the interstellar gas. Cool stars are not suitable for study because their own hosts of absorption lines entirely mask the weak effects of

Fig. 18.9:1. Interstellar atoms between a star and the observer may absorb photons proceeding from the star; interstellar absorption lines are then imprinted on the spectrum of the star.

the interstellar atoms. The known interstellar lines arise from neutral sodium, neutral potassium, both neutral and ionized calcium, ionized titanium, and neutral iron. Also present are molecules of CH, CH$^+$, and CN, along with several unidentified absorption bands. The relative abundance of the known interstellar atoms resembles that in the stars, and the temptation is therefore strong to look for interstellar hydrogen. From our stellar studies we can guess that there may be 1000 atoms of hydrogen to every atom of the heavy elements in interstellar space. A search for interstellar absorption lines of the Balmer series shows nothing, however, and for a very good reason. The electron of a neutral hydrogen atom in cool interstellar space spends nearly all of its time in the innermost orbit and thus can only absorb Lyman photons. A passing Balmer photon can be absorbed by a neutral hydrogen atom only if it arrives during that infinitesimal fraction of the time that the electron spends in the second orbit. The same situation prevails for the heavier atoms; all of the known interstellar absorption lines represent upward jumps from the innermost unexcited orbit.

Comparison of the blackness of the singly ionized calcium lines at 3934 A and 3968 A with that of the neutral calcium line at 4227 A indicates that in any volume of interstellar space there are about 100 singly ionized calcium atoms for every neutral one. At first it seems astonishing that a calcium atom spends only a minute fraction of its time with its outer electron in an excited orbit and yet spends all but about 1 percent of its time as an ion. After all, it takes less energy to excite an atom than to ionize it. The essential clue is the extreme rarity of the gas. Imagine a single neutral calcium atom far from any star. Surrounding it is the celestial sphere, looking much as we see the sky at night. After a time an ultraviolet photon from one of the stars and with wavelength less than 2000 A strikes the atom and ionizes it. Because of the rarity of the surrounding gas the ion must wait a long time before it can find a free electron to capture and re-establish its neutrality. On the average a single calcium atom spends 100 times as much of its life singly ionized as it does neutral. During its ionized hours it may of course absorb a stellar photon of wavelength 3934 A or 3968 A and help produce the interstellar lines we record, and during its neutrality it may absorb a 4227 A photon and assist in producing the interstellar line of neutral calcium.

The interstellar lines in the spectra of many stars are multiple. Each line is split into two or more narrow lines. These separations are caused by the Doppler effect, and the multiplicity is produced by several gas clouds moving with different radial velocities, as shown in Fig. 18.9:2. Cloud A produces a small red shift, B a larger red shift, and C an appreciable violet shift. The picture of the tenuous interstellar material emerges, then, not as a smooth and homogeneous medium but as a gathering into lumps. Instead of resembling a smooth sheet of cirrostratus cloud, the distribution is similar to the cotton-like cumulus of a fair summer afternoon. The radial velocity differences indicate that the gas clouds have random velocities, much like the atoms of a gas or the stars near the sun. The average random radial

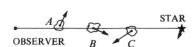

Fig. 18.9:2. Interstellar lines are often multiple because of the different radial velocities of gas clouds lying between the star and the observer.

velocity is about 5 mi/sec and the average random space velocity is twice as great, or 10 mi/sec. Studies of certain very distant blue stars reveal multiple interstellar lines with a much larger spread in radial velocity. These results do not imply that distant gas clouds have faster

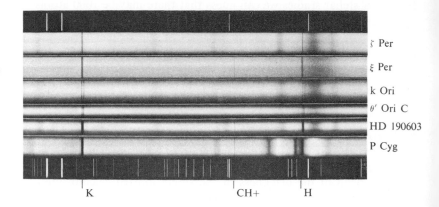

Fig. 18.9:3. Interstellar lines in the spectra of several stars. Marked are the H and K lines of ionized calcium and a line between them due to CH⁺ Note the multiple radial velocities in some of the lines. (*Lick Observatory photographs*)

random motions, but rather that their motions reflect the rotation of the entire galaxy. We shall return to this matter in Chapter 20 when we study the over-all nature of our Milky Way system.

10. Neutral Hydrogen and Radio Studies

IN THE EARLY decades of this century it was tantalizing to guess at the large abundance of hydrogen in interstellar space but to have no way of observing interstellar Lyman lines through our opaque atmosphere. A major breakthrough occurred in 1945 when the Dutch astronomer H. C. Van de Hulst suggested that interstellar neutral hydrogen might be observed with a radio telescope tuned to 21 cm. The prediction was realized in 1951 when Milky Way radiation at this wavelength was discovered at Harvard University and confirmed some weeks later in both Holland and Australia.

This type of radiation is rather different from the kinds we have met before. Jumps of electrons between orbits and in and out of atoms create or absorb photons that are largely in the visual part of the spectrum. But transitions involving much lower energies also occur, and the associated photons are therefore of much lower frequency or longer wavelength. Picture a single neutral hydrogen atom in interstellar space, with its electron circling in the inner unexcited orbit. As with the sun–earth system, there is not only orbital motion but also axial rotation of the two bodies. The electron spins and so does the proton. By the rules of quantum theory the spins can only be parallel or antiparallel, as shown in Fig. 18.10:1. In the upper atom the spins are parallel and the angular momentum and energy of the proton–electron pair are slightly greater than for the lower antiparallel pair. The

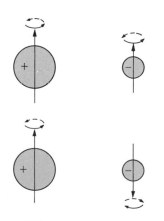

Fig. 18.10:1. In the upper neutral hydrogen atom the spins of proton and electron are parallel; in the lower atom they are antiparallel.

difference in energy of the two can be converted to frequency by the Planck formula, $E = hf$, and is 1420 megacycles per second, somewhat above the frequencies employed by UHF television, which range from 470 mc/sec to 890 mc/sec. The frequency of 1420 mc/sec is a wavelength of 21 cm, some 400,000 times greater than that of green light. Thus the energy difference between parallel and antiparallel spins is only about 1/400,000 as great as that involved in electron jumps that produce photons at visual wavelengths.

Suppose our neutral hydrogen atom is in the excited state with the electron and proton spinning parallel to each other. The electron may spontaneously flip its spin with the emission of a 21-cm photon in some random direction. But the spontaneity is of an entirely different order than with downward orbital jumps that produce Balmer emission lines or forbidden oxygen lines. Recall that the hydrogen electron lingers in an outer orbit for only about 10^{-8} second, whereas the green and violet nebular photons of forbidden oxygen are produced after electrons linger in their excited states for minutes or hours. But the average time our electron spends spinning parallel to its proton is 11 million years before it "spontaneously" reverses and emits a quantum of 21-cm radio radiation. Leisurely as this process may seem, it is clear that if we start with all atoms having parallel spins and then wait 100 million years there will be no excited atoms left to emit 21-cm photons. For equilibrium we need a competing process that lifts atoms into the parallel state at the same rate that others enter the antiparallel state. One possibility is that a hydrogen atom may absorb a Lyman photon from a star, jump upward, and then cascade downward to the first orbit but with parallel spin. The dominant process, however, occurs during atomic collisions. Every 25 years or so a hydrogen atom passes close enough to another so that the pair may be thought of as an exceedingly temporary hydrogen molecule. During such an encounter the electron spins are sometimes unchanged and sometimes reversed. In a large number of such collisions, flips up to the parallel state happen three times as frequently as flops down to the antiparallel state. Such encounters ensure that there are always enough hydrogen atoms in the more energetic state that will radiate 21-cm photons. At any one time very nearly three-quarters of the atoms are in the parallel state and one-quarter in the antiparallel state. A given hydrogen atom averages about 150 years in the parallel state and 50 years in the antiparallel state. In one visit out of every 70,000 or so to the upper state the hydrogen atom will emit a photon of frequency 1420 mc/sec.

Radio surveys of the 21-cm sky have indicated that the interstellar neutral hydrogen is at a temperature of about 100°K and that the average number density in our part of galactic space is about one hydrogen atom per cubic centimeter. Combining these and other studies, astronomers have found that the relative abundance of interstellar atoms resembles that in stars, with the overwhelming majority being hydrogen. In mass the dust particles contribute only a small fraction of the interstellar matter, perhaps 1 percent. The gas contributes the great majority, with hydrogen accounting for most of it.

In one cubic parsec there are 3×10^{55} cubic centimeters, and with one hydrogen atom in each the combined mass in a cubic parsec is 5×10^{31} grams, or about $\frac{1}{40}$ of the sun's mass. The known stars contribute on the average about $\frac{1}{20}$ of the sun's mass to each cubic parsec. Roughly, then, in our part of the galaxy the amount of matter between stars is comparable with that inside stars.

Radio studies confirm the cloudy structure of the interstellar matter. Inside a cloud there are perhaps 10 atoms per cubic centimeter, whereas outside there are only 1 percent as many. The clouds occupy about 10 percent of space in our part of the galaxy, and a typical cloud has a radius of several parsecs and a mass several hundred times that of the sun. The random velocities are about 10 mi/sec and the clouds spend roughly 10 percent of their time interpenetrating each other.

The 21-cm line is not the only one found by radio telescopes. In 1963 a pair of lines at 1665 and 1667 mc/sec was first detected. They are produced by OH molecules in interstellar space, and preliminary indications are that there is one OH molecule for every 10^7 or 10^8 hydrogen atoms between the stars. The study of such spectral lines at radio frequencies has made it possible to study Doppler shifts of photons that have been emitted from remote parts of the galaxy, and we shall deal with this important work in Chapter 20.

11. Dust, Star Clusters, and Galaxies

THE TENUOUS interstellar gas reveals itself by interstellar spectral lines at visual wavelengths and by radio astronomical studies. The pervasive interstellar dust was first identified, as we learned in the last chapter, through a comparison of the distances of galactic clusters as gauged by their angular diameters and as gauged by their HR diagrams. Another major piece of evidence for obscuring matter between the stars is the apparent absence of external galaxies along the Milky Way. The 1932 survey of bright galaxies by Shapley and Miss Ames at the Harvard Observatory lists more than 1200 galaxies brighter than thirteenth magnitude. And not one of these 1200 distant systems lies within 10° of the galactic circle. Since this belt contains 17 percent of the entire sky, we are therefore entitled to expect about 200 bright galaxies in it. Not one is found. This vacancy is not a result of chance; the reason for it must be a local one arising from a thin layer of obscuring material in the equatorial plane of our own galaxy. The complete absence of bright galaxies indicates that light traversing the galactic plane is dimmed by many magnitudes.

12. Dust and Star Counts

THE EXISTENCE of obscuring dust particles may also be inferred from star counts. Let us suppose for a moment that all stars are equally luminous and uniformly spread throughout transparent space. Next we count all the stars in the sky brighter than visual magnitude 10 and find that there are 340,000 such stars. Now let us ask how many stars in the whole sky are brighter than visual magnitude 15 *if* our assumptions are correct. This estimate will include all the 340,000 brightest plus many fainter and thus more distant stars. How many should we expect? A star of magnitude 15 delivers only $\frac{1}{100}$ as much radiation to us as does a star of magnitude 10. The inverse-square law tells us that the fainter star must be 10 times as far as the brighter if both have the same absolute magnitude. Our survey to fifteenth magnitude therefore reaches 10 times as far into space and encompasses a volume 1000 times as great. We thus anticipate finding 1000 times as many stars, or 340,000,000, brighter than $m_v = 15$. The actual number is only 37,000,000, scarcely over 10 percent of our expectation. What is the matter? One or more of the following assumptions: (1) We know that not all stars are equally luminous. This effect is disastrous when we try to estimate the distance of a dark nebula, but here it does not affect our argument very much. (2) The stars may thin out with distance from the sun. And it is true that they do thin out at right angles to the equatorial plane of the galaxy. But since most stars are in or near the Milky Way, we have to conclude somewhat implausibly that our sun is in a favored region where the number density of stars is high. (3) Space is transparent. But suppose it is not. Then a star that would be of magnitude 15 if space were clear is actually recorded as fainter and fails to be included in our survey. The observed numbers are less than the expected ones and the discrepancies get worse the fainter and further we go. Our third assumption turns out to be false, and we infer that dust particles exist, tenuously spread, in and near the plane of our galaxy.

Our argument is too simple, and what is done in practice is to work with photographs of a limited area of the sky, let us say in Cygnus. The analysis yields the number of stars per square degree brighter than magnitude 8, 9, 10, and so on, in this particular direction. If our assumptions were all justified, the ratio of increase in numbers should be the fifth root of 1000, or 3.98, for every magnitude. Actually, at an average point in the Milky Way the observed ratio of increase is only about 2.8 per magnitude for stars brighter than tenth magnitude and is down to 1.8 near magnitude 20.

The results of star counts suggest that starlight traversing the galactic plane is dimmed on the average by about one magnitude per 1000 parsecs of travel. This figure refers to blue-violet light and is only an over-all average; the variations are wide, and detailed results from various areas indicate that the tenuous dust is not a smooth layer but is lumped into clouds. Since gas and dust go together, we may assume that the dust clouds and gas clouds are for the most part one and the same. These clouds have lower densities than do the more obvious bright and dark nebulae, but they have substantially higher densities than do the intercloud regions. The light from a distant star passes through many clouds before reaching us. If the star is 5000 parsecs away and in the galactic plane, its light may be dimmed by roughly 5 magnitudes before reaching us. Thus we record only one out of each 100 photons it tries to send us; the other 99 are scattered by intervening dust. The light from a distant galaxy in or near the extended plane of the Milky Way must penetrate several thousand parsecs of dust at the very least. Little wonder that we do not see bright galaxies close to the galactic circle.

13. Dust and Reddening

THE SPECTRUM of a distant star in the Milky Way indicates, let us say, that it is of class B0; its lines of neutral helium are especially prominent. When its color index is measured, however, it is found to be $+0.3$, approximately the color of a cooler star of class F5. The B0 spectrum of the star indicates that it is radiating somewhat like a black body at a temperature of $22,000°K$. Its color index should be about -0.4 instead of $+0.3$. What is the trouble? Again the interstellar dust is to blame. The light is indeed bluish on leaving the star, but the interstellar matter scatters short-wave light more efficiently than long-wave light, and therefore more of the longer wavelengths get through. The star thus looks redder than it is, like the setting sun. The dust reddens not only blue stars but objects of all spectral types. The upper curve of Fig. 18.13:1 shows the Planck curve of a solar-type star whose surface temperature is $6000°K$. When the same star is put about 1000 parsecs away on the galactic circle, its observed Planck curve resembles the lower curve. The blue light is dimmed by about one magnitude and is thus only 40 percent as intense, while the red light is dimmed less. The *color excess* of a star, CE, is its observed color index minus the normal color index for a star of its spectral type. For the B0 object we have

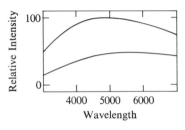

Fig. 18.13:1. The upper curve shows the Planck radiation of a star with surface temperature $6000°K$. The lower curve shows how the upper one is distorted and reddened when the light traverses 1000 parsecs of interstellar dust.

$$CE = \text{observed } CI \text{ minus normal } CI = +0.3 - (-0.4) = +0.7.$$

The color excess of a star can be used to find the total dimming of light between the star and the earth and it is proportional to the amount of dust in the long cone.

Something can be deduced about the nature of the interstellar obscuring material from the observed dependence of scattering on wavelength. The shorter their wavelength the greater the proportion of photons scattered by the interstellar particles. This result means that the scattering particles cannot be large, because a collection of large objects, such as a flock of birds, blocks light of all wavelengths equally. The particles must instead be of dimensions about the wavelength of visual light and perhaps smaller. But they cannot be as small as atoms or molecules, which scatter short-wave light with extreme efficiency and cause the intense blue of our daylight sky. Also, to produce the observed amount of scattering in interstellar space would require gas many thousands or even millions of times as dense as the observed number density of one atom per cubic centimeter. It is likely, then, that the particles have intermediate diameters of 10^{-5} cm or smaller. It is not yet determined whether they are tiny bits of metal such as iron or whether they are small crystals of ices such as water, ammonia, and methane.

In the figure: Relative Intensity (vertical axis) with values 0 and 100; Wavelength (horizontal axis) with values 4000, 5000, 6000.

14. Polarized Starlight

WHEN WE CONCEIVE of light as a wave phenomenon, we recall that radiant energy is transported from one place to another by transverse waves. If a rope is tied at one end and shaken up and down at the other, energy is transported along the rope at a certain rate, while a knot in the rope moves up and down. If the rope is then shaken sidewise with the same frequency and vigor, energy is transported along it at the same rate. The only difference between the two operations is the orientation of the plane containing the shaking rope: in the first case it is vertical and in the second it is horizontal. The *polarization* of the two waves is different. Light waves from such natural sources as stars are randomly polarized; a given wavelet may be vibrating back and forth in any plane that contains the star and the observer. If a polaroid filter is placed in front of the observer, however, only those wavelets vibrating in one particular plane are allowed to pass through.

When the light from a typical star is collected by a telescope and passed through a polaroid filter before impinging on a photoelectric cell, it is found that the intensity of the recorded light is the same no matter how the polaroid filter is rotated. Thus as many arriving waves are vibrating in one plane as in any other. For certain stars, however, the intensity varies as the filter is turned. The light of these stars is therefore partially polarized. And it is just these stars that also have large color excesses. The correlation of reddening and polarization indicates therefore that the dust is responsible for both. In particular, the interstellar particles not only scatter a part of the oncoming light, the blue more than the red, but they also modify the light waves that get through to us by partially polarizing them. Now if the dust particles were spherical, or even if they were elongated but randomly oriented in space, they could not polarize light passing through a cloud of them. To unrandomize natural starlight the particles must be elongated in shape and as a group they must be more or less aligned with one another, something like a school of minnows or like iron filings near a magnet. Polarization studies of stars in different parts of the Milky Way have shown that the partial alignment of particles is not confined to any one localized region, but occurs rather generally in the galactic plane. It appears certain that the elongated particles are aligned by forces exerted on them by weak but extensive magnetic fields that pervade interstellar space. The observation of polarization in the light of dust-reddened stars thus implies indirectly that our galaxy possesses a general magnetic field.

A SUMMARY

15. Gas, Dust, and Our Galaxy

IN THIS CHAPTER we have surveyed the astronomer's knowledge of the interstellar matter in our part of the galaxy. The material is confined rather strongly to a thin layer in the galactic plane. In these regions it is grouped into the denser nebulae that can be photographed directly and into the less dense clouds that are revealed only by more subtle studies. This turbulent structure is apparently superposed on a more rarefied general medium. In this tenuous substratum the number density of hydrogen atoms is perhaps 0.1 per cubic centimeter, whereas in the clouds it may be a hundred times as great, and in the nebulae 1,000 or 10,000 per cubic centimeter. Other atoms are present in lesser abundance, following roughly the chemical composition of stars. One atom in a hundred or a thousand or more is part of a small solid grain of dust that is elongated and has a diameter of 10^{-5} cm or less. In most parts of space the gas and dust are found together; only in the hot H II regions surrounding blue stars is it likely that the interstellar matter is completely gaseous.

The average smoothed-out interstellar stuff in our neighborhood contains one hydrogen atom per cubic centimeter and accounts for perhaps one-third of the total mass, stellar plus interstellar, in any large volume of space. The average separation of nearest-neighboring hydrogen atoms is about $\frac{1}{4}$ inch, of helium atoms $\frac{1}{2}$ inch, of heavy atoms 2 to 3 inches. Neighboring dust particles are about 200 feet apart if they are chiefly 10^{-5} cm in diameter. If it is discovered in the future that they are smaller, then they would have to be somewhat more neighborly to produce the average obscuration we measure.

When we study our galaxy as a whole in Chapter 20, we shall find that much of our knowledge of its structure and motions comes from investigations of the interstellar matter. Of great interest are surveys of the locations of blue supergiants and associated Strömgren spheres that help to delineate the spiral arms of the galaxy. Studies of radio radiation at 21 cm and other wavelengths are extending our knowledge of the spiral structure and of the more tenuous intervening regions because the material of interstellar space is largely transparent to radio waves. But before we examine our home galaxy as an entity, we must pull together our knowledge of the sun, the stars, clusters, and interstellar matter and try to see what we can understand of the birth, growth, and death of the stars.

PROBLEMS

1. Classify the types of nebulae according to the processes by which they shine.

2. (a) What is meant by a forbidden line? (b) Give three examples of forbidden lines that may be seen in the spectrum of an emission nebula.

3. (a) Describe the physical conditions inside and immediately outside a Strömgren sphere. (b) Give examples of the sizes of such spheres for various characteristics of the parent star and the surrounding interstellar matter.

4. Explain why, when each one of the following is increased separately, you would expect the apparent magnitude of a reflection nebula as seen from the earth to become larger or smaller: distance from earth, luminosity of parent star, number density of surrounding interstellar particles, albedo of surrounding interstellar particles, radius of the nebula.

5. Light from stars behind a dark nebula is dimmed by 3 magnitudes. What fraction of incident light gets straight through the nebula?

6. Why do astronomers believe that gas and dust are for the most part located together in the same places in the galaxy?

7. List the kinds of evidence that point to the existence of interstellar gas.

8. Although the temperature of interstellar matter is only about $100°K$, the great majority of interstellar calcium is ionized. Why?

9. How is the 21-cm line produced?

10. Approximately what percentage of the total matter per cubic parsec in our part of the galaxy is (a) inside stars, (b) in interstellar space, (c) in the form of interstellar dust?

11. List the kinds of evidence that point to the existence of interstellar dust.

12. Suppose that star counts in a certain area of the sky indicate that the ratio of increase of star numbers per magnitude is greater than 3.98. What are your conclusions about conditions in that particular direction?

13. The spectrum of a star indicates that it is of class A0; photoelectric observations indicate that for this star $m_p = 9.4$ and $m_v = 8.8$. What is the color excess of the star, and what does this finite color excess mean?

14. How do we know that a weak magnetic field pervades interstellar space?

19

THE STARS: EVOLUTION

W HEN we studied the sun and its interior, we treated it as a gaseous body in equilibrium, with its mass and size and energy output as fixed quantities. We also measured or deduced the masses, radii, and luminosities of other stable stars, recording the results as though each of these quantities were a constant quantity as time flows by. This implicit assumption of constancy is indeed a valid one to make for normal stars and for short enough intervals of time. The radius of Sirius will be the same next Wednesday as it is today; the absolute magnitude of Arcturus will not be different a decade from now; the mass of the sun will not be measurably less a thousand years hence. But in the long run, over millions or billions of years, the changes in stars may be profound. An acquaintance seen today and again tomorrow usually looks the same on each occasion, but 30 years from now he is likely to look rather different. Our study in this chapter focuses on the long-range evolution of the stars: birth, growth, and death. By ordinary standards most evolutionary processes in stars are exceedingly slow, and it would be a dull business for an ultra-long-lived astronomer to sit around and wait for Vega to become a red giant star. In studies of stellar evolution we do not sit and wait. Instead we bring together a host of physical ideas and such results of astronomical observation as the HR diagrams of star clusters; we then proceed to deduce indirectly something of the life a star has had in the past and will have in the future. The deductions that do not accord with the observed facts are discarded;

those that meet the test are accepted—unless new and better data come along that overthrow them.

The history of theories of stellar evolution is a confused one, and it is only recently that understanding has increased at a sharp rate. Advance had to await the recognition a few decades ago that the major energy source of the stars is the atom. In particular, the breath-taking pace of recent years owes much to current developments in nuclear physics and to the emergence of high-speed computers that can cope with the complex calculations required before theory can be compared with observation. Stellar evolution is one of the major themes of research astronomy at the present time, and therefore our knowledge is changing rapidly. An enormous amount of work remains to be done, and our review here must be a snapshot that catches the subject at a particular moment rather early in its life.

1. Ages

A FUNDAMENTAL guide to ideas on the evolution of stars is provided by the principle of conservation. We have already noted that energy is conserved, even though it may appear in such different forms as kinetic energy, gravitational potential energy, and radiant energy. Now, a star is not a star unless it emits photons from its surface and therefore loses energy into space. There is virtually no replenishment from outside. An occasional meteorite may crash into the sun before evaporating. A star receives light from other distant stars, but an isolated solar-type star takes in only one photon for every several trillion it gives out. Therefore the energy radiated by a star must be provided almost entirely from energy sources inside its own volume. But since no finite sphere can contain an infinite store of energy, no star can radiate for eternity. The life of every star is finite: Spica, Polaris, and Proxima have not been with us for an infinite time in the past, nor can they be with us as luminous stars for an infinite time in the future.

Given that the lives of stars are finite in duration, we should like next to know whether all types of stars live equally long and whether all stars were born at some common moment in the past and are now all of the same age. Or is the situation more like the human population? Births and deaths occur every day, and at any one time the populace comprises people of many different ages. The answers to our stellar questions have been revealed in earlier chapters, but it is perhaps well to pause here and see how the answers can be found without recourse to the details of nuclear physics. All we need are Einstein's formula, $E = mc^2$, and the empirical mass-luminosity relationship described in Chapter 15, Section 6. The Einstein formula tells us that a star radiating energy is losing mass. In particular, the rate of loss of mass is proportional to the luminosity of the star, as we learned in Chapter 12, Section 30. Next let us simplify the argument and assume that the luminosity of a star remains fixed throughout its life. The assumption is a bad one for detailed studies, but it is reasonable enough for our present inquiry. Now, the time a star can last is proportional to its initial mass divided by the rate at which it loses mass, just as the "life" of a case of ginger ale is proportional to the initial amount purchased divided by the average rate at which it is used up. Thus 12 bottles drunk at 2 bottles per day are all empty in 6 days; 24 bottles consumed at one per day will therefore ensure a supply that last 4 times as long. Returning to the stars and remembering that from Einstein's formula the rate of loss of mass is proportional to luminosity, we conclude that

$$\tau \propto \frac{M}{L}.$$

Here τ is the life expectancy of a new star, M its mass, and L its luminosity. Next recall the mass-luminosity correlation as well as our finding that the luminosity of a star is proportional to the cube or perhaps the fourth power of its mass. Let us adopt the average of 3.5. Algebraically, this relation is expressed as

$$L \propto M^{3.5}.$$

Substituting in the formula for life expectancy, we have

$$\tau \propto \frac{M}{M^{3.5}} = \frac{1}{M^{2.5}}.$$

Think of a star four times as massive as the sun. Now

$$4^{2.5} = 4^2 \times 4^{0.5} = 4 \times 4 \times \sqrt{4} = 16 \times 2 = 32,$$

and this more massive star can expect to last only $\frac{1}{32}$ as long as the sun. A star of 16 solar masses can look forward to a life of $(\frac{1}{32})^2$, or only about one-thousandth that of the sun. At the other extreme a star $\frac{1}{16}$ as massive as the sun can live a thousand times as long. Other things being equal, the more massive star has more material to feed on and might be expected to lead a longer life. But other things are not equal because of the much greater luminosity of the massive star. Consider the rich spendthrift who has $16,000 in the bank and the poor tightwad whose balance is only $1000. The spendthrift withdraws at a rate that is $16^{3.5}$, or 16,384, times as great as the tightwad's rate of expenditure. For simplicity, let us make this ratio 16,000. The tightwad makes ends meet, we assume, by taking out 20 cents each week. Thus his balance has a lifetime of

$$\frac{\$1000}{\$0.20/\text{week}} = 5000 \text{ weeks} = 96 \text{ years}.$$

The spendthrift withdraws at 16,000 times this rate, or at $3200 per week. His money is therefore all gone in five weeks; the life of his account is only one-thousandth that of his frugal fellow, even though he started with a much larger balance. The stars behave in the same general way: the massive ones radiate photons into space very lavishly while the feeble dwarfs spend their resources very slowly. Our conclusion is that at birth stars of different masses have very different life expectancies. And because we see ultraluminous stars in our own times it is certain that at least some stars are, relatively speaking, extremely young. We may reasonably guess that some of the subluminous stars we see today are also young but that others may be very old.

In Chapter 12 we examined the kind of thermonuclear reaction that maintains the radiant output of the sun. The fusion of hydrogen into helium provides the major energy source in the life of any star, with the proton–proton reaction dominant in the sun and cooler stars and the carbon–nitrogen cycle dominant in the hotter stars. And every type of star spends the great majority of its luminous life consuming hydrogen in its core. We also calculated in Chapter 12 that the sun itself can last roughly another 10 billion years. A more refined estimate indicates that the sun is now about 5 billion years old and has another 5 billion to go before exhausting the hydrogen deep in its interior. Thus its life expectancy at birth was 10^{10} years. Life expectancy, or more strictly the time spent in hydrogen-burning, may then be computed roughly for other stars, using the formula for τ. In Table 19.1:1 such

TABLE 19.1:1. Approximate Life Expectancy of Seven Stars

Mass in Terms of Sun	Luminosity in Terms of Sun	Bolometric Abs. Mag.	Spectral Type	Life Expectancy in Years
30	150,000	−8	O5	2×10^6
10	3,200	−4	B3	3×10^7
3	47	+1	A0	6×10^8
1	1	+5	G2	1×10^{10}
1/3	1/47	+9	M3	2×10^{11}
1/10	1/3,200	+14	M7	3×10^{12}
1/30	1/150,000	+18	M8	5×10^{13}

estimates, along with other data, are given for seven stars. The bolometric absolute magnitudes refer to the total luminosity rather than to the energy output in the visual part of the spectrum, and the spectral types are those appropriate to each kind of star only while it is on the main sequence and burning hydrogen. The numerical values should be regarded as indicative rather than exact, but the essential conclusion cannot be altered by moderate changes in the numbers: the more massive a star the shorter its life.

2. Evidence for Young Stars

BEFORE PROCEEDING to the details of stellar evolution, let us see if there is additional evidence that some stars are indeed young. Thus far we have relied on the Einstein formula and the observed mass–luminosity correlation. Now we shall turn to observational results of a very different sort in order to confirm the relative youthfulness of O and B stars of the main sequence. Quite generally, we should expect to find a newborn star not very far from its place of birth, for even if it wanders away from the scene at 10 mi/sec, it moves only 16 parsecs every million years. Also, since stars must be born out of matter, we should expect to find young ones closely associated with the nebulae and clouds of interstellar material. The observations do in fact reveal a strict correlation: wherever luminous blue stars are found, interstellar gas and dust are also found in the neighborhood. Recall from Chapter 18 that the emission, reflection, and dark nebulae are very strongly confined to a thin layer in the galactic plane; in Chapter 17 we found that the galactic clusters and stellar associations are similarly distributed in the equatorial disk. Within this layer the O and B stars and the interstellar matter are found together in clouds and clumps here and there along the great spiral arms of our galaxy.

Fig. 19.2:1. The great nebula near Eta Carinae, a complex region of interstellar matter and luminous stars. (*Photographed by Burt J. Bok, Mount Stromlo Observatory, Australia*)

Additional evidence of youth is provided by the expanding stellar associations. Ages computed from the rates of expansion are in reasonable accord with the ages estimated by the techniques we used to construct Table 19.1:1. We saw in Chapter 17, Section 5 that the O and B stars of the Zeta Persei association have been moving outward from a common center for 1.3 million years. Now the most luminous member of the group is Zeta Persei itself, a B1 supergiant with $M_v = -6.0$. This star has already departed from the main sequence and is slowly moving to the right on the HR diagram. With this great luminosity, Zeta Persei cannot be older than a few million years, and thus the maximum possible age of this O-association is only a few million years. The extensive Scorpio–Centaurus association, on the other hand, has been expanding for several tens of millions of years and one expects any O stars originally present to have run out of fuel long ago and evolved away from the main sequence. This expectation is borne out: there are no stars in the Scorpio–Centaurus with spectral class bluer than B0 and the most luminous member has $M_v = -4.5$.

A negative argument for the youthfulness of certain stars is provided by such clusters as the Pleiades, the Hyades, and Messier 13. The stars in each one of these groups were all born at the same time. At birth each group presumably contained stars of all spectral types, but today the Pleiades have no members bluer than B6, the Hyades have stars of class A1 or later, and the globular cluster Messier 13 is nearly devoid of main-sequence stars hotter than class F5. The implication of Table 19.1:1 is that these differences are caused by differing ages. The O stars run out of hydrogen first because of their enormous luminosities and they are forced to vacate the main sequence. Then the B stars leave, followed by the A stars, and so on. The general picture afforded by the HR diagrams of clusters, the expanding associations, and the common spatial distribution of interstellar matter and blue supergiants is nicely consistent with the arguments cited in Section 1. We can be confident that stars have lives of differing lengths and also that stars are being born in our times.

3. The Zero-Age Main Sequence

IMAGINE A cluster of several hundred stars of different masses but all born at the same time. Early in the history of the cluster the massive stars contracted swiftly, their central temperatures rose, and they began to burn hydrogen by the carbon–nitrogen cycle. We would then find them on the HR diagram at the top of the main sequence. At the same time their less massive fellows were still undergoing gravitational contraction and were probably T Tauri stars; they were migrating to the left but had not yet reached the main sequence. At a much later moment in the history of the cluster the stars of low mass were burning hydrogen by the proton–proton chain and living on the main sequence, while the heavy luminous stars had exhausted themselves and evolved to the right away from the main sequence. In general, then, only a certain segment of the main sequence of a cluster was populated at any given time.

A useful concept that helps us to visualize the long-run evolutionary flow of stars is a fixed reference line on the HR diagram. It is called the *zero-age main sequence*. Figure 19.3:1 shows this line over the range of color and magnitude for which it has been carefully established by observations of stars in galactic clusters. By age zero we mean that moment when a star begins the longest part of its luminous life. This moment occurs when gravitational contraction ends and the star begins to derive its radiant energy exclusively by converting hydrogen into helium. Like people, the stars spend a fraction of their history with negative age. For both people and stars it is simply a more definite procedure to reckon ages from the moment of birth rather than from the moment of conception.

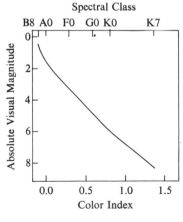

Fig. 19.3:1. The zero-age main sequence.

Let us imagine a nebula of typical chemical composition that fragments into a cluster of protostars of different masses. Each protostar contracts at a rate that depends on its mass, and at age zero it is located at some point on the zero-age main sequence and is beginning to operate solely by burning hydrogen. For a fixed chemical composition, then, the zero-age main sequence defines those points on the HR diagram where stars of different mass, and therefore different luminosity, begin the most important part of their careers. Because contracting stars move from right to left and exhausted stars move from left to right, the zero-age main sequence also represents the maximum leftward penetration that stars of differing masses can make. Regarded in this light, the zero-age main sequence is a bit like the western boundary of the continental United States. It represents the maximum possible westward migration. A survey at any one moment may or may not reveal people standing on the shore of Cape Flattery in Washington or of Cape Blanco in Oregon; but it will certainly not reveal people standing on the Pacific ocean offshore. We shall see later that this containing wall is not absolute for the stars; at very late stages of their lives dying stars may cross into the blue territory denied to hydrogen-burning stars.

4. Evolutionary Tracks for Stars of Moderate Mass

WHEN A PROTOSTAR begins to contract gravitationally, it is large and cool and radiates very little. Thus its position on the HR diagram is far to the right and downward, well outside the limits of the diagram as we ordinarily plot it. As the radius of the body decreases, half of the gravitational potential energy released is emitted into space as radiant energy and the other half is added to the kinetic energy of the interior atoms, thereby increasing the internal temperature. The star crosses the HR diagram moving to the left and slightly upward, as the luminosity and surface temperature increase and the radius decreases. The approximate tracks of 3 contracting stars are shown in Fig. 19.4:1, and the ticks on each track indicate the progress of each star across the diagram in an interval of 3 million years. Note that a star twice as massive as the sun spends far less time contracting than does the sun, whereas the lightest star makes very little progress in 3 million years.

As each star progresses toward its position on the zero-age main sequence, it slows down its pace along the track. When it reaches maximum luminosity, the central temperature is high enough so that hydrogen-burning begins in the core and the core stops contracting. When these central regions stop shrinking, they can release no further gravitational energy to help contribute to the total radiation of the star. The luminosity slowly decreases by half a magnitude while the increasing thermonuclear reactions try to remedy the situation. Finally comes age zero, when all contraction ceases and the entire radiant energy output is supplied by the thermonuclear conversion of hydrogen into helium. The time of evolution from peak luminosity to age zero is about 2 million years for the most massive star in Fig. 19.4:1, over 10 million

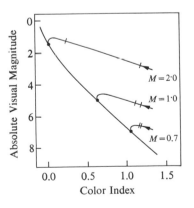

Fig. 19.4:1. The evolutionary paths of stars contracting toward the main sequence. Dots indicate the locations at age zero, and masses are expressed in terms of the sun.

for a star of solar mass, and perhaps 50 million for a star 70 percent as massive as the sun.

Once on the main sequence a star spends the great majority of its brilliant life at very nearly the same place on the HR diagram. The life expectancies given in Table 19.1:1 suggest the times involved for stars of different mass. Remember from Chapter 12 that a star in equilibrium must generate energy inside itself at precisely the same rate that its surface radiates energy into space. Therefore the measured luminosity of a main-sequence star reveals the rate of consumption of hydrogen in its core. At any point inside, this rate depends on the square of the number density of atoms and on a high power of the temperature. (1) The frequency with which one proton encounters other ones depends on the number of other protons per unit volume in the vicinity, and so the total number of close meetings of pairs of protons is proportional to the square of the number density. (2) The frequency of encounters depends on the average speed of the protons and therefore on the kinetic temperature. (3) The specific reactions that bring the proton–proton chain or the carbon–nitrogen cycle into operation require that some of the atoms move extremely fast. The higher the temperature the more probable it is that a colliding pair of nuclei can overcome their mutual force of electrostatic repulsion and join together as a single heavier nucleus. Thus it is that thermonuclear reactions are confined to the central zone of all main-sequence stars. Only there are the number densities and temperatures adequately high. And thus it is that hydrogen-burning goes very fast in massive stars, where the central number densities and temperatures are especially large.

During these years the hydrogen-burning core of a star slowly but steadily becomes poorer in hydrogen and richer in helium. But because the star as a whole is not stirred or mixed by large scale currents of moving matter, the cooler outer regions retain their original chemical composition. The general result of the slow conversion of hydrogen into helium inside a star of moderate mass is a minor increase in the luminosity and radius, so that an evolving star remains quite near the zero-age main sequence during these times. Ultimately, of course, the central zone of the star becomes nearly pure helium and there is so little hydrogen that not much thermonuclear energy can be released. When the hydrogen-poor core has reached out to embrace about 10 percent of the star's mass, the hydrogen-burning in it virtually ceases. At this time the core is an ultrahot constant-temperature region composed of essentially pure helium. From now on the hydrogen reactions are confined to a thin spherical shell that expands slowly outward, leaving an increasingly large core of helium inside it. The situation is not unlike a grass fire on a windless day: the ring of fire expands to feed on unused fuel and leaves a larger and larger burned circle that is no longer releasing energy.

Simultaneously, the helium core enters a stage of gravitational contraction, with some of the energy increasing the temperature and the rest radiating from the surface of the core. While the helium core contracts, the radiation from its surface pushes outward on the outer layers of the star and expands them. The star, as it grows larger and more luminous, picks up speed in its evolution through the HR diagram. It is now headed upward and to the right to become a red giant. The approximate track of a star of 1.1 solar masses is shown in Fig. 19.4:2. The arrival track from the protostar stage terminates at a point on the zero-age main sequence, where the star lingers for perhaps 5 billion years. It then moves along the track toward the red giant branch, swelling enormously as its goes. About 100 million years elapse from the time of minimum color index to the beginning of the nearly vertical rise; only about 40 million years then carry the star to the top of the giant branch. During this time the helium core contracts and its density becomes greater. The temperature increases from about 15,000,000°K at the main sequence to values approaching 100,000,000°K at the most luminous and reddest point of the track.

At the red end of the track the core is so hot that its helium nuclei are dashing about at hundreds of miles per second. At these speeds two of them may combine to form an atom of beryllium, $_4Be^8$, with the release of a gamma ray. Now, Be^8 is an extraordinarily unstable isotope; an atom of Be^8 spontaneously disrupts into two helium nuclei again after an ultrashort interval. Thus at any moment there is only a tiny amount of Be^8 in the core. What there is, however, may react with a third helium nucleus to give a carbon atom, $_6C^{12}$, plus another gamma ray. At this stage of its life, then, a red giant begins to convert helium into carbon. The carbon core grows and helium burns in a shell around it, while hydrogen burns even farther out. The over-all characteristics of the star alter in response to these changes in its internal structure: with the onset of helium-to-carbon reactions the evolutionary track reverses and the star moves relatively rapidly down the giant branch. The path of such a star after its reversal has not been computed in detail, but it is likely that it leads through the horizontal branch. As we learned in Chapter 16, it seems certain that an old star passes through a phase where it must pulsate. Stars somewhat more massive than the sun and living in the old globular clusters are about the right age to be going through the giant and horizontal branches at the present time; some of these stars are now oscillating as RR Lyrae variables.

THE PATHS OF stars of moderate mass through the HR diagram have been studied extensively because the results can be compared with the observed color-magnitude diagrams of globular clusters. The tracks of extremely massive stars have not been studied so extensively, although it is known that heavy unmixed stars start to evolve upward and to the right away from the main sequence as they lose their central hydrogen. Probably the motion is chiefly to the right, without any large increase in luminosity, slowing down as the color index increases. Paths of this sort can explain the few supergiants of all spectral types that we find in the general field. They also can explain the red supergiants of the Double Cluster in Perseus. This cluster is only a few

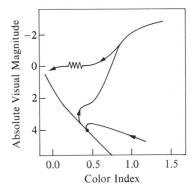

Fig. 19.4:2. The approximate evolutionary track of a star with 1.1 solar masses. After initial contraction the star spends most of its time near the dot. Later it evolves into a red giant. Still later it may move leftward, pulsating for a part of its elderly life.

5. Evolutionary Tracks for Stars of Extreme Mass

million years old, as judged by the presence of several blue supergiants with $M_v = -7$; it is reasonable to suppose that the red supergiants have evolved very rapidly from blue to red in response to their high rate of consumption of hydrogen and are now lingering for a time as enormous objects of low surface temperature.

The tracks of the low-mass red dwarfs are not well known and for a very good reason. Even the eldest of them have plenty of hydrogen left. A star of 0.1 solar mass can last hundreds of times the present age of the galaxy because it radiates so feebly. Thus no M dwarf has had time to evolve noticeably, and there is now no means of checking theory against fact. It seems a good guess that when their time finally comes these little stars will also move upward and right from the zero-age line.

6. Evolution and Color-Magnitude Diagrams

THEORETICAL studies of the long-run evolution of stars through the HR diagram have been inspired and guided by observational studies of star clusters, as we have seen. The pace of such studies has quickened since 1944, when Walter Baade of the Mount Wilson Observatory segregated the two stellar populations and noted that Population I objects are largely confined to the disk of our galaxy, whereas Population II objects tend to be spherically distributed in the galactic halo and more densely in the galactic nucleus. Since that time observations of the magnitudes and colors of stars in different clusters have refined our knowledge: the Population I galactic clusters differ one from the other, and to a lesser extent the Population II globular clusters differ among themselves. When such differences are announced, the specialist in stellar interiors is impelled to attempt an explanation. And so the subject develops.

To correlate theory and observation, we need first a very general statement provided by the theory of stellar interiors. Given the initial *mass* and *chemical composition* of a star, its evolution in time can be completely determined. In principle, that is, we can compute the density, temperature, and composition in each spherical shell of the interior at all times. Moreover, we can calculate the over-all observable characteristics such as luminosity, radius, and surface temperature at all times. Given these quantities at every moment, it follows that the star travels a unique and calculable path in the HR diagram as it moves toward the zero-age main sequence and much later as it migrates away again. It must be understood that this statement is a general theorem; we are only beginning to learn a few of the actual tracks with the aid of high-speed computers.

From the theorem that the mass and the initial relative abundance of hydrogen, helium, and heavy elements determine the evolution of a star, what can be learned from studies of the color-magnitude diagrams of star clusters? Recall that all the stars in any one cluster are very nearly the same age. And because they formed out of a relatively localized and well-mixed cloud of interstellar gas and dust, it is likely that at birth each member had the same chemical composition. Therefore the observed HR diagram of a cluster is a snapshot of a group of stars that have the same age and the same initial chemical composition but different masses. That of another cluster reveals the stage of evolution of a second group of stars with a variety of masses but with a different common age and chemical composition. Thus, by comparing the diagrams of many clusters, we may hope to learn something about their ages and compositions.

Figure 19.6:1 shows an approximate composite plot of the color-magnitude diagrams of several galactic clusters. For simplicity, each group is represented by a single line, although the individual stars themselves actually occupy a thin band for each cluster. The Double Cluster in Perseus contains the most luminous blue stars in the plot and also some red supergiants. It is also interesting to note that there are no main-sequence stars in the Double Cluster with spectral classes later than A. Thus the stars of low mass are presumably still undergoing gravitational contraction, and those of greatest mass have already evolved away to the region of the red supergiants. The estimated age of the Double Cluster is only 2 to 3 million years. The Pleiades is next in order of age, with its turn-off point near $M_v = +0.5$ and no stars bluer than $CI = -0.1$; it is 10^8 years old or perhaps somewhat less. Messier 11 in Scutum has a slightly fainter turn-off point and is estimated to be about 2×10^8 years old. The Hyades and Praesepe are plotted together because they are very similar; their turn-off points

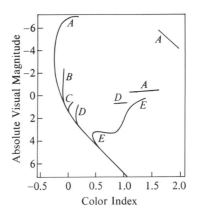

Fig. 19.6:1. The HR diagrams of several galactic clusters are superposed. The youngest cluster shown, *A*, is the Double Cluster in Perseus; *B* is the Pleiades; *C* is Messier 11; *D* represents both the Hyades and Praesepe; and *E* is the oldest of the group, Messier 67.

Fig. 19.6:2. Messier 11, a cluster that is intermediate in age between the Pleiades and the Hyades. (*Yerkes Observatory photograph*)

are near $M_v = +2.5$, and each cluster contains 4 red giants with $M_v = +1$. Both are nearly a billion years of age. One of the oldest galactic clusters known is Messier 67 in Cancer. This cluster is rather far from the galactic plane and its age is estimated to be about 5 billion years. All of its giant-branch stars have evolved to their present positions from a small segment of the zero-age main sequence just above the turn-off point. Note also that stars fainter than $M_v = +4$ have not had time, even in 5 billion years, to evolve appreciably away from the main sequence. Thus the color-magnitude diagrams of galactic clusters confirm the prediction that luminous stars are young, and the location of the turn-off point permits an estimate of the age of each group.

Fig. 19.6:3. Messier 67, a very old galactic cluster, photographed with the 24–33-inch Jewett Schmidt telescope. (*Harvard College Observatory photograph*)

The globular clusters, as we have learned, are very old systems, with ages of 5 billion years or more. It is likely that they differ from one another in age, but very little is yet known about such differences. In addition to variations in age, we have seen that variations in initial chemical composition can give rise to detectable effects. Already cited in Chapter 17, Section 11 is the fact that globular clusters in the galactic nucleus and disk differ from their fellow clusters far out in the galactic halo; stars in the latter contain less of the heavy elements. A very conspicuous discrepancy reveals itself when we compare the color-magnitude diagrams of a globular cluster like Messier 3, as shown in Fig. 17.10:1, with those of an old galactic cluster like Messier 67. Both have turn-off points at nearly the same magnitude and they are thought to be roughly the same age. But the most luminous red giants in Messier 3 are 3 magnitudes brighter than those in Messier 67. This effect almost certainly arises from differing initial chemical composition. In particular, the theory of stellar interiors indicates that the more luminous red giants of globular clusters contain less of the heavy elements than do the feebler red giants of Messier 67. It appears that star clusters born long ago in the halo originated from nebulae having an extremely low abundance of heavy elements, whereas the breeding grounds in the galactic nucleus and especially in the disk were substantially richer in their concentrations of such elements.

When we turn away from clusters and look at the HR diagram for stars in the general vicinity of the sun, as in Fig. 13.15:2, we note objects of all luminosities. The reason of course is that the stars visible to the unaided eye are a mixture of bodies of different masses, compositions, and ages. The blue stars of Orion are massive and very young and now lie on the upper main sequence. Such red supergiants as Betelgeuse and Antares are also massive and therefore young. The red giants like Aldebaran and Arcturus are old and are now evolving away from the main sequence. The sun is of middle age and has not wandered far in the HR diagram since it began burning hydrogen. The red dwarfs of the lower main sequence are a mixture of ages; some are old and some are young. And the white dwarfs we see are now dying stars; some of them have had very long lives, and others, like Sirius B, are less than a billion years old because their binary partners are known to be reasonably youthful stars. It is little wonder that the early history of evolutionary theories is a confusing one, because the first HR diagrams displayed the very complicated mixture of nearby stars. Only recently, with the advent of large reflectors capable of focusing on faint stars in distant clusters, has it been possible to unscramble some of the complexities and begin to lay a firm observational foundation for the theory of stellar evolution.

7. Chemical Evolution

IN THE LAST section we noted evidence that the initial chemical composition of stars seems to depend on their birthplace in the galaxy. Halo globular clusters and their parent interstellar clouds contained a minimum percentage of heavy elements, globular clusters in the nucleus and disk contained more, and old galactic clusters had a maximum. Thus at any given moment in the past, say 5 billion years ago, the composition of the interstellar material probably differed from place to place in our galaxy. Better established is a general change in composition with time. We saw in Chapter 15, Section 9 that the younger Population I stars have about ten times as many heavy elements as do the old Population II stars. The differing strengths of the metallic lines in stellar spectra show that instead of just two groups there is a continuous gradation in composition. The middle-aged sun contains one heavy atom for every thousand atoms of hydrogen and helium, and the older stars have less. In a general way the older the star the lower its abundance of massive atoms; some objects are known that have less than 1 percent of the solar abundance of heavy elements. Since stars are born from the interstellar matter, this result means that the birth material in the oldest days was virtually devoid of such elements as calcium and iron. As time passed, somehow the nebulae and interstellar clouds gradually became richer and richer in such elements. In summary, the observed facts combine to suggest that at any one moment in the history of the galaxy the concentration of heavy elements in the interstellar gas differs from place to place, while at any one place the concentration increases with time.

What can be responsible for such variations? The temperature and density of the interstellar material are far too low for thermonuclear reactions to occur there. Under these conditions hydrogen cannot possibly fuse into helium, nor can helium fuse into carbon. The answer must be sought in the stars themselves. They synthesize heavy elements in their cores, as we know, and by some means or other they eject some of their internal matter back into space. A star is born out of a cloud with given chemical composition, later and inside itself the star manufactures heavy elements at the expense of hydrogen, and finally it gives some of this enriched material back to the interstellar material. In any part of the galaxy at any stage of its history many stars are feeding heavy elements back into space. There the heavy atoms join with the existing interstellar gas to provide a slightly different mixture for the succeeding generation of protostars. In the long run, therefore, the relative abundance of heavy elements increases with time, both inside and outside of the stars. The general process is not unlike the evolution of the earth's oceans as described in Chapter 2, Section 16. Originally fresh, the waters have gradually increased in salinity because the input of salts from the rivers has been greater than the outgo as salt deposits and sedimentary rocks are built. Any given terrestrial atom of sodium may have been in and out of the sea many times, just as a given carbon atom may have been in and out of many stars. But the long-run effect is a slow increase in saltiness.

At any particular moment in galactic history the differences in composition between halo, nucleus, and disk can only be explained by a more detailed picture. Suppose, for simplicity, that the galaxy began as an enormous contracting cloud of pure hydrogen. Now, if stars are born at the same rate every place, we may guess that the feedback should be the same everywhere, and that the gradual addition of heavy elements to interstellar space should proceed at the same rate everywhere. The observations suggest otherwise, and we may hypothesize that the rate of star birth is faster the greater the interstellar gas density in the vicinity. Very early in galactic times the rate was slow everywhere because the density of the gaseous protogalaxy was low. Somewhat later the partly depleted gaseous sphere contracted to a higher density and the rate of star birth inside it increased. Finally, but nevertheless early in galactic history, the contraction and flattening of the gas were well advanced and inside the nucleus and disk the rate of star birth was a maximum. In the earliest stages a few luminous blue supergiants were born throughout the galaxy, quickly ran the course of their evolution, and ejected a small amount of heavy elements into space. Later on many blue supergiants were born, but they were confined to the nucleus and disk where the denser contracting gas was located. They quickly evolved and ejected matter and since there were many of them they supplied lots of heavy elements to the interstellar material of the galactic nucleus and disk, but not to the halo. Today most of

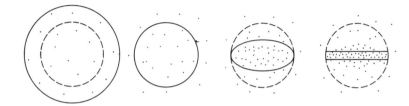

Fig. 19.7:1. Several stages in the probable evolution of the galaxy. Solid lines bound the volume occupied by the contracting interstellar gas; dotted lines indicate the size of the gaseous sphere at the time flattening begins.

the gas is inside the stars; what remains in space has fully contracted and is now strongly concentrated in the galactic disk. As we have seen, the disk with its nebulae and clouds is the only region of the galaxy where stars are now being born at an appreciable rate. And these protostars contain a maximum of heavy atoms—atoms that were synthesized long ago inside stars of earlier generations.

8. Synthesis of Heavy Elements in Stars

IT IS SCARCELY surprising that the galaxy as a whole is losing hydrogen and gaining more massive atoms, because thermonuclear reactions provide the major source of the radiant energy emitted by its 100 billion stars. Of all the possible kinds of nuclear fusion, the conversion of hydrogen to helium provides by far the most energy. But a question we have not yet faced is the actual origin of the heavy elements, such as iron and gold and uranium, that we know exist in nature. We have learned the processes by which hydrogen turns into helium inside main-sequence stars, and we saw in Section 4 how three helium nuclei may, at very high temperatures, join to become a carbon atom. Are there ways of building heavier atoms inside stars? The answer is yes, if the central cores of stars get even hotter than the 100,000,000°K temperature of the red giants. Although the evolutionary tracks of stars after they leave the realm of the red giants are not well known, it is certain that heavy elements are produced in these late stages of development. As an example we may note that absorption lines of technetium are seen in the spectrum of R Andromedae, a red star of spectral class S. Technetium is an unstable element, its longest-lived isotope having a half-life of only 2×10^5 years. Thus, if we still see such lines, the atoms that produce them were born rather recently inside this star and have been brought by currents to the stellar surface.

The study of element-building is called *nucleosynthesis*; it belongs to nuclear physics and uses giant particle accelerators as well as the stars as testing grounds for its predictions. We saw in Chapter 12 how the proton–proton chain involves only isotopes of hydrogen and helium.

But once carbon is built by helium fusion, it gets involved in a variety of reactions. We also learned in Chapter 12 about the carbon–nitrogen cycle, which involves the production of various isotopes of carbon, nitrogen, and oxygen. But to complete the cycle these are destroyed again and fresh helium and carbon appear. At very high temperatures, however, heavy elements can be produced when heavy nuclei capture helium nuclei. Among such reactions are

$$_6C^{12} + {}_2He^4 \rightarrow {}_8O^{16} + \text{gamma ray,}$$
$$_8O^{16} + {}_2He^4 \rightarrow {}_{10}Ne^{20} + \text{gamma ray,}$$
$$_{10}Ne^{20} + {}_2He^4 \rightarrow {}_{12}Mg^{24} + \text{gamma ray.}$$

Thus are built the relatively abundant oxygen, neon, and magnesium. To build even heavier elements by adding helium nuclei, the temperature must be still greater because the nuclei must collide at ultrahigh speed if they are to overcome their very strong forces of electrostatic repulsion. It is probable that elements as heavy as iron, $_{26}Fe^{56}$, are produced in this way, but the temperatures required are about $3 \times 10^9\ °K$. We have not encountered such extreme temperatures thus far, but because iron and adjacent elements are relatively abundant in the galaxy as compared with other heavy elements, we must suppose that such temperatures can and do occur. We shall return to this point soon.

Other reactions are important for producing odd-numbered isotopes. If some hydrogen is present, for example, heavy carbon is built by

$$_6C^{12} + {}_1H^1 \rightarrow {}_7N^{13} + \text{gamma ray,}$$
$$_7N^{13} \rightarrow {}_6C^{13} + {}_1e^0 + \text{neutrino.}$$

Heavy neon is produced by

$$_{10}Ne^{20} + {}_1H^1 \rightarrow {}_{11}Na^{21} + \text{gamma ray,}$$
$$_{11}Na^{21} \rightarrow {}_{10}Ne^{21} + {}_1e^0 + \text{neutrino.}$$

Such reactions are critical because they create isotopes that can react with helium nuclei to produce neutrons. Also, recall that many neutrons are required to manufacture atoms of large atomic number. The fate of $_6C^{13}$ and $_{10}Ne^{21}$, for example, may be

$$_6C^{13} + {}_2He^4 \rightarrow {}_8O^{16} + {}_0n^1$$

and

$$_{10}Ne^{21} + {}_2He^4 \rightarrow {}_{12}Mg^{24} + {}_0n^1.$$

Not only are oxygen and magnesium created in these reactions, but in each one a neutron is ejected away from the scene at a speed of about 10,000 mi/sec. After about 15 minutes a free neutron spontaneously decays into a proton, an electron, and a neutrino. But in the dense core of a star, long before this decay occurs, the neutron is slowed down by collisions so that its average kinetic energy equals that of the other particles of the gas. Before its short life ends spontaneously, it is captured by a nucleus in the vicinity, with the emission of a gamma photon.

Imagine a single heavy nucleus rushing about in a hot gas that contains free neutrons. Suppose it captures a free neutron and increases its mass number by one. In the absence of other competing processes, two things may happen. First, if the number density of free neutrons is very low, the nucleus will not capture a second one very soon. And if the nucleus is now an unstable isotope, it does not live with itself for long. After a certain time it spontaneously releases a free electron into the surroundings and therefore increases its atomic number by one while its mass number remains the same. The new nucleus much later captures another free neutron and perhaps yet another, and then hops up again as it spontaneously emits an electron. Thus the nucleus may slowly zigzag uphill. Such processes produce the various known isotopes up to a mass number of about 50 in the late stages of evolution of normal stars. In addition, isotopes up to bismuth, $_{83}Bi^{209}$, are produced in this fashion in regions where the temperature is measured in the billions of degrees. No heavier nuclei can be made in this way because any further neutron captures give highly radioactive isotopes that spontaneously eject helium nuclei long before fresh free neutrons come along. The general character of radioactive decay was described in Chapter 2, Section 17.

A second general process occurs under conditions when the number density of free neutrons is very great. An atomic nucleus dashing around under these conditions captures one free neutron after another because there are so many available. Its atomic number remains the same, but its mass number increases by one with every neutron it takes in. Ultimately, it will become an unstable isotope that is too rich in neutrons to live with itself until the next neutron comes along. It very quickly rids itself of an electron and changes into the next higher chemical element; then it may be able to accept additional neutrons. When the supply of free neutrons dwindles, these neutron-rich isotopes spontaneously hop upward until they exist as stable isotopes. This process can account for the neutron-rich isotopes we find in nature and in particular for the existence of thorium and uranium, whose stable isotopes last for billions of years before radioactive decay. The ultra-heavy transuranic elements are built in this way too, but they decay spontaneously rather fast and thus are not found abundantly in nature.

Although the lighter isotopes may be manufactured in the late stages of evolution in normal massive stars, the production of isotopes heavier than iron requires extreme conditions. It is thought that the "occasional" capture of neutrons to build very heavy isotopes occurs only in supernovae, during the final stages of their pre-explosion evolution. It is also believed that the "rapid" capture of neutrons occurs only in supernovae and only during the brief explosions themselves; thus the synthesis of many known isotopes and of elements like uranium seems to be confined to a few moments in the life of these stars. The silver of your cup and the gold of your ring were not made in the alchemist's laboratory but probably in supernovae that blew up long ago.

Research in nucleosynthesis is recent and active, and much remains to be learned. The picture sketched here will doubtless have to be touched up and possibly redrawn. But despite our ignorance of the evolutionary tracks of massive stars in their late years, it seems certain that the heavy elements come into being during these times, when all sorts of nuclear reactions occur. Recall that the relative abundances of the different chemical elements and their individual isotopes can be measured in terrestrial matter and in meteorites, and they can be inferred indirectly by spectral studies of the sun, the stars, and the interstellar gas. We have noted differences in chemical composition here and there, but equally striking is the over-all uniformity, with hydrogen ranking first and helium second. Carbon, nitrogen, and oxygen account for most of the remaining atoms in our galaxy. In a general way the heavier the atom the less its abundance. Thus for every million atoms of oxygen there are roughly a million atoms of carbon and of nitrogen; these elements have atomic numbers 6, 7, and 8. But for every million atoms of oxygen there are several hundred million of helium and a few billion of hydrogen. Going the other way, our sample contains only about a thousand atoms of titanium at atomic number 22, and only about one atom of strontium at atomic number 37. For a very heavy element selected at random there is only about one chance in a hundred that a single atom of it will be found in the sample.

These figures are rough and are typical. But there are many well-established departures from the average decrease in abundance with increasing atomic number. We have already learned that lithium, beryllium, and boron are exceedingly rare in spite of their low atomic numbers of 3, 4, and 5. Iron, on the other hand, is about a hundred times as abundant as the smooth trend of our sample might suggest. These are but two examples of a host of known details. The aim of nucleosynthetic studies is to explain all these details in terms of the processes of nuclear physics and of the rates of these processes as they operate in different stars at different times. The beginnings of this discipline are full of promise and the end may some day witness a detailed accounting of how a protogalaxy of hydrogen can evolve chemically, through stellar alchemy, into the complicated distribution of isotopic abundances we see today.

9. The Birth of Stars

WE HAVE SEEN something of the way a star of moderate mass evolves during much of its life, and we have made reasonable guesses about the tracks of massive stars and of the little red dwarfs. Each kind of star spends a minor part of its luminous life in gravitational contraction, then at age zero begins the much longer interval of hydrogen-burning, and finally there follows a shorter time of evolution toward the upper right region of the HR diagram. We come finally to the extreme moments of a star's life: its earliest history and its ultimate death. Our knowledge of both is very incomplete and much of it is necessarily speculative at this early stage in the theory of stellar evolution.

Turning first to stellar birth, we know from many kinds of evidence that some stars are old, that others are young, and that still others are now being born in the great clouds of interstellar matter in the galactic disk. It is clear from the statistics of binary stars that multiple stars are a very frequent phenomenon. Furthermore, studies of definitely young stellar associations and galactic clusters suggest that most stars are born in groups. Thus the problem of individual stellar birth interlocks with the additional problems of how a cluster originates and how it fragments into single and multiple protostars. A look at present-day nebulae shows at once that they are turbulent structures. As the millenniums pass by, randomly moving currents carry material from one place to another, and at any one point the density fluctuates. Photographs of the nebulae tens or hundreds of thousands of years from now will reveal large changes in their appearances. It is possible that a major dense eddy may form inside a nebula and that it may be able to survive. Normally, such a random fluctuation will subside, just as in tossing a coin an improbably long series of heads must ultimately be followed by tails. But there may be forces that tend to keep the eddy together. One such is the mutual gravitational pull of all the eddy particles on one another. If dust exists inside the eddy, a more important force may be the radiation pressure of surrounding stars; the photons from outside drive the dust grains toward the eddy center and the inbound dust carries the gas along with it.

The interior of the eddy is turbulent on a smaller scale, and similar processes may help to form the protostars themselves. Many of these smaller eddies dissolve, but some survive either because they are dense enough or because external radiation pressure squeezes them together. Each prestellar eddy has some net angular momentum to start with, and as the contraction proceeds the rate of rotation must increase. A single contracting object will ultimately fly apart at its equator if it has much angular momentum to start with. It therefore is likely that most of the contracting prestellar eddies that survive manage to break into pairs or little groups, with the bulk of the angular momentum going ultimately into the orbital motion of the individual binary stars around one another or of protoplanets around a single star. Any one subeddy that manages to get this far along its obstacle course is a protostar; it may one day become a full-fledged star. A very large sphere of gas and dust to begin with, the protostar begins to contract gravitationally. The energy is fed partly into increasing internal temperature and partly into radiation by the young star. Like the T Tauri stars, it presumably varies irregularly in luminosity during these years. As time passes, the shrinkage continues against the increasing pressure of the internal gases. The star moves toward the moment of zero age, its core hydrogen begins to react, and life begins.

10. The Death of Stars

AT THE OTHER end of stellar life there are, in principle, two extreme ways a star may reach its end. Conceivably, a body can explode its entire mass outward at such a speed that all its atoms escape from one another and join the interstellar matter. At the other end of the range of possibilities, it is conceivable that another body can evolve without losing matter into space; ultimately, its nuclear and gravitational energy are completely used up, and because it can radiate no more it is a dense black sphere and no longer a star. The truth appears to be contained between these extremes; many heavy stars are known to be losing mass into space, while the many white dwarfs are evolving slowly and rather calmly toward their final ruin. A given star probably gets involved in both processes during its evolution; we shall now look at them in turn.

Loss of mass is a very common phenomenon among stars, as we have learned. Most spectacular of all are the supernovae, described in Chapter 16, Section 15 and again in the present chapter. When a supernova explodes, a good share of its mass flies into space at high speed. It seems likely that most heavy elements are synthesized in supernovae before and during their outbursts, and there is little doubt that cosmic-ray particles and ultraenergetic radio-emitting electrons are created too. But at the same time that gold and silver come into being, destruction is occurring at a prodigious rate. Since these explosions are the most spectacular ever witnessed, it may be that such stars have contracted and heated as severely as any star can stand. Recall that temperatures of a few billion degrees are required for the creation of massive nuclei. But in this same range of temperature a heavy atomic nucleus may be knocked apart if it collides with another superspeed nucleus or if it absorbs an extremely energetic gamma photon. Only the lucky heavy nuclei get out intact. Perhaps the most destructive omen for such a star is its neutrino problem. We encountered neutrinos in Chapter 12, Section 28 and noted their role in the proton–proton reaction. In the sun they carry away only a minor fraction of the energy that is released in the fusion of hydrogen. But in a climate where the temperature is 4 to 5 billion degrees and rising, the neutrinos carry an ever-increasing amount of energy out of the star at the speed of light. As all of this energy is more and more rapidly removed from the interior, the gas pressure inside decreases. The star collapses gravitationally in minutes or seconds, its central regions heat up very suddenly, a multitude of new nuclear reactions occur, and the star blows up. Thus proceeds the most rapid kind of stellar evolution we know, but what remains of the star after its catastrophe we do not know.

The ordinary novae and the recurrent novae are less spectacular. But spectroscopic evidence and the expanding nova envelopes show that these stars are losing mass too. From the evidence cited in Chapter 16, Section 14, it is tempting to suppose that all such stars are repeaters and that as the millions of years go by their masses dwindle significantly. Recall that these stars occupy the blue territory of the HR diagram that is reserved for stars in the late stages of evolution. Some astronomers have suggested that an old star on the horizontal branch may migrate leftward across the main sequence and begin to lose mass. Accompanying the decrease in mass is a slow decrease in luminosity, punctuated occasionally by bright eruptions. As the blue star sinks down the left side of the HR diagram, it gets smaller and smaller in size and is finally ready for admission to the realm of the white dwarfs. Consistent with this picture is the interesting theoretical finding that a star with mass greater than 1.2 solar masses cannot find any normal physical processes to use in order to become a white dwarf. The only recourse of a massive star is to lose mass by ejecting matter into space.

Several other processes of mass loss deserve mention. In Chapter 16 the shell stars, the ring stars, and the central stars of planetary nebulae all revealed a release of mass. All of these stars are blue, and at least some of them are old and far along on their evolutionary tracks. Evolving close binaries tear gases away from their partners, as we learned in Chapter 14, Section 9. Finally we look at our own sun. Not only is it losing mass into radiation at a known rate, but it is also losing atoms into interplanetary space. In Chapter 12, Section 14 we learned that many particles evaporate away from the hot corona in escape orbits and are lost to the sun; perhaps 1000 tons of matter leaves in this way every second. Active regions on the sun emit great clouds of ions and electrons from time to time, as described in Chapter 9, Section 32, and the average rate of ejection of mass from such disturbed zones is probably many times as great as that from the normal corona. Thus mass loss ranges from the catastrophic ejection of supernovae all of the way down to the relatively feeble release by a normal main-sequence star like the sun. We do not yet know whether the sun itself, during late evolution, will have to run through a catastrophic stage or whether it will evolve rather calmly into a white dwarf. It is at least possible that it will take the quieter route.

Let us now turn to the slow type of late evolution as it is followed by the white dwarfs. Remember from Fig. 13.15:2 that these little stars occupy a band in the HR diagram that lies parallel to the main sequence but about 10 magnitudes below it. And Section 8 of Chapter 15 demonstrated that the average density of matter inside a white dwarf is at least 1000 times that of solid lead. The most celebrated star of this kind is Sirius B. Its mass as deduced from its effect on Sirius A is very close to that of the sun, but its radius as calculated from its absolute magnitude and surface temperature is only about 8000 miles, or twice the earth's. The average density of Sirius B turns out to be about 200,000 times that of water.

The course of evolution of a white dwarf is very different from anything we have encountered before. The density is very great, and the star has already contracted to the maximum possible extent. There is simply no more gravitational energy that can be made available for radiation into space. Moreover, the star has no more thermonuclear reactions to perform; if it were still a thermonuclear furnace, it would not be a dying star. But we know that Sirius B and Procyon B do radiate into space, and therefore they must still have some energy store on which to draw. Now, under the extreme conditions inside a white dwarf the atoms are almost completely ionized and, as we have seen, the nuclei can be closely packed together even while they and the free electrons remain in the gaseous state. But the behavior of the free electrons is quite different from that of the gas particles described in Chapter 11, Section 2; in a white dwarf these electrons constitute what

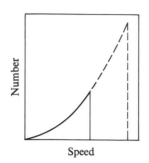

Fig. 19.10:1. The number of electrons moving at different speeds in a degenerate gas. As more electrons are added, their speeds must be greater. Compare this with the situation in a normal gas (Fig. 11.2 :1), where only a few particles move very rapidly.

is called a *degenerate gas*. In considering a normal gas, we learned that at any one moment the atoms were moving in random directions but with a well-defined set of speeds, as illustrated in Fig. 11.2:1. In a degenerate gas, however, things are different. The rules of quantum theory dictate that in a close-packed group there is only so much room for slow-moving free electrons. As more are added, they must have very high velocities. Contrast the distribution of speeds in a normal gas with that of a dense and degenerate gas, as shown in Fig. 19.10:1. The degenerate gas is a bit like a crowd: if only a few are gathered, they are close to the center of attention; but if the throng is huge, the late arrivals must stay far out on the periphery. Here, however, we are concerned with the *speeds* of electrons rather than the *positions* of people. Unlike the free electrons, however, the atomic nuclei inside a white dwarf are not restricted by the quantum rules, and their speeds are like those in a normal gas.

The electrons inside a white dwarf are victims of their circumstances. They cannot slow down because there is no more allowed room for slowpokes, and thus they cannot give up kinetic energy to help the star radiate. The only remaining energy source that we can call on seems to be the random motions of the atomic nuclei, and it is probable that their kinetic energies slowly diminish and keep the white dwarfs radiating feebly for long periods of time. Thus a white dwarf cools down slowly, and as its surface temperature and luminosity decline, it moves to the right and downward on the HR diagram, its motion becoming slower and slower. Perhaps 10 percent of the stars near the sun are white dwarfs. Once upon a time they were relatively massive stars tracking in toward the moment of zero age. Now, later and much feebler, they are slowly sliding down a reverse route. Some day blackness and death will come, and these cinders will bear little resemblance to their earlier luminous selves. But perhaps it is unfair to say that these lost stars will be totally lifeless. After all, they will still be endowed with mass and therefore they will continue to respond to the ceaseless force of galactic gravitation, moving darkly through space.

PROBLEMS

1. How do we know that a star cannot radiate energy for an infinite period of time?

2. (a) Calculate the approximate life expectancies of a star of 7 solar masses and of another of 0.2 solar mass, counting from zero age. (b) Use the mass-luminosity diagram of Chapter 15 and the HR diagrams of Chapter 13 to estimate the absolute visual magnitude and the spectral type of each of these stars while it remains on the main sequence.

3. What observational evidence do we have that some stars are very young?

4. (a) What is meant by the zero-age main sequence? (b) Why can the stars of a given cluster never occupy the entire zero-age line?

5. On what essential physical conditions inside a star does the rate of thermonuclear reactions depend? Why?

6. (a) Sketch the approximate track of the sun on the HR diagram from its early contraction until it reaches the top of the giant branch. (b) Describe in a general way the alterations of structure of the star as it evolves along this route.

7. Explain the differences in the HR diagrams of the clusters in Fig. 19.6:1 in terms of the present theories of stellar evolution.

8. (a) What is the observational evidence that the initial chemical composition of a star born in our times is different from that of a star born a few billion years ago? (b) How can the difference be explained?

9. List some of the various thermonuclear reactions that use helium nuclei to build elements heavier than helium.

10. (a) Why are a large number of neutrons needed in order for the heavier elements to be built inside a star? (b) Give an example of a reaction that supplies free neutrons.

11. What physical conditions are necessary for elements heavier than iron to be synthesized?

12. Explain the forces that assist in contracting a large but tenuous cloud of gas and dust into a star.

13. Mention some of the events that go on inside a star as the central temperature rises to several billion degrees.

14. List the various types of stars that are known to contribute matter to interstellar space.

15. Sketch the track of a white dwarf on the HR diagram and explain the probable source of the radiant energy emitted by such a star.

20

THE HOME GALAXY

Thus far we have largely dealt with the properties and motions of the individual things that comprise our galaxy: atoms, interstellar dust, planets, stars, multiple stars, and clusters. Now it is time to integrate our knowledge and study the galaxy as a whole. We shall first examine the structure of the system and seek to guess how it might look to an observer a million parsecs away. Then we shall proceed to the dynamics of the system and see how the things in it move with time. Finally we shall look briefly at a young topic: the evolution of the galaxy from birth to now to death. Some of our findings have been hinted at in previous chapters, but most will be new. Also, although the astronomer's methods of collecting data are already familiar, the point of view of our interpretation will now be rather different. No longer do we want to measure the parallax of Pollux and the magnitude of Canopus for their own sakes. Instead our chief concern will be to put together all we know statistically in order to grope toward the total picture. The task is by no means easy, nor is the view yet complete, living as we do at a particularly dusty point inside the system we wish to survey. Our job has been likened to that of the surveyor who is supposed to construct a street map of Chicago, but whose observations must be made from the roof of a garage 10 miles out in the suburbs on a foggy day.

Our own larger dwelling place goes by several names. With the same kind of fondness that a typical person has for his home town, a number of astronomers talk of *our galaxy* or *the galaxy*, and a few speak of the *home galaxy*. What we see of the entire structure from our eccentric location inside is the Milky Way, and one sometimes hears the total structure called the *Milky Way system* or the *Milky Way galaxy*.

STRUCTURE OF THE GALAXY

1. The Milky Way

REMOVE ALL of the several thousand visible stars from the evening sky and while you are at it remove the whole solar system, including the earth beneath you. Nearly all that remains visible is the Milky Way; the three exceptions are other neighboring galaxies, which we

Fig. 20.1:1. A drawing of the entire celestial sphere; the central line is the galactic circle. The Scorpio-Sagittarius region is at the center, the Great Rift in Aquila and Cygnus is left of center, and the dimmer winter Milky Way lies at the extreme left and right. Three extragalactic objects are shown: the Clouds of Magellan below and right of center and the Andromeda spiral at galactic latitude −20° near the left edge of the chart. (*Lund Observatory, Sweden*)

shall leave until the next chapter. As we saw in Chapter 13, the Milky Way is a circular belt of light that courses entirely around the sky and divides the celestial sphere into two equal parts. In a general way this strip of light is broadest and brightest in one particular direction. As one scans the circle, going either way from this direction, the belt becomes dimmer and its angular width decreases until the scan is completed after 180°; there, opposite the brightest direction, the Milky Way is feeblest and dimmest. Away from any point on the circle the surface brightness of the Milky Way decreases rapidly and the majority of each hemisphere appears black. A detailed look with the unaided eye or with a pair of good binoculars reveals that the Milky Way has many localized features superposed on this general smooth background. Patches of excess light appear here and there and black regions occur as well.

Let us bring back the stars, sun, and earth and recall that only half of the celestial sphere can be seen at any one moment. It follows that only half of the Milky Way is above your horizon at any one instant. And a good share of this half is at such low altitude that its light is much dimmed on penetrating the earth's atmosphere. Thus the Milky

Fig. 20.1:2. The Milky Way in the Sagittarius region. The area shown measures 20° by 20°, and the direction to the center of the galaxy lies to the right of center, 40 percent of the way from the center to edge. (*From Atlas of the Northern Milky Way, by Ross and Calvert, University of Chicago Press, 1934; Yerkes Observatory photograph*)

Way must be studied from hour to hour as the earth's rotation carries it across the sky and from season to season as its different segments become further removed from the direction of the sun. From northern latitudes the brightest part of the Milky Way, in Sagittarius, is best studied during early evenings in summer. The belt courses from Scorpio through Sagittarius and up into Aquila. From there it passes prominently through Cygnus and becomes fainter as it continues on to Cepheus and Cassiopeia. These parts of the Milky Way are best seen after dark in early autumn. In the winter one can study the feebler section of the strip where it runs through Perseus down through Auriga, between Gemini and Orion, between Sirius and Procyon, and down to the horizon. Least conspicuous in Auriga, the winter Milky Way ought to be observed on a clear and moonless night away from the competition of man-made lights. The far southern Milky Way runs

THE HOME GALAXY

Fig. 20.1:3. The Milky Way in Auriga and Taurus. The galactic equator runs from upper right to center bottom, and the anticenter is below and to the right of center, left of the bright star Beta Tauri. (*From* Atlas of the Northern Milky Way, *by Ross and Calvert, University of Chicago Press, 1934; Yerkes Observatory photograph*)

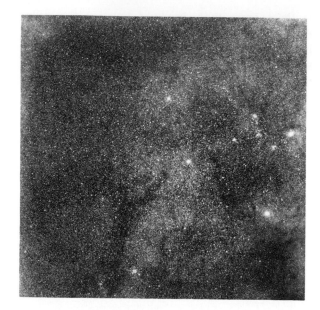

from Canis Major down through Vela and the Southern Cross, on between Alpha and Beta Centauri, and then up into Scorpio to complete the circuit.

2. Galactic Coordinates

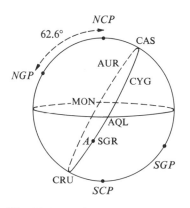

Fig. 20.2:1. The relationship of galactic and equatorial coordinates.

IN STUDYING the galaxy it is a great convenience to use galactic coordinates, which were described in Chapter 4, Section 7. The galactic circle, or galactic equator, is the best great circle that can be plotted so as to bisect the Milky Way along its entire length. It represents the intersection of the extended equatorial plane of the galaxy with the celestial sphere. Figure 20.2:1 shows the relationship between galactic and equatorial coordinates and the location of several constellations through which the Milky Way passes. Cygnus, Aquila, and Sagittarius are on the near side of the celestial sphere; Auriga and Monoceros are on the far side. The point A in this illustration and also in Fig. 4.7:2 marks the direction to the center of our galaxy and is about 5° west of Gamma Sagittarii, the star which marks the spout of the teapot. Point A has galactic longitude 0° and galactic latitude 0°. As an example, the bright star Capella, in Auriga, is a bit north of the galactic circle and near the feeblest part of the Milky Way; its galactic longitude is about 165° and its galactic latitude about +5°. Altair, in Aquila, is somewhat south of the galactic equator; its galactic coordinates are approximately 50° and −10°.

3. Star Gauges

THE STUDY OF galactic structure began around 1610 when Galileo first pointed his telescope to the Milky Way and found that it was composed of hosts of stars. The great majority of its individual stars are too far and too faint to be seen by the unaided eye; their combined light, however, is easily visible as a continuous belt of moderate to feeble surface brightness. Thomas Wright in 1750 interpreted the Milky

Way as our view of an enormous flat disk of stars from a position inside it and near its center. As we learned in Chapter 13, Section 2, the first quantitative studies of galactic structure were made by William Herschel in England in the late eighteenth century. He pointed his 18-inch telescope in a given direction and counted all stars visible in a 15′ by 15′ square in that direction; then he turned to another direction and repeated the procedure. His son, John Herschel, took the same telescope to the Cape of Good Hope and early in the nineteenth century made many of these gauges in the far southern sky, which is inaccessible to observers in England. Between them they accumulated nearly 6000 counts. To analyze the results, one begins with the simplest possible assumptions: that all stars have the same luminosity, that the number density of stars

Fig. 20.2:2. A mosaic of the Milky Way, from Scorpio on the right to Cassiopeia on the left. Altair is the bright star at the center and slightly below the Milky Way; Vega lies to the left of center and above the galactic equator. Messier 31 shows at lower left. (*Mount Wilson and Palomar Observatories photographs*)

is constant inside the galaxy and zero outside, and that space is transparent. Given these assumptions, the extent of the galaxy in any particular direction is proportional to the cube root of the number of stars counted. Figure 20.3:1 shows the situation roughly. In any given pointing a telescope surveys the volume of a cone with the observer at the vertex. In one direction the extent of the system is twice that in the other; a given telescope therefore probes eight times as much spatial volume and reveals eight times as many stars in the longer cone. By analyzing their many gauges in different directions, the Herschels were led to an interpretation similar to Wright's: the sun is close to the center of a somewhat ragged wheel-shaped volume of space. And all this was done before a single stellar distance was measured. As with the solar system, a three-dimensional model could be constructed many years before a scale of miles could be assigned to it.

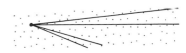

Fig. 20.3:1. Star gauges in two different directions.

4. Star Counts

WE LEARNED in Chapter 18, Section 12 that deductions from star counts are bedeviled by the interstellar dust. Furthermore, we know that stars are not equally luminous and that the luminosity function varies from place to place in the galaxy. Bright blue supergiants are found in clusters and associations near the galactic plane, whereas far from the plane there are few if any such powerful radiators. The road of analysis appears smooth at first, but the more we travel along it the more it is pitted with holes that can cause accidents. Because of the dust in particular, it is hopeless to try to pinpoint the present location of every star in the galaxy and thus to assess the detailed over-all structure of the system. Suppose we had a dozen 200-inch telescopes around the world dedicated to photographing the whole sky, a task that would take the better part of a century. The total number of stars in the galaxy that could be detected is probably between 2 and 3 billion. Independent estimates, which we shall discuss later, suggest that there are about 100 billion stars in our home galaxy, and thus only a very small percentage of the members can be photographed even with the world's largest telescope.

But all is not lost, and star counts at different galactic latitudes have yielded valuable information on some of the major structural features of our own part of the galaxy. One interesting result is the *galactic concentration* at different magnitudes. Suppose we conduct an analysis like that shown in skeleton form in Table 20.4:1. Columns 2 and 4

TABLE 20.4:1. Results from Star Counts

Limiting Visual Magnitude	Number at Equator	Ratio of Increase at Equator	Number at Poles	Ratio of Increase at Poles	Galactic Concentration
6	0.25		0.062		4.0
		210		140	
11	52		8.9		5.8
		100		40	
16	5,200		360		14
		37		8.3	
21	190,000		3,000		63

give the average number of stars per square degree of sky that are brighter than the magnitude listed in column 1; column 2 contains the number for an average point on the galactic equator and column 4 gives the average at the galactic poles. The galactic concentration is the ratio of these two numbers at any magnitude. The ratios of increase are found by dividing any entry by the entry vertically above it. We have met these latter quantities before, in Chapter 18, Section 12, where we learned that the theoretical ratio of increase is 1000 every time we step 5 magnitudes fainter. The fact that the *observed* ratios are much less at the galactic equator arises from the interstellar dust. And the fainter we go the farther we survey and the more severe the obscuration. At the galactic poles the effect of the dust is minor and the declining ratios reflect a real thinning out perpendicularly away from the galactic plane; the number density declines rather rapidly. The run of galactic concentrations is explained by Fig. 20.4:1. The closest nearby stars, for example those within 4 parsecs as given in Table 13.3:1, are found in all directions from us. Since there are as many per unit area at high galactic latitude as there are closer to the Milky Way, their galactic concentration is unity. This effect is illustrated by the inner sphere of the figure. A census to greater distances finds vacancies in the polar regions while in the plane the stars run on and on. In spite of the dust they far outnumber the stars near the galactic poles in Coma Berenices and Sculptor. If the interstellar dust could be blown away, the concentrations would be even more extreme at the fainter limiting magnitudes.

Analyses of star counts at different galactic latitudes tell us of the rate of decrease of their abundance with distance from the galactic plane. In our neighborhood the number density of stars is about 0.14 per cubic parsec. At 100 parsecs above or below the plane the number density is 0.12 per cubic parsec, at 200 parsecs it has decreased to 0.08 per cubic parsec, and at 1000 parsecs it is only 0.01 per cubic parsec. When, by contrast, we move 1000 parsecs away from the sun *in* the galactic plane, the number density differs only by minor amounts from its value near the sun.

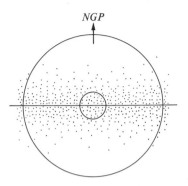

NGP

Fig. 20.4:1. Galactic concentrations are explained by the distribution of stars as shown. The sun is at the center and assumed to lie in the galactic plane.

5. Spatial Distribution of Different Kinds of Objects

ALTHOUGH MOST stars occupy a disk-shaped region in space, we have already learned that not all types of galactic objects occupy the same spatial volume. The nebulae and the tenuous interstellar matter occupy a very thin disk centered in the galactic plane. Here too are the young clusters and associations and the superluminous blue stars of spectral classes O and early B. These objects comprise the extreme Population I; they are young, and within the plane they are rather closely confined to the spiral arms of the galaxy. Older Population I stars, such as those of spectral classes late B and A, have had time to wander from their places of birth and occupy a somewhat less flattened disk. The ordinary novae define an intermediate distribution that is not so highly flattened. And the family of planetary nebulae is concentrated strongly toward the galactic nucleus, showing the characteristic distribution of Population II. The RR Lyrae variables are found in large abundance in the nuclear part of the galaxy and far out in the halo; they are old stars. Finally, as we learned in Chapter 17, Section 13, the globular clusters are extreme Population II objects and occupy an enormous sphere centered on the galactic nucleus and extending out beyond the sun. Although the great majority of globular clusters are in the central region of the galaxy, a few are found as far out as 100,000 parsecs. Thus the galaxy is a superposition of subsystems of differing ages. Each subsystem is centered at the galactic nucleus and has its plane of symmetry coincident with the galactic plane. The spatial volume occupied by the oldest subsystems is nearly spherical, and the younger a subsystem the flatter the oblate spheroid in which its members roam.

6. Radio Radiation from the Milky Way

WE SAW IN Chapter 18 that many emission nebulae have been recorded by radio telescopes; radio waves are emitted as a consequence of free-free transitions in the rarefied ionized hydrogen of these nebulae. In addition, many studies have been made of the 21-cm radiation by cool neutral hydrogen between the stars. But by far the strongest cosmic radio radiation at wavelengths of one meter or more originates in an entirely different way. When Karl Jansky first discovered celestial radio radiation with his New Jersey antenna in 1932 and when Grote Reber made pioneering studies in Illinois in the early 1940s, their instruments were recording this major type of radio energy from

Fig. 20.6:1. The late Karl Jansky, shown with the rotating antenna which he used in the discovery of cosmic radio radiation in the early 1930s. (*Bell Telephone Laboratories*)

space. It reaches us from all directions of the celestial sphere, but is strongest along the Milky Way. A contour map of the radio brightness of the sky strongly resembles a plot of the visual brightness of the Milky Way; maximum intensity is in Sagittarius, and the angular width and brightness decrease as one moves around the galactic equator in either direction toward the anticenter in Auriga.

This radiation is far too intense to be coming from individual stars like the sun. Instead it is emitted by interstellar matter. It seems fairly certain that it is synchrotron radiation, which we learned in Chapter 16, Section 15 is also emitted in the vicinity of supernovae. But the general radio radiation we are dealing with now is not confined to regions near known supernovae. Rather it comes from the entire oblate-spheroidal part of the galaxy occupied by solar-type stars, and in lesser amount from the spherical galactic halo. Synchrotron radiation is emitted by extremely energetic electrons that are circling around the lines of force in a magnetic field. Recall from Chapter 18 that the light of some stars is partly polarized, indicating that a weak but extensive magnetic field pervades the galaxy. At any moment a tiny fraction of all interstellar electrons are spiraling around the lines of force at nearly the speed of light, and as they go round they emit radiant energy. A very small part of this energy will eventually reach a radio telescope and help to reveal a bit more about the structure of the radio galaxy. A great advantage of such studies is that the radio radiation is not stopped by the interstellar dust, and we can examine the galaxy as a whole rather than only that local sample of it near the sun.

The high-speed electrons are not as strongly concentrated to the galactic disk as are the usual interstellar atoms. Indeed, they are present in low abundance in the halo. Thus, although the bulk of the interstellar matter lies in the galactic disk, a small part of it moves far from the plane. The gas in the halo is of extremely low density and is nearly all ionized; its presence is revealed by the synchrotron radiation emitted by a small percentage of its electrons. The combined energy output of all the spiraling electrons in the galaxy is respectable. Their total emission in the wavelengths covered by the radio-astronomical spectrum equals the rate of energy release in visual wavelengths by about 10,000 suns. On the other hand, the radio radiation by interstellar electrons is only about one-millionth as great as the entire light energy emitted by all of the stars in our galaxy.

7. Spiral Structure

WHEN WE STUDY pictures of other galaxies, we find that some systems are chaotic and irregular and filled with interstellar matter, and that others are clean and symmetrical oblate spheroids without obvious interstellar gas and dust. Between these extremes are the spiral galaxies. Like Messier 81 in Fig. 20.7:1, they have nuclear regions that appear free of gas and dust; and out from the central zones wind the spiral arms with their supergiants and gaseous nebulae and knots and lanes of dust. The arms occupy a thin discoidal volume of space, as can be seen when we look at an edge-on galaxy like NGC 4565, shown in Fig. 20.7:2. Here a part of the central bulge is hidden by outlying dust in the disk. Astronomers have long suspected that the Milky Way system is a galaxy of the spiral type. The bulk of the stars in the solar neighborhood are strongly concentrated toward the galactic plane, as we have seen. And Shapley's studies of the globular clusters revealed that we are far from the nucleus of the galaxy. These two results suggest that the sun is in or near the main plane, but far out toward one edge, as indicated in Fig. 20.7:3. This idea is reinforced by the fact that our galaxy contains an intermediate amount of interstellar matter, more than the clear spheroidal or elliptical galaxies and less than the turbulent irregular galaxies.

If our galaxy is a spiral, where are the spiral arms? Finding them is a difficult business because of our own location inside a rather dusty galaxy. The first evidence was found by W. W. Morgan and his associates in 1951, from photographs that showed Strömgren spheres surrounding blue supergiants. More recent studies in the southern hemisphere have been led by B. J. Bok in Australia. Given the galactic latitude and longitude of each object and the estimated distance of the

Fig. 20.7:1. Messier 81, a spiral galaxy in Ursa Major, photographed with the 200-inch telescope. (*Mount Wilson and Palomar Observatories photograph*)

THE HOME GALAXY

parent star after careful correction for the effect of interstellar dust, an astronomer can plot the location of each nebula and see whether as a group they tend to lie along arms. The general results are shown schematically in Fig. 20.7:4. The sun appears to lie inside a spiral

Fig. 20.7:2. NGC 4565, an edge-on spiral galaxy in Coma Berenices, as recorded by the 200-inch telescope. (*Mount Wilson and Palomar Observatories photograph*)

arm and fairly close to its inner edge. The local arm is referred to as the Orion arm because the Orion Nebula is one of its prominent nebulae. The Perseus arm lies between 2000 and 3000 parsecs beyond the sun and contains the Double Cluster as one of its prominent features. The Sagittarius arm passes between us and the galactic nucleus at a distance of about 2000 parsecs. The width of a given arm is 500 parsecs or more in the galactic plane, but the thickness at right angles to the plane is only about 200 parsecs.

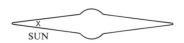

Fig. 20.7:3. A schematic view of the home galaxy, seen edge-on.

Fig. 20.7:4. Spiral arms in our part of the galaxy.

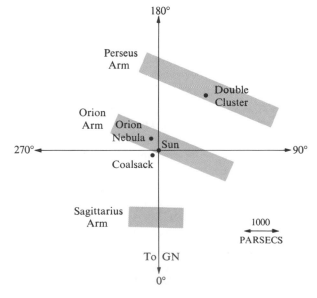

Studies of the spiral structure far from the sun have been made with radio telescopes. One important kind of work has been done at 21 cm, as we shall see later. It is also possible to analyze the synchrotron radiation at longer wavelengths with very large radio telescopes. B. Y. Mills of Australia recorded the radiation received from various longitudes along the galactic equator and found peaks at certain well-defined longitudes. If the gas density is a maximum in the spiral arms and much smaller between them, we may expect to record the greatest amount of radiation when we point in a direction that lies tangent to a spiral arm. Figure 20.7:5 shows the pattern of two spiral arms that best fits the observed peaks of radio brightness. The arrows indicate several galactic longitudes where the radiation is most intense. It should be stressed that the arms of other galaxies are not perfectly spiral in shape; they break here and there and they often branch. But the over-all pattern probably resembles that of the illustration.

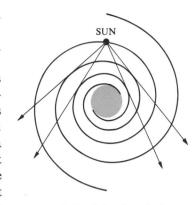

Fig. 20.7:5. Galactic spiral structure as deduced from radio studies.

8. Size, Shape, and Census

A FUNDAMENTAL quantity is the distance of the sun from the center of the galaxy. As with the astronomical unit in the solar system, a knowledge of this distance fixes the scale of our galaxy. At the present time most estimates are confined to between 8,000 parsecs and 11,000 parsecs, and we shall adopt 9,000 parsecs, or 30,000 light-years, as the most likely value. In principle there are several good geometrical methods of finding this distance, but in practice the interstellar dust causes uncertainties. One possibility is to estimate the distance to the center of the system of globular clusters, but most of these systems are near the galactic nucleus and are badly veiled by obscuration. Another possibility is to find the distance to the center of the system of planetary nebulae, but the absolute magnitudes of their central stars differ rather widely from one another. Studies of RR Lyrae stars in the direction of Sagittarius show that some are very faint and some are relatively bright. But the great majority have about the same apparent magnitude and are therefore in the nucleus. Measurement of their color excesses allows us to correct approximately for the dimming due to dust.

Little is known about the size and shape of the central spheroidal nucleus of the galaxy. Infrared photographic and photoelectric studies have recorded an excess of radiation from an oval spot in Sagittarius that is centered near longitude 0° and latitude 0°. Because infrared radiation is less scattered by dust than is visual light, it appears likely that this radiation comes from the nucleus and reveals a flattened spheroid of stars with a maximum diameter of 1,000 to 1,500 parsecs. Surrounding this central bulge is the galactic disk, with a radius of about 15,000 parsecs and a thickness of only a few hundred parsecs. Enveloping all is the low-density spherical halo, containing Population II objects and rarefied ionized gas. The majority of the mass of the halo lies within 15,000 parsecs of the nucleus, although we have seen that a few globular clusters are roaming much farther out, at distances up to 100,000 parsecs. The solar system, at about 9,000 parsecs, is about two-thirds of the way from center to edge of the disk and is about 15 parsecs north of the equatorial plane of the galaxy.

The total number of stars in the galaxy may be estimated from star counts, after correcting for the rather drastic effects of interstellar dust. Another rough estimate may be made if we recall that the number density of stars near the sun is 0.14 per cubic parsec. Let us multiply this figure by the volume of a disk of radius 15,000 parsecs and thickness 1,000 parsecs. We choose 1,000 parsecs to allow for squeezing the halo stars down into the disk and for our underestimate of the greater number density of stars in the central part of the galaxy. Both estimates suggest that there are about 10^{11} stars in the home galaxy.

DYNAMICS OF THE GALAXY

9. Rotation and Flattening

WE HAVE SEEN that rotation is a universal phenomenon. Protons and electrons spin, and so do planets and stars and the nebulosities around ring stars. And wherever the rotation is rapid enough, we observe flattening. The earth's polar diameter is 27 miles less than its equatorial diameter, and Jupiter and Saturn are seen through the telescope to be appreciably flattened. The planetary system itself is strongly confined to a thin disk. Even some of the stately globular clusters show evidence of flattening owing to their rotations. A look at Figs. 20.7:1 and 20.7:2 suggests that the great galaxies are not static systems, but are turning around their minor axes. The flattening and the semiorderly spiral arms of our own galaxy strongly suggest that it is spinning too. The first evidences of galactic rotation were cited in 1926 and 1927 by B. Lindblad of Sweden and J. H. Oort of Holland.

10. Local Effects of Galactic Rotation

LET US SUPPOSE that each star in the galactic disk moves in an essentially circular orbit around the distant nucleus in response to the combined gravitational attraction of the great mass of stars there. The situation may be pictured as something like the motion of planets around the sun or of the particles in Saturn's ring system around Saturn itself. Stars closer to the nucleus than is the solar system answer the greater gravitational force by moving faster than the sun; those at greater distances move at slower speeds. Figure 20.10:1 shows the velocity vectors of several stars as they move around the galactic center. But we are observing the motions of these stars from the moving sun. Subtracting the sun's arrow from that of each surrounding star, we may expect the measured space velocity of each to be given by the arrows in Fig. 20.10:2, in which the scale is doubled for clarity. Suppose our ideas are correct and that we measure the radial velocities of moderately distant and luminous B stars at different galactic longitudes. Stars in Sagittarius toward the center and in Auriga at the anticenter should show no average radial velocity, while stars in Cygnus and Vela

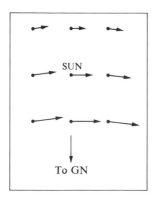

Fig. 20.10:1. Circular motions around the galactic nucleus.

should show no radial motion either. Near longitude 45° in Aquila, however, the stars should run away from us and show red shifts in their spectra. Stars in Perseus should approach, those in Canis Major should recede, and those in Centaurus should approach.

Observations of stellar radial velocities confirm our expectations, and we conclude that our part of the galaxy is rotating in response to the gravitational pull of the central mass of stars. Studies of the Doppler shifts of interstellar spectral lines imprinted on the spectra of blue supergiants show that the interstellar gas clouds are moving in the same general way. Additional verification of this type of rotation is provided by proper-motion surveys of moderately distant stars. For example, Fig. 20.10:2 shows that the galactic longitudes of stars in both Sagittarius and Auriga should increase slowly as the years go by. And so they do. The general conclusion from all such studies is that the nearby Population I stars are moving in nearly circular orbits around the galactic nucleus. At the moment they are moving toward Cygnus. The orbital period of the sun is approximately 230 million years. Stars 1000 parsecs closer to the center move 7 to 8 mi/sec faster in their galactic orbits than do those in the immediate solar neighborhood, while stars 1000 parsecs farther out move more slowly by 7 to 8 mi/sec. If we adopt a distance of 9000 parsecs for the sun's distance from the hub of the galaxy, the circular velocity of stars in the solar neighborhood turns out to be about 150 mi/sec.

STARS ON THE opposite side of the galaxy are too much dimmed for radial velocity measurements. But at radio wavelengths the galaxy is essentially transparent, and several surveys of interstellar neutral hydrogen have been carried out by radio telescopes operating at 21 cm. When pointed in a given direction, a radio telescope collects radiation emitted toward it from all points in a long narrow cone of space. How the emitting atoms are distributed along the line of sight cannot be directly determined, but indirect evidence is provided by the Doppler shifts of the radiation. In Fig. 20.11:1 a radio telescope is examining a long thin cone of space with vertex at the sun and centered on the line AB at galactic longitude 25°. The radial velocity of all emitting hydrogen between the sun and point B is positive and red-shifted. The maximum red shift is shown by material at A, which in its circular orbit is running straight away from the sun. Hydrogen at the point B is running away at the same rate the sun is chasing it and thus is not Doppler-shifted. Matter outside the right-hand semicircle is all approaching the sun and thus the arriving radiation is violet-shifted. In the left-hand semicircle the situation is reversed, with hydrogen in the interior approaching the sun and that beyond 9000 parsecs receding.

An observation in a given direction consists in obtaining a line profile of the 21-cm radiation by recording the number of photons incident at each wavelength in the vicinity of 21 cm. The Doppler shifts are then translated into radial velocities, as shown schematically in Fig. 20.11:2. The intense radiation receding at about 85 mi/sec may be

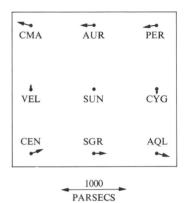

Fig. 20.10:2. Velocity vectors of stars as observed from the moving sun.

11. General Effects of Galactic Rotation

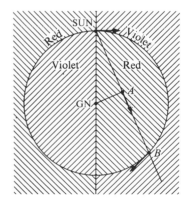

Fig. 20.11:1. Doppler shifts of interstellar hydrogen help to reveal the nature of galactic rotation.

THE HOME GALAXY

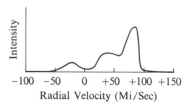

Intensity

−100 −50 0 +50 +100 +150
Radial Velocity (Mi/Sec)

Fig. 20.11:2. A line profile at 21 cm.

Fig. 20.11:3. The 60-foot radio telescope at Harvard's Agassiz Station, 30 miles northwest of Boston, devoted to studies at 21 cm. (*Harvard College Observatory photograph*)

Fig. 20.11:4. The trend of circular speed with distance from the galactic nucleus.

interpreted as a segment of a spiral arm near point *A*, whereas the lower peak near 40 mi/sec may be caused by looking across a spiral arm between the sun and *A* and across another arm between *A* and *B*. An outer arm is revealed by the small peak at −25 mi/sec. Such studies at many longitudes have permitted a preliminary mapping of the spiral structure of the galaxy.

By looking at the extreme radial velocity in any interior direction and correcting for the effect of random gas-cloud velocities of 10 mi/sec, it is also possible to build up a picture of how the circular speed varies with distance from the galactic nucleus. Figure 20.11:4 shows an approximate plot of the circular velocity against distance from the galactic nucleus. An object in the galactic plane and moving in a circle at a given distance from the center has a speed that can be read roughly from the graph. The velocity curve is pieced together from 21-cm data, from optical data on O and B stars, and also from dynamical requirements. Since the dynamical ideas involved are of some interest, let us deal with them briefly. Stars that are extremely far from the nucleus, and thus well beyond the limits of the diagram, see the galaxy as a distant point and therefore move in Keplerian orbits. Recall from Chapter 7 that the circular velocities of the planets are inversely proportional to the square roots of their distances from the sun. Similarly, the far-out portion of the galactic velocity curve must decrease in the same fashion. A star very close to the galactic nucleus, on the other hand, experiences a much reduced net gravitational attraction. Other stars are pulling on it in all directions and the individual force vectors tend to cancel each other. Close to the nucleus the rotation is like that of a solid body. Every star in a circular orbit has the same orbital period, perhaps 100,000,000 years. Just as with particles inside the earth and on its equatorial plane, the rotational velocity is proportional to distance from the center. Thus the inner part of the galactic velocity curve is a straight line, with speed directly proportional to distance. The actual curve of Fig. 20.11:4 is a blend, with solid-body motion occurring close to the center and Keplerian motion occurring far out. Stars somewhat closer to the galactic nucleus than is the sun have the maximum circular speed. In our part of the galaxy, as we have seen, the circular velocity decreases with distance from the nucleus by 7 to 8 mi/sec each kiloparsec.

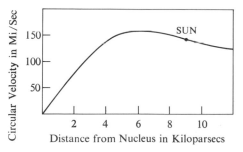

SUN

150

100

50

2   4   6   8   10
Distance from Nucleus in Kiloparsecs

Circular Velocity in Mi/Sec

Let us stress once again that our knowledge of the sun's distance from the nucleus is uncertain by 10 to 15 percent, and its orbital period is also somewhat uncertain. The circular velocity of 150 mi/sec that we have adopted is probably only correct to within 20 percent; some estimates run as low as 130 mi/sec and others as high as 190 mi/sec.

Thus the curve of Fig. 20.11:4 is only approximate; refinements will come in time. One entertaining prospect for improving our knowledge of the sun's circular speed is to observe the radial velocities of nearby galaxies and analyze them by exactly the same technique we used in Chapter 13. There we looked at the radial velocities of nearby stars in order to find the solar motion relative to neighboring stars. Now we look farther afield at galaxies outside our own. When our analysis is complete, we find that relative to the nearest dozen galaxies the sun is moving toward a point in Cepheus at 180 mi/sec. But can we adopt 180 mi/sec as the circular velocity of the sun around the galactic nucleus? No. Just as nearby stars mill about at speeds of 10 to 15 mi/sec, so do galaxies wander in random directions at 50 to 100 mi/sec. Therefore our analysis only gives us a combination of the sun's velocity vector around the galactic nucleus and the velocity vector of the home galaxy through the local swarm. The two separate vectors have not yet been unscrambled, as shown in Fig. 20.11:5. The motion of the sun relative to the nearby galaxies is shown by the solid arrows. Two of the many possible galactic orbital speeds are shown. If our circular velocity is 150 mi/sec, then the galaxy as a whole is moving through the other galaxies in one direction at 50 to 60 mi/sec. If instead we travel around the galactic center at 190 mi/sec, the galaxy's motion is some other direction at 50 to 60 mi/sec.

THUS FAR IN our study of galactic rotation we have been content to think of each star moving in a perfectly circular path in the galactic plane. The diagram of Fig. 20.10:1 resembles an orderly parade around a circular track, with the marchers closer to the center moving at a somewhat faster pace than those farther out, and with all marchers at the same distance from the center going at the same speed and thus remaining always the same distance apart. Actually the situation is not quite so ideal. Recall our finding in Chapter 13, Section 8 that the stars near the sun move relative to each other in random directions with speeds that average about 15 mi/sec. What implications do these local motions have for our over-all picture of the galactic rotation?

Let us think of the sun in particular. It moves through the local swarm at 12 mi/sec approximately toward Vega. When this velocity vector is broken down into its three parts, the sun is rising toward the galactic pole at 4 mi/sec, approaching the galactic center at 6 mi/sec, and heading

DYNAMICS OF THE GALAXY

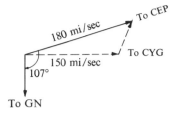

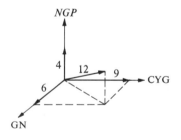

Fig. 20.11:5. Two possible motions of the sun around the galactic nucleus.

12. Galactic Orbits of the Nearby Stars

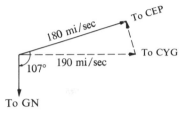

Fig. 20.12:1. The sun's motion through the local swarm, at 12 mi/sec toward Vega.

Fig. 20.12:2. The velocity vector of the sun relative to the center of the galaxy.

toward galactic longitude 90° at 9 mi/sec, as shown in Fig. 20.12:1. And in turn the local swarm as a whole is moving in a circular track around the galactic nucleus. The swarm speed is approximately 150

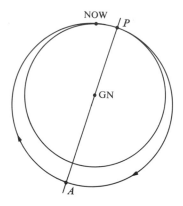

Fig. 20.12:3. The sun's galactic track and that of a star in a circular orbit of radius 9 kiloparsecs.

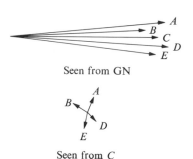

Seen from GN

Seen from *C*

Fig. 20.12:4. Local random motions are explained by slightly different galactic orbits for the individual stars.

13. Vertical Motions of the Nearby Stars

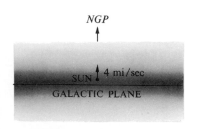

Fig. 20.13:1. The sun's up-and-down motion.

mi/sec and is directed toward galactic longitude 90° and galactic latitude 0° in the direction of Cygnus. If we ignore, for the moment, the motion of the sun toward the north galactic pole, we can combine these data and see how the sun itself is now moving relative to the galactic nucleus. Figure 20.12:2 shows that the sun is moving a little faster than the circular velocity and that it is slightly inbound toward the nucleus. The galactic orbit of the sun is approximately a Keplerian ellipse of small eccentricity. Now approaching the galactic nucleus, the sun will reach the perigalactic point of its path somewhat more than 10 million years from now. Its mean distance from the galactic center is about one kiloparsec greater than its present distance and the eccentricity of its orbit is about 0.1. In Fig. 20.12:3 is shown the track of the sun, its present location, and the perigalactic and apogalactic points of its track. The inscribed circle centered on the galactic nucleus is the path of a star moving in a circular orbit with radius equal to the sun's present distance.

Now we can interpret the local random motions of nearby stars like Altair, Capella, or Regulus. Each one has its own slightly eccentric path, just as does the sun. Each one deviates slightly from the circular velocity. As measured from a star moving in a circle, then, these objects have small motions that average 15 mi/sec and are directed at random. Figure 20.12:4 relates the over-all motions to the local motions seen from *C* in its circular orbit. It is clear that the slightly ragged parade of stars in the galactic disk will carry present neighbors rather far away from one another in the long run. Thus as the millions of years go by, Altair, Capella, and Regulus will no longer be numbered among our first-magnitude stars. And if we have the patience to wait 230 million years until we have completed a full circuit of the galactic nucleus, these stars will not necessarily be close to us again because their orbital periods in general are somewhat different from our own.

WE HAVE JUST seen that the sun moves in a slightly eccentric path, in response to the inward gravitational pull of the billions of stars in the central part of the galaxy. But we have yet to account for its motion at right angles to the galactic plane. At the present time the sun is about 15 parsecs north of the plane and rising at the rate of 4 mi/sec. These figures imply that it passed through the plane northbound some 2 million years ago and that even longer ago it was below the equatorial plane. What is responsible for this vertical motion? The gravitational effect of the massive but distant nucleus on the up-and-down motion of a star is zero when it is in the plane and very small when it is not too far above or below the plane. The major part of the vertical acceleration of a star in the disk is caused by neighboring stars and interstellar matter. Let us smear out all of the matter in the nearby stars of the galactic disk and ask how the gravitational pull of this matter will affect the vertical motion of the sun. In Fig. 20.13:1 the sun has been placed 15 parsecs above the plane with an upward velocity of 4 mi/sec. As the sun rises, it leaves more and more of the stars and interstellar matter below it and sees less and less above it. It is therefore accelerated downward and its upward speed decreases. Finally it stops rising at a height of 100 parsecs and begins to sink downward again. It is accelerated to a maximum speed of just over 4 mi/sec as it crosses the plane. It moves 100 parsecs south of the plane before being pulled back again. Thus the sun oscillates slowly up and down in response to the gravitational pull of stars and interstellar matter in the disk. The total period of oscillation is about 80 million years. The over-all motion of the sun is very much like that of the horseback rider on a merry-go-round. His major motion is circular in the horizontal plane, but at the same time he moves up and down with the horse, making some three complete vertical oscillations as the merry-go-round spins once.

The sun is not alone in its vertical motion; the other stars and the interstellar atoms and dust particles also move slowly up and down while they move in faster tracks around the center of the galaxy. A star that passes vertically through the plane at 10 mi/sec is decelerated exactly as is the sun, but because of its greater speed it moves more than 200 parsecs above and below the plane before being drawn back. Its greater travel is compensated by its faster average vertical speed, so that the time for a complete oscillation is again about 80 million years. Another star that is in the plane and has no vertical motion will stay there. With as much mass above as below, no net vertical force is exerted on such a star; it can neither rise nor sink. Vertical stellar motions rather resemble those of a child on a swing. The farther to one side he is drawn, the greater the arc through which he swings when he is let go and the faster his speed as he passes through the vertical.

What determines that the sun should pass through the plane at 4 mi/sec while another star passes through at 10 mi/sec? These figures are governed by its place of birth and any random vertical motion it may have acquired when born. Many Population II stars were born rather far from the plane and thus plunge through it periodically at high speed. At any moment some of these old stars are near us as they move through the plane, but most are rather far above or below us. As a group, therefore, they are not strongly concentrated in the galactic plane. The extreme Population I stars are born from the gas and dust that lies very near the plane. Their vertical speeds are generally very small and they therefore remain very near the plane. Thus young clusters and associations, blue supergiants, and interstellar gas and dust are confined strikingly to a very thin disk. In our part of the galaxy the number density of stars is a maximum in the galactic plane because Population I stars always stay close to it and because all older stars periodically must pass through it. The farther one moves from the plane the smaller the number of stars that can attain that height and thus the smaller the number density.

14. High-Velocity Stars

When we studied the motions of the nearby stars, we learned that a few like Barnard's Star, 61 Cygni, and Kapteyn's Star have very large

THE HOME GALAXY

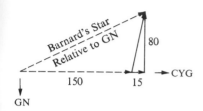

Fig. 20.14:1. The motion of Barnard's Star.

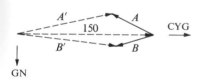

Fig. 20.14:2. Two high-velocity stars.

space velocities. Most stars have smaller space velocities, and it follows that these normal objects move in nearly circular orbits around the galactic nucleus while oscillating vertically at low speed. Let us now examine the few fast renegades. Table 13.3:1 shows, for example, that Barnard's Star has a space velocity of 87 mi/sec relative to the sun. When the space velocity vector is referred to galactic coordinates and to the local swarm of stars instead of to the sun, it turns out that Barnard's Star is rising toward the north galactic pole at about 20 mi/sec, moving toward Cygnus about 15 mi/sec faster than the circular velocity of the local swarm, and receding from the galactic nucleus at nearly 80 mi/sec. The rather fast vertical velocity of Barnard's Star implies that it gets as far as 300 parsecs from the galactic plane. Its present velocity vector in the plane is diagramed in Fig. 20.14:1. Barnard's Star is therefore now outbound toward its apogalactic point on a track that is far more eccentric than that of the sun. Its present speed relative to the galactic nucleus is about 185 mi/sec, but as it recedes it will obey the law of areas and slow down. The apogalactic distance of Barnard's Star is more than 20 kiloparsecs, and therefore the conventional boundary of the galactic disk at 15 kiloparsecs is not observed by all stars. When passing its perigalactic point tens of millions of years ago, Barnard's Star was only 6 or 7 kiloparsecs from the center of the galaxy. In a similar way, the tracks of other high-velocity stars may be imagined as rather eccentric ones. When one such star passes through our neighborhood, its motion *relative to us* is rather fast.

In Chapter 13, Section 8 we learned that a typical star moves in a random direction at a speed of about 15 mi/sec relative to the local swarm. But if we next plot the velocity vectors of the high-velocity stars relative to the local swarm, the results are very different. Suppose we isolate all those stars moving 40 mi/sec or faster relative to the local swarm. With very few exceptions the velocity arrows of these stars point toward the celestial hemisphere *away* from Cygnus. Barnard's Star is one of the few exceptions, as can be seen from Fig. 20.14:1. Two examples of more typical high-velocity stars are shown in Fig. 20.14:2. Both A and B avoid the Cygnus hemisphere as seen by us. But their velocities around the galaxy are given by A' and B', which represent present orbital speeds of *less* than 150 mi/sec. What from our local point of view we call high-velocity stars are, in the main, actually slow-moving stars. Star A' is now outbound toward its apogalactic point along a rather eccentric path. Its mean distance from the galactic nucleus is less than 9 kiloparsecs. The law of areas dictates that its orbital velocity is relatively low. The path of B' is generally similar to that of A', but it has already passed its apogalactic point and is now inbound as it passes through our neighborhood.

When the RR Lyrae stars of Population II are analyzed statistically, it is found that they are lagging, on the average, about 70 mi/sec behind the circular velocity of the local swarm. Some are moving rapidly inward and some rapidly outward; some are moving rapidly upward and some rapidly downward. But for every inbound star there must be another outbound star, and for every rising star there must be another that is falling. Thus when we average the radial or the vertical velocities, we find that they are zero. But the average velocity of the nearby RR Lyrae stars toward Cygnus is substantially less than our own. Again we are led to the picture of eccentric orbits; most RR Lyrae stars that pass near us have mean distances that are substantially less than 9 kiloparsecs. The vertical motions of the individual RR Lyrae variables are relatively large, with a typical value of about 30 mi/sec. Thus these stars can move far from the plane. As a group, therefore, they are not at all strongly concentrated in the galactic disk.

We are now able to interpret the long-standing puzzle mentioned in Chapter 13, Section 13. Recall that the more luminous stars have the lowest space velocities and the less luminous stars have faster space motions. The reason for this correlation is that the high-velocity Population II stars are old. Therefore all of their luminous brothers of the same age have long since evolved out of the upper part of the HR diagram. The young Population I stars, on the other hand, move in nearly circular orbits in the disk, and therefore their velocities as measured by us are relatively small. Some of these young stars are feeble, but some of them are luminous blue or red supergiants. On the average, therefore, youth and luminosity and low space motions go together at the one extreme and old age and feebleness and large space motion go together at the other.

The globular clusters lag even further behind the local swarm than do the RR Lyrae stars. Also, their individual vertical motions must be very large because these objects occupy a spherical space around the galactic nucleus. The average speed of the globular clusters around the nucleus is only 50 mi/sec or so, suggesting that they formed long ago when the protogalaxy was large and rotating slowly. Only at a later stage of the contraction, with the flattening and increasing angular velocity of the gas and dust, were clusters and stars born in the disk with the high circular velocities we see today.

Let us return to Fig. 20.14:2 and imagine a high-velocity star whose velocity vector relative to the local swarm is 70 to 80 mi/sec and which is directed more or less toward Cygnus. What will be the destiny of such a star? Its velocity relative to the galactic nucleus is some 220 to 230 mi/sec. Such high speed will carry the star on a hyperbolic orbit right out of the galaxy and into intergalactic space. Its velocity is greater than the escape velocity at our distance from the nucleus. It is not surprising that we observe very few high-velocity stars heading into the Cygnus hemisphere. Most such objects are making their getaways and will never be back again. Only a very few stars, perhaps ten altogether, are now suspected of being escapees.

15. Is Our Galaxy Contracting or Expanding?

IF THE GALAXY as a whole were shrinking, we would observe that the average radial velocity of all stars is a negative quantity, because statistically all stars would be coming together. Conversely, if the galaxy were growing in size, the average Doppler shift in stellar spectra would be to the red. There is at present no clear-cut evidence that the average radial velocity of the stars is other than zero. Thus, as far as we know, our stellar system is not changing in size.

Recent 21-cm observations suggest that the interstellar matter in the central part of the galaxy moves in a fashion quite unlike that of any stars. When line profiles are recorded in the Sagittarius region, it is found that the neutral hydrogen in the nucleus is in rapid motion. A gaseous spiral arm 3 kiloparsecs from the center is expanding outward away from the nucleus at a rate of 30 mi/sec. Thus, although the stars of the galaxy are not expanding away from one another appreciably, the inner gas is heading outward at the same time that it shares in the general galactic rotation. We may logically ask where all of this outbound gas comes from and why it has not by this time left the central regions empty of interstellar matter. It appears likely that the interstellar gas slows down as it moves outward in the plane, because observations of interstellar lines show that its outward radial speed can be no more than a few miles per second when it reaches the solar neighborhood. The nuclear regions are apparently replenished continually by a backward and inward flow through the halo and a sinking of the gas down the rotational axis of the galaxy and back into the nucleus once again. The precise nature and cause of this flow remains in doubt. There are two major parts to the puzzle. (1) The bulk of the interstellar hydrogen in the spiral arms is cool and neutral and can be observed by the 21-cm technique. But why should this gas hold together in great spiral whirls as it rotates and expands? (2) The halo hydrogen is highly rarefied and, like the material of the outer solar corona, at a high kinetic temperature. Because it is virtually all ionized, we are unable to observe it with a 21-cm radio telescope. If indeed hydrogen far out in the galactic plane rises and then flows inward through the halo, what forces are responsible for this motion? The answers may be found in the magnetic fields of the galaxy. Their existence is established by studies of the polarization of starlight and substantiated by observations of synchrotron radiation at radio wavelengths. The direct effects of a magnetic field on charged particles may be profound and its indirect effects on neutral atoms may likewise be important.

16. Mass of the Galaxy

THERE ARE two crude but simple ways of estimating the mass of our stellar system. In Section 8 we found the total number of stars to be about 10^{11}. The average mass of all stars is somewhat less than the mass of the sun because of the very numerous small red dwarfs. On the other hand, we must add the interstellar matter to the total. These adjustments do not affect the argument strongly, and in round numbers the mass of the galaxy is about 10^{11} solar masses. An alternative computation may be made by using Newton's generalized formula for Kepler's third law. We used this relation in Chapter 14, Section 3 to deduce the sum of the masses of a pair of visual binary stars. Here we may estimate the mass of the galaxy from the fact that a star in circular motion at 9 kiloparsecs takes about 230 million years to complete one circuit of the galactic nucleus. Since 9 kiloparsecs = 1.9 × 10⁹ a.u., we have

$$M \simeq \frac{(1.9 \times 10^9)^3}{(2.3 \times 10^8)^2} = \frac{6.8 \times 10^{27}}{5.3 \times 10^{16}} = 1.3 \times 10^{11} \text{ solar masses.}$$

This calculation has two defects: (1) our knowledge of distance and period is somewhat uncertain, and (2) we are assuming the galaxy to be a point mass at the nucleus instead of a spread-out assembly of stars. It is reassuring, however, that the two separate estimates give roughly the same result. More refined estimates indicate that the mass of the galaxy is rather close to 10^{11} solar masses, or 2×10^{44} grams.

A different group of data can tell us something about the mass in our own part of the galaxy. Recall from Section 13 that the vertical motion of each star is chiefly controlled by the nearby stars and the local interstellar matter. If in Fig. 20.13:1 we remove all gravitating material except for the sun, the vertical acceleration of the sun would be zero. On the other hand, if we put twice as many stars in every cubic parsec, the acceleration would be doubled and the oscillation time much less than 80 million years. By analyzing the known vertical velocities of many stars at different distances from the galactic plane, it is possible to work backward and compute the vertical acceleration at each level. From these data one can then deduce how the matter in the disk must be distributed in order to cause these accelerations. A major result of such analyses is the so-called *Oort limit* of 0.10 solar mass per cubic parsec. Oort found that the smeared-out density of matter in our vicinity can be no greater than this figure. If it *were* greater, the stars would move up and down at paces brisker than those we observe. We saw in Chapter 18, Section 10 that the known nearby stars contribute, on the average, one-twentieth of the sun's mass to each cubic parsec and the interstellar hydrogen about half as much again. Together they amount to three-fourths of the Oort limit. It is of interest that the agreement is so close, because the various estimates are arrived at in very different ways. It is also tempting to speculate whether the missing fourth is a result of uncertainties in the different observational investigations or whether there is really matter in our neighborhood that we know nothing about. For example, if there were two interstellar hydrogen atoms per cubic centimeter instead of one, the stars and interstellar matter would contribute equally to the total mass in each cubic parsec, and the total would agree with the Oort limit. Alternatively, we might suppose that there are feeble red dwarfs, white dwarfs, or black dwarfs in our neighborhood that remain undiscovered. Although uncertainties remain, it is clear that the local density of all matter is not far from 0.10 solar mass per cubic parsec and that the mass of the entire galaxy is close to 100 billion solar masses.

17. The Galaxy Today

OUR HOME system is a spiral galaxy and is composed of three parts. The relatively small central nucleus is an oblate spheroid and there the star density is a maximum. The stars are dominantly Population II, and their orbital periods around the center are all about the same. Interstellar hydrogen also exists in the nucleus, and it participates in the rotation while expanding outward into the disk.

The galactic disk has an over-all diameter of 30,000 parsecs but a thickness of only a few hundred parsecs. It contains virtually all of the Population I objects in the galaxy, and also every Population II object spends a fraction of its time passing vertically through it. The entire disk rotates around a perpendicular axis through the nucleus. In an outward direction the circular rotational velocity increases until it reaches a maximum, probably near 6000 parsecs. Beyond this point it declines because the net gravitational force on a star is weaker. The sun is about 9000 parsecs from the nucleus but only 15 parsecs north of the galactic plane. Moving around the nucleus at about 150 mi/sec, it completes a revolution every 230 million years. In all of its 5-billion-year history the solar system has completed only 20 or 25 circuits of the nucleus.

The young objects of the galaxy inhabit the disk, and the youngest of all comprise the dramatic spiral arms. Along these spiral tracks are found the great nebulae of interstellar matter as well as the clusters and associations that were recently born out of this material. The arms are thus highlighted and lowlighted by blue supergiants, bright emission nebulae, and dark dust clouds. The sun is now near the inner edge of a spiral arm, and the interstellar matter in our neighborhood consists in the main of one hydrogen atom per cubic centimeter. Although the stuff between the stars accounts for perhaps one-third of all the matter in our vicinity, we are in a rather special location today. In the disk as a whole the interstellar matter contributes a much smaller percentage to the entire mass. Studies at 21 cm indicate that only 1 to 2 percent of the entire galactic mass is in interstellar space; the rest is in the stars.

The older stars are less concentrated in the disk; their motions carry them relatively far from the galactic plane and toward and away from the nucleus. They dwell in the halo and each one of them passes through the disk twice during every revolution around the nucleus. The halo is a spherical zone centered on the nucleus, with a radius of about 15,000 parsecs. Its edge is of course not abrupt; outward from the nucleus and into the halo the star density steadily decreases. Beyond 15,000 parsecs most of the halo material has been left behind. The most obvious members of the halo are the great globular clusters, and the most distant of them are about 100,000 parsecs from the nucleus; these remote systems are probably close to their apogalactic points as they sweep in enormous paths around the nucleus. Also in the halo are found single Population II stars, and radio surveys indicate that a tenuous ionized gas extends throughout this large spherical space.

If it could be seen from a million parsecs or 3 million light-years out in intergalactic space, the home galaxy would appear as a fuzzy patch of light of fifth magnitude. If it could be photographed with a large telescope, it would probably resemble NGC 4565 if seen edge-on and Messier 81 if viewed face-on. From a million parsecs the angular diameter of its disk would be about 2°, or about 4 times that of the moon. There is scarcely any doubt that our hypothetical photograph would be a splendid thing to behold.

EVOLUTION OF THE GALAXY

WE HAVE ALREADY hinted, in Chapter 19, Section 7, at the probable trends of galactic evolution. Let us reopen the question, remembering the clues provided both by the theory of stellar evolution and by our knowledge of the structure and dynamics of the galaxy as a whole. The first problem centers on the nature of the galaxy at the time of its birth. The age of our stellar system is probably around 10 billion years and at least 5. We have strong evidence both from the rate of solar evolution and from radioactive studies here on earth that the solar system is about 5 billion years old. Yet the motion of the sun is rather strongly confined to the galactic disk and its content of heavy elements is relatively high. Both lines of evidence indicate that the sun is an old Population I star. The Population II objects are older. Let us therefore assume that the protogalaxy began as a separate entity 10 billion years ago.

What was this primeval system like? We have already learned that stars are made out of interstellar matter. And as time goes by, more and more mass is tied up inside the white dwarf stars. Although exploding stars and normal evolving stars eject atoms back into the interstellar medium, those stars that have made the full evolutionary journey all the way to the white dwarf stage are near death. And they carry their mass with them to the grave. In the long run more matter goes into stars than comes out, and ultimately nearly every atom in the galaxy will be inside a star. Conversely, at the time of its origin the system was probably a medium of tenuous gas without stars. We have also seen that the interstellar material has gradually but steadily gained more and more heavy elements as a result of nucleosynthesis inside stars. It therefore appears plausible that the protogalaxy was a mass of tenuous hydrogen, with helium and other atoms coming into being later on in the cores of stars. Although future research may disprove us, let us assume for simplicity that the protogalaxy was an enormous and detached mass of extremely rarefied hydrogen gas, and that the date was 10 billion years ago.

We shall try to go even further back into the shadowy beginnings in the final chapter after we have surveyed the entire known universe of galaxies. For now we shall be content with the picture of a universal expanding gas that was tenuous but turbulent. At a certain stage it broke up into mammoth gaseous blobs that were the protogalaxies, and one of them was our home system. As neighboring blobs moved away from our own, they exerted no appreciable net gravitational force on us; Fig. 20.18:1 shows the general tug-of-war in which the individual forces tended to cancel each other. We were thus left alone

18. Early Days

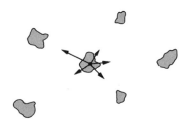

Fig. 20.18:1. Protogalaxies receding in various directions. Their net pull on our home system was not great enough to interfere with its development.

to develop without much outside interference. Because each proto-galaxy was turbulent, it had random currents of gas moving around in its interior. For each protogalaxy the sum of the angular momentum vectors of all the individual small volumes of gas was the net total angular momentum of the whole protogalaxy around some axis in space. Because of the principle of conservation of angular momentum, the present axis of our own system coincides with the original axis of rotation.

To begin with, our galaxy was probably a ragged sphere of tenuous hydrogen somewhat larger than the stellar system today. Because of the gravitational pull by each of its 10^{68} atoms on all of the others, the system began to shrink. Turbulent gas currents collided and blended their motions and angular momenta together. As the contraction proceeded and the ingredients were mixed, some order was imposed on the gigantic sphere, and a general slow rotation began. As tens or hundreds of millions of years rolled by, the contraction continued and the rotation rate was forced to increase. As the sphere diminished in size, a given mass was squeezed into a smaller and smaller volume. And thus the average gas density increased as time passed by. Through-out this time the matter was turbulent, with small-scale eddies spon-taneously forming and then disappearing. At a critical stage the average density became high enough so that extradense eddies, once they had formed spontaneously, were able to hold together gravitationally. At this time the first clusters and stars were born here and there throughout a large sphere. Today they are the eldest citizens of our galactic community, and the most illustrious of them are the halo globular clusters.

Once a star or cluster is born, it moves through the local surrounding gas without being appreciably influenced by it; rather it moves in response to the net gravitational force exerted on it by the entire galactic mass. In a general way the pull on such a body is toward the center of mass of the system. Now, these early objects were born when the general rotation of the gas sphere was slow. Therefore they inherited only a small rotational speed. From the sun we now see these Population II objects moving with high velocity. Their motions around the center of the galaxy lag well behind those of the younger stars, as we learned in Section 14. Since these early objects also inherited an inward radial component from the shrinking gas, they began to move in elongated tracks around the center. Those that were born far from today's galactic plane plunge through it twice each revolution, but spend the majority of their time far above and below it. Statistically speaking, as these objects move around the galaxy, they occupy the same volume of space in which they were born billions of years ago. This space com-prises the nucleus and the halo.

19. Later Days

THE FIRST generation of stars and clusters consumed only a minor fraction of the hydrogen. The rest of it continued contracting, its average density gradually increasing. The massive first-generation stars built helium quickly in their cores, and some of the heavier elements as well, and sent a proportion of their new products back into space to modify slightly the composition of the contracting sphere of gas. As the shrinkage continued, the sphere spun more rapidly, and the system began to flatten somewhat. The greater density made better conditions for star birth, and thus a second generation came into being throughout a smaller and somewhat flattened sphere. Each of these stars contained a minor amount of elements heavier than helium. Many of the RR Lyrae stars belong to this group. Today they move in somewhat elongated orbits and fill the same oblate-spheroidal volume of space in which they were born. Their rotational motions lag behind the sun's because the parent gas sphere was not rotating very fast at the time of their birth.

The contraction and flattening of the gas continued, and succeeding generations of stars sprinkled out. They contained more and more heavy elements and they occupied successively flatter spheroids. At some stage the gas could no longer contract toward the nucleus because of its large rotational velocity, but the vertical contraction continued. Old Population I stars were born in great abundance, the sun among them. They were born in the disk and remain in it today; their orbital velocities are large because the parent birth-cloud had contracted as much as possible toward the nucleus. Because angular momentum was conserved, when minimum size was reached so was maximum rotational velocity at every distance from the nucleus. These speeds were essentially those of today, as graphed in the curve of Fig. 20.11:4. Thus the old Population I stars are rather strongly concentrated in the galactic plane, their vertical motions are small, and their heavy-element concentrations are greater than those of the even older stars of Population II.

20. Today

STARS ARE STILL being born in the home galaxy now, but the birth rate is much lower today than it was when the sun was born. The rate was low during the first generation because the low gas density was not very favorable for birth. Later the density was higher and the birth rate increased. Ultimately, the gas supply dwindled, however, and the birth rate declined. Today the contraction and flattening of the interstellar matter is extreme, with most of the gas and dust occupying a disk that is relatively as thin as a long-play record. Star birth is almost exclusively confined to the disk; it is there that we find the blue supergiants and T Tauri stars of clusters and associations. Their galactic orbits are very nearly circular, their vertical motions are small, and they contain a maximum concentration of heavy elements. For reasons we do not understand, the gas and dust and very young stars are confined to spiral arms in the flat disk. Certainly the semiorderly shapes of the spinning spiral arms, as defined by their gas, dust, and luminous stars, are governed somehow by the galactic rotation. But whatever the explanation of the arms, it is clear that they comprise the remaining breeding ground of stars in our galaxy and in other spiral galaxies.

21. Tomorrow

ONLY 1 OR 2 percent of the galactic mass is now in interstellar space. As time goes on, an increasing percentage will go into new stars at the expense of the interstellar matter. At the same time, of course, existing stars will send atoms back into space, reasonably quietly if they are like the sun, but explosively if they are massive objects. As the future billions of years pass by, the process will continue until a large-scale equilibrium is established. At that time new stars will be born only rarely, consuming interstellar gas at the same statistical rate that stars expel atoms into space. Ultimately, blue supergiants will be a great rarity as will be the Strömgren spheres and emission nebulae that they illuminate. As the gas and dust and young stars in the arms are depleted, it seems certain that our spiral structure will become less and less spectacular.

The stars will continue their motions indefinitely around the galactic nucleus. But with the passage of time each star will evolve through the HR diagram at a rate that depends on its mass. In the long run only the feeble red dwarf stars will still remain on the main sequence. The galaxy will finally be almost free of interstellar matter, the spiral structure will be undetectable, and most stars will be small and dim. From a distance the galaxy will show a very faint reddish halo sliced through by a brighter reddish disk with a reddish nuclear region at its center. Beyond that we may expect blackness, with nothing remaining but dark spheres moving ceaselessly in their galactic orbits under the universal force of gravitation.

PROBLEMS

1. (a) Use the star maps of Chapter 4 to find the major constellations through which the Milky Way passes, beginning at galactic longitude 0°. (b) Use the same maps to estimate the galactic coordinates of Betelgeuse, Sirius, Alpha Centauri, Gamma Cassiopeiae, Deneb, and the north ecliptic pole.

2. (a) What do the data of Table 20.4:1 tell us about the structure of the galaxy? (b) In what way has the interstellar dust affected the various entries?

3. What is synchrotron radiation, how is it produced, and where has it been found in the galaxy?

4. Discuss the several methods that have been employed to study the spiral structure of the home galaxy.

5. (a) Give the dimensions and shape of the galactic nucleus, the galactic disk, and the galactic halo. (b) Locate the sun.

6. Explain how observations of moderately distant B stars at different galactic longitudes prove that the galaxy is rotating.

7. From the known rate of decrease of the circular velocity with distance from the galactic nucleus, compute the circular velocity and orbital period of stars at 8,000, 9,000, and 10,000 parsecs from the nucleus (one parsec $= 2 \times 10^{13}$ miles).

8. Explain how 21-cm observations help reveal motions in the galaxy.

9. Interpret the local random motions of the nearby stars in terms of the galactic orbits of these stars.

10. Explain why the so-called high-velocity stars are actually moving rather slowly.

11. Account for the fact first noted in Chapter 13 that the low-luminosity stars have, on the average, higher space velocities relative to the sun than do the high-luminosity stars.

12. Discuss two methods of estimating the total mass of the galaxy, and criticize both of them.

13. What is the Oort limit and what does it tell us?

14. Discuss the probable course of events in the early days of galactic evolution.

15. What will the galaxy look like if viewed from afar 100 billion years from now?

21

GALAXIES

THE earth yielded its exalted position of centrality in Copernican times; the sun then assumed the chief role. Not until the nineteenth century was the sun certainly established as just one star among many, and in the early decades of the twentieth century the sun and local stars were discovered to lie far from the center of our larger home, the Milky Way galaxy. The last frontier we know was crossed in 1924 when Edwin P. Hubble at the Mount Wilson Observatory showed that we are not alone; the home galaxy is but one of multitudes. And the repeated lessons of the past warn us loudly to make no claim that our system is the biggest galaxy in the universe or that it lies at the center of the universe. We shall soon see that the astronomical observations of the past few decades support the early lessons. In the largest domain we can survey with great optical and radio telescopes the galaxies are the individual members. And there is now no evidence that our own home system is specially favored, either in its size and structure or in its spatial location.

1. Early Speculations

NEBULAE HAVE been known, in small numbers, from pretelescopic times. With his telescopes Galileo was able to resolve a few such feebly luminous patches as Praesepe and show that they are clusters of stars. As the centuries passed, more and more fainter clouds were discovered and catalogued, but their true nature remained unknown.

By the middle of the eighteenth century these objects could be described generally as very faint, of small angular diameter, and more or less elliptical in shape. Some thought that they were holes in the star-studded sphere that afforded a glimpse of the fiery highest heaven beyond. In 1750 Thomas Wright of England conceived of the Milky Way as a finite and flattened assembly of stars and speculated that it was not isolated in space. He believed that the little dim clouds were other similar stellar systems, far away and unresolved. In 1755 Immanuel Kant, the German philosopher, extended Wright's notions to the theory of island universes. Assuming the Milky Way to be a circular disk of stars and other Milky Ways to be strewn at random far from each other in space, Kant reasoned that some such disks would be seen edge-on as highly elongated ellipses and that others would be seen face-on as circles. He also pointed out that the nebulae could not be resolved into individual stars because of their enormous distances. Nevertheless, the disks themselves were big enough to appear not as points but as patches of finite angular size. The ideas of Wright and Kant accounted for the observations of nebulae in a rational way, but proof of their general validity had to wait nearly two centuries for the construction of great reflecting telescopes.

New nebulae were discovered with increasing rapidity in the century that followed, especially by William and John Herschel. But nobody knew whether the little clouds were unresolved clusters of stars or perhaps enormous lumps of luminous fluid. In the 1860s, not very long after the spectra of chemical elements were beginning to be recorded in the laboratory, William Huggins of England discovered that some nebulae have emission lines in their spectra. These systems were therefore proved to be clouds of rarefied gas. During the latter years of the nineteenth century some of the patches were known to be star clusters and some were known to be gaseous nebulae. Since both groups were found close to the belt of the Milky Way, it was generally agreed that clusters and gaseous nebulae belong to our stellar system.

But what of the great majority, the dim blotches here and there all over the sky away from the Milky Way? Already it was known that some of the brighter of these patches showed a spiral pattern, including Messier 31 in Andromeda. The great Andromeda spiral is visible to the unaided eye as a hazy spot of fourth magnitude; telescopes revealed its over-all elliptical shape and spiral whirls. Interest in the true nature of the unidentified nebulae was awakened by the 1885 discovery of a nova, S Andromedae, in the middle of Messier 31. With a peak brightness of seventh magnitude and an assumed absolute magnitude of -8, its distance could be roughly estimated as 10,000 parsecs. Granted that the nova belonged to the Andromeda spiral and knowing that the long axis of the spiral measures about $2°$, astronomers could then estimate the maximum linear diameter of the nebula to be 350 parsecs. This dimension is very small in comparison with the size of the Milky Way and therefore would suggest that Messier 31 and other unidentified nebulae are small and not terribly distant members of our great galactic system. In the early years of this century it became possible to obtain the spectra of some of the more conspicuous patches, and two important findings emerged. (1) The spectra were continuous and were crossed by absorption lines, suggesting that the objects were collections of stars. (2) The measured radial velocities were, on the average, astonishingly large, and far greater than those of individual stars.

Fig. 21.1:1. The great spiral in Andromeda, Messier 31, with its two elliptical companions, Messier 32 at the left and NGC 205 at the lower right, photographed with the 48-inch Schmidt. (*Mount Wilson and Palomar Observatories photograph*)

But although the large radial velocities hinted that these systems were in a class by themselves and perhaps outside of the Milky Way, measures were also being made of the proper motions of various features in the spiral arms of nebulae. The deduced proper motions came out rather large, supporting the idea that these nebulae are relatively close to us and actual members of our galaxy. Into this confusing arena came eminent astronomers, some to debate the merits of the local-and-small hypothesis and others to champion the idea of island universes. Both sides had strong evidence at their command. Finally, late in 1924, Hubble took the stage; his work settled the long controversy and opened up for exploration an entirely new realm—the realm of the galaxies.

2. The New Realm

THE LARGE reflectors on Mount Wilson were able to resolve individual stars in the outlying parts of some of the bright galaxies, and Hubble discovered a number of Cepheid variables in the Andromeda spiral. Analysis of many photographs established the light curves of a dozen variable stars; for each star the period of light variation and the average apparent magnitude were known. The light curves were similar in range and shape to those of Cepheids in our galaxy and in the Clouds of Magellan, and the period-luminosity relationship described in Chapter 16, Section 6 was also shown by the variables in Messier 31. There could be little doubt that they were Cepheids. Given the period and average apparent magnitude of any one of these stars and the period-luminosity diagram, Hubble was able to estimate the distance of the Andromeda spiral as about 300,000 parsecs. More recently, with the absolute magnitude of Cepheids known to be 1.5 magnitudes brighter than originally thought, the distance to Messier 31 has been revised upward to 600,000 parsecs. Hubble also studied Cepheids in the bright spiral Messier 33 in Triangulum and in the irregular system NGC 6822 in Capricornus, establishing them also as very distant. Thus the little patches that Wright and Kant wrote about in the mideighteenth century were proved to be other galaxies, far beyond our own and comparable with our own.

The controversial evidence of the earlier years was studied again. The spectra confirmed that galaxies were assemblies of stars and that their radial motions were rapid. The large angular proper motions were not confirmed; the original findings originated in some obscure kind of measuring errors and did not reflect real transverse motions in the spirals. The puzzle of the 1885 nova in Messier 31 was settled with the recognition of many ordinary novae in that galaxy, with peak apparent magnitudes near 16. The 1885 star had actually been a supernova explosion, and the distinction between novae and supernovae was entirely unknown in those days. Thus the misleading clues were eventually explained, the correct clues were validated, and the case was clinched by the Cepheids. No longer were astronomers confined to the study of stars in one galaxy with dimensions of tens of thousands of parsecs. Suddenly in 1924 a new and enormously greater territory was opened to exploration; the known physical universe became a universe of galaxies—stellar assemblies here and there in space, some nearer, some farther, with the most distant detectable systems lying hundreds of millions of parsecs away.

3. The Distance of a Neighboring Galaxy

ASTRONOMERS are permanently and rightly concerned with finding the distances of objects; distances have to be determined reasonably correctly if we are to grope toward an understanding of the structure of the solar system, the home galaxy, and the universe of galaxies. Distances in the solar system are known rather precisely, because they have been studied for a very long time and also because they are not extremely great. The history of stellar distance measurement began more recently and the lengths involved are much greater. Distances of the nearby stars are known with less precision than are those in the solar system; the catalogued parallax of Alpha Centauri is probably within 1 percent of the true parallax. Farther afield the errors are bigger, and the distance of the sun from the galactic nucleus is uncertain by 10 to 20 percent. Astronomers have surveyed the universe of galaxies only since 1924, and the lengths to be measured are of course enormous. The estimated distances are accordingly rather doubtful; concerted research continues today to seek improvement in our knowledge of the distances of galaxies and thus of the scale of the universe.

The earth's orbit is thousands of times too small to serve as a base line for measuring the parallax of the closer galaxies, and we must be content with less direct methods. The most useful technique is exemplified by Hubble's investigations of Messier 31, Messier 33, and

NGC 6822. Individual luminous stars can be resolved in many of the nearby galaxies. When Cepheids are found, the period-luminosity relation can be employed to estimate the distance of their parent galaxy, provided the dimming of their light by interstellar dust in the parent galaxy and in our own is taken into account. Also useful are studies of the light curves of the ordinary novae that burst forth periodically in a galaxy. We know something of their peak absolute magnitudes from studies in our own system; from the peak apparent magnitude we can compute the distance of the system in which they appear. Another method is the comparison of the average apparent magnitude of the ten brightest stars in a given system with the absolute magnitude of the most luminous stars in our own galaxy.

It is of some interest to note that two of these methods conspired to give consistent but wrong distances during the first three decades of extragalactic studies. The Cepheids are the most trustworthy tool because of the well-established correlation of period and luminosity. But recall from Chapter 16, Section 6 that the luminosities of Cepheids were at first underestimated by about 1.5 magnitudes, and the error was not discovered until 1952. Now 1.5 in absolute magnitude corresponds to a factor of 3.98 in luminosity. And if an object is really four times more luminous than was thought, it must be twice as far away in order to have the apparent magnitude we observe. The method of brightest stars yielded distances which were consistent with those derived from Cepheids but which are now known to be too small. The brightest images in a number of galaxies were actually not stars at all, but unresolved emission nebulae some 1.5 to 2 magnitudes brighter than the most luminous stars. Thus again the distances to nearby galaxies were underestimated by a factor of 2 or even more in the first reconnaissance of the universe. Just as with the stars, the distances of remote galaxies are estimated by techniques that depend on a knowledge of the distances of the close ones. And so the whole detectable universe of galaxies was judged to be two or more times smaller than we believe it to be today.

The implications of the early and incorrect distance scale prompted occasional nightmares in the astronomical community before 1952. The novae in Messier 31 and other local galaxies seemed to be a somewhat different breed than our own. And the several hundred globular clusters in Messier 31 averaged four times less luminous than our own. The unhappiest note of all was the special status of the home galaxy; it was apparently the biggest galaxy in the universe. From the angular diameter of a galaxy and its distance, its linear diameter is calculated. But if all the distances used are only half what they should be, so are the computed linear diameters. As the decades passed, the influence of interstellar dust was recognized and the early over-estimates of distances *within* our galaxy were corrected. The estimated size of the Milky Way system steadily shrank. At the same time increasingly longer exposures of other galaxies revealed their fainter outlying parts, and their estimated angular diameters increased. But in spite of the approach to comparability we remained the biggest known galaxy until 1952. At that time the estimated extragalactic distances were increased twofold, as were the linear diameters of galaxies beyond our own. Since then the Andromeda spiral has taken over the leading role among the nearby systems. We are a giant spiral, but Messier 31 is somewhat bigger and more massive. The assumption of special status for our own home had long proved a wrong one, and the apparent early results on our own mammoth size engendered bad dreams. No longer are we the biggest of all.

The general problem of finding the distances to nearby galaxies demands that we use Cepheids, novae, brightest stars, globular clusters, and indeed any object within the parent galaxy that is luminous enough for identification. Our final choice of distance is then made so as to be consistent with the apparent magnitudes of the various indicators and with what we know of their absolute magnitudes from studies in our own galaxy. Some or all of these criteria can be used in nearby spirals and irregular galaxies, but the elliptical galaxies of Population II contain no superluminous stars. In them we can look for globular clusters or for an occasional nova outburst, but Cepheids are missing and the most luminous nonvariable stars of Population II are red giants with absolute magnitudes of only -2 or -3. Not until 1944 was it possible to resolve individual stars in elliptical systems. In that year Walter Baade used the 100-inch reflector on Mount Wilson to photograph the nucleus of Messier 31 and its two small elliptical companion galaxies. Helped by the wartime dim-out of lights in Los Angeles below, he was able for the first time to obtain images of single stars.

Fig. 21.3:1. NGC 147, a neighboring elliptical galaxy in which individual stars are resolved by the 200-inch telescope. (*Mount Wilson and Palomar Observatories photograph*)

Their resemblance to the brightest stars in the HR diagrams of Milky Way globular clusters led him to formulate the idea of two distinct stellar populations. At present the 200-inch Hale telescope is able to photograph the brightest red stars in a few of the nearby elliptical galaxies and thus help in the determination of their distances.

More remote galaxies must be studied by other techniques because their individual stars or globular clusters are not within the range of the greatest telescopes. What can be done here is first to compute the absolute magnitude of each nearby galaxy from a knowledge of its distance and its apparent magnitude. The median absolute magnitude is found to be about −15, equal to the light of 100 million suns. Then, when the apparent magnitude of a very distant galaxy is measured and its absolute magnitude is assumed to be −15, the distance can be calculated. Unfortunately, however, the estimate may well be wrong by a factor of 10 either way because galaxies are not all equally luminous. We shall later encounter this problem again.

PROPERTIES OF INDIVIDUAL GALAXIES

4. Classifying Galaxies

IN ANY GROUP of people a list of common features as well as individual traits can be tallied. Common to all or most of the group are arms, breathing, the ability to move, and the capacity to speak a language. Special identifying features, on the other hand, might be violet eyes, a violent temper, or three missing teeth. Similarly, all galaxies share at least two characteristics as far as we know. (1) Each one is enormous in size, and far larger than any nebula, cluster, or other unit studied thus far. (2) Each one contains, at the very least, an enormous number of stars. But beyond that there are great individual differences from one galaxy to the next. And an early task, taken up chiefly by Hubble, was to see if the great variety of objects could be placed in some kind of orderly sequence.

The classification of galaxies was and still is an empirical undertaking. The primary data are photographs of the nearer systems made with large reflectors, and the primary criterion for assigning a galaxy to one class or another is its appearance in the pictures. Additional information may be provided by spectrograms of the brighter central regions of a galaxy. About 3 percent of the thousand brightest galaxies are chaotic-looking affairs and bear no obvious resemblance to the remainder; they are the *irregulars*. The great majority are regular galaxies in the sense that each can be assigned its place along a fairly neat sequence of forms. These galaxies divide into two broad classes, the *spirals* and the *ellipticals*. Among the brighter systems the spirals account for about 77 percent of the total and the ellipticals for about 20 percent.

5. Irregular Galaxies

A SMALL proportion of the bright galaxies show no clear evidence of the symmetrical structure that is imposed by rapid rotation. These systems are the irregular galaxies and are symbolized by Irr. The most celebrated examples are the satellites of our own galaxy, the Large Magellanic Cloud and the Small Magellanic Cloud. Deep in the southern celestial hemisphere, these systems appear like two ragged and detached portions of the Milky Way. They are about 20° from one

Fig. 21.5:1. The Clouds of Magellan, photographed with a small wide-angle telescope. The Large Cloud is at the left and the Small Cloud is at the lower right. Achernar is the bright star at the upper right; the south celestial pole is off the picture at the bottom. (*Harvard College Observatory photograph*)

Edge-on View

SUN

LMC

SMC

Plan View

SUN

LMC

SMC

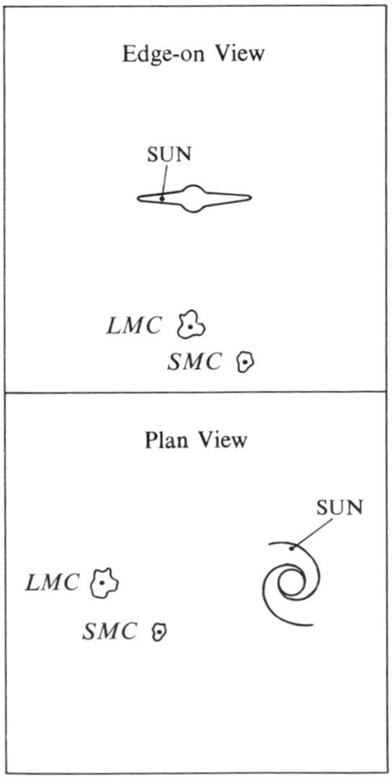

Fig. 21.5:2. Spatial location of the Magellanic Clouds.

another, and each is about 20° from the south celestial pole, appearing to circle it once a day as a consequence of the earth's rotation. The combined light from the Large Cloud is equivalent to that from a star of visual magnitude zero, and the Small Cloud is about 2 magnitudes fainter. The distances to the Clouds are uncertain by perhaps 20 percent, with the average estimate about 60,000 parsecs for both. Their approximate spatial locations are shown in Fig. 21.5:2. In the edge-on view the sun is moving away from the observer and in the plan view our galaxy is spinning clockwise and the trio is seen by a hypothetical observer who has traveled toward the north galactic pole to a distant point in intergalactic space.

The clouds and other Magellanic-type irregular galaxies have no clearly defined spiral structure; they are nevertheless known to contain interstellar gas and dust and luminous blue stars of spectral classes O and B. When the light of a galaxy is spread out into a spectrogram, the continuous spectrum and the spectral lines reveal the joint contribution of its more luminous contents. The composite spectra of Magellanic-type systems show the forbidden emission line of oxygen, indicating the presence of interstellar gas. Also, the trend of the continuous spectra proves that a major part of the light comes from stars whose spectral class is close to B0. The evidence is strong, therefore, that galaxies of this type are rich in young stars and interstellar matter.

Fig. 21.5:3. The Large Cloud of Magellan, photographed with a 6-inch telescope. (*Lick Observatory photograph*)

In the Clouds of Magellan themselves, however, globular clusters and individual RR Lyrae stars are known, and therefore such systems are not entirely composed of young stars. A major distinction between the young Population I objects of irregular galaxies and those in our own

Fig. 21.5:4. The Small Cloud of Magellan, photographed with the 33–36-inch Armagh-Dunsink-Harvard Schmidt telescope near Bloemfontein, South Africa. At the right edge is a part of 47 Tucanae, one of the brightest globular clusters of our own galaxy. (*Harvard College Observatory photograph*)

galaxy appears to be their spatial distribution. In the former their arrangement is irregular, whereas in the Milky Way they are confined strongly to the spiral arms in the thin equatorial plane.

A somewhat different kind of irregular galaxy is represented by Messier 82. Again, these systems have no rotational symmetry and thus defy easy description. But unlike galaxies of the Magellanic

Fig. 21.5:5. The irregular galaxy Messier 82 in Ursa Major, photographed with the 200-inch telescope. (*Mount Wilson and Palomar Observatories photograph*)

type, this class is not resolved into stars. Messier 82 itself is about 3,000,000 parsecs away, and photographs taken with the largest telescopes should reveal individual stars or nebulae brighter than absolute magnitude -4 or -5. None are seen, however, and the most prominent features are the lanes and wisps of overlying dust. Another example of these puzzling systems is NGC 5195, the irregular companion of the Whirlpool Galaxy shown in the title page illustration.

6. Normal Spirals

MOST BRIGHT galaxies are spirals. This class is divided into two major categories, the *normal spirals* designated by S and the *barred spirals* designated by SB. The two major arms of a normal spiral emerge from opposite points of a smooth bright nuclear region and coil around and outward until they are too faint to be seen. The normal spirals can be arranged in a sequence determined by how tightly the arms are wound and the extent to which stars and nebulae can be resolved. The loosest coiling is found among the Sc galaxies, such as Messier 33, our neighboring spiral in Triangulum, and Messier 51, the Whirlpool Galaxy. Individual luminous stars and H II nebulosities are easily seen. Ordinarily the nuclei of Sc spirals are relatively small whereas the spiral arms are broad and bright and often branch in their outer parts. These systems are rather blue, indicating they have a fairly heavy population of young stars. When photographs of many Sc galaxies and Irr galaxies of Magellanic type are inspected, we find a smooth transition from one class to the other. The contents of both types are reasonably similar, but the spiral pattern so prominent in the Sc's is not seen in the irregulars.

Galaxies of type Sb have tighter spiral windings, and usually their smooth nuclei are bigger than in Sc systems. Messier 31 in Andromeda,

Fig. 21.1:1, is classified as Sb, and so indeed is our own galaxy. Both systems have spiral arms that are made of interstellar gas and dust and luminous young stars. Baade's wartime photographs showed that the nuclear part of Messier 31 contains, as its brightest members, red giants of absolute magnitude -2 to -3. It is therefore a region in which elderly Population II objects predominate. The disk of the system is populated with a substratum of Population II stars in addition to the more obvious spiral features of Population I. Since the rotational axis of Messier 31 is inclined at an angle of 75° to the line of sight, we see our great neighbor nearly edge-on, but not quite. Another fine

Fig. 21.6:1. Messier 33, a neighboring Sc spiral in Triangulum, photographed in red light with the 48-inch Schmidt. (*Mount Wilson and Palomar Observatories photograph*)

Sb system, seen almost perfectly edge-on, is NGC 4565, illustrated in Fig. 20.7:2. As with Messier 31, the diameter of the bright nucleus is only about one-tenth as great as that of the visible major axis of the disk. The central dust layer is very thin, like that of our own system. The rotational axis of Messier 81, Fig. 20.7:1, is less inclined to the line of sight than are the axes of the other two Sb systems illustrated. The nucleus is a collection of Population II stars, and the innermost spiral features are lanes of dust. Only farther out are the arms highlighted by knots of bright nebulae and individual luminous blue stars. The distance of Messier 81 is about 3,000,000 parsecs, or 10 million light-years. It is sometimes disconcerting to realize that we see galaxies as they were very long ago. In the last 10 million years Messier 81 has rotated a fraction of a turn and the more luminous individual stars in the spiral arms have evolved rapidly and declined in brillance. Gone too are their associated H II spheres. The spiral arms are doubtless still prominent, because new blue supergiants have surely been born. But the detailed structure of the arms is different now from what it is in the photographs *we* make of Messier 81 now.

The arms of Sa galaxies are even more tightly wound than are those of Sb systems, and they are usually smooth. NGC 1302 is an example. The arms are usually almost circular in shape and no individual stars are resolved. Most Sa's have dominant bright nuclei that are relatively large. The color indexes of the Sa spirals average larger than those of the Sc's and the composite spectral type is of class G. It appears that there is a continuous sequence from the irregulars, whose light is chiefly contributed by blue stars, through Sc and Sb to Sa galaxies. The light of the latter is dominated by photons from red giant stars.

Fig. 21.6:2. Two views of NGC 1302, an Sa spiral, photographed with the 200-inch telescope. (*Mount Wilson and Palomar Observatories photographs*)

Fig. 21.6:3. Two views of the S0 system NGC 4762, the larger photograph made with the 100-inch and the insert negative with the 48-inch telescope. (*Mount Wilson and Palomar Observatories photographs*)

The next and final kind of normal spiral is that represented by the S0 systems. They provide a bridge between the galaxies that show spiral structure and the smooth and featureless elliptical galaxies. A few of these systems show circular dust lanes, but there is no evidence of any spiral shape. Most S0's are free of obvious dust and are classified by their over-all distribution of light. A splendid example is NGC 4762, which is seen edge-on and is exceedingly flat. The structure of an S0 galaxy resembles that of a normal spiral with all of its interstellar matter and youngest stars removed from their spiral-shaped volume of space. Remaining is a bright spheroidal nucleus fading away into a flatter and bigger lens. Surrounding these parts is an enormous but thin disk of stars in a plane perpendicular to the axis of rotation. NGC 3115 is sometimes classified as S0 and sometimes as elliptical.

Fig. 21.6:4. The edge-on S0 galaxy NGC 3115, photographed with the 200-inch telescope. (*Mount Wilson and Palomar Observatories photograph*)

Its structure consists of a nearly globular nucleus and an outlying thin disk. Less flattened than NGC 4762, either its rotational axis is not quite perpendicular to the line of sight or its intrinsic flattening is not quite so severe.

7. Barred Spirals

A MINORITY of spirals, about one in five, have a bright bar that slices across the nucleus. The arms begin at the two ends of the bar and wind outward much as they do in normal spirals. The barred spiral galaxies can be ordered in a sequence that parallels that of the ordinary spirals and depends on both the openness of the arms and the degree of resolution into stars and nebulosities. The most open class is designated SBc. As in the normal Sc's, the spiral arms are well resolved into individual knots. Furthermore, the transverse bars in these galaxies sometimes show a series of bright lumps. These systems are relatively blue in color and contain many Population I objects.

Galaxies of type SBb have more tightly wound arms that are not so highly resolved, and their bars are smooth, without bright knots. Some have a thin ring-shaped arm that surrounds the nucleus and bar, with spiral-shaped arms coiling outward from the ring. Others, like NGC 1300, show no rings at all. Instead, the arms spring from the end of the bar and spiral outward for the better part of one complete turn. The softer light of the arms is smooth in texture, and superposed on it are many small bright knots and a few dark lanes of dust. The bar and nucleus show no bright nebulae, but each wing of the bar has an overlying straight rod of dust.

The next class of barred spiral is designated SBa, and here the arms are generally smooth and unresolved and are so tightly wrapped that they often appear to be complete rings instead of spirals. These systems are redder than their SBc counterparts, and as with the normal spirals there is a progression along the sequence of decreasing numbers of young blue stars.

The final group of barred spirals, SB0, is intermediate between the elliptical galaxies and the SBa systems. To be classified as SB0 a galaxy must have a bar but it cannot show spiral arms. In some of these

Fig. 21.7:1. NGC 1300, a beautiful SBb barred spiral in Eridanus, photographed with the 200-inch Hale telescope. (*Mount Wilson and Palomar Observatories photograph*)

systems the bar is bright and very prominent; in others it is only a minor brightening of the lens in two diametrically opposite regions. Occasional SB0 galaxies are surrounded by very faint envelopes or rings. These dim features are centered on the nucleus and have diameters two or three times the length of the bar.

8. Elliptical Galaxies

About 20 percent of the bright galaxies are beautifully symmetric but featureless systems. They are the ellipticals and are symbolized by the letter E. Some have highly flattened contours, lenticular in shape; others are ellipses of moderate eccentricity; and still others appear circular. The surface brightness of E galaxies is generally very great at the center and falls off smoothly to indefinite and unknown boundaries. Because there are no distinctive markings such as spiral arms or superluminous stars, and only occasionally are there small dark patches, the classification of E systems is based solely on the observed shape of the contours. If the measured semimajor axis of an E galaxy is a and the semiminor axis b, the ellipticity is defined as $(a - b)/a$, and the galaxy is assigned to a numerical subclass equal to ten times the ellipticity. Thus a circular E system has $b = a$ and an ellipticity of zero and belongs to class E0. NGC 205, the more elongated companion of Messier 31 shown in Fig. 21.1:1, has axes of about 10′ and 5′. Thus $b/a = 0.5$ and the ellipticity is also 0.5; thus NGC 205 is designated E5. The smaller companion, Messier 32, is an E2 galaxy. The most flattened class recognized is E7; regular galaxies flatter than this are probably all spirals. NGC 3115, Fig. 21.6:4, is now usually assigned to class S0, but has very nearly the characteristics of an E7 galaxy.

In three dimensions the E galaxies are shaped like oblate spheroids because of their rotations. But in general we do not know the true degree of flattening of any given galaxy because we cannot tell the angle between the rotational axis and the line of sight. All we know is that a particular galaxy is at least as flat as it appears in projection on the sky; it may be flatter if it could be viewed from other points in space. Thus an edge-on E7 shows its true shape. An E0 system, on the other hand, may be globular in three dimensions or it may be lenticular in three dimensions with its rotational axis pointing toward

Fig. 21.8:1. NGC 205, an E5 galaxy in company with Messier 31 and 32, recorded by the 200-inch telescope. (*Mount Wilson and Palomar Observatories photograph*)

us. When all the bright E galaxies in the sky are examined statistically, however, it is possible to make a deduction from the data on the ellipticities. Let us assume that the rotational axis of each E galaxy points in a random direction. First suppose all these systems are true globes; we should then see them all in projection as E0 systems—at odds with the facts. Next suppose they are all thin circular disks oriented in all ways; we should then see half of all galaxies rounder than E5 and the other half flatter than E5. This time our assumption is too severe; only about 20 percent are actually classified as flatter than E5. The observed data indicate that all degrees of true flattening occur; some ellipticals are true globes, others are moderately flattened oblate spheroids, while the most extreme are lens-shaped with $b/a = 0.3$. More flattened galaxies belong to the spiral family.

Only the nearest ellipticals, those within about 1,000,000 parsecs, have been resolved into stars. A celebrated example is NGC 205, the outer companion of the Andromeda spiral. The granular structure of the outlying parts is caused by individual red giant stars of absolute magnitude -2 to -3. The brighter images are stars of our own galaxy, through and past which we look to see NGC 205 as it was about 2 million years ago. The character of the brightest stars, the over-all reddish color, and the composite spectrum show conclusively that NGC 205 and other elliptical galaxies are Population II systems. Gone is the evidence of youth; only rarely do luminous blue supergiants disrupt the extreme smoothness and serenity of these old assemblies. Farther afield, at a distance of perhaps 10 million parsecs, is the giant E0 galaxy, Messier 87, shown in Fig. 21.8:2. Its brightest stars are several magnitudes too faint to show as individual images; instead the joint

Fig. 21.8:2. The great E0 galaxy Messier 87, in the Virgo cluster and a strong source of radio radiation, photographed with the 200-inch telescope. (*Mount Wilson and Palomar Observatories photograph*)

light of all member stars contributes to the smooth distribution of light. Surrounding Messier 87 are hundreds of nonstellar and slightly fuzzy images. These are globular clusters dwelling in the outer halo of the system. Also visible are several very distant galaxies; the smaller and fainter of these little elongated patches are more than a billion light-years away.

An entirely different sort of E galaxy is the dwarf elliptical. These galaxies are so underpopulated that they are found only if they are relatively nearby. We can look right through the closer ones and see distant galaxies. Many RR Lyrae stars and an occasional globular cluster have been identified in these dwarfs and thus, like the larger ellipticals, they contain Population II objects. They are called Sculptor-type galaxies after the prototype, which lies near the south galactic pole and was discovered in 1938.

9. The Sequence of Galaxies

THE ENTIRE array of the thousand brightest galaxies can be arranged into a reasonably regular sequence, as shown in Fig. 21.9:1. It should be remembered, however, that the progression is not perfectly orderly, but rather indicative of a general trend from the chaotic irregulars with their many young stars through the spiral sequences to the placid ellipticals with their old stars. The division between normal spirals and barred spirals is not complete, and a number of galaxies are intermediate in their structure. At one end of the sequence the irregulars are not pure Population I systems, for some of them are known to contain RR Lyrae stars and globular clusters. At the other end the ellipticals are not necessarily perfectly pure Population II systems. In NGC 205, for example, there are some weak dust patches and about a

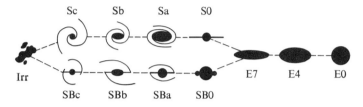

Fig. 21.9:1. The sequence of galaxies of different types.

dozen B stars have been found. Moreover, a fair proportion of E galaxies show the oxygen emission line at 3727 A, revealing the presence of interstellar gas. Finally, it should be stressed again that the galaxies resemble a collection of people: all have certain features in common, they can be sorted approximately into groups according to their appearance, and yet most have distinctive characteristics that allow us to recognize them as individuals.

10. Luminosities

WHEN THE DISTANCE of a galaxy is known and its apparent magnitude is measured, we can compute its correct absolute magnitude if it is possible to account for the effect of intervening dust. Among the 17 nearest known galaxies the Andromeda spiral is the most luminous, with $M_v = -21$. Thus our giant neighbor emits the light of 20 to 30 billion suns, some of it coming from luminous stars and the majority from feeble stars. Our own galaxy ranks a fairly close second, followed by the Large Magellanic Cloud, Messier 33, and the Small Magellanic Cloud. The close elliptical satellites of Messier 31 are nearly 5 magnitudes fainter than their parent, each emitting only 1 to 2 percent as much radiation. The remaining neighboring galaxies are all dwarfs, eight of elliptical type and two irregulars. The feeblest probably have $M_v = -10$ and therefore radiate less than one ten-thousandth of the energy emitted by Messier 31. The median absolute magnitude of the entire group is close to $M_v = -15$, or 100 million suns, but the greater spatial abundance of the feeble dwarfs is far more than balanced by the much greater candle power of the few luminous systems. In fact, it is likely that the joint light of Messier 31 and our own system exceeds that of all the other 15 galaxies combined.

The luminosity function of galaxies calls to mind that of the stars near the sun. The ultraluminous systems are very rare in space, those of middling luminosity are most abundant, and the feeble galaxies are the most frequent of all. As far as we now know, however, there is a minimum luminosity for galaxies, perhaps near $M_v = -10$. Next downward in the hierarchy of astronomical systems are the feebler and much smaller globular clusters. The globular clusters are not small galaxies but distinct subunits of lesser dimensions. They are found associated not only with big galaxies but also with some of the smaller elliptical galaxies of our greater neighborhood.

11. Sizes and Masses

THE MAJOR AXIS of the Andromeda spiral measures about 2.2° when the brighter main body is examined, but the fainter outlying parts extend the length of the major axis almost twofold. If the distance is 600,000 parsecs the linear diameter of Messier 31 is about 45,000 parsecs. That of the home galaxy is about 30,000 parsecs. The Large Cloud and Messier 33 are both about 10,000 parsecs in diameter, and the Small Cloud perhaps 6,000 parsecs. The smallest nearby dwarfs measure only about 1,000 parsecs in diameter. The median linear diameter of the 17 nearest known galaxies is between 2,000 and 2,500 parsecs.

The masses of galaxies may be calculated by various methods. We shall see in the next section that the rotational speeds of a number of galaxies have been measured spectrographically. As a crude first estimate we can examine an edge-on galaxy and use the Doppler effect to deduce the orbital speed of an outlying bright nebula around the nucleus. In the Andromeda spiral, for example, objects in the disk at 1.2°, or 13,000 parsecs, from the nucleus are found to be circling the center at a speed of 190 mi/sec. The period of rotation at that distance is therefore about 3×10^8 years. We may then use Kepler's third law to deduce the mass, just as we did in Chapter 14 to find the masses of double stars. The mass of giant Messier 31 found in this way is near 2×10^{11} solar masses, or about twice the mass of our galaxy. Having seen that the Andromeda spiral and our own rank first and second in luminosity and size among our neighbors, it is not surprising that their same status is preserved in being the most massive. The Magellanic Clouds and Messier 33 have substantially smaller masses, perhaps a few billion suns each. Although not very much less luminous than the great Sb spirals, these Sc and Irr galaxies have a greater proportion of young blue supergiant stars. They are thus very luminous for their masses. The elliptical galaxies, on the other hand, are dominated by old stars that have retained virtually all of their mass but have declined in energy output. Although relatively feeble, the companions of Andromeda are estimated to have masses of a few billion suns each. Very little is known about the smallest dwarf galaxies, but it is likely that their masses are only 10^7 to 10^6 suns. It would take many thousands of them to equal the mass of one giant galaxy.

12. Rotations

THE FLATTENED forms of galaxies indicate that they are spinning around their minor axes. In Chapter 20 we saw abundant evidence from the proper motions of stars and from the radial velocities of stars and interstellar gas clouds that the home galaxy is spinning in this same way. Spectra have been made of a number of the brighter edge-on galaxies, with the slit of the spectrograph oriented along the major axes. The resulting spectrograms have absorption lines that are slightly tipped, as shown schematically in Fig. 21.12:1. The effect is exaggerated for clarity. Light coming from the part of the galaxy near *A* is violet-shifted compared with light proceeding from the center, while light from the vicinity of *B* is red-shifted. Thus the *A* end is approaching, the *B* end receding, and the center moving transverse to the line of sight. Measurement of the Doppler shifts allows the determination of the rotational speed. The straightness of the sloped spectral lines in the figure indicates that we are observing the solid-body type of rotation that occurs in the central bright regions of the galaxy. Rotational speeds of the order of 100 mi/sec are found from spectrograms of this sort. The method fails for galaxies that are nearly face-on because the rotational motions are then not radial but at right angles to the line of sight.

For the closest bright galaxies it has been possible to obtain spectrograms of bright nebulosities here and there over the face of the system and also to observe the Doppler shifts of the 21-cm line in different zones. Both techniques confirm the rotations. Each of the Clouds of Magellan is turning rather slowly, whereas the motions in the Andromeda spiral are much faster as a consequence of its great mass. Figure 21.12:2 shows the approximate observed velocity curve for the major axis of Messier 31. The southwest side is approaching and the northeast side is receding. The center of mass approaches us at 170 mi/sec, chiefly because of the sun's orbital motion around our galactic nucleus. The peak rotational velocity occurs about 1.2°, or 13,000 parsecs, from the nucleus and is about 190 mi/sec. The straight part of the curve near the center suggests that the circular velocity is approximately proportional to distance from the nucleus in the inner regions. Recent spectrographic observations with the 120-inch reflector at the Lick Observatory show that the velocity curve in the innermost part of Messier 31 is more complicated than the figure indicates. The measurements reveal a very small core of radius 2", or about 6 parsecs, that is spinning surprisingly fast. This tiny core appears to rotate once every million years or so, as contrasted with periods that are several hundred times as long in the outer parts of the galaxy.

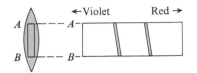

PROPERTIES OF
INDIVIDUAL GALAXIES

Fig. 21.12:1. Galaxy rotations are sometimes revealed by the tilt of their spectral lines.

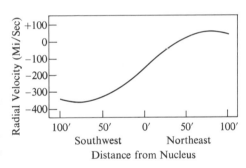

Fig. 21.12:2. Radial velocities at different points along the major axis of Messier 31.

13. Relative Frequency of Types

WE SAW IN Section 4 that the great majority of the thousand brightest galaxies are spirals. About 3 percent are irregular, 77 percent spiral, and 20 percent elliptical. But these figures are misleading. Recall from Chapter 13 that most of the *apparently* brightest stars are intrinsically very luminous. Although rare in space, their great radiative powers admit them to the group of first-magnitude stars in spite of their generally great distances. When, however, we examine the stars in a given *volume* of space, we find that the feeble red dwarfs are actually in the majority. The same situation holds for the galaxies. When we examine the best sample we know, the *local group*, the relative numbers change remarkably. These 17 nearest known systems are listed in Table 22.4:1 (page 511). Included are four irregulars, three spirals, and ten ellipticals. Thus the ellipticals account for about 60 percent of the total and the spirals for less than 20 percent. Future discoveries of nearby galaxies will reveal more dwarfs; the luminous neighbors have already been found. The essential reason for the very different results from the two kinds of surveys is simply that the average luminosity of the spirals is several times greater than that of the other types. Thus a survey to a given limiting apparent magnitude reaches two or three times as far into space for the spirals as for the others and hence includes a disproportionate number of spiral galaxies.

In our stellar studies we found that the feebler main-sequence stars were the most frequent of all, and that they contained a majority of the total mass of all the stars in a given volume of space. With the galaxies the situation is rather different, if we can assume that the local group is a reasonable sample of the universe. In sheer numbers the dwarf ellipticals are in the majority. But it is the great spirals that occupy the largest fraction of space, that contain the majority of all stars and therefore the majority of the mass. And it is also the stars of the great spirals that emit the majority of all the radiation that goes into intergalactic space.

THE EVOLUTION OF GALAXIES

14. Significance of Galaxy Classification

THE SEQUENCE of galaxy types begins with the chaotic irregulars. Although they contain a substratum of very old objects, their most striking characteristic is the high abundance of irregularly distributed young stars and interstellar material. Star-birth is going on vigorously in these systems. The Sc and SBc systems also abound in luminous blue stars, their associated Strömgren spheres, and clouds of dust, all spread along loosely coiled spiral arms. The Sb and SBb galaxies are not so highly resolved, except in their outer parts, and their over-all color indexes are not so blue. The Sa and SBa systems are redder still, and their arms are not well resolved; young blue supergiants are less abundant. Galaxies of type S0 and SB0 appear to be spirals and barred spirals in their essential structure, but with the bright and obvious spiral markers missing; youthful stars and the interstellar gas and dust out of which such stars are born seem to be either almost or entirely absent. Finally, the elliptical galaxies are almost totally composed of

Population II objects. Occasionally they have dust patches or a clump of blue stars and some of their spectra reveal interstellar matter. But apart from these minor impurities they are very mature and orderly systems, rather red in color. Some E galaxies are shaped like lenses, others are oblate spheroids of lesser ellipticity, and some are globes. A few ellipticals, like Messier 87, are giants in size and are surrounded by hundreds of globular clusters. In our own neighborhood all the ellipticals are smaller, and the less luminous and massive dwarfs have no globular clusters at all.

The general trend along the sequence of galaxies is one of decreasing concentration of young stars and presumably, therefore, of birth material. It is very significant that the steady decline in numbers of resolved blue supergiants and nebulosites is confirmed separately by the decreasing blueness as revealed by the photoelectrically measured color indexes of different galaxies and by analyses of their composite spectra. The light of the irregulars is dominated by blue O and B supergiants of Population I, whereas that of the ellipticals is dominated by red giants of Population II, and there is a steady and progressive change along the sequence.

Independent evidence has recently been provided by 21-cm studies of our own and other galaxies. In the Clouds of Magellan the interstellar neutral hydrogen has been variously estimated to account for 10 to 50 percent of the total mass. If the true figures indeed lie in this range, these representatives of the irregular galaxies contain a larger percentage of interstellar matter than do any of the regular galaxies that have been measured. Interstellar hydrogen in Messier 33, of type Sc, accounts for only about 5 to 10 percent of the total mass of that system. Our galaxy and Messier 31, both Sb spirals, have only 1 to 2 percent of their masses external to stars. The failure to detect 21-cm radiation from ellipticals suggests that in them the ratio of interstellar matter to total mass is less than one part in a hundred. Thus the early results from radio investigations indicate a steady decline in interstellar matter along the sequence of galaxy types. Recall that in our own galaxy the dense regions of interstellar matter are the regions where young stars are found. This correspondence extends to other galaxies: where interstellar gas and dust abound, stars are born. And the sequence of galaxy types runs the gamut from the irregulars which are rich in stellar breeding grounds to the ellipticals which have little or no signs of youth.

15. Protogalaxies and Their Development

A SATISFACTORY theory for the evolution of galaxies must account for the varying degrees of maturity we observe among assemblies of different types. And no fully acceptable theory has been proposed. A reasonable starting point, however, is the assumption that individual galaxies begin their careers as huge and turbulent clouds of gas. A given protogalaxy or cluster of protogalaxies begins as one or more detached blobs that form in a universal expanding gas. Only those clouds that are dense enough can hold together; the rest dissolve, perhaps to form again at a later time. The different clouds probably have a variety of masses and dimensions. Some are endowed with much angular momentum and others with little. Some may be born in relative isolation and thus be left more or less free to develop by themselves; others come into being in dense clusters and may lead highly disturbed young lives. The great diversity of possible conditions at birth may account in part for the many types of galaxies we observe today.

Although it may be assumed that a galaxy will emerge once a protogalaxy has come into being, there remains a fundamental and unsolved question. Are the galaxies all of the same age? Or are they being born at a constant rate as time goes by? Or does the truth lie somewhere in between? Nobody has yet given final and compelling answers to these queries. At first, it is appealing to make the hypothesis that protogalaxies are always coming into being at a constant rate. The irregulars, with all their interstellar gas, may then be regarded as young systems that have much star-building material left. The spirals are older. And the ellipticals are very old and clean and red in color. On second thought, one wonders why old globular clusters and RR Lyrae stars are found in the Clouds of Magellan. When will we find an ultra-ancient and extremely red elliptical galaxy that now contains only lower main-sequence stars? And where are the youthful blue galaxies of pure Population I?

At the other extreme one can argue that all protogalaxies were born simultaneously, but that different types evolved at different rates. For the sake of argument, assume that the birth date was 10 billion years ago. A protogalaxy with little or no angular momentum perhaps contracted rapidly, the blue supergiants sprinkling forth early and quickly running their course of evolution; we see it now as an elliptical system. Another protogalaxy with more rotation was perhaps prevented from maturing at such a rapid pace, and now, 10 billion years later, it is still producing stars in a flattened equatorial disk. It is a spiral galaxy. But where do the irregular systems fit into the picture? Their abundance of interstellar matter and young stars argues for immaturity. On the other hand, they seem to possess little angular momentum; in this respect they are more like the ellipticals than like the spirals.

Whatever the definitive theory of evolution may turn out to be, it appears reasonably clear that the scheme of development of a normal galaxy generally follows the sequence for our home system described at the end of the preceding chapter. A protogalaxy of gas shrinks, the first stars and star clusters are born, shrinkage continues, and more stars and clusters come into being. As the process continues, the interstellar material is continually enriched in its content of heavy elements— elements that were previously synthesized inside stars. But the over-all ratio of interstellar mass to total mass decreases steadily as more and more matter becomes tied up in white dwarf stars. In a galaxy with large angular momentum, like our own, successively younger generations of stars occupy more and more flattened oblate spheroids. The youngest stars and the interstellar gas and dust are finally confined to a flattened equatorial region. A protogalaxy with little angular momentum may become a system of type E, and one with no angular momentum a globular galaxy with a very large number density of stars in its central parts. Thus the ellipticals of different degrees of flattening and the highly flattened spirals can probably be interpreted as protogalaxies with less or more original angular momentum. Outstanding problems still to be solved are the explanations of spiral arms, of barred spiral galaxies, and of the place of irregular systems in the story of galaxy evolution.

PROBLEMS

1. Explain how Hubble discovered that the Andromeda spiral lies far outside our galaxy.

2. Discuss the methods by which we can determine the distance of a relatively nearby galaxy.

3. Before 1952 it seemed fairly certain that the home galaxy was the biggest one of all. Why have our ideas changed since that time?

4. Describe the two types of irregular galaxies.

5. Distinguish between the appearance of the different kinds of (**a**) normal spiral galaxies and (**b**) barred spirals.

6. (**a**) Describe the classification system for elliptical galaxies. (**b**) What is the designation of an elliptical whose apparent axis ratio is 0.62?

7. Why do astronomers believe that elliptical galaxies range in true shape from highly flattened oblate spheroids to spheres?

8. What is the observational evidence that elliptical galaxies are Population II systems?

9. How do we know that irregular galaxies are not absolutely pure Population I systems and that ellipticals are not absolutely pure Population II systems?

10. The visual absolute magnitude of our own galaxy is $M_v = -20$. What is the luminosity of the galaxy in terms of the luminosity of the sun?

11. Discuss the luminosity function of the nearby galaxies.

12. Explain and criticize one method of finding the mass of a relatively nearby galaxy.

13. Describe two kinds of observations that can provide us with information on the rotations of galaxies.

14. About three-quarters of the thousand brightest galaxies are spirals, but the ellipticals are the most abundant per unit volume of space. Explain the discrepancy.

15. Discuss the correlation between young stars and interstellar matter in galaxies beyond our own.

22

THE UNIVERSE OF

GALAXIES

In the last chapter we studied galaxies as individual aggregations of stars. Now we shall survey the known physical universe as a whole, the vast domain in which the galaxies are isolated points. The task is a triple one. (1) Let us find out what we can about the structure of the known universe. Are galaxies distributed uniformly in space, like the atoms in a pailful of air? Or are there major changes in density from one point to another, as at different levels in the earth's atmosphere? (2) We wish to learn how galaxies move in space. Are they stationary or not? (3) We shall make an excursion into the realm of cosmology, the science which seeks to assess the over-all nature and behavior of the physical universe. The cosmologist employs the facts and statistical data on galaxies that observational astronomers provide; he then attempts to devise a theory or model of the universe of galaxies that does no violence to the facts and that suggests future observations as tests for his ideas.

THE SPATIAL DISTRIBUTION OF GALAXIES

1. Arrangement on the Celestial Sphere

Studies of the distribution of stars in our home galaxy reveal that their arrangement is anything but uniform. There are many more faint stars in a square degree near the galactic equator than in the same

THE UNIVERSE OF
GALAXIES

area near the galactic poles. Similar studies can be made of the galaxies, for example by plotting on a globe the positions of all systems brighter than a given magnitude. We can then estimate whether our Milky Way system lies in a wheel-shaped congregation of galaxies or near the edge of a spherical congregation, or at the center of an apparently endless universe. Such investigations are analogous to William Herschel's star gauges. What have astronomers learned from their gauges of galaxies?

2. Zone of Obscuration

WE LEARNED in Chapter 18, Section 11 that not a single one of the 1200 brightest galaxies is located within 10° of the galactic equator. The vacancy of this belt is perhaps the most striking feature when we look at the general arrangement of galaxies over the whole sky. It is, however, a strictly local effect. Many lines of evidence prove the existence of a tenuous layer of dust clouds in and near the main plane of the home galaxy. And the belt of nearly complete obscuration arises without question from our own galactic dust. There most certainly are bright galaxies at low galactic latitude, but their light is dimmed by many magnitudes on traversing the disk of our own system.

Our analyses of galaxy counts must account not only for the more or less complete dimming of external systems located in the galactic belt, but also for the partial dimming of galaxies at the greater galactic latitudes. As shown in Fig. 22.2:1, light from a galaxy toward the north galactic pole suffers the least possible extinction by a layer of dust, about one-fourth of a magnitude. Light arriving from a galaxy at latitude 30° encounters a path of interstellar dust that is twice as long and therefore less of the light reaches our telescopes. The general effect is that if there are really equal numbers of galaxies per square degree in both directions, we will count only about 70 percent as many at latitude 30° as at the galactic poles. When the local effects of dust are assessed and eliminated, it appears that galaxies lie in all directions from us. What is more, when sample counts of galaxies are made down to very faint magnitudes, it is found that the number of galaxies per unit area of the sky is about the same in any one direction as in any other. As far as such studies have told us, the distribution of galaxies on the celestial sphere is statistically *isotropic*, the same in every direction. There is no clear evidence of a major piling up of galaxies in any given part of the sky, no evidence of a dense "center" of the observable universe.

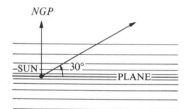

Fig. 22.2:1. Galactic dust dims the light arriving from external systems. The lower the galactic latitude the greater the effect.

3. Clusterings

IF THE OVER-ALL arrangement of galaxies on the celestial sphere is uniform, the detailed distribution is assuredly not. Here we find deficiencies and there we find excesses. The picture is spotty and clumpy. We see not only close pairs of galaxies and triplets, but here and there small groups, such as Stephan's Quintet in Pegasus, and larger groups of perhaps a few dozen members. Conspicuous too are even more populous clusters of galaxies. The great Virgo cluster accounts for the

Fig. 22.3:1. Stephan's Quintet, a small group of bright galaxies, photographed with the 120-inch telescope. (*Lick Observatory photograph*)

Fig. 22.3:2. The Corona Borealis cluster of galaxies, photographed with the 120-inch telescope. (*Lick Observatory photograph*)

excess of bright galaxies near the north galactic pole. Farther and fainter and more concentrated are such great assemblies of galaxies as the Corona Borealis cluster, which contains about 400 individual galaxies in an area no larger than that of the moon. These clusters are a few examples of the nearly 3000 that have been catalogued. On an even higher order there appears to be strong evidence of superclusters—

Fig. 22.3:3. A part of the Hercules multiple cluster of galaxies, showing systems of many different types, photographed with the 200-inch telescope. (*Mount Wilson and Palomar Observatories photograph*)

clusters of clusters. In Hercules, for example, there is a multiple cluster, its various components containing several hundred galaxies each and perhaps overlapping one another. The irregularity of the distribution is striking, and the isotropic arrangement of galaxies on the celestial sphere does not reveal itself when we compare the number of galaxies per square degree in neighboring squares. Only when we compare areas of some hundreds of square degrees with one another does the whole-sky uniformity disclose itself.

4. The Local Group

OUR OWN SYSTEM belongs to a concentration of galaxies. The 17 known members are listed in Table 22.4:1 and several more are suspected of membership. The distances and dimensions are approximate only and are subject to revision. Our Milky Way galaxy and the two Clouds of Magellan are the major members of a localized subgroup that also includes five dwarf ellipticals. The dominant members of a second family, the M31 subgroup, are Messier 31 itself and Messier 33. These two spirals are separated by a distance of some 150,000 parsecs. Also belonging to this family are the two close elliptical companions of M31 and two outlying ellipticals, NGC 147 and NGC 185. Isolated on the periphery of the whole local group are NGC 6822, the Leo I system, and IC 1613. Except for these three galaxies, the known members of the local group can be enclosed by an elongated spheroid with our own galaxy at one focus and Messier 31 at the other focus 600,000 parsecs away. The major axis of this egg-shaped volume is 900,000 parsecs long and the minor axis about 800,000 parsecs. In millions of parsecs, or megaparsecs, these dimensions are 0.9 megaparsec by 0.8 megaparsec. The volume of this great spheroid is one-third of a

TABLE 22.4:1. The Local Group of Galaxies

Name	Distance (parsecs)	Ang. Diam.	Linear Diam.	M_v	Type	Sub-group
Our galaxy			30,000	-20	Sb	Gal.
Large Magellanic Cloud	60,000	550′	10,000	-19	Irr	Gal.
Small Magellanic Cloud	60,000	330′	6,000	-17	Irr	Gal.
Draco Dwarf	80,000	30′	700		E	Gal.
Ursa Minor Dwarf	80,000	60′	1,400		E	Gal.
Sculptor Dwarf	90,000	60′	1,600	-14	E	Gal.
Fornax Dwarf	180,000	60′	3,100	-15	E	Gal.
Leo II Dwarf	250,000	12′	900	-10	E	Gal.
NGC 6822	400,000	20′	2,300	-15	Irr	Isol.
Leo I Dwarf	500,000	13′	1,900		E	Isol.
IC 1613	600,000	17′	3,000	-15	Irr	Isol.
Messier 31	600,000	260′	45,000	-21	Sb	M31
Messier 32	600,000	8′	1,400	-16	E2	M31
Messier 33	600,000	60′	10,000	-19	Sc	M31
NGC 147	600,000	13′	2,300	-15	E	M31
NGC 185	600,000	13′	2,300	-15	E	M31
NGC 205	600,000	10′	1,700	-16	E5	M31

cubic megaparsec. With 14 known galaxies inside this region, the local number density of galaxies is about 40 to 50 galaxies per cubic megaparsec. If instead we reach out to embrace the three outlying members of the local group, the calculated average number density is reduced to about 20 per cubic megaparsec.

The mass of the local group is chiefly supplied by Messier 31 and ourselves. Assuming the total to be 4×10^{11} solar masses, the smeared-out density of matter in the volume occupied by the local group is only about 10^{-6} solar mass per cubic parsec. Compare this figure with that for our part of the galaxy as given in Chapter 20, Section 16. It is only a hundred-thousandth as large. Very crudely put, the members of the local group occupy only about 1/100,000 of the room available inside the great spheroidal envelope.

When we go farther afield, the apparent number density of galaxies is much reduced, and so also is the estimated smeared-out mass density of the observable universe. These discrepancies have at least two causes. (1) We do indeed live in a region where galaxies are rather neighborly;

the local condensation is a real one. (2) At greater distances our discoveries of the subluminous dwarf systems are incomplete. Recall from Chapter 13 that our census of the stars is reasonably complete only to distances of a few parsecs; more distant red and white dwarfs tend to elude discovery. Similarly, many dwarf galaxies are missing from our lists. At distances as great as 10 megaparsecs, for example, our tally is complete only for the more luminous galaxies—and for them only if they lie outside the dusty zone of obscuration in our own Milky Way system.

5. Distance of a Remote Galaxy

BEFORE STUDYING the distribution of galaxies at distances of many megaparsecs, it is useful to see if we can estimate how far away they are. As so often in the determination of astronomical distances, the methods used here hinge on first finding the distances of nearer objects. In Chapter 21, Section 3 we saw that the reasonable approach for a neighboring galaxy involves measuring the apparent magnitudes of such indicators as Cepheids, novae, or globular clusters in the system. We then choose a distance so that the computed absolute magnitudes of these indicators accord as well as possible with the absolute magnitudes of the same species in our own galaxy.

Several hundred galaxies are near enough so that such indicators can be found and measured with the help of the great reflecting telescopes. In principle, then, we can find the distances of these few hundred systems. Going further, we can measure the integrated apparent magnitude and color index of each of these galaxies photoelectrically or photographically. From photographs we can estimate the angular diameter and type of each one. Then we are able to compute the absolute visual magnitude and linear diameter of each one.

To find the distance of a remote galaxy, we can measure or estimate the same data: magnitude, color, angular diameter, and type if possible. Assuming the uniformity of nature, we then select a distance for the galaxy so that its absolute magnitude and linear diameter are consistent with the absolute magnitude and linear diameter of nearby systems of the same color and type. In practice, the astronomer feels uncertain about such a procedure. Types are hard to estimate for distant galaxies and the colors of Sa, S0, and E systems are all about the same. Estimated angular diameters do not refer to any precise boundary, and the absolute magnitudes of galaxies of even one type show a spread. Little wonder, then, that distance estimates of individual remote galaxies are only roughly approximate.

The situation is somewhat better when we are interested in finding the distance of a cluster of galaxies, for there is the extra information that all members are at essentially the same distance. When all the apparent magnitudes are measured and the results surveyed, we can estimate the distance by assuming for example that the median absolute magnitude of the members is -15, in agreement with that for the local group. Another and simpler possibility is the guess that the brightest cluster member has an absolute magnitude equal to or somewhat brighter than that of Messier 31. More stable is the assumption that the average absolute visual magnitude of the 10 brightest galaxies in a big cluster is close to −21.5.

HAVING SEEN that galaxies lie more or less uniformly in all *directions* from us, we now inquire whether they lie at all *distances* from us. The simplest question is whether there is an end to galaxies fainter than some certain apparent magnitude. The answer is no. On maximum exposures with the 200-inch telescope there is no cut-off. The photographs abound with tiny fuzzy images that are barely discernible;

6. Distribution of Galaxies in Depth

Fig. 22.6:1. At the center is a faint cluster of galaxies several billion light-years away, near the limit of today's observable universe. A minority of the images are local Milky Way stars; the great majority are ultradistant galaxies. Photographed with the 200-inch telescope. (*Mount Wilson and Palomar Observatories photograph*)

each of these images is an ultradistant galaxy. There is no reason to suspect that the entire realm of galaxies is now within our range of study.

A more searching inquiry asks *how* galaxies are distributed in depth. Is the number density of galaxies the same hundreds of millions of parsecs away as it is here? Or does it decrease with distance? Or does it, perhaps, increase with distance, so that we are in a central hollow? We have already seen that the over-all arrangement of the galaxies is statistically the same in all *directions*; now we ask if it is the same at all *distances*. A preliminary answer can be found by the same kind of analysis we reviewed in Chapter 18, Section 12. If the number density of galaxies in space is constant, we are entitled to expect that the total number brighter than apparent magnitude 18 is 3.98 times the total number brighter than 17, that the total brighter than 17 is 3.98 times the total brighter than 16, and so on. The argument holds good even though galaxies have different intrinsic luminosities.

In practice, the numbers of galaxies per square degree of the sky are found from photographs made with different telescopes to different limiting magnitudes. Regions at low galactic latitude are avoided because of the obscuring dust layer in the home galaxy. It is also customary to pool results from many different sample areas so that the statistics will not be ruined by the chance occurrence of a great cluster of galaxies here and there. Hubble's studies in the 1930s continue today to suggest the general results of such surveys. At the brighter magnitudes the ratio of increase indeed seems to be close to 3.98. But a decline sets in at magnitude 19 and fainter; the ratio of increase for the most distant galaxies is only about 3.1 or 3.2.

How are we to interpret this result? It could arise in a variety of ways. First, perhaps the number density of galaxies does indeed decrease with distance, the nearer galaxies inhabiting an extradense part of the known universe. But it seems folly to think we are at the center of things when there may be better explanations. Another possibility is the existence of a tenuous medium of intergalactic dust. A few other conceivable explanations are also worth mentioning now. For one thing, we see a very remote galaxy as it was hundreds of millions or even billions of years ago. Was its luminosity then the same as it is "now"? Or was it greater, or less? For another thing, the amount of radiant energy reaching us from a distant galaxy depends on how that galaxy is moving. If a galaxy is approaching us, the photons reaching our instruments have greater individual energies and arrive at a faster rate than do those from a receding galaxy. Let us leave these questions open for the moment and conclude that, very roughly, the distribution of galaxies in depth is not far from uniform. The number density of galaxies does not change dramatically with distance outward to a billion parsecs. Whatever changes there may be are not stunning and not immediately perceived; they are elusive, subtle, and still imperfectly known.

THE MOTIONS OF GALAXIES

7. Observations

KNOWLEDGE OF the angular coordinates and distance of a galaxy suffices to fix its position uniquely in space. But is it possible to deduce the space velocity of a galaxy from measurements of its proper motion and radial velocity? Recall from Chapter 13 that we used the measured proper motion and parallax of a nearby star to deduce its transverse velocity. Then we combined the computed transverse velocity and the observed radial velocity in order to deduce the space velocity of the star relative to the sun. Our measurements for galaxies are not so complete because of their enormous distances. The proper motions of galaxies remain complete secrets; they are much too small to detect. Imagine a reasonably nearby galaxy like Messier 31 at 0.6 megaparsec.

Suppose its transverse velocity is 100 mi/sec. Even at such a speed Messier 31 would take a long time to change its position on the celestial sphere by an appreciable amount. To move through an angle of 0.01″ would take 300 years and to move 0.1″ would take 10 times as long, or 3000 years.

Our knowledge of galaxy motions to date is confined to the results of measuring radial velocities. Because a galaxy is a huge aggregate of stars, a spectrogram reveals the integrated average spectrum of the aggregate. The absorption lines of ionized calcium at 3934 A and 3968 A are prominent in the spectra, just as they are very intense in the solar spectrum. And in many galaxies containing interstellar gas the emission line of ionized oxygen at 3727 A stands out clearly. The lines are often tilted because of the rotation of the galaxy under study and they are broadened because any one point of the image is composed of the joint light of many stars moving with different individual radial velocities. Despite these problems it has been possible for skillful and patient observers to deduce reliable radial velocities for about a thousand galaxies.

8. Random Motions

WHEN THE radial velocities of the local group are examined, the members located in the hemisphere centered on Cygnus are found to be approaching us and those in the other hemisphere centered on Carina are receding. Among the latter group are the two Magellanic Clouds and among the former are the members of the Messier 31 subgroup. These motions are chiefly a reflection of the sun's own velocity toward Cygnus at about 150 mi/sec as it participates in the galactic rotation. And to some extent they also reflect the fact that our galaxy as a whole has a random velocity vector through the local swarm. We saw evidence in Chapter 20, Section 11 that the magnitude of this random velocity is very roughly estimated to be about 50 mi/sec. The local velocities of the other nearby galaxies are in random directions at speeds of some 50 mi/sec to 100 mi/sec relative to the framework defined by them all. When we look farther afield, the motions of distant galaxies relative to *their* neighbors seem to be of the same general character.

9. Motions in Clusters of Galaxies

WHEN THE individual radial velocities are known for several members of one of the great clusters, a large spread is noted. In the Coma cluster, with its thousand galaxies, the individual values differ rather dramatically from the average. The typical velocity of a member galaxy relative to the center of mass of the cluster is about 1000 mi/sec. The same general situation holds in other great clusters like Virgo and in small groups like Stephan's Quintet. The interpretation of these very fast motions inside clusters is not clear. One possibility is that a galaxy wandering around inside a cluster is accelerated to high speed by the combined gravitational pull of the other members. A second possibility is that a given group or cluster was born in a smaller volume of space and the individual galaxies are now flying apart. In a few billion years the members would then merge with the general field and the assembly would be unrecognizable. The similarity to star clusters and stellar associations is strong. In Chapter 17 we saw that young associations are expanding while the denser globular clusters are stable and able to retain their member stars for enormously long intervals. Among the clusters of galaxies we may guess that the looser groups are disintegrating while the compact groups are able to hold together.

Whatever the correct interpretation may be, it is instructive to ask about the conditions in a relatively dense cluster of galaxies. As an individual system wanders at high speed through the cluster, it will cross or circle several times in 10 billion years, visiting many parts of the system. It may collide with other galaxies one or more times in this long interval of time. If two galaxies of typical size collide head-on at a relative speed of 1000 mi/sec, it takes about 10 million years until the collision is complete and the two systems are separate once again. During such a collision the individual stars do not ram one another because they occupy only an infinitesimal fraction of the space available. Indeed the odds are strongly against any of the billions of stars in the first galaxy making a direct hit on any of the billions of stars in the second galaxy. But if interstellar gas is present in the two systems, things are very different. The gas clouds ram at high speed, stopping one another. As the stars pass on through, the interstellar gas clouds of the two galaxies presumably pile up and interact at their common front, more fresh gas speeding into the melee as the collision continues. Some of the original organized kinetic energy of the two approaching volumes of gas is now randomized by the high-speed collisions of the individual atoms. In other words, the kinetic temperature, which is a measure of the random atomic speeds, increases very greatly. Radiation characteristic of high temperature is emitted from the scene.

Such collisions of galaxies may provide the explanation for at least two puzzling phenomena. The most intense extragalactic radio source in the sky is located in Cygnus and is called Cygnus A. Photographs of the area with the 200-inch Hale telescope reveal a faint distorted

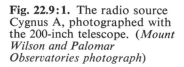

Fig. 22.9:1. The radio source Cygnus A, photographed with the 200-inch telescope. (*Mount Wilson and Palomar Observatories photograph*)

pair of galaxies. They are members of a relatively dense cluster, and the spectrum of the pair reveals wide bright lines of hydrogen and highly ionized stages of heavier elements. The unusual spectrum and the powerful radio radiation, which is about a million times as great as that of our whole galaxy, may arise from a grandiose collision of the pair. A second and long-standing puzzle is the observation that dense clusters have a strong preponderance of luminous E and S0 galaxies and a deficiency of spirals, as compared with galaxies in the general field. It appears likely that a majority of the members have engaged in one or more collisions in the past and that these encounters have swept the galaxies clean. As we have seen, an S0 system looks very much like a spiral that has lost its interstellar matter. A final problem is to find all the swept-out gas. Perhaps it escapes from the scene and gradually diffuses throughout the cluster. Another possibility is that the remaining disk of gas is dense enough so that it can hold together gravitationally. Ultimately, it has been suggested, such a great pool of gas may begin to condense into stars and become a new galaxy.

Although collisions may account for certain curious phenomena in clusters of galaxies, it has recently become clear that some isolated extragalactic radio sources are also very strange fellows when examined on photographs and spectra made at visual wavelengths. Several were found in 1963, both inside clusters and in the general field, to be almost starlike in appearance, with outlying wisps of nebulosity. Doppler measures indicate that the wisps are moving outward explosively from the central nuclei at thousands of miles per second. Most striking is the early evidence that some of these galaxies are variable in luminosity, with periods of only months or even days. These irregular fluctuations have not yet been interpreted with any certainty. If a typically bright galaxy is to change its total brightness in a short time by half a magnitude, it must somehow manage, for example, to set off hundreds or even thousands of supernovae within a few light-months or light-days of each other at approximately the same moment of time.

10. Correlations: Velocity–Magnitude Diagrams

WHEN THE ENTIRE list of galaxy velocities is surveyed, three striking phenomena are revealed. The first is the extremely high velocities of most galaxies, providing one interprets the shifts of the spectral lines as arising from the Doppler effect. The largest shift measured through 1963 is for a faint galaxy a few degrees from the last star in the handle of the Big Dipper. The ionized calcium lines in its spectrum are displaced from their normal positions in the violet to wavelengths in the green part of the spectrum near 5600 A. The shifts are 46 percent of the laboratory wavelengths themselves and the implication is that this galaxy has a radial velocity some 46 percent of the speed of light, or about 86,000 mi/sec. A second astonishing result is that nearly all of the shifts are toward the red end of the spectrum. Indeed, when the effect of the sun's motion around the galaxy is eliminated, only four galaxies out of about a thousand are approaching our home system. These four galaxies are all relatively nearby, and the local randomness

518

THE UNIVERSE OF
GALAXIES

of motions is responsible for these few violet shifts. There are no large violet shifts whatever; all the big ones are to the red, implying that the vast majority of galaxies are receding from us. One is tempted to ask what is the trouble with us that the other systems are running away from the home system.

The third phenomenon may be called the velocity–magnitude relationship. When both the Doppler shift and the apparent magnitude of a galaxy have been measured, its characteristics can be plotted as a point on a velocity–magnitude diagram. When all known points are plotted, a strong correlation appears. In general, the fainter a galaxy the greater its red shift. There is considerable scatter in the diagram

Fig. 22.10:1. A 200-inch photograph of the radio source 3C295. The spectrum of the source is shown to the right; its red shift indicates a radial velocity of 86,000 mi/sec. (*Mount Wilson and Palomar Observatories photographs*)

because galaxies have a variety of intrinsic luminosities, as we have seen. But the general trend is clear: on the average, the fainter the source the larger the shift. To interpret this relationship, let us assume that the red shifts observed in galaxy spectra are indeed caused by the Doppler effect. Some astronomers have wished to ascribe the redward displacements to other causes, but then a new and unknown principle of nature would have to be invented. The great majority of astronomers prefer to ascribe them to actual recessional velocities. Thus a small shift indicates a low speed, and a large shift a high speed. Now let us turn to the apparent magnitudes. In a statistical sense the fainter a galaxy the farther away it is. Thus a typical extremely faint galaxy is very remote. The correlation of velocity and magnitude thus becomes a correlation of velocity and distance. A fairly nearby galaxy recedes only slowly, another in the middle distance at greater speed, and a very remote one at ultrahigh speed.

The precise character of the correlation is not fully known. Additional data on the red shifts and magnitudes of galaxies are needed. Moreover, the theoretical apparatus of the general theory of relativity has to be employed for the interpretation because we are dealing with very great speeds in the universe of galaxies. But an approximate picture of the relationship is given in Fig. 22.10:2. Each of the ten plotted points refers to an entire cluster of galaxies rather than to an individual galaxy. In this way the effects of different galaxy luminosities and random motions are reduced. Each cluster velocity is the average of two

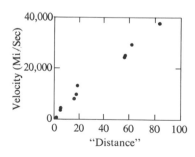

Fig. 22.10:2. The velocity-distance correlation for galaxies. The "distances" shown are based solely on the inverse-square law of intensity. Correction of these estimates is discussed in Section 12.

or more single galaxy velocities in the cluster, as measured by M. L. Humason at the Mount Wilson and Palomar Observatories. The "distances" are in units of the distance to the Virgo cluster, shown at the lower left. They are arrived at in the following somewhat devious way. We first compute the average photographic magnitude of the brightest, third brightest, fifth brightest, and tenth brightest galaxy for each cluster, the data being from A. R. Sandage, also of Mount Wilson and Palomar. These values range from $m_p = 9.57$ for the Virgo cluster to $m_p = 19.17$ for the point farthest to the right, the Hydra cluster. The latter "average" galaxy is thus 9.60 magnitudes fainter than the former. Recall that 10 magnitudes corresponds to an intensity ratio of 10,000. And if the two objects have the same absolute magnitude or luminosity, the inverse-square law tells us that the object 10 magnitudes fainter is 100 times as far away as the brighter object. Similarly, 9.60 magnitudes corresponds to an intensity ratio of 6920. And the square root of 6920 is 83.2. Thus, as a first crude estimate, the distance of the Hydra cluster is something like 83 times that of the Virgo cluster. The remaining points of the diagram were found by the same type of calculation.

The general lessons, but by no means the final detailed lessons, are several. Figure 22.10:2 suggests a fairly close correlation of velocity and distance. Roughly, if cluster B is twice as far away as cluster A, it is receding twice as fast. Another point worth noting is that the clusters in the graph lie in different *directions* from us. We have already seen, however, that the over-all arrangement of the galaxies and clusters of galaxies is isotropic. Similarly, the velocity–magnitude correlation is found in whatever direction we look; it is also isotropic. In summary, the totality of galaxy observations leads to a picture of general recession that is much the same in all directions. And the speed of recession is greater for the more distant galaxies than for the closer ones.

11. The Expanding Universe

AN ESSENTIAL point to be gained from Fig. 22.10:2 is that our own galaxy is not unique. We have seen that, apart from a few neighbors, all of the other galaxies are receding from us. But the isotropic velocity-magnitude correlation implies that all galaxies are running away from each other. Again we are ignoring the effects of the local random motions of galaxies within a few megaparsecs of each other and are dealing with the observable universe as a whole. Thus we are not alone in witnessing a general recession; the same effect would be recorded by a hypothetical astronomer in any other galaxy. To illustrate the point, Fig. 22.11:1 shows two views of an artificial arrangement of galaxies in a straight line. The radial velocities observed from galaxy C are plotted as arrows at the top; those of the same galaxies observed from E are at the bottom. Note that each observer sees all other galaxies receding. Furthermore, each observer finds that any given galaxy is moving away faster than all closer ones. Generalizing to three-dimensional space, we may regard the observed isotropic correlation of velocities and magnitude as evidence that the universe of galaxies is expanding. Except for relatively close neighbors, all galaxies are

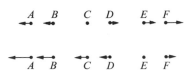

Fig. 22.11:1. If an observer in galaxy C finds that speeds are proportional to distances, then observers in galaxy E and all other galaxies experience the same proportionality.

hastening away from one another. The general recession is statistically the same no matter where one surveys it from. And thus there is no favored central point in the expanding universe.

An analogy that is helpful, although not complete, is that of an expanding balloon. Imagine, as in Fig. 22.11:2, a spherical balloon that is being inflated. Arranged at random on the surface are many points, each representing a galaxy. Think only of the two-dimensional spherical surface; nothing happens inside it or outside it. Light emitted by one galaxy travels outward along the balloon surface on great-circle paths, some of it reaching other galaxies. First, note that there is no favored spot on the spherical surface; each point has just as much claim to fame as every other one. Second, if the balloon is growing in size, then every point recedes from every other one. Whether the circumference of the sphere at any moment is small, as on the top, or bigger, as on the bottom, all points recede from one another no matter what the rate of inflation or how this rate changes with time. Only if the inflation stops or if collapse sets in, does the general expansion stop. Because red shifts are found for all distant galaxies, let us assume the balloon is now expanding and has been for a long time. A third feature of the swelling balloon is that it mimics the velocity-distance correlation of galaxies. Imagine an observer on galaxy O. For him, galaxy C is relatively close and galaxy F is rather far away. As the arrows indicate, the observer on O finds that the recessional speed of F is proportionately greater than that of C. A plot of the velocity against the great-circle distance of all dots shows that the two quantities are proportional to one another. If F is twice as far as C from O, then its recessional speed is twice as great. And the proportionality is seen not only from O but from any dot whatever. At a later instant when the dots are farther apart, O finds the same proportionality, even though the *rate* of inflation may then be less or more. Whatever the radial velocity of F at this later moment, it is still twice that of C. Thus at any fixed instant every observer sees the same general expansion.

Useful though it may be, our balloon analogy breaks down on several counts. First, of course, the balloon surface has two dimensions whereas the universe of galaxies is embedded in a space of three dimensions. Second, there is nothing about our hypothetical balloon to prevent light signals from circling the surface time after time, just as an astronaut may travel around the earth for many circuits. Photons emitted by any dot will go in all directions into the surface, traveling along great-circle tracks. Those that are not absorbed by other dots will complete their orbits and converge *from* all surface directions on O once again. The three-dimensional extension of the argument suggests that the photons radiated by our galaxy a long time ago may now be seen as a faint smear of light reaching us from all parts of the celestial sphere. As we shall see later, it now seems very doubtful that we live in a "closed" universe. In other words, radiation emitted from our galaxy is not expected to come back.

A third point that merits reflection is the question of time effects. On any balloon of manageable size, light travels almost instantaneously

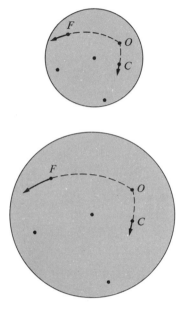

Fig. 22.11:2. The velocity-distance relationship is illustrated by points on a swelling balloon.

from one dot to any other. In the universe of galaxies the situation is very different. If a galaxy is 10 million light-years away, we see it as it was and where it was and as it was moving 10 million years ago. Now 10 million years is a relatively short interval compared with the ages of most stars and galaxies, and the universe as a whole has not changed much in that time. But think of another galaxy 5 billion light-years away. What is it like "now"? What are its distance and radial velocity "now"? We shall not know through earth-made measurements until 5 billion years from today. Thus the farther out we look the more into the past we probe. For a variety of reasons, we have no right to expect that we can draw a straight line through all the clusters of Fig. 22.10:2. At any fixed moment a diagram of velocity against distance for the dots on an expanding balloon actually shows that the plotted points lie on a straight line. But in the universe of galaxies it is only the relatively nearby systems that can instruct us about conditions in the present history of the universe and that may be expected to show a proportionality of velocity and distance. The far-out galaxies can only teach us ancient history. And long ago galaxies may have been systematically more or less luminous than today. Long ago the expansion may have been more rapid than today, or perhaps more leisurely. We shall scrutinize some of these problems with a more critical eye in the next section.

12. A Closer Look

LET US FIRST try to estimate the actual distances of galaxies and clusters of galaxies in our greater neighborhood. We have seen that the most distant members of the local group lie at about 0.6 megaparsec, or 2 million light-years. From Table 22.4:1 the average absolute visual magnitude of the two most luminous local members, Messier 31 and ourselves, is found to be about -20.5. The color index of both systems is not far from 1.0, and so their average absolute photographic magnitude is about -19.5. The Virgo cluster is many times as populous as the local group, and it therefore seems likely that the "average" apparent photographic magnitude of 9.57 given in Section 10 refers to galaxies somewhat more luminous than Messier 31 or ourselves. Present information suggests that $M_p = -20.5$ for the average bright galaxy in the Virgo cluster. The distance then is found by the formula

$$M_p = m_p + 5 - 5 \log r.$$

Solving for $\log r$ and substituting the magnitudes, we have

$$\begin{aligned}
\log r &= 0.2(m_p - M_p) + 1 \\
&= 0.2(9.6 + 20.5) + 1 \\
&= 7.02.
\end{aligned}$$

Thus the distance is a shade over 10^7 parsecs, or 10 megaparsecs. Let us adopt 10 megaparsecs as the distance. More elaborate arguments give values both less and greater than this, but the average current estimate is not far from this figure.

Given a distance to the Virgo cluster which hopefully is not far from the truth, let us return to Fig. 22.10:2 and find a numerical relationship between velocity and distance in our greater neighborhood. The three closest clusters are plotted on an expanded scale in Fig. 22.12:2. From the discussion of the previous section it is legitimate to assume that velocities and distances are proportional in our greater neighborhood where time effects are not severe. The straight line through ourselves and the Virgo, Perseus, and Coma clusters indicates that a galaxy recedes at a rate of some 70 mi/sec for each megaparsec of its

Fig. 22.12:1. A part of the Virgo cluster of galaxies, photographed with the 24–33-inch Schmidt at Harvard's Agassiz Station. The field is approximately 5° by 5°. (*Harvard College Observatory photograph*)

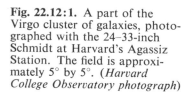

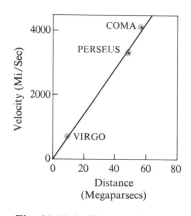

Fig. 22.12:2. Data on clusters of galaxies in our greater neighborhood suggest that the present expansion rate of the universe is about 70 mi/sec for each megaparsec of distance.

distance. The center of mass of the Virgo cluster is receding at 700 mi/sec, Perseus at almost 3400 mi/sec, and Coma more than 4100 mi/sec. Given that the center of the Virgo cluster is 10 megaparsecs away, the other two are then at 48 megaparsecs and 57 megaparsecs respectively. If the distances are correct, we therefore see these 3 clusters as they were 33 million, 160 million, and 180 million years ago respectively.

It is interesting, although possibly illusory, to calculate the times needed for these clusters to have reached their present distance from us *if* they have always been traveling at the same outward speed. At 700 mi/sec how long does it take to travel 10 megaparsecs? At 3400 mi/sec how long does it take to travel 48 megaparsecs? Because the points in Fig. 22.12:2 are represented by a straight line, the computed times all come out the same. Quantitatively, a body moving at 100 mi/sec moves 165 parsecs in a million years. Another at 700 mi/sec therefore moves 1155 parsecs in a million years or 1.155 megaparsecs in a billion years. Thus to move 10 megaparsecs takes about 8.7 billion years. Imagine now a uniformly expanding system of galaxies. The implication is that all galaxies were close together roughly 10 billion years ago, and this time interval is comparable with our estimate of the ages of the eldest objects in our galaxy and thus of the Milky Way system itself. Recall, however, that the rate of expansion need not have been the same in the past as it is now. Thus our computation, although suggestive, is certainly no unique estimate of the "age" of the universe. Perhaps the expansion began very slowly and accelerated with time. Or perhaps it began with a bang and decelerated as the galaxies drew apart from one another.

Next let us look farther afield. Imagine the straight line of Fig. 22.12:2 transferred onto the diagram of Fig. 22.10:2, passing through the three closest clusters. All of the seven farthest clusters then lie below and to the right of the line. On the face of it, the computed "distances" are too large for the observed red shifts, or else the red shifts are too small for the computed "distances." One explanation that comes to mind is that the expansion was slower in the past than it is today. The light now reaching us from the Hydra cluster was emitted an exceedingly long time ago, when its member galaxies were not receding as fast as they are "now." This explanation, however, ignores several complicating but very interesting effects.

A first point to be made is that the meanings of the terms *radial velocity* and *distance* are not self-evident when we turn to the general theory of relativity as our theoretical tool for interpreting the expanding universe. Fortunately, the differences between our everyday concepts and those required in relativity theory are not great when we confine our attention to the Hydra cluster and other closer ones. It seems doubtful that properly defined distances and velocities will differ from those we commonly use by more than 10 percent out to the Hydra

Fig. 22.12:3. The Hydra cluster of galaxies, photographed with the 200-inch reflector. (*Mount Wilson and Palomar Observatories photograph*)

galaxies, whose spectral lines are shifted redward by 20.2 percent of their normal wavelengths. Let us therefore bypass the complexities of general relativity, although we shall later need to refer to results based on that theory.

Returning to the actual observations on which Fig. 22.10:2 is based, we look first at the red shifts. Imagine the radiation emitted by stars that belong to the galaxies in the Hydra cluster. In particular, think of the photons emitted in the wavelength band between 4500 A and 5500 A. Measurement of the 20.2 percent shift of the absorption lines indicates that an emitted photon at 4500 A reaches us shifted 909 A to the red, or at 5409 A. Another emitted at 5500 A reaches us shifted by 1111 A and is therefore located at 6611 A. Thus the radiation in a wavelength band of 1000 A at the emitter is spread into a broader band 1202 A wide at the receiver. This width is therefore 20.2 percent larger. Not only is there a spreading effect, but the energy of each arriving photon is 20.2 percent less than at the time of emission. Recall from Chapter 11, Section 15 that the energy of a photon is proportional to its frequency, $E = hf$, and therefore inversely proportional to its wavelength. Thus with a given receiving apparatus here on earth that is responsive to a fixed wavelength region, the arriving radiation is reduced by these two effects. The more remote a galaxy the narrower the band of wavelengths at the emitter that is spread out to cover the wavelength band we record here. In addition, the energy of each photon we *do* catch is reduced the more remote the galaxy. Both of these effects reduce the intensity of a galaxy as compared with what we *would* observe if there were no red shift. Thus the observed brightnesses are too dim and the "distances" of Fig. 22.10:2 too great.

Another effect comes into play when we choose to interpret the red shifts as actual Doppler shifts. As our telescope records photons arriving from the Hydra galaxies, it is receding from the source at nearly 40,000 mi/sec. Therefore the number of photons that strike the objective each second is reduced below the number it would receive if there were no runaway motion, again by 20.2 percent. If a machine gun is aimed at a rapidly receding target, the rate of impact on the target is less than the rate of release at the gun. The effect is similar for radiation in an expanding universe, and it further reduces the intensity of a distant galaxy.

A fourth consequence of the red shift has to do with the apparent spectral distribution of the light we receive from a distant galaxy. For simplicity, let us think of a galaxy as a collection of solar-type stars, all emitting like black bodies at 6000°K. The solid line of Fig. 22.12:4 shows the Planck curve of such an emitter when there is no red shift, peaking in the visual part of the spectrum. The dotted curve shows the Planck curve of the same emitter when the red shift is 50 percent, corresponding closely with the greatest shift yet observed among the galaxies. Notice that near P, where photographic magnitudes are obtained, and also near V, where visual magnitudes are measured, the amount of arriving light is reduced. The relatively weak ultraviolet emission of such a galaxy is displaced into the wavelength regions we

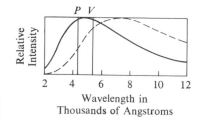

P *V*

Relative
Intensity

2   4   6   8   10   12

Wavelength in
Thousands of Angstroms

Fig. 22.12:4. The radiation curve of a rapidly receding galaxy is shifted far to the red. The two curves are here adjusted so that their tops are at the same height.

record, while the relatively strong visual emission is shifted to the infra-red when it reaches us. The reduction is more aggravated in the photographic region near 4400 A than in the visual region near 5450 A. As a result the galaxy appears not only too faint but also too red; its observed color index is substantially greater than its true color index.

All four of these effects conspire to make the radiation we receive from a distant galaxy weaker than it would be if there were no red shifts. A final consideration is the influence of aging on a galaxy. If galaxies are of all different ages, no problem arises; but if all or most galaxies were born at a common time in the past, then the intrinsic luminosity and color of a galaxy will depend on its distance from us. We see very remote systems as they were long in the past, and therefore when they were younger. At those remote epochs a typical galaxy may have contained a higher proportion of blue supergiants and thus emitted more and bluer radiation. Although such evolutionary effects would seem to go in the opposite direction of the other four effects, precise predictions of their amounts require elaborate knowledge of the stellar content and evolution in galaxies of different kinds. They cannot be made at the present time.

The over-all consequence of these various effects is still tentative, because the effects of aging are not at all well known. If we assume them to be small, the consequence of the other four effects is rather astonishing. When the observations are properly analyzed through use of relativity theory, the "distances" of the outer seven galaxies of Fig. 22.10:2 are very much reduced. The plotted points fall to the *left* of the line supplied by Virgo, Perseus, and Coma. It appears preliminarily, then, that the expansion was *more* rapid long ago than it is today, as though there were some universal force over and above gravitation that has been retarding or decelerating the expansion. A further consequence of making proper allowance for these dimming effects returns us to the subject of Section 6, the distribution of the galaxies in depth. We saw there that the galaxies seem to thin out with distance, the ratio of increase at the faint magnitudes being less than 3.98. Now, without needing to blame intergalactic dust at all, the conclusion appears to be reversed. The number density of galaxies probably *increases* somewhat with distance. Thus we may be living in the hole of the dough-nut. Independent evidence of such an increase is suggested by the results of surveys with radio telescopes. Over and above the known radio sources like supernova shells and emission nebulae that lie in our own galaxy, numerous faint radio sources have been found here and there all over the celestial sphere. The most intense is Cygnus A, but thousands of fainter ones have been catalogued. The few that have been identified with the help of optical telescopes are either normal galaxies like Messier 31 or peculiar galaxies—odd individuals, close interacting pairs, or pairs in collision. The isotropic arrangement of these sources hints strongly that they are all extragalactic. Also, analyses of the number of sources of different magnitudes seems to indicate that their number density increases with distance.

Although all of these results are tentative as of 1963, it is tempting to seek an explanation should they be confirmed. The distant congestion may be interpreted if we recall that the ultradistant galaxies and radio sources are seen as they were long ago. The general expansion had not then progressed as far as it has today. Thus the galaxies were, on the average, closer together; their number density was greater than it is "now," or at least greater than it is in our own neighborhood where we can investigate the character of the universe now. The correlation of red shifts with corrected magnitudes suggests, in addition, that the expansion rate long in the past was somewhat greater than it is in our time.

COSMOLOGIES

13. Infinity, Eternity, or Not?

MANY MODELS of the universe of galaxies have been constructed by cosmologists, and most of them have been developed within the framework of Einstein's general theory of relativity. The Newtonian theory of gravitation fails at the enormous speeds encountered in the universe of galaxies, whereas Einstein's special theory of relativity contends with very high speeds but not with the phenomenon of gravitation. General relativity is competent to cope simultaneously with the effects of gravitation and of very great relative velocities. Given the knowledge that general relativity is the superior theoretical structure, the cosmologist then turns to the astronomer's observational data on galaxies. At first he may be impressed by the apparent confusion of the universe: here a giant spiral, there a dwarf elliptical; now a blue galaxy, then a red galaxy; in one direction a distorted pair that sends us strong radio radiation, in another direction a ragged swarm of several hundred galaxies. But then he remembers that his interpretive concern is not with individual galaxies but with the observable universe as a whole. Each galaxy provides a bit of information; each becomes but one item in a large statistical analysis. To simplify his work, the cosmologist drops his concern with the peculiarities of individual systems and instead deals with the average characteristics of large numbers. Each galaxy is a single atom in a supergas; the structure and motion of the individual are forgotten and the over-all macroscopic characteristics of the gas are now the focus of attention: density, pressure, mass motions.

Once the decision has been made to employ general relativity and, in imagination, to smear out the galaxies into a universal supergas, it is essential that the cosmologist settle in his own mind just what general observable characteristics this gas may have. If he is in a vacuum without any knowledge of the facts and statistics about galaxies, he can concoct all sorts of possible cosmologies that may suit his fancy and not do violence to relativity theory. But he is not in a vacuum; astronomers have provided him with several statistical results. A few of them are on firm footing; others cannot be on firm footing until many more data have been gathered. Well established are the isotropic arrangement of galaxies on the celestial sphere and a general correlation of red shift with apparent magnitude. If the cosmologist accepts the red shifts as actual recessional motions, then the data of observation show that in our greater neighborhood velocity is proportional to distance. Also, the number density of galaxies is statistically constant as we move outward through our greater neighborhood. Farther afield a variety of complicating effects influence the apparent magnitudes we observe, and the trend of red shift and number density with distance is only imperfectly known.

Given these several observed features, one begins to wonder whether the system of galaxies extends to infinity. Or is it perhaps confined to the three-dimensional analogue of a spherical surface, whereon one can travel infinitely far on a bounded area? And one wonders whether there have always been galaxies and whether there always will be. Or is there a beginning and an end? At the present time the available astronomical data are neither extensive enough nor precise enough to give us answers to these questions. The cosmologist cannot choose one specific model from all possible models of the universe and claim that it alone faithfully represents the observed universe. In principle, the astronomical data dictate the answer; in practice, the day has not yet come when the data are well-enough known. Let us now review two rather different conceptions of the universe that attempt to fit the facts. The ultimate fate of these theories cannot be guessed in advance. But the fact that both have serious proponents in 1963 and the fact that both are discussed side by side indicates the necessity for sharpened observations if one or the other or both of the theories are to be shot down.

14. A Steady-State Universe

ONE OF THE fundamental axioms of most cosmologies is that the universe of galaxies is statistically the same no matter from what point it is viewed. If one can imagine a superobserver able to hurdle the time barrier and witness the universe as it is "now," he would find that the number density of galaxies "now" is the same at every point in space. There is no preferred center where the population density is a maximum. And the general expansion of the system of galaxies is the same "now" no matter where our superobserver is located. The steady-state theory has a second fundamental axiom: the universe is statistically the same *whenever* it is viewed. Thus no matter where one goes or when one goes there, the surrounding array of galaxies is always observed to behave in the same fashion. The precept of a steady state, of no long-run changes with time, is not at all demanded by the data of observation. But it does have the undeniable merit of simplicity.

Some of the consequences of the assumptions of the steady-state theory can be appreciated without difficulty. (1) If the universe cannot alter its gross characteristics with time, then it has lasted for an eternity in the past and will last for an eternity in the future. (2) The red-shift effect is interpreted as an actual recession; therefore some galaxies have been receding for an infinite time and so the system is infinite in size. (3) A steady state in time implies that the number density of galaxies remains constant as the billions of years roll on. But the expansion is carrying the galaxies away from one another. To reconcile the thinning-out of existing galaxies with the requirement of a statistically steady state, it is necessary to introduce fresh galaxies in the spaces left void by the older receding ones. In other words, the high-speed galaxies that move out of the range of the 200-inch Hale telescope every century must be replaced in the same interval of time by an equal number of new galaxies inside the sphere of space that is within the range of the same instrument. In one version of the theory, hydrogen atoms come into being at random points in space at a rate that just compensates for the expansion of existing systems. This proposed process of continual creation requires the appearance of one atom per century in each cube of space 1000 to 2000 feet on a side. The hydrogen atoms that come into existence in intergalactic space are thought to convene eventually into protogalaxies, with the gravitational assistance of existing galaxies. A typical galaxy moves in a random direction at 50 to 100 mi/sec through the tenuous intergalactic gas, experiencing a wind as it goes. Hydrogen atoms far enough from the galaxy to avoid capture move on past in hyperbolic paths. Like droplets running down the outside of a wine glass and converging on the thin stem, the intergalactic gas congregates in the wake of the existing galaxy. According to the theory, the piled-up gas ultimately becomes a more or less isolated protogalaxy, free to evolve into a stellar system.

The axioms of the steady-state picture also have an important consequence concerning the motions in the universe. A sample volume of galaxies 5 billion light-years away is of course seen as it was 5 billion years ago. But if there are to be no long-run statistical changes, there is another similar sample of different galaxies at the same place "now" and moving in the same way. The only way that this similarity can be preserved is for the expansion to be accelerated. Think of a particular galaxy born many billions of years ago 10 megaparsecs away from us and receding at 700 mi/sec. After about 6 billion years it has receded to 20 megaparsecs and is moving at 1400 mi/sec. In another 6 billion years it is at 40 megaparsecs and running away at 2800 mi/sec, and so on. A rather different prediction concerns the ages of galaxies. To maintain a steady state in the face of the expansion, systems must be coming into being at all times in all parts of the universe. Thus any one neighborhood, our own for example, must contain galaxies of all ages. The majority in any volume are relatively young, a few billion years at most, for the expansion has not had time to carry them off. A smaller percentage are middle-aged. And a very few are extremely ancient relics, many tens of billions of years old.

A variety of charges have been filed against the steady-state theory. One problem is that it violates the principles of conservation of energy. As we have seen, matter is a highly concentrated form of energy. Therefore the continual appearance of hydrogen steadily adds to the energy store of the universe. Now, on a smaller scale the principle of conservation has survived a multitude of tests; the question of whether it holds on the tremendous scale of the universe of galaxies is a challenging one. If it does, the steady-state theory must be discarded. If, on the other hand, the steady-state picture is correct, the conservation principle has to be modified so that the energy per unit volume of space stays the same.

Another problem concerns the ages of galaxies. The majority of galaxies in any large sample of space must be young—not more than a few billion years old; otherwise the expansion would have carried them far away. Indeed, some should be extremely young. We saw in Chapter 21 that the irregular galaxies appear to be chaotic and under-developed. But such systems as the Magellanic Clouds are known to contain Population II objects. At least two interesting questions remain to be settled. Will further studies reveal truly young galaxies that contain no old objects? And if so, are there other mechanisms such as galaxy collisions that can spawn new systems, or is continual creation of matter required? At the other end of the time scale are extraordinarily old galaxies. The expansion has carried them very far away, but nevertheless the theory predicts that there is an infinite number of them *somewhere*, and it would be interesting to see at least one. Such a fossil galaxy would presumably be subluminous and very red because its stars would have been evolving for tens of billions of years. Further-more, as a galaxy ages, more and more hydrogen is created inside of it and is unable to escape. And as the system moves at random through the intergalactic gas, it captures more and more matter. In the long run the mass of the galaxy increases, enabling it to capture intergalactic matter at an even greater rate. And so on without limit. Apparently, then, a consequence of the steady-state theory is that the older the fossil the greater its mass, until it becomes infinitely massive after a life of perhaps 30 billion years.

An interesting consequence of the steady-state theory is that the average smeared-out density of matter in the universe is substantially larger than has been accounted for by known matter. The required density is the equivalent of about ten hydrogen atoms per cubic yard or per cubic meter of space. This value just about matches the smeared-out value for the local group of galaxies, which as far as we know is a relatively dense part of the universe. The average for our much greater neighborhood appears to be lower by tenfold or even a hundredfold. Thus if the steady-state theory is valid, it appears likely that 90 or even 99 percent of the matter of the universe remains undetected, chiefly perhaps as the uncondensed and continually created intergalactic gas.

Finally, we saw in Section 12 that current observations of the red shifts and apparent magnitudes of galaxies hint that the expansion was more rapid in the past than it is today. Also, the number counts of galaxies and remote radio sources suggest an apparent increase in number density with distance. Whether or not these statistical results are substantiated by future work, it is worth mentioning that they are both contrary to the predictions of the steady-state theory. In a steady-state universe every galaxy is in accelerated motion away from the observer, and the number density of galaxies must be constant with distance.

15. A Time-Varying Universe

IN SHARP CONTRAST to the steady-state picture are those models of the universe in which the large-scale features of the system of galaxies are allowed to change with time. Cosmologists have given most of their attention to uniform models; at the basis of these models is once again the fundamental axiom that the universe of galaxies looks much the same no matter where one views it from. In other words, at any given instant of time the number density of galaxies is the same in every region of space. And the velocity-magnitude correlation is assumed to be statistically the same no matter where the observer is in space, provided he is making his measurements "now." Thus far the assumptions are identical with those of steady-state theory. But here the resemblance ends, for no longer is there any postulate that the universe stays the same as time flows by.

A consequence is that time-varying models are less restrictive than the steady-state model. In the latter kind of universe, the imposition of steadiness leads to some quite definite predictions, as we have seen. These predictions can in principle be tested against the results of astronomical observation. In the time-varying models there is an enormous number of *possible* ways the universe may behave. For example, the number density of galaxies in our greater neighborhood may now be decreasing with time. At a later stage the density may decrease less rapidly and stop and then increase again. Or it may not. The hope here is to eliminate more and more of the many possible kinds of behavior by a continual appeal to the astronomical data. The more accurate and more extensive the data the larger the percentage of possibilities that can be ruled out. Perhaps some day all choices but one will have been discarded, but that day appears to be a long way ahead.

One conclusion is clear, again with the proviso that the red shifts are indeed caused by the Doppler effect. The galaxies in our greater neighborhood are receding with speeds in proportion to their distances. Statistically, they will be farther apart tomorrow than today; they were closer together yesterday than today. Therefore the average smeared-out density of matter must now be decreasing with time. And because of the axiom of uniformity the thinning-out is occurring at the same rate "now" in all regions of the universe. A second firm conclusion is that the galaxies have been thinning out for at least several billion years. If the corrected velocity-magnitude curve tipped over and became essentially horizontal at great distances, we could conclude that all ultraremote galaxies have the same runaway speed and thus that they are essentially motionless with respect to each other. But no such trend has been recorded; the curve rises even for the faintest magnitudes. The consequence, then, is that the number density of galaxies several billion years ago was everywhere much greater than it is today.

If we attempt to judge more closely which particular time-varying model best fits the facts, we encounter too few and too inaccurate facts. Several conclusions appear probable, but they may be altered by future investigations. At present the data suggest but do not prove that the rate of expansion is slowing down. When the apparent magnitudes of very faint galaxies are corrected for the several effects described in Section 12, the velocity-magnitude correlation indicates that the ultradistant galaxies, seen as they were billions of years ago, were then receding excessively fast. The rate seems to have slowed since then, as is revealed by data on nearby galaxies and clusters. Today a galaxy at 10 megaparsecs recedes at about 700 mi/sec; an observer 100 million years from now will perhaps detect a galaxy at 10 megaparsecs to be receding only at 680 to 690 mi/sec. A second probable conclusion is that gravitational forces between galaxies are not sufficient to brake the expansion at the observed rate. But what the physical nature of the extra retarding *cosmical force* may be is a completely open question. A third probable conclusion is that the universe is open and infinite rather than closed and bounded. The two-dimensional analogue is not the surface of a sphere, nor even the infinite surface of a plane sheet, but instead the hyperbolic surface of a saddle.

Two generally different types of time-varying models deserve our attention. One is the *oscillating universe* and the other is the *dispersing universe*. Both types are possible within the framework of the existing data. In dealing with each, we agree that the number density of galaxies a few billion years ago was everywhere much greater than it is today. If the universe is oscillating, the future scheme of events will follow a pattern in which the number density of galaxies decreases with time at first. But as the braking action of mutual gravitation and of the cosmical force takes hold, the expansion slows down. In billions of years it stops, and the universe begins to contract. Astronomers in that remote era would begin to record violet shifts first for the nearer galaxies and then later for the more distant ones. Ultimately, all galaxies and stars come together vigorously into a superdense state. The organized energy of the contraction is converted to random thermal energy, and with the attendant enormous temperatures all traces of galaxies and stars and atoms and even atomic nuclei are destroyed. In the subsequent rebound the universe of atoms, stars, and galaxies is presumably recreated afresh, the new system of galaxies expanding once again. Every few tens of billions of years the universe completes an expansion and contraction; at the end of each pulsation all of the previous details vanish and a new phase of the universe begins. The galaxies we know today came into being as products of the most recent great squeeze, very roughly 10 billion years ago. What the universe was like before then we cannot know.

The dispersing universe resembles the oscillating model except that the braking action of the gravitational and cosmical forces is insufficient to stop the expansion. The contrast between the two models is something like that between two earth satellites. If one is launched at less than the escape velocity of the earth, it moves around us periodically; if another is launched at greater than escape velocity, it moves away from us indefinitely, never to return. The future historian of a dispersing universe would record the galaxies getting farther and farther apart as their number density continually decreases. Ultimately, an observer in one cluster of galaxies would see no others, all systems having dispersed infinitely far from one another. In the past the number density of galaxies was far higher than it is today. And as in the oscillating model, most of today's galaxies came into being shortly after the big squeeze. Again, all vestiges of a previous collapsing universe were erased during the era of maximum compression.

Although it is impossible with today's data to decide whether the oscillating model or the dispersing model is correct, or even whether both are incorrect, it is of some interest to speculate on the course of events that may have followed the era of extreme compression. For it seems certain that enormous densities did occur if one of the time-varying models of the universe is to be the final answer. A previous collapse probably resulted in ultrahigh density and temperature, with the matter of all stars and galaxies jumbled together, atoms fully ionized and even atomic nuclei thoroughly split asunder. The hot, packed matter may have been a medium of pure neutrons. At the time of maximum density a rebound set in and the matter started to expand. As the neutrons flew apart, the density and temperature both decreased and each neutron decayed into a proton and an electron, so that the universe was a turbulent expanding plasma of hydrogen that was steadily getting cooler and more rarefied. In the early stages of the expansion the temperature was so great that most of the energy in any given volume was in the form of photons of high-energy radiation; less was in the mass energy of particles. Much later the density of radiation decreased below the density of matter and no longer did matter ride helplessly on the winds of radiation. Gravitation then became a ruling force, and the turbulent mass broke up into supereddies, the protogalaxies. Each surviving eddy was held together by the mutual gravitational attraction of its several parts. But the protogalaxies themselves continued to separate from one another and are still doing so today. The internal evolution of a single protogalaxy of hydrogen followed more or less the pattern outlined in Chapter 21, regardless of whether it originated as a turbulent eddy, as here suggested, or as an isolated mass in the wake of an old galaxy, as suggested in the previous section.

Time-varying models of the universe escape criticism provided our attention is focused on the system of galaxies as we see it today and as we see it changing today. Moreover, we can delve relatively far into the past by observing very distant galaxies, although the messages those objects send us are likely to be somewhat fuzzy. The chief difficulties arise when we try to extrapolate the expansion backward and ask what happened during the early phases of the swelling universe. One problem is that the cosmologist's best weapon is an analysis of the behavior of a smoothed-out gas within the framework of relativity theory. But at the birthday of the universe the density of matter is found to have been infinite. A more elaborate and realistic theory must therefore be built if that impossible situation is to be avoided. A second problem is that no galaxy or star or atom can be older than the moment of maximum squeeze. The day may come when the student of stellar evolution can point to a star and assert correctly that it is 50 billion years old. If it does, our rough time scale of 10 billion years will require alteration. A third problem is the physical theory of the break-up of expanding hydrogen into protogalaxies. The details are not clear, but neither are those of galaxy formation in the steady-state theory. All in all, the time-varying models are less open to criticism than is the steady-state model. The latter embraces the extra axiom of changelessness with time, which leads in turn to some fairly specific predictions about the mean density of matter in the universe, the outward acceleration of galaxies, and so on. The time-varying models are more flexible and can accommodate more of the emerging data provided by the astronomer. In fact, it is just these data that will be needed if some day the cosmologist is to be able to single out precisely what kind of universe we live in.

PROBLEMS

1. What general effect does the interstellar dust of our own galaxy have on counts of galaxies per square degree of the sky?

2. What is meant by the statement that the distribution of galaxies is isotropic?

3. Our galaxy belongs to several different groups or subgroups. Discuss.

4. (a) What is the approximate number density of galaxies in the local group? (b) What is the approximate average mass density of matter in this region of space?

5. Describe the nature of the random motions of galaxies in the general field and of galaxies that belong to large clusters.

6. Collisions of galaxies may explain several puzzling observations. What are they?

7. What is the velocity-magnitude diagram, and what are its implications?

8. Criticize the balloon analogy of the expanding universe.

9. Calculate the proper motions of two or three galaxies at different distances if their transverse velocities were as large as their radial velocities.

10. Review the principles involved in computing the distance of the Virgo and Coma clusters.

11. Explain the various effects that weaken the intensity of a rapidly receding galaxy as recorded here on the earth.

12. (a) What are the fundamental axioms of the steady-state model of the universe? (b) What are some of the necessary features of such a universe?

13. What are some of the criticisms that have been made of the steady-state theory?

14. (a) What are the fundamental axioms of the time-varying models of the universe? (b) Distinguish between the oscillating and the dispersing universes.

15. What are some of the criticisms that have been made of time-varying models of the universe?

23

RETROSPECT

As CENTURY has followed century, men's conceptions of the astronomical universe have undergone radical alterations. Horizons have receded beyond all advance expectations, and the place of the earth has become less and less central. For thousands of years civilization had conceived a finite universe, with the stationary earth fixed at the center of a daily-wheeling, crystalline sphere of stars. From the times of classical Greece until the sixteenth century men thought of sun and moon circling the central earth, and of the bright planets on epicycles whose centers also circled the earth. All of these motions were referred to the background sphere of stars, the entire assemblage wheeling from east to west once every day.

The revolutionary ideas of Copernicus were published in 1543. Men had been plying the world's oceans on their voyages of discovery, trade and commerce were bringing minds together at the market place, and thoughts were turning outward. The Reformation suggested that there was no longer a single unique religious center of the world. And circumnavigation of the globe proved strikingly that there was no unique geographical center. Copernicus went further and renounced the fixity and centrality of the earth itself. To his mind it was preferable to locate the great light-giver, the sun, at the center of all. Thus the earth was put into annual motion around the sun, planet number three of the six he knew. Because to his mind it was also preferable that the crystalline sphere of stars remain stationary, the earth was set to spinning from west to east every day. At first these radical notions seized the minds of only a few thinkers, but the number gradually grew. And the observations of Galileo in the early 1600s put the older Ptolemaic picture to a very severe test.

In 1576 Digges dared to suggest that the stars lie at different distances in three-dimensional space; to him the celestial sphere was only a fiction and not a physical reality. Shortly afterwards Bruno advocated that the stars were other suns. Although proofs of these ideas had to wait a long time, practicing astronomers became fairly well convinced of their validity in the intervening years. In 1718 Halley proved that the stars move relative to one another, and later in the eighteenth century William Herschel found the sun itself to be moving through the stars. Thus the sun took on the same status as the stars, and no longer was it the motionless center of the universe. The enormous scale of stellar distances was estimated as early as the era of Newton, but the first measurement of stellar parallax did not issue until 1838, with Bessel. By then it was certain that stars are at different distances, distributed at random in space and moving among one another.

On a grander scale, Galileo found the Milky Way to be hosts of individual faint stars. In 1750 Wright suggested that our stellar system is an enormous wheel-shaped aggregation of stars, with the sun near the main plane and near the center. The pioneering gauges of the Herschels later put Wright's ideas on a firm observational basis. The size of our galaxy had been estimated by many astronomers, but it was not until Shapley's 1917 studies of globular clusters that the first overestimate was made. The announced extent of about 100,000 parsecs was exciting enough, but even more dramatic was the dethronement of the sun and nearby stars from their central position in the home galaxy. Suddenly they took up their posts far out in the galactic disk. A decade later the milling motions of the nearby stars were shown by Lindblad and Oort to be but local effects of a far bigger and more majestic phenomenon—the rotation of the whole galaxy every 200 million years.

The many faint little elliptical patches in the sky were thought by Wright to be other stellar islands here and there in space, other Milky Ways. Five years later, in 1755, Kant extended these ideas. But nearly two centuries elapsed before Hubble's work provided the proof. In 1924 his studies of Cepheids in several of the brighter systems proved that the little patches were very far away, galaxies comparable with our own. The new conceptual picture was of galaxies strewn here and there in space. The scale of the universe suddenly increased a thousand-fold. Spectral observations of galaxies, mainly with American telescopes, soon showed the red-shift effect, and there emerged the dramatic idea of an expanding universe of galaxies, chiefly owing to the interpretive work of Hubble.

Today the seeming centrality and fixity of our own galaxy is apparent only. We can survey a sphere of galaxies out to distances of 5 billion light-years or more. With improved instruments it may some day be possible to survey a bigger sphere that is limited not by our observational apparatus but by the fact that more distant galaxies are receding faster than the speed of light; their radiation is unable to reach us. But our apparent centrality is illusory; the same effect is seen by an observer in any galaxy. The same is true of motions; the expansion is recorded by an observer in any galaxy who studies it at the same instant of time that we do. The central place of rest in the universe is everywhere and nowhere.

BIBLIOGRAPHY FOR

MORE EXTENDED STUDY

CHAPTER 2

Allen, C. W., *Astrophysical Quantities*. University of London, The Athlone Press, London, 1955. (Useful tables and data covering all branches of astronomy.)

Bates, D. R., ed., *The Planet Earth*. Pergamon Press, New York, 1957.

Jeffreys, H., *The Earth*. The University Press, Cambridge, England, 1952.

Kuiper, G. P., ed., *The Earth as a Planet*. University of Chicago Press, Chicago, 1954.

Massey, H. S. W., and R. L. F. Boyd, *The Upper Atmosphere*. Hutchinson and Company, London, 1958.

Russell, H. N., R. S. Dugan, and J. Q. Stewart, *Astronomy*, Vol. I, rev. ed. Ginn and Company, Boston, 1945.

CHAPTER 3

Jeffreys, H., *The Earth*. The University Press, Cambridge, England, 1952.

Kuiper, G. P., ed., *The Earth as a Planet*. University of Chicago Press, Chicago, 1954.

Nassau, J. J., *Practical Astronomy*, 2nd ed. McGraw-Hill Book Company, New York, 1948.

CHAPTER 4

Allen, R. H., *Star-Names and Their Meanings*. G. E. Stechert, New York, 1899.

The American Ephemeris and Nautical Almanac. Superintendent of Documents, U.S. Government Printing Office, Washington, issued annually.

BIBLIOGRAPHY FOR
MORE EXTENDED
STUDY

Becvar, A., *Skalnate Pleso Atlas of the Heavens, 1950.0*. Sky Publishing Corporation, Cambridge, Mass., 1958.

Nassau, J. J., *Practical Astronomy*, 2nd ed. McGraw-Hill Book Company, New York, 1948.

Northcott, Ruth J., ed., *The Observer's Handbook*. The Royal Astronomical Society of Canada, Toronto, issued annually.

Norton, A. P., *A Star Atlas and Reference Handbook*, 14th ed. Sky Publishing Corporation, Cambridge, Mass., 1959.

Schlesinger, F., and Louise F. Jenkins, *Catalogue of Bright Stars*, 2nd ed. Yale University Observatory, New Haven, Conn., 1940.

CHAPTER 5

Flügge, S., ed., *Encyclopedia of Physics*, Vol. 54. Springer-Verlag, Berlin, 1962.

Hiltner, W. A., ed., *Astronomical Techniques*. University of Chicago Press, Chicago, 1962.

Kuiper, G. K., and Barbara M. Middlehurst, eds., *Telescopes*. University of Chicago Press, Chicago, 1960.

Miczaika, G. R., and W. M. Sinton, *Tools of the Astronomer*. Harvard University Press, Cambridge, Mass., 1961.

Steinberg, J. L., and J. Lequeux, *Radio Astronomy*, trans. by R. N. Bracewell. McGraw-Hill Book Company, New York, 1963.

Thackeray, A. D., *Astronomical Spectroscopy*. Eyre and Spottiswoode, London, 1961.

Vaucouleurs, G. de, *Astronomical Photography*. The Macmillan Company, New York, 1961.

CHAPTER 6

Baldwin, R. B., *The Face of the Moon*. University of Chicago Press, Chicago, 1949.

Kopal, Z., *The Moon, Our Nearest Celestial Neighbor*. Academic Press, New York, 1960.

Mitchell, S. A., *Eclipses of the Sun*, 5th ed. Columbia University Press, New York, 1951.

CHAPTER 7

Abetti, G., *The History of Astronomy*, trans. by Betty B. Abetti. Henry Schuman, New York, 1952.

Blanco, V. M., and S. W. McCuskey, *Basic Physics of the Solar System*. Addison-Wesley Publishing Company, Reading, Mass., 1961.

Moulton, F. R., *An Introduction to Celestial Mechanics*, 2nd rev. ed. The Macmillan Company, New York, 1914.

Pannekoek, A., *A History of Astronomy*. Interscience Publishers, New York, 1961.

Russell, H. N., R. S. Dugan, and J. Q. Stewart, *Astronomy*, Vol. I, rev. ed. Ginn and Company, Boston, 1945.

Shapley, H., ed., *Source Book in Astronomy, 1900–1950*. Harvard University Press, Cambridge, Mass., 1960. (Useful original articles by many astronomers during the first half of the twentieth century, dealing with planetary, stellar, and galactic astronomy.)

Shapley, H., and Helen E. Howarth, *A Source Book in Astronomy*. McGraw-Hill Book Company, New York, 1929. (Useful original articles by many astronomers prior to 1900, dealing with many topics.)

Sterne, T. E., *An Introduction to Celestial Mechanics*. Interscience Publishers, New York, 1960.

CHAPTER 8

Alexander, A. F. O'D., *The Planet Saturn*. Faber and Faber, London, 1962.

Blanco, V. M., and S. W. McCuskey, *Basic Physics of the Solar System*. Addison-Wesley Publishing Company, Reading, Mass., 1961.

Flügge, S., ed., *Encyclopedia of Physics*, Vol. 52. Springer-Verlag, Berlin, 1959.

Kuiper, G. P., ed., *The Atmospheres of the Earth and Planets*, 2nd ed. University of Chicago Press, Chicago, 1952.

Kuiper, G. P., ed., *Planets and Satellites*. University of Chicago Press, Chicago, 1961.

Moore, P., *The Planet Venus*. The Macmillan Company, New York, 1956.

Peek, B. M., *The Planet Jupiter*. Faber and Faber, London, 1958.

Slipher, E. C., *The Photographic Story of Mars*. Sky Publishing Corporation, Cambridge, Mass., 1962.

Urey, H. C., *The Planets, Their Origin and Development*. Yale University Press, New Haven, Conn., 1952.

Vaucouleurs, G. de., *Physics of the Planet Mars*. Faber and Faber, London, 1954.

Whipple, F. L., *Earth, Moon, and Planets*, rev. ed. Harvard University Press, Cambridge, Mass., 1963.

CHAPTER 9

Flügge, S., ed., *Encyclopedia of Physics*, Vol. 52. Springer-Verlag, Berlin, 1959.

Hynek, J. A., ed., *Astrophysics*. McGraw-Hill Book Company, New York, 1951.

Lovell, A. C. B., *Meteor Astronomy*. The Clarendon Press, Oxford, 1954.

McKinley, D. W. R., *Meteor Science and Engineering*. McGraw-Hill Book Company, New York, 1961.

Öpik, E. J., *Physics of Meteor Flight in the Atmosphere*. Interscience Publishers, New York, 1958.

Porter, J. G., *Comets and Meteor Streams*. John Wiley and Sons, New York, 1952.

Watson, F. G., *Between the Planets*, rev. ed. Harvard University Press, Cambridge, Mass., 1956.

CHAPTER 10

Bates, D. R., ed., *The Planet Earth*. Pergamon Press, New York, 1957.

BIBLIOGRAPHY FOR MORE EXTENDED STUDY

Hynek, J. A., ed., *Astrophysics*. McGraw-Hill Book Company, New York, 1951.

Urey, H. C., *The Planets, Their Origin and Development*. Yale University Press, New Haven, Conn., 1952.

CHAPTER 11

Goldberg, L., and L. H. Aller, *Atoms, Stars, and Nebulae*. Harvard University Press, Cambridge, Mass., 1946.

Jeans, J., *An Introduction to the Kinetic Theory of Gases*. The University Press, Cambridge, England, 1940.

McCrea, W. H., *Physics of the Sun and Stars*. Hutchinson's University Library, London, 1950.

Richtmyer, F. K., E. H. Kennard, and T. Lauritsen, *Introduction to Modern Physics*, 5th ed. McGraw-Hill Book Company, New York, 1955.

CHAPTER 12

Abetti, G., *The Sun*, trans. by J. B. Sidgwick. The Macmillan Company, New York, 1957.

Aller, L. H., *Astrophysics: The Atmospheres of the Sun and Stars*. The Ronald Press Company, New York, 1953.

Ellison, M. A., *The Sun and Its Influence*. Routledge and Kegan Paul, London, 1955.

Flügge, S., ed., *Encyclopedia of Physics*, Vol. 52. Springer-Verlag, Berlin, 1959.

Kiepenheuer, K., *The Sun*. The University of Michigan Press, Ann Arbor, 1959.

Kuiper, G. P., ed., *The Sun*. University of Chicago Press, Chicago, 1953.

McCrea, W. H., *Physics of the Sun and Stars*. Hutchinson's University Library, London, 1950.

Menzel, D. H., *Our Sun*, rev. ed. Harvard University Press, Cambridge, Mass., 1959.

Steinberg, J. L., and J. Lequeux, *Radio Astronomy*, trans. by R. N. Bracewell. McGraw-Hill Book Company, New York, 1963.

CHAPTER 13

Aller, L. H., *Astrophysics: The Atmospheres of the Sun and Stars*. The Ronald Press Company, New York, 1953.

Flügge, S., ed., *Encyclopedia of Physics*, Vol. 50. Springer-Verlag, Berlin, 1958.

Flügge, S., ed., *Encyclopedia of Physics*, Vol. 51. Springer-Verlag, Berlin, 1958.

Goldberg, L., and L. H. Aller, *Atoms, Stars, and Nebulae*. Harvard University Press, Cambridge, Mass., 1946.

Greenstein, J. L., ed., *Stellar Atmospheres*. University of Chicago Press, Chicago, 1961.

Hynek, J. A., ed., *Astrophysics*. McGraw-Hill Book Company, New York, 1951.

Morgan, W. W., P. C. Keenan, and Edith Kellman, *An Atlas of Stellar Spectra*. University of Chicago Press, Chicago, 1943.

U S. DEPARTMENT OF COMMERCE
MARITIME ADMINISTRATION
U. S. MERCHANT MARINE ACADEMY
KINGS POINT, N. Y. 11024

November 18, 1965

CIRCULAR NO. 65-12

From: Superintendent

To: Cadet-Midshipmen of all classes

Subject: Participation in Extra-Curricular
          Activities During Setback Status

Effective July, 1966,
It shall be the general academic policy that:

(1)   Cadet-Midshipmen in their setback year must not participate
      in any extra-curricular activities without the specific written
      recommendation of the Dean and the approval of the Super-
      intendent.

(2)   A Cadet-Midshipman who successfully completes his academic
      work during the setback year may subsequently participate in
      extra-curricular activities as long as the required academic
      standards are then maintained.

GORDON MCLINTOCK
Rear Admiral, USMS
Superintendent

Schlesinger, F., and Louise F. Jenkins, *Catalogue of Bright Stars*, 2nd ed. Yale University Observatory, New Haven, Conn., 1940.

Thackeray, A. D., *Astronomical Spectroscopy*. Eyre and Spottiswoode, London, 1961.

CHAPTER 14

Aitken, R. G., *The Binary Stars*, 2nd ed. McGraw-Hill Book Company, New York, 1935.

Binnendijk, L., *Properties of Double Stars*. University of Pennsylvania Press, Philadelphia, 1960.

Flügge, S., ed., *Encyclopedia of Physics*, Vol. 50. Springer-Verlag, Berlin, 1958.

Hynek, J. A., ed., *Astrophysics*. McGraw-Hill Book Company, New York, 1951.

Struve, O., *Stellar Evolution*. Princeton University Press, Princeton, N.J., 1950.

CHAPTER 15

Aller, L. H., *The Abundance of the Elements*. Interscience Publishers, New York, 1961.

Aller, L. H., *Astrophysics: The Atmospheres of the Sun and Stars*. The Ronald Press Company, New York, 1953.

Aller, L. H., *Astrophysics: Nuclear Transformations, Stellar Interiors, and Nebulae*. The Ronald Press Company, New York, 1954.

Flügge, S., ed., *Encyclopedia of Physics*, Vol. 50. Springer-Verlag, Berlin, 1958.

Flügge, S., ed., *Encyclopedia of Physics*, Vol. 51. Springer-Verlag, Berlin, 1958.

Greenstein, J. L., ed., *Stellar Atmospheres*. University of Chicago Press, Chicago, 1961.

McCrea, W. H., *Physics of the Sun and Stars*. Hutchinson's University Library, London, 1950.

CHAPTER 16

Campbell, L., and L. Jacchia, *The Story of Variable Stars*. Harvard University Press, Cambridge, Mass., 1946.

Flügge, S., ed., *Encyclopedia of Physics*, Vol. 51. Springer-Verlag, Berlin, 1958.

Goldberg, L., and L. H. Aller, *Atoms, Stars, and Nebulae*. Harvard University Press, Cambridge, Mass., 1946.

Greenstein, J. L., ed., *Stellar Atmospheres*. University of Chicago Press, Chicago, 1961.

Payne-Gaposchkin, Cecilia, *Variable Stars and Galactic Structure*. University of London, The Athlone Press, London, 1954.

Payne-Gaposchkin, Cecilia, and S. Gaposchkin, *Variable Stars*. Harvard College Observatory, Cambridge, Mass., 1938.

CHAPTER 17

Flügge, S., ed., *Encyclopedia of Physics*, Vol. 53. Springer-Verlag, Berlin, 1959.

Shapley, H., *Star Clusters*. McGraw-Hill Book Company, New York, 1930.

BIBLIOGRAPHY FOR
MORE EXTENDED
STUDY

CHAPTER 18

Aller, L. H., *Astrophysics: Nuclear Transformations, Stellar Interiors, and Nebulae.* The Ronald Press Company, New York, 1954.
Aller, L. H., *Gaseous Nebulae.* John Wiley and Sons, New York, 1956.
Dufay, J., *Galactic Nebulae and Interstellar Matter*, trans. by A. J. Pomerans. Philosophical Library, New York, 1957.
Hynek, J. A., ed., *Astrophysics.* McGraw-Hill Book Company, New York, 1951.

CHAPTER 19

Flügge, S., ed., *Encyclopedia of Physics*, Vol. 51. Springer-Verlag, Berlin, 1958.
Payne-Gaposchkin, Cecilia, *Stars in the Making.* Harvard University Press, Cambridge, Mass., 1952.
Schwarzschild, M., *Structure and Evolution of the Stars.* Princeton University Press, Princeton, N.J., 1958.
Struve, O., *Stellar Evolution.* Princeton University Press, Princeton, N.J., 1950.

CHAPTER 20

Bok, B. J., and Priscilla F. Bok, *The Milky Way*, 3rd ed. Harvard University Press, Cambridge, Mass., 1957.
Flügge, S., ed., *Encyclopedia of Physics*, Vol. 53. Springer-Verlag, Berlin, 1959.
Payne-Gaposchkin, Cecilia, *Variable Stars and Galactic Structure.* University of London, The Athlone Press, London, 1954.
Ross, F. E., and Mary R. Calvert, *Atlas of the Northern Milky Way.* University of Chicago Press, Chicago, 1934–36.
Steinberg, J. L., and J. Lequeux, *Radio Astronomy*, trans. by R. N. Bracewell. McGraw-Hill Book Company, New York, 1963.

CHAPTER 21

Flügge, S., ed., *Encyclopedia of Physics*, Vol. 53. Springer-Verlag, Berlin, 1959.
Hubble, E. P., *The Realm of the Nebulae.* Dover Publications, New York, 1958.
Sandage, A., *The Hubble Atlas of Galaxies.* Carnegie Institution of Washington, Washington, D.C., 1961.
Shapley, H., *Galaxies*, rev. ed. Harvard University Press, Cambridge, Mass., 1961.

CHAPTER 22

Bondi, H., *Cosmology.* The University Press, Cambridge, England, 1952.
Flügge, S., ed., *Encyclopedia of Physics*, Vol. 53. Springer-Verlag, Berlin, 1959.
Hubble, E. P., *The Realm of the Nebulae.* Dover Publications, New York, 1958.
McVittie, G. C., *Fact and Theory in Cosmology.* Eyre and Spottiswoode, London, 1961.
Shapley, H., *Galaxies*, rev. ed. Harvard University Press, Cambridge, Mass., 1961.

Shapley, H., *The Inner Metagalaxy*. Yale University Press, New Haven, Conn., 1957.

Whitrow, G. J., *The Structure and Evolution of the Universe*, rev. ed. Harper Torchbooks, New York, 1959.

BIBLIOGRAPHY OF PERIODICALS

The first six journals listed below are among those that present the current results of astronomical research in the English language. The following five are devoted to astronomy and report current research results as well as offer review articles and other features. The final two are broader in scope but often contain authoritative reviews of astronomical subjects.

The Astronomical Journal, 10 issues a year, The American Institute of Physics, 335 East 45th Street, New York 17, N.Y.

The Astrophysical Journal, 8 issues a year, University of Chicago Press, Chicago 37, Ill.

Monthly Notices of the Royal Astronomical Society, 6 to 12 issues a year, Burlington House, London, W.1, England.

Icarus, International Journal of the Solar System, 6 issues a year, Academic Press Inc., 111 Fifth Avenue, New York 3, N.Y.

Planetary and Space Science, 6 to 12 issues a year, Pergamon Press Inc., 125 East 55th Street, New York 22, N.Y.

Transactions of the International Astronomical Union, published every 3 years, Academic Press Inc., 111 Fifth Avenue, New York 3, N.Y.

Publications of the Astronomical Society of the Pacific, 6 issues a year, California Academy of Sciences, Golden Gate Park, San Francisco 18, Calif.

The Observatory, 6 issues a year, The Editors, Royal Greenwich Observatory, Herstmonceux Castle, Hailsham, Sussex, England.

The Journal of the British Astronomical Association, about 8 issues a year, 303 Bath Road, Hounslow West, Middlesex, England.

The Journal of the Royal Astronomical Society of Canada, 6 issues a year, 252 College Street, Toronto 2B, Canada.

Sky and Telescope, published monthly, Sky Publishing Corporation, Harvard College Observatory, Cambridge 38, Mass.

Physics Today, published monthly, The American Institute of Physics, 335 East 45th Street, New York 17, N.Y.

Scientific American, published monthly, 415 Madison Avenue, New York 17, N.Y.

APPENDIX

CONSTANTS AND CONVERSION FACTORS

Velocity of light	$c = 3.00 \times 10^5$ km/sec $= 186,000$ mi/sec
Constant of gravitation	$G = 6.67 \times 10^{-8}$ cm^3/gm sec^2
Planck's constant	$h = 6.62 \times 10^{-27}$ erg sec
Wien's constant	$= 0.290$ cm deg
Stefan's constant	$= 5.67 \times 10^{-5}$ erg/cm^2 sec deg^4
Fahrenheit temperature	$T_F = 1.8T_C + 32 = 1.8T_K - 460$
Absolute temperature	$T_K = T_C + 273$
Angstrom unit	$1 \text{ A} = 10^{-8}$ cm
Inch	$1 \text{ in} = 2.54$ cm
Kilometer	$1 \text{ km} = 10^5$ cm
Mile	$1 \text{ mi} = 1.61$ km
Mean radius of earth	$= 6371$ km $= 3959$ mi
Radius of sun	$= 696,000$ km $= 432,000$ mi
Astronomical unit	$1 \text{ a.u.} = 1.50 \times 10^8$ km $= 0.930 \times 10^8$ mi
Light-year	$1 \text{ l.y.} = 0.946 \times 10^{18}$ cm $= 5.88 \times 10^{12}$ mi
Parsec	$1 \text{ pc} = 3.08 \times 10^{18}$ cm $= 206,265$ a.u. $= 3.26$ l.y.
Kiloparsec	$1 \text{ kpc} = 1000$ pc
Megaparsec	$1 \text{ mpc} = 10^6$ pc $= 1000$ kpc
Present period of earth's rotation	$= 86,164$ sec
Tropical or ordinary year	$1 \text{ yr} = 365.2422$ mean solar days $= 3.16 \times 10^7$ sec
Mass of electron	$= 9.11 \times 10^{-28}$ gm
Mass of hydrogen atom	$= 1.67 \times 10^{-24}$ gm $= 1840$ electron masses
Mass of earth	$= 5.98 \times 10^{27}$ gm
Mass of sun	$= 1.99 \times 10^{33}$ gm $= 333,000$ earth masses
Luminosity of sun	$= 3.86 \times 10^{33}$ erg/sec

INDEX